NONLINEAR ANALYSIS OF PLATES

£19.40 R⌐

ᵐⱽ

**McGRAW-HILL
INTERNATIONAL
BOOK COMPANY**
New York
St Louis
San Francisco
Auckland
Bogotá
Guatemala
Hamburg
Johannesburg
Lisbon
London
Madrid
Mexico
Montreal
New Delhi
Panama
Paris
San Juan
São Paulo
Singapore
Sydney
Tokyo
Toronto

CHUEN-YUAN CHIA

Professor of Solid Mechanics
Department of Civil Engineering
The University of Calgary
Canada

Nonlinear
Analysis
of Plates

British Library Cataloguing in Publication Data

Chia, Chuen-Yuan
    Nonlinear analysis of plates.
    1. Plates (Engineering) 2. Nonlinear
    theories   3. Mathematical analysis
    I. Title
    624'.1776   TA660.P6

    ISBN 0-07-010746-7

Printed and bound in the United States of America

CONTENTS

7   Moderately Large Deflections of Unsymmetrically Laminated Anisotropic Plates   337

8   Postbuckling Behavior and Nonlinear Flexural Vibration of Unsymmetrically Laminated Anisotropic Plates   372

Appendices

PREFACE

This book has been developed from a series of seminars given by the author in the Department of Engineering Mechanics at the University of Wisconsin-Madison, during the academic year of 1974–1975, and from lecture notes of a senior graduate course in the nonlinear theory of plates offered later on by the author in the Department of Civil Engineering at the University of Calgary. The text contains more material than will ordinarily be covered in a semester course. Prerequisites for this book are some knowledge in the nonlinear theory of three-dimensional elasticity for the formulation of the present nonlinear plate theory and some knowledge in the linear theory of plates for a better understanding of the plate problems considered herein. The former, however, can be avoided by virtue of the ad hoc assumption as indicated in Sec. 1.5, or by some other formulation.

The historical background of the classical plate theory for homogeneous plates can be found in some texts such as *Theory and Analysis of Plates* by R. Szilard. Thus only the development of the theories of laminated anisotropic plates is briefly summarized in the following pages.

In recent years the use of laminated anisotropic composites as structural members has increased considerably. This arises from the fact that, by taking advantage of its anisotropic material properties and light weight with high strength, the materials can be used very efficiently. They are found in various industries such as aircraft, missile, hydrospace, shipbuilding, transportation, and building construction. Composite technology will play an even more important role in view of the forecast of acute future shortage of mineral materials. A considerable amount of research work, therefore, has been under progress regarding the elastic behavior of laminated composites, particularly thin plates. Since the formulation by E. Reissner and Y. Stavsky in 1961 of the static small deflection theory of laminated plates, taking into account the effect of bending-stretching coupling, a great number of investigators have applied the theory to study bending and buckling of unsymmetric laminates, and extended the theory to the dynamic case. Furthermore, the transverse shear deformation has been included in some analyses. For a compendium, see the references in the text, and also *Theory of Laminated Plates*, by J. E. Ashton and J. M. Whitney. In 1964 Y. Stavsky formulated a static large deflection theory of heterogeneous anisotropic plates in the sense of von Kármán. In 1969 J. M. Whitney and A. W. Leissa included the inertia terms in the von Kármán-type large deflection theory of generally laminated anisotropic plates. Later on, numerous solutions for nonlinear behavior of such plates based on these theories have appeared in literature. Comprehensive references are given at the ends of respective chapters in this book.

The material covered in this work is all limited to elastic behavior of plates with moderately large deflection, postbuckling, and nonlinear vibration. The nonlinear laminated plate theory in the sense of von Kármán is used throughout this book. Problems related to sandwich constructions and the effects of transverse shear, rotatory inertia, temperature, etc., on the elastic behavior of plates will be treated in another book. The present chapter and section titles are a significant indication of the total content. The derivation of the governing equations is presented in Chap. 1. The other chapters, except for relating to the first, are not significantly interdependent and represent nearly distinct blocks of the total structure. Chapters 2, 3, and 4 are devoted to isotropic plates. Some of the topics on static large deflections of these plates discussed in a few texts are re-treated by different methods, and new results are also included. Some numerical results in postbuckling behavior and nonlinear flexural vibration of isotropic plates are discussed in a few reference texts, but generally not the mathematical part. In this book the formulation of solutions is stressed and much additional information regarding postbuckling and moderately large-amplitude vibration of isotropic plates is presented. Chapters 5 to 8 deal with static and dynamic nonlinear problems of homogeneous and laminated anisotropic plates, with isotropic plates treated as a special case. Most of the solutions presented in these chapters are the results of investigation made by the author and his research associates since 1972. The material covered in this book may be regarded as an extension of bending and elastic stability of isotropic plates discussed in some texts such as *Theory of Plates and Shells* by S. Timoshenko and S. Woinowsky-Krieger, to nonlinear bending and postbuckling of isotropic, anisotropic, and laminated plates, and also as an extension of bending, buckling, and vibration of laminates treated in the text *Theory of Laminated Plates* by J. E. Ashton and J. M. Whitney to geometrically nonlinear behavior of such plates.

At the time of publishing this book, despite a number of existing texts in the theory and analysis of plates, there is not a single text which is devoted entirely to the geometrically nonlinear problems of homogeneous isotropic and laminated anisotropic elastic plates. It is hoped that this book will fill the gap to some extent and that it might be used as a valuable information source for senior graduate students, engineers, designers, scientists, and applied mathematicians in this field.

The author wishes to record his appreciation to the National Research Council of Canada for the partially financial support of this work, to Professor M. A. Ward and Dr. M. Sathyamoorthy for various assistance, and to his wife for encouragement and forbearance.

C. Y. Chia

LIST OF SYMBOLS

A_{ij}, B_{ij}, D_{ij}	Extensional, coupling and flexural rigidities of laminated plate defined by Eq. (1-53), $i, j = 1, 2, 6$
$A_{ij}^*, B_{ij}^*, D_{ij}^*$	Constants for laminated plate defined by Eq. (1-127), $i, j = 1, 2, 6$
a, b	Length and width of rectangular plate
a_0, b_0	Half-length and half-width of rectangular plate
C_{ij}	Reduced stiffnesses of anisotropic plate, $i, j = 1, 2, 6$
D	Flexural rigidity of isotropic plate
D_i	Principal bending and twisting rigidities of orthotropic plate defined by Eq. (1-112), $i = 1, 2, 4$
E	Modulus of elasticity of isotropic plate
E_1, E_2	Principal moduli of elasticity of orthotropic plate
E_L, E_T	Principal moduli of elasticity of generally orthotropic layer or plate
G	Modulus of rigidity of isotropic plate
G_{12}	Modulus of rigidity of orthotropic plate
G_{LT}	Modulus of rigidity of orthotropic layer in laminated plate
h	Thickness of plate
$M_r, M_\theta, M_{r\theta}$	Bending and twisting moments per unit length in polar coordinates
M_x, M_y, M_{xy}	Bending and twisting moments per unit length in rectangular cartesian coordinates
N_r, N_θ, N_{rs}	Membrane forces per unit length in polar coordinates
N_x, N_y, N_{xy}	Membrane forces per unit length in rectangular cartesian coordinates
n_{cr}	Critical buckling load per unit length in x direction
n_x, n_y	Inplane edge compressions per unit length in x and y directions, respectively
P	Concentrated load or total partial load
P_x, P_y	Resultant inplane edge loads in x and y directions, respectively

p_{cr}	Critical buckling pressure in x direction
p_x, p_y	Inplane compressive edge stresses in x and y directions, respectively
Q_r, Q_θ	Transverse shear forces per unit length in polar coordinates
Q_x, Q_y	Transverse shear forces per unit length in rectangular cartesian coordinates
q	Intensity of distributed transverse normal load
q_0	Intensity of uniformly distributed lateral load
r, θ, z	Cylindrical polar coordinates
t	Time
u, v, w	Displacement components at a point off the midsurface in the x, y, and z directions, respectively
u°, v°, w	Displacement components in midsurface in x, y, z directions, respectively
u_r, u_θ, w	Displacement components in midsurface in r, θ, z directions, respectively
x, y, z	Rectangular cartesian coordinates
$\varepsilon_r, \varepsilon_\theta, \varepsilon_{r\theta}$	Total strain components in polar coordinates
$\varepsilon_r^\circ, \varepsilon_\theta^\circ, \varepsilon_{r\theta}^\circ$	Midsurface strain components in polar coordinates
$\varepsilon_x, \varepsilon_y, \varepsilon_{xy}$	Total strain components in rectangular cartesian coordinates
$\varepsilon_x^\circ, \varepsilon_y^\circ, \varepsilon_{xy}^\circ$	Midsurface strain components in rectangular cartesian coordinates
$\kappa_x, \kappa_y, \kappa_{xy}$	Changes of bending and twisting curvatures of midsurface
λ	Aspect ratio of rectangular plate ($= a/b$)
v	Poisson's ratio of isotropic plate
v_{12}, v_{21}	Poisson's ratios of orthotropic plate
v_{LT}, v_{TL}	Poisson's ratios of orthotropic layer in laminated plate
ρ	Mass per unit area of plate
ρ_0	Mass density
$\sigma_r, \sigma_\theta, \sigma_{r\theta}$	Total stress components in polar coordinates
$\sigma_r^b, \sigma_\theta^b, \sigma_{r\theta}^b$	Bending stress components in polar coordinates
$\sigma_r^m, \sigma_\theta^m, \sigma_{r\theta}^m$	Membrane stress components in polar coordinates
$\sigma_x, \sigma_y, \sigma_{xy}$	Total stress components in rectangular cartesian coordinates
$\sigma_x^b, \sigma_y^b, \sigma_{xy}^b$	Bending stress components in rectangular cartesian coordinates
$\sigma_x^m, \sigma_y^m, \sigma_{xy}^m$	Membrane stress components in rectangular cartesian coordinates
ψ	Force function
∇^2	Two-dimensional Laplace operator
$(\ )_{,i}^2$	Square of differentiation with respect to i coordinate
$(\ )_{,i}$	Partial (or ordinary) differentiation with respect to i coordinate

Other symbols are defined when they appear in the text.

NONLINEAR THEORY OF LAMINATED PLATES

A nonlinear theory of unsymmetrically laminated anisotropic elastic plates is derived from the three-dimensional nonlinear theory of elasticity by the classical method of integration. The plate equations of motion, bending moments, membrane forces, and transverse shear forces are expressed in terms of three-displacement components as well as in terms of transverse deflection and stress function. In each case these equations are specified for unsymmetric angle-ply, cross-ply, and isotropic laminates, for symmetric anisotropic laminates, and for anisotropic, orthotropic, and isotropic plates. The corresponding static equations of isotropic plates are those of von Kármán nonlinear plate theory. In addition some fundamentals of plates and methods of solution are also discussed in this chapter.

1.1 STRESS AND STRAIN

When a deformable body is under the action of external forces such as applied loads, body forces, and support reactions, the body will be deformed and the internal forces interacting between elemental portions of the body will be developed. In discussing internal forces, stress is defined as the internal force per unit area. The state of stress at a point within the body is specified, at most, by nine components of stress. The deformation of the body is characterized by the extension of line elements and the distortion of the angles between line elements. The extensional and shearing components of strain in engineering are defined as unit elongations of line elements and the changes in the values of initially right angles between line elements, whereas those of a strain tensor are defined in terms

1

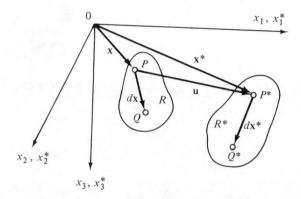

Figure 1.1 Deformation of a line element.

of displacement. The deformation, however, may be either finite or infinitesimally small. In the theory of finite deformations or the nonlinear theory of elasticity, stress and strain can be described by two different coordinate systems of reference, namely, the eulerian coordinates describing the material particles with respect to the deformed configuration, and the lagrangian coordinates describing these particles with respect to the original or undeformed configuration. In the former the independent variables are the coordinates of the particles in the deformed state at the time of interest. In the latter all quantities are expressed in terms of the initial position coordinates of each particle and time during all subsequent motions. Thus the initial material lines and rectangular planes are deformed to curves and curved surfaces in the lagrangian description.

Consider a material particle $P(x_1, x_2, x_3)$ in an unstrained continuum occupying a region R as shown in Fig. 1.1. At a later instant of time the continuum is deformed to occupy the region R^* and the particle is deformed to a new location $P^*(x_1^*, x_2^*, x_3^*)$ by a displacement vector **u**. In the description of initial and current configurations of the continuum, the same system of rectangular cartesian coordinates is used herein. The deformation from the initial configuration to the deformed configuration is assumed to be continuous with one-to-one correspondence. From Fig. 1.1 the two sets of coordinates are related by

$$x_i^* = x_i + u_i \qquad (i = 1, 2, 3) \tag{1-1}$$

The square of the length ds_0 connecting the particle $P(x_1, x_2, x_3)$ to a neighboring particle $Q(x_1 + dx_1, x_2 + dx_2, x_3 + dx_3)$, both lying on a line element in the undeformed state, is

$$ds_0^2 = dx_i \, dx_i \tag{1-2}$$

in which the repeated index in a term indicates summation with respect to this index. During deformation the particles P and Q are displaced to $P^*(x_1^*, x_2^*, x_3^*)$ and $Q^*(x_1^* + dx_1^*, x_2^* + dx_2^*, x_3^* + dx_3^*)$, respectively. The square of the length ds of the new line element P^*Q^* is given by

$$ds^2 = dx_i^* \, dx_i^* \tag{1-3}$$

The difference $(ds^2 - ds_0^2)$ is a measure of strain. In the lagrangian description the coordinates x_1, x_2, x_3 are regarded as independent variables such that $ds^2 = (\partial x_i^*/\partial x_j)(\partial x_i^*/\partial x_k)\, dx_j\, dx_k$. Thus

$$ds^2 - ds_0^2 = dx_i^*\, dx_i^* - dx_i\, dx_i = 2\varepsilon_{ij}\, dx_i\, dx_j \tag{1-4}$$

where

$$\varepsilon_{ij} = \frac{1}{2}\left(\frac{\partial u_i}{\partial x_j} + \frac{\partial u_j}{\partial x_i} + \frac{\partial u_k}{\partial x_i}\frac{\partial u_k}{\partial x_j}\right) \tag{1-5}$$

is called the Green strain tensor or the lagrangian strain components. In the eulerian description the coordinates x_1^*, x_2^*, x_3^* are regarded as independent variables and hence

$$ds^2 - ds_0^2 = 2\varepsilon_{ij}^*\, dx_i^*\, dx_j^* \tag{1-6}$$

in which

$$\varepsilon_{ij}^* = \frac{1}{2}\left(\frac{\partial u_i}{\partial x_j^*} + \frac{\partial u_j}{\partial x_i^*} - \frac{\partial u_k}{\partial x_i^*}\frac{\partial u_k}{\partial x_j^*}\right) \tag{1-7}$$

is called the Almansi strain tensor or eulerian strain components.

In the case of infinitesimally small deformation, the products of displacement derivatives in equations (1-5) and (1-7) can be neglected, thus there is no need to distinguish between these strain tensors.

In discussing stress it is natural to employ the eulerian coordinates. Stresses, however, are related to strains, thus either the eulerian or the lagrangian description may be used. The components of a stress tensor per unit area of the deformed state are defined to be those of the eulerian stress tensor, whereas the Kirchhoff stress tensor is measured with reference to the initial state. All these stress and strain tensors are symmetric in the system of cartesian coordinates.

In the following discussion the lagrangian description is adopted. The normal components of the Kirchhoff stress tensor in the direction of cartesian coordinate axes x, y, z are denoted by σ_x, σ_y, σ_z, respectively, and the shearing components by σ_{xy}, σ_{yx}, σ_{xz}, σ_{zx}, σ_{yz}, σ_{zy}. The first subscript in shearing stress components indicates the direction of the normal to the plane under consideration, and the second the direction of the stress component. The senses of positive stress components are depicted in Fig. 1.2. The extensional components of the Green strain tensor (or the extensional components of strain in engineering) in the directions of the coordinate axes x, y, z are represented by ε_x, ε_y, ε_z, and the shearing components of strain in engineering by ε_{xy}, ε_{yx}, ε_{xz}, ε_{zx}, ε_{yz}, ε_{zy}. It is observed that the engineering shearing strain is twice larger than the corresponding shearing component of the strain tensor.

For a given state of stress at a point in the cartesian system of coordinates x, y, z, the components of stress in a new system of rectangular coordinates x', y', z' can be computed by the classical formulas of transformation

$$\boldsymbol{\sigma}' = \mathbf{A}\boldsymbol{\sigma} \tag{1-8}$$

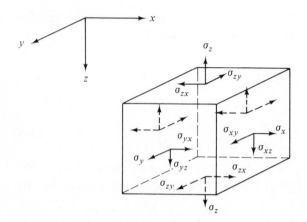

Figure 1.2 Sign conventions for stresses in rectangular cartesian coordinates.

where

$$\boldsymbol{\sigma}' = [\sigma'_x \ \sigma'_y \ \sigma'_z \ \sigma'_{yz} \ \sigma'_{zx} \ \sigma'_{xy}]^T$$
$$\boldsymbol{\sigma} = [\sigma_x \ \sigma_y \ \sigma_z \ \sigma_{yz} \ \sigma_{zx} \ \sigma_{xy}]^T$$

$$
\begin{aligned}
b_{44} &= a_{22}a_{33} + a_{23}a_{32} & b_{45} &= a_{23}a_{31} + a_{21}a_{33} \\
b_{46} &= a_{21}a_{32} + a_{22}a_{31} & b_{54} &= a_{13}a_{32} + a_{12}a_{33} \\
b_{55} &= a_{11}a_{33} + a_{13}a_{31} & b_{56} &= a_{12}a_{31} + a_{11}a_{32} \\
b_{64} &= a_{12}a_{23} + a_{13}a_{22} & b_{65} &= a_{13}a_{21} + a_{11}a_{23} \\
b_{66} &= a_{11}a_{22} + a_{12}a_{21}
\end{aligned}
\tag{1-9}
$$

$$
\mathbf{A} = \begin{bmatrix}
a_{11}^2 & a_{12}^2 & a_{13}^2 & \alpha a_{12}a_{13} & \alpha a_{11}a_{13} & \alpha a_{11}a_{12} \\
a_{21}^2 & a_{22}^2 & a_{23}^2 & \alpha a_{22}a_{23} & \alpha a_{21}a_{23} & \alpha a_{21}a_{22} \\
a_{31}^2 & a_{32}^2 & a_{33}^2 & \alpha a_{32}a_{33} & \alpha a_{31}a_{33} & \alpha a_{31}a_{32} \\
\beta a_{21}a_{31} & \beta a_{22}a_{32} & \beta a_{23}a_{33} & b_{44} & b_{45} & b_{46} \\
\beta a_{11}a_{31} & \beta a_{12}a_{32} & \beta a_{13}a_{33} & b_{54} & b_{55} & b_{56} \\
\beta a_{11}a_{21} & \beta a_{12}a_{22} & \beta a_{13}a_{23} & b_{64} & b_{65} & b_{66}
\end{bmatrix}
\tag{1-10}
$$

In equation (1-9) the superscript T stands for the matrix transpose, and in the square matrix (1-10), $\alpha = 2$, $\beta = 1$, and a_{ij} are the direction cosines defined in Table 1.1.

Table 1.1 Direction cosines

	x	y	z
x'	a_{11}	a_{12}	a_{13}
y'	a_{21}	a_{22}	a_{23}
z'	a_{31}	a_{32}	a_{33}

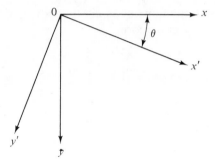

Figure 1.3 A rotation of coordinate system through an angle θ about the z axis.

Similarly, the equations of the transformation for the components of strain also can be written in the matrix form

$$\varepsilon' = A\varepsilon \tag{1-11}$$

where **A** is given by expression (1-10), with $\alpha = 1$ and $\beta = 2$, and where

$$\varepsilon' = \begin{bmatrix} \varepsilon'_x & \varepsilon'_y & \varepsilon'_z & \varepsilon'_{yz} & \varepsilon'_{zx} & \varepsilon'_{xy} \end{bmatrix}^T$$
$$\varepsilon = \begin{bmatrix} \varepsilon_x & \varepsilon_y & \varepsilon_z & \varepsilon_{yz} & \varepsilon_{zx} & \varepsilon_{xy} \end{bmatrix}^T \tag{1-12}$$

In the case of plates, often only a rotation of the coordinates x and y about the z axis in the thickness direction is required. Transformation matrix (1-10) then simplifies to

$$A = \begin{bmatrix} c^2 & s^2 & 0 & 0 & 0 & \alpha cs \\ s^2 & c^2 & 0 & 0 & 0 & -\alpha cs \\ 0 & 0 & 1 & 0 & 0 & 0 \\ 0 & 0 & 0 & c & -s & 0 \\ 0 & 0 & 0 & s & c & 0 \\ -\beta cs & \beta cs & 0 & 0 & 0 & c^2 - s^2 \end{bmatrix} \tag{1-13}$$

in which $\alpha = 2$, $\beta = 1$ for transformation of stress components and $\alpha = 1$, $\beta = 2$ for transformation of strain components, and in which

$$c = \cos\theta \qquad s = \sin\theta \tag{1-14}$$

with θ being the angle of rotation about the z axis (Fig. 1.3).

1.2 BASIC EQUATIONS IN NONLINEAR ELASTICITY

The strain-displacement relations, equations of motion, and the generalized Hooke's law in the nonlinear theory of three-dimensional elasticity will be reduced to a simplified version of the nonlinear theory under appropriate assumptions.

In the lagrangian description for finite deformations of an elastic body, the strain-displacement relations (1-5) can be written in the form

$$\varepsilon_x = e_x + \tfrac{1}{2}[e_x^2 + (\tfrac{1}{2}e_{yx} + \omega_z)^2 + (\tfrac{1}{2}e_{zx} - \omega_y)^2]$$

$$\varepsilon_y = e_y + \tfrac{1}{2}[e_y^2 + (\tfrac{1}{2}e_{xy} - \omega_z)^2 + (\tfrac{1}{2}e_{yz} + \omega_x)^2]$$

$$\varepsilon_z = e_z + \tfrac{1}{2}[e_z^2 + (\tfrac{1}{2}e_{xz} + \omega_y)^2 + (\tfrac{1}{2}e_{yz} - \omega_x)^2]$$

$$\varepsilon_{yz} = e_{yz} + e_y(\tfrac{1}{2}e_{yz} - \omega_x) + e_z(\tfrac{1}{2}e_{zy} + \omega_x)$$
$$+ (\tfrac{1}{2}e_{xy} - \omega_z)(\tfrac{1}{2}e_{xz} + \omega_y) \qquad (1\text{-}15)$$

$$\varepsilon_{zx} = e_{zx} + e_x(\tfrac{1}{2}e_{xz} + \omega_y) + e_z(\tfrac{1}{2}e_{zx} - \omega_y)$$
$$+ (\tfrac{1}{2}e_{yz} - \omega_x)(\tfrac{1}{2}e_{xy} + \omega_z)$$

$$\varepsilon_{xy} = e_{xy} + e_x(\tfrac{1}{2}e_{xy} - \omega_z) + e_y(\tfrac{1}{2}e_{yx} + \omega_z)$$
$$+ (\tfrac{1}{2}e_{zx} - \omega_y)(\tfrac{1}{2}e_{zy} + \omega_x)$$

in which ε_{ij} are finite (or nonlinear) strains, e_{ij} are infinitesimal (or linear) strains, and ω_i are rotations of an element about the i axis. These strains and rotations are, respectively, defined by

$$e_x = u_{,x} \qquad e_y = v_{,y} \qquad e_z = w_{,z}$$

$$e_{yz} = w_{,y} + v_{,z} \qquad e_{zx} = u_{,z} + w_{,x}$$

$$e_{xy} = u_{,y} + v_{,x} \qquad \omega_x = \tfrac{1}{2}(w_{,y} - v_{,z}) \qquad (1\text{-}16)$$

$$\omega_y = \tfrac{1}{2}(u_{,z} - w_{,x}) \qquad \omega_z = \tfrac{1}{2}(v_{,x} - u_{,y})$$

In this equation u, v, w are the displacement components in the x, y, and z directions, respectively, and a comma denotes partial differentiation with respect to the corresponding coordinates.

The Kirchhoff stress tensor corresponds to the Green strain tensor, both referring to the initial undeformed configuration. The nonlinear equations of motion expressed in terms of these stress components (Ref. 1.1) can be expressed in the conventional form

$$\{\sigma_x(1 + e_x) + \sigma_{xy}(\tfrac{1}{2}e_{xy} - \omega_z) + \sigma_{xz}(\tfrac{1}{2}e_{zx} + \omega_y)\}_{,x}$$
$$+ \{\sigma_{yx}(1 + e_x) + \sigma_y(\tfrac{1}{2}e_{xy} - \omega_z) + \sigma_{yz}(\tfrac{1}{2}e_{zx} + \omega_y)\}_{,y}$$
$$+ \{\sigma_{zx}(1 + e_x) + \sigma_{zy}(\tfrac{1}{2}e_{xy} - \omega_z) + \sigma_z(\tfrac{1}{2}e_{zx} + \omega_y)\}_{,z}$$
$$+ f_x = \rho_0 u_{,tt} \qquad (1\text{-}17)$$

$$\{\sigma_x(\tfrac{1}{2}e_{xy} + \omega_z) + \sigma_{xy}(1 + e_y) + \sigma_{xz}(\tfrac{1}{2}e_{yz} - \omega_x)\}_{,x}$$
$$+ \{\sigma_{yx}(\tfrac{1}{2}e_{xy} + \omega_z) + \sigma_y(1 + e_y) + \sigma_{yz}(\tfrac{1}{2}e_{yz} - \omega_x)\}_{,y}$$
$$+ \{\sigma_{zx}(\tfrac{1}{2}e_{xy} + \omega_z) + \sigma_{zy}(1 + e_y) + \sigma_z(\tfrac{1}{2}e_{yz} - \omega_x)\}_{,z}$$
$$+ f_y = \rho_0 v_{,tt}$$

▼

▼

$$\{\sigma_x(\tfrac{1}{2}e_{zx} - \omega_y) + \sigma_{xy}(\tfrac{1}{2}e_{yz} + \omega_x) + \sigma_{xz}(1 + e_x)\}_{,x}$$

$$+ \{\sigma_{yx}(\tfrac{1}{2}e_{zx} - \omega_y) + \sigma_y(\tfrac{1}{2}e_{yz} + \omega_x) + \sigma_{yz}(1 + e_z)\}_{,y}$$

$$+ \{\sigma_{zx}(\tfrac{1}{2}e_{zx} - \omega_y) + \sigma_{zy}(\tfrac{1}{2}e_{yz} + \omega_x) + \sigma_z(1 + e_z)\}_{,z}$$

$$+ f_z = \rho_0 w_{,tt}$$

in which f_x, f_y, f_z are the components of the body force in the x, y, and z directions, respectively, ρ_0 is the mass density, both referring to the original volume, and t denotes the time.

In the case when linear strains and the squares of angles of rotation are small compared to unity, equations (1-15) may be simplified to yield

$$\varepsilon_x = e_x + \tfrac{1}{2}(\omega_z^2 + \omega_y^2)$$

$$\varepsilon_y = e_y + \tfrac{1}{2}(\omega_z^2 + \omega_x^2)$$

$$\varepsilon_z = e_z + \tfrac{1}{2}(\omega_y^2 + \omega_x^2)$$

$$\varepsilon_{yz} = e_{yz} - \omega_y\omega_z \tag{1-18}$$

$$\varepsilon_{zx} = e_{zx} - \omega_z\omega_x$$

$$\varepsilon_{xy} = e_{xy} - \omega_x\omega_y$$

and equations (1-17) to

$$(\sigma_x - \sigma_{xy}\omega_z + \sigma_{xz}\omega_y)_{,x} + (\sigma_{xy} - \sigma_y\omega_z + \sigma_{yz}\omega_y)_{,y}$$

$$+ (\sigma_{zx} - \sigma_{zy}\omega_z + \sigma_z\omega_y)_{,z} + f_x = \rho_0 u_{,tt}$$

$$(\sigma_x\omega_z + \sigma_{xy} - \sigma_{xz}\omega_x)_{,x} + (\sigma_{yx}\omega_z + \sigma_y - \sigma_{yz}\omega_x)_{,y}$$

$$+ (\sigma_{zx}\omega_z + \sigma_{yz} - \sigma_z\omega_x)_{,z} + f_y = \rho_0 v_{,tt} \tag{1-19}$$

$$(\sigma_{xz} - \sigma_x\omega_y + \sigma_{xy}\omega_x)_{,x} + (\sigma_{yz} - \sigma_{yx}\omega_y + \sigma_y\omega_x)_{,y}$$

$$+ (\sigma_z - \sigma_{zx}\omega_y + \sigma_{zy}\omega_x)_{,z} + f_z = \rho_0 w_{,tt}$$

It should be noted (Ref. 1.2) that equations (1-19) are not the consequence of equations (1-18), and that these two sets of equations represent a simplified version of equations (1-15) and (1-17).

In the case when a plate is a massive body in its plane, the rotation about an axis normal to the plate is generally much smaller than those about axes in the plane of the plate, especially for the thickness of a plate much smaller than the other plate dimensions. Therefore, the terms containing ω_z may be neglected in calculation of strains and stresses. Applying this assumption to equations (1-18) and (1-19) leads to the strain-displacement relations

$$\varepsilon_x = e_x + \tfrac{1}{2}\omega_y^2 \qquad \varepsilon_y = e_y + \tfrac{1}{2}\omega_x^2$$

$$\varepsilon_z = e_z + \tfrac{1}{2}(\omega_x^2 + \omega_y^2) \qquad \varepsilon_{yz} = e_{yz} \tag{1-20}$$

$$\varepsilon_{zx} = e_{zx} \qquad \varepsilon_{xy} = e_{xy} - \omega_x\omega_y$$

and the equations of motion

$$
\begin{aligned}
&\left(\sigma_x + \sigma_{xz}\omega_y\right)_{,x} + \left(\sigma_{xy} + \sigma_{yz}\omega_y\right)_{,y} \\
&\quad + \left(\sigma_{zx} + \sigma_z\omega_y\right)_{,z} + f_x = \rho_0 u_{,tt} \\
&\left(\sigma_{xy} - \sigma_{xz}\omega_x\right)_{,x} + \left(\sigma_y - \sigma_{yz}\omega_x\right)_{,y} \\
&\quad + \left(\sigma_{yz} - \sigma_z\omega_x\right)_{,z} + f_y = \rho_0 v_{,tt} \\
&\left(\sigma_{xz} - \sigma_x\omega_y + \sigma_{xy}\omega_x\right)_{,x} + \left(\sigma_{yz} - \sigma_{xy}\omega_y + \sigma_y\omega_x\right)_{,y} \\
&\quad + \left(\sigma_z - \sigma_{zx}\omega_y + \sigma_{zy}\omega_x\right)_{,z} + f_z = \rho_0 w_{,tt}
\end{aligned}
\tag{1-21}
$$

The strain-displacement relations (1-20) and equations of motion (1-21), as well as the constitutive relations for anisotropic material discussed in the next section, constitute a simplified nonlinear theory of anisotropic elasticity. This theory will be used in the derivation of nonlinear equations of motion of plates.

1.3 GENERALIZED HOOKE'S LAW

Throughout the book the material of a body or plate is assumed to be linearly elastic. The stress then depends only on the deformation and not on the history of that deformation. A body whose elastic properties are different for different directions is called anisotropic. The generalized Hooke's law for a homogeneous elastic body of general anisotropy can be expressed in the matrix form

$$
\begin{Bmatrix}
\varepsilon_x \\ \varepsilon_y \\ \varepsilon_z \\ \varepsilon_{yz} \\ \varepsilon_{zx} \\ \varepsilon_{xy}
\end{Bmatrix}
=
\begin{bmatrix}
r_{11} & r_{12} & r_{13} & r_{14} & r_{15} & r_{16} \\
r_{12} & r_{22} & r_{23} & r_{24} & r_{25} & r_{26} \\
r_{13} & r_{23} & r_{33} & r_{34} & r_{35} & r_{36} \\
r_{14} & r_{24} & r_{34} & r_{44} & r_{45} & r_{46} \\
r_{15} & r_{25} & r_{35} & r_{45} & r_{55} & r_{56} \\
r_{16} & r_{26} & r_{36} & r_{46} & r_{56} & r_{66}
\end{bmatrix}
\begin{Bmatrix}
\sigma_x \\ \sigma_y \\ \sigma_z \\ \sigma_{yz} \\ \sigma_{zx} \\ \sigma_{xy}
\end{Bmatrix}
\tag{1-22}
$$

where the coefficients r_{ij} are the elastic compliances. The number of independent elastic constants is 21 in the general case. If, however, any planes of elastic symmetry are present in elastic properties, this number is reduced.

For an anisotropic body having elastic symmetry with respect to a plane, say, $z = \text{const}$, each point of the body has a plane normal to the z axis with such elastic properties that any two directions symmetrical with respect to the plane are identical. In this case the compliance matrix in equation (1-22) reduces to

$$
\begin{bmatrix}
r_{11} & r_{12} & r_{13} & 0 & 0 & r_{16} \\
r_{12} & r_{22} & r_{23} & 0 & 0 & r_{26} \\
r_{13} & r_{23} & r_{33} & 0 & 0 & r_{36} \\
0 & 0 & 0 & r_{44} & r_{45} & 0 \\
0 & 0 & 0 & r_{45} & r_{55} & 0 \\
r_{16} & r_{26} & r_{36} & 0 & 0 & r_{66}
\end{bmatrix}
\tag{1-23}
$$

in which the independent elastic constants are 13 in number.

In the case of an orthotropic body there are three mutually perpendicular planes of elastic symmetry. The matrix (1-23) becomes

$$
\begin{bmatrix}
r_{11} & r_{12} & r_{13} & 0 & 0 & 0 \\
r_{12} & r_{22} & r_{23} & 0 & 0 & 0 \\
r_{13} & r_{23} & r_{33} & 0 & 0 & 0 \\
0 & 0 & 0 & r_{44} & 0 & 0 \\
0 & 0 & 0 & 0 & r_{55} & 0 \\
0 & 0 & 0 & 0 & 0 & r_{66}
\end{bmatrix}
\tag{1-24}
$$

where there are nine independent elastic constants.

For a body having a plane of isotropy at every material point, the elastic properties in the plane are identical in all directions. Such a body is called transversely isotropic or transtropic. If the x axis is perpendicular to this plane, then the matrix (1-24) reduces to

$$
\begin{bmatrix}
r_{11} & r_{12} & r_{12} & 0 & 0 & 0 \\
r_{12} & r_{22} & r_{23} & 0 & 0 & 0 \\
r_{12} & r_{23} & r_{22} & 0 & 0 & 0 \\
0 & 0 & 0 & 2(r_{22}-r_{23}) & 0 & 0 \\
0 & 0 & 0 & 0 & r_{66} & 0 \\
0 & 0 & 0 & 0 & 0 & r_{66}
\end{bmatrix}
\tag{1-25}
$$

in which there are five independent elastic constants. In the case of completely isotropic material, the elastic properties are independent of direction such that

$$
r_{22} = r_{11} \qquad r_{23} = r_{12} \qquad r_{66} = 2(r_{11} - r_{12})
\tag{1-26}
$$

and the number of independent elastic constants is reduced to two.

It is evident from the symmetric compliance matrix (1-24) that the constitutive relations for an orthotropic material can be written in the so-called engineering constants as follows

$$
\begin{Bmatrix}
\varepsilon_x \\
\varepsilon_y \\
\varepsilon_z \\
\varepsilon_{yz} \\
\varepsilon_{zx} \\
\varepsilon_{xy}
\end{Bmatrix}
=
\begin{bmatrix}
\dfrac{1}{E_1} & -\dfrac{v_{21}}{E_2} & -\dfrac{v_{31}}{E_3} & 0 & 0 & 0 \\[2mm]
-\dfrac{v_{12}}{E_1} & \dfrac{1}{E_2} & -\dfrac{v_{32}}{E_3} & 0 & 0 & 0 \\[2mm]
-\dfrac{v_{13}}{E_1} & -\dfrac{v_{23}}{E_2} & \dfrac{1}{E_3} & 0 & 0 & 0 \\[2mm]
0 & 0 & 0 & \dfrac{1}{G_{23}} & 0 & 0 \\[2mm]
0 & 0 & 0 & 0 & \dfrac{1}{G_{13}} & 0 \\[2mm]
0 & 0 & 0 & 0 & 0 & \dfrac{1}{G_{12}}
\end{bmatrix}
\begin{Bmatrix}
\sigma_x \\
\sigma_y \\
\sigma_z \\
\sigma_{yz} \\
\sigma_{zx} \\
\sigma_{xy}
\end{Bmatrix}
\tag{1-27}
$$

in which E_i are the Young's moduli along the i principal direction of elasticity, v_{ij} are the Poisson's ratios characterizing contraction in the j direction during tension applied in the i direction, and G_{ij} are the shear moduli characterizing changes of angles in the ij planes. Due to the symmetric compliance matrix the elastic constants in equations (1-27) are related by

$$v_{12} E_2 = v_{21} E_1 \qquad v_{23} E_3 = v_{32} E_2$$

$$v_{31} E_1 = v_{13} E_3 \tag{1-28}$$

The constitutive relations for transversely isotropic material can be expressed in terms of engineering constants as

$$\varepsilon_x = \frac{1}{E_1} \sigma_x - \frac{v_{12}}{E_1} (\sigma_y + \sigma_z) \qquad \varepsilon_{yz} = \frac{1}{G} \sigma_{yz}$$

$$\varepsilon_y = \frac{1}{E} (\sigma_y - v\sigma_z) - \frac{v_{12}}{E_1} \sigma_x \qquad \varepsilon_{zx} = \frac{1}{G_{12}} \sigma_{zx} \tag{1-29}$$

$$\varepsilon_z = \frac{1}{E} (\sigma_z - v\sigma_y) - \frac{v_{12}}{E_1} \sigma_x \qquad \varepsilon_{xy} = \frac{1}{G_{12}} \sigma_{xy}$$

where E, v, and $G = E/[2(1 + v)]$ are the modulus of elasticity (or Young's modulus), Poisson's ratio, and shear modulus in the plane of isotropy, respectively and where E_1 is Young's modulus in the direction perpendicular to this plane, G_{12} is the shear modulus characterizing change of the angle between the isotropic plane and its normal, and v_{12} is Poisson's ratio representing the contraction in the plane of isotropy for tension applied perpendicular to this plane. For an isotropic body, equations (1-29) reduce to

$$\varepsilon_x = \frac{1}{E} [\sigma_x - v(\sigma_y + \sigma_z)] \qquad \varepsilon_{yz} = \frac{1}{G} \sigma_{yz}$$

$$\varepsilon_y = \frac{1}{E} [\sigma_y - v(\sigma_x + \sigma_z)] \qquad \varepsilon_{zx} = \frac{1}{G} \sigma_{zx} \tag{1-30}$$

$$\varepsilon_z = \frac{1}{E} [\sigma_z - v(\sigma_x + \sigma_y)] \qquad \varepsilon_{xy} = \frac{1}{G} \sigma_{xy}$$

In the case of cylindrical anisotropy the equations of the generalized Hooke's law can be similarly obtained by use of cylindrical coordinates r, θ, z. For example, the constitutive relations for a cylindrically orthotropic material are given by

$$
\begin{Bmatrix} \varepsilon_r \\ \varepsilon_\theta \\ \varepsilon_z \\ \varepsilon_{\theta z} \\ \varepsilon_{zr} \\ \varepsilon_{r\theta} \end{Bmatrix}
=
\begin{bmatrix}
\dfrac{1}{E_r} & -\dfrac{v_{\theta r}}{E_\theta} & -\dfrac{v_{zr}}{E_z} & 0 & 0 & 0 \\[2mm]
-\dfrac{v_{r\theta}}{E_r} & \dfrac{1}{E_\theta} & -\dfrac{v_{z\theta}}{E_z} & 0 & 0 & 0 \\[2mm]
-\dfrac{v_{rz}}{E_r} & -\dfrac{v_{\theta z}}{E_\theta} & \dfrac{1}{E_z} & 0 & 0 & 0 \\[2mm]
0 & 0 & 0 & \dfrac{1}{G_{\theta z}} & 0 & 0 \\[2mm]
0 & 0 & 0 & 0 & \dfrac{1}{G_{rz}} & 0 \\[2mm]
0 & 0 & 0 & 0 & 0 & \dfrac{1}{G_{r\theta}}
\end{bmatrix}
\begin{Bmatrix} \sigma_r \\ \sigma_\theta \\ \sigma_z \\ \sigma_{\theta z} \\ \sigma_{zr} \\ \sigma_{r\theta} \end{Bmatrix}
\tag{1-31}
$$

in which ε's and σ's are components of stress and strain in cylindrical coordinates and E's and v's are similarly defined as in equation (1-27) and satisfy the relations similar to expressions (1-28).

1.4 EQUATIONS OF TRANSFORMATION FOR ELASTIC CONSTANTS

In practical problems the elastic constants of a body are sometimes known in a reference coordinate system, but required to be determined with reference to a new coordinate system. In the case of general anisotropy the classical transformation equations for a rotation of the coordinate axes through an angle θ about the z axis (Fig. 1.3) are given by

$$r'_{11} = c^4 r_{11} + c^2 s^2 (2r_{12} + r_{66}) + 2cs(c^2 r_{16} + s^2 r_{26}) + s^4 r_{22}$$

$$r'_{12} = c^2 s^2 (r_{11} + r_{22} - r_{66}) + (c^4 + s^4) r_{12}$$
$$\quad + cs(s^2 - c^2)(r_{16} - r_{26})$$

$$r'_{13} = c^2 r_{13} + s^2 r_{23} + csr_{36}$$

$$r'_{14} = c^3 r_{14} - cs[c(r_{15} - r_{46}) - s(r_{24} - r_{56})] - s^3 r_{25}$$

$$r'_{15} = c^3 r_{15} + cs[c(r_{14} + r_{56}) + s(r_{25} + r_{46})] + s^3 r_{24}$$

$$r'_{16} = c^2(c^2 - 3s^2) r_{16} - cs$$
$$\quad \cdot [2c^2 r_{11} - 2s^2 r_{22} - (c^2 - s^2)(2r_{12} + r_{66})]$$
$$\quad + s^2(3c^2 - s^2) r_{26}$$

$$r'_{22} = s^4 r_{11} + c^2 s^2 (2r_{12} + r_{66}) - 2cs(s^2 r_{16} + c^2 r_{26} + c^4 r_{22})$$

$$r'_{23} = s^2 r_{13} + c^2 r_{23} - csr_{36}$$

$$r'_{24} = c^3 r_{24} - s^3 r_{15} + cs[s(r_{14} + r_{56}) - c(r_{25} + r_{46})]$$

▼

$$r'_{25} = s^3 r_{14} + cs^2(r_{15} - r_{46}) + c^2 s(r_{24} - r_{56}) + c^3 r_{25}$$

$$r'_{26} = cs[(s^2 - c^2)(2r_{12} + r_{66}) - 2(s^2 r_{11} - c^2 r_{22})]$$
$$+ s^2(3c^2 - s^2)r_{16} + c^2(c^2 - 3s^2)r_{26}$$

$$r'_{33} = r_{33}$$

$$r'_{34} = cr_{34} - sr_{35}$$

$$r'_{35} = sr_{34} + cr_{35}$$

$$r'_{36} = 2cs(r_{23} - r_{13}) + (c^2 - s^2)r_{36}$$

$$r'_{44} = c^2 r_{44} - 2csr_{45} + s^2 r_{55}$$

$$r'_{45} = cs(r_{44} - r_{55}) + (c^2 - s^2)r_{45} \qquad (1\text{-}32)$$

$$r'_{46} = 2cs[s(r_{15} - r_{25}) - c(r_{14} - r_{24})] + (c^3 - cs^2)r_{46}$$
$$+ (s^3 - c^2 s)r_{56}$$

$$r'_{55} = s^2 r_{44} + 2csr_{45} + c^2 r_{55}$$

$$r'_{56} = 2cs[s(r_{24} - r_{14}) - c(r_{15} - r_{25})] + (c^2 s - s^3)r_{46}$$
$$+ (c^3 - cs^2)r_{56}$$

$$r'_{66} = 4c^2 s^2(r_{11} - 2r_{12} + r_{22}) + 4cs(s^2 - c^2)(r_{16} - r_{26})$$
$$+ (c^2 - s^2)^2 r_{66}$$

in which r'_{ij} are the elastic compliances referred to the new system of rectangular cartesian coordinates x', y', z, and in which c and s are given by equations (1-14).

For an anisotropic material having elastic symmetry with respect to the plane, $z = $ const, the generalized Hooke's law with the compliance matrix (1-23) can be written in the form

$$
\begin{Bmatrix} \sigma_x \\ \sigma_y \\ \sigma_z \\ \sigma_{yz} \\ \sigma_{zx} \\ \sigma_{xy} \end{Bmatrix}
=
\begin{bmatrix}
s_{11} & s_{12} & s_{13} & 0 & 0 & s_{16} \\
s_{12} & s_{22} & s_{23} & 0 & 0 & s_{26} \\
s_{13} & s_{23} & s_{33} & 0 & 0 & s_{36} \\
0 & 0 & 0 & s_{44} & s_{45} & 0 \\
0 & 0 & 0 & s_{45} & s_{55} & 0 \\
s_{16} & s_{26} & s_{36} & 0 & 0 & s_{66}
\end{bmatrix}
\begin{Bmatrix} \varepsilon_x \\ \varepsilon_y \\ \varepsilon_z \\ \varepsilon_{yz} \\ \varepsilon_{zx} \\ \varepsilon_{xy} \end{Bmatrix}
\qquad (1\text{-}33)
$$

in which s_{ij} are the elastic stiffnesses. In the case of the generalized plane stress (say, $\sigma_z = \sigma_{yz} = \sigma_{zx} = 0$) ε_z can be expressed in terms of ε_x, ε_y, and ε_{xy} by use of the third of relations (1-33). Consequently, the constitutive equations (1-33) simplify to yield

$$
\begin{Bmatrix} \sigma_x \\ \sigma_y \\ \sigma_{xy} \end{Bmatrix}
=
\begin{bmatrix}
C_{11} & C_{12} & C_{16} \\
C_{12} & C_{22} & C_{26} \\
C_{16} & C_{26} & C_{66}
\end{bmatrix}
\begin{Bmatrix} \varepsilon_x \\ \varepsilon_y \\ \varepsilon_{xy} \end{Bmatrix}
\qquad (1\text{-}34)
$$

where C_{ij} are the reduced stiffnesses given by

$$C_{ij} = s_{ij} - \frac{s_{i3} s_{j3}}{s_{33}} \qquad (i, j = 1, 2, 6) \tag{1-35}$$

It is observed that equation (1-34) also represents the stress-strain relations for an orthotropic plate having arbitrary principal directions of elasticity with respect to the plate axes. In engineering applications the elastic properties of an orthotropic plate are usually known in the principal directions (L, T) of elasticity. The plane-stress reduced stiffnesses are related to these material axes of symmetry by

$$C_L = \frac{E_L}{\mu} \qquad C_{LT} = \frac{v_{LT} E_T}{\mu}$$

$$C_T = \frac{E_T}{\mu} \qquad C_S = G_{LT} \tag{1-36}$$

in which E_L and E_T are major and minor Young's moduli, v_{LT} and v_{TL} are the Poisson's ratios, and G_{LT} is the shear modulus, and in which

$$\mu = 1 - v_{LT} v_{TL}$$

$$v_{TL} E_L = v_{LT} E_T \tag{1-37}$$

The elastic constants of the material with reference to arbitrary orthogonal directions (1, 2) can be found by the following transformation equations

$$\begin{Bmatrix} C_{11} \\ C_{12} \\ C_{22} \\ C_{16} \\ C_{26} \\ C_{66} \end{Bmatrix} = \begin{bmatrix} c^4 & 2c^2s^2 & s^4 & 4c^2s^2 \\ c^2s^2 & c^4 + s^4 & c^2s^2 & -4c^2s^2 \\ s^4 & 2c^2s^2 & c^4 & 4c^2s^2 \\ c^3s & cs^3 - c^3s & -cs^3 & -2cs(c^2 - s^2) \\ cs^3 & c^3s - cs^3 & -c^3s & 2cs(c^2 - s^2) \\ c^2s^2 & -2c^2s^2 & c^2s^2 & (c^2 - s^2)^2 \end{bmatrix} \begin{Bmatrix} C_L \\ C_{LT} \\ C_T \\ C_S \end{Bmatrix} \tag{1-38}$$

where c and s are given by equations (1-14) with θ being the angle measured from the L axis to the x axis.

1.5 NONLINEAR EQUATIONS OF MOTION OF GENERALLY LAMINATED PLATES

Consider a thin plane plate of variable thickness referred to a right-handed cartesian system of coordinates x, y, z. The reference plane $z = 0$ may be chosen at an arbitrary location through the undeformed plate and the z axis is directed normal to the reference plane. The generators of the cylindrical boundaries of the undeformed plate lie along the normal to the reference plane. In the application of equations (1-20) and (1-21) to the thin plate, some further assumptions will be made in the due course of derivation of plate equations.

In most practical applications, the thickness of a plate is small in comparison with its smallest lateral dimension, and hence Kirchhoff's hypothesis may be assumed to be valid. That is, tractions on surfaces parallel to the reference plane are negligibly small as compared with the inplane stresses, and the inplane displacements are linear functions of z. Under this assumption the inplane displacements u, v and the transverse deflection w at an arbitrary point of the plate in the x, y, and z directions may be approximated by

$$u(x, y, z, t) = u°(x, y, t) - zw°_{,x}$$
$$v(x, y, z, t) = v°(x, y, t) - zw°_{,y} \qquad (1\text{-}39)$$
$$w(x, y, z, t) = w°(x, y, t)$$

in which $u°$, $v°$, and $w°$ are the values of u, v, and w at the reference plane. In the case of constant thickness with the reference plane at the midplane of the undeformed plate, $w°$ characterizes the classical plate theory, $u°$ and $v°$ serve to describe the displacements in the plane of the plate, and the static displacements given by equations (1-39) are those of the von Kármán plate theory (Ref. 1.3).

Introduction of equations (1-39) into (1-16) yields

$$e_x = u°_{,x} - zw_{,xx} \qquad e_y = v°_{,y} - zw_{,yy}$$
$$e_{xy} = u°_{,y} + v°_{,x} - 2zw_{,xy} \qquad (1\text{-}40)$$
$$\omega_x = w_{,y} \qquad \omega_y = -w_{,x}$$

where the superscript o to w has been omitted for convenience. In view of relations (1-40), equations (1-20) become

$$\varepsilon_x = \varepsilon°_x + z\kappa_x \qquad \varepsilon_y = \varepsilon°_y + z\kappa_y$$
$$\varepsilon_{xy} = \varepsilon°_{xy} + z\kappa_{xy} \qquad (1\text{-}41)$$

in which the nonvanishing strain ε_z has not been presented herein and in which $\varepsilon°_x$, $\varepsilon°_y$, and $\varepsilon°_{xy}$ are reference surface strains at $z = 0$ defined by

$$\varepsilon°_x = u°_{,x} + \tfrac{1}{2}w^2_{,x} \qquad \varepsilon°_y = v°_{,y} + \tfrac{1}{2}w^2_{,y}$$
$$\varepsilon°_{xy} = u°_{,y} + v°_{,x} + w_{,x}w_{,y} \qquad (1\text{-}42)$$

and κ_x, κ_y, and κ_{xy} are the plate curvatures given by

$$\kappa_x = -w_{,xx} \qquad \kappa_y = -w_{,yy} \qquad \kappa_{xy} = -2w_{,xy} \qquad (1\text{-}43)$$

The nonlinear strain-displacement relations given by equations (1-42) are those of von Kármán (Ref. 1.4), and equations (1-43) imply that the squares of plate slopes (or rotations) are small compared to unity.

Applying Kirchhoff's hypothesis to equations (1-21) and taking into account equations (1-39) and (1-40) leads to the following equations of motion

$$\sigma_{x,x} + \sigma_{xy,y} + \sigma_{zx,z} + f_x = \rho_0(u°_{,tt} - zw_{,xtt}) \qquad (1\text{-}44)$$
$$\sigma_{xy,x} + \sigma_{y,y} + \sigma_{yz,z} + f_y = \rho_0(v°_{,tt} - zw_{,ytt}) \qquad (1\text{-}45)$$

$$(\sigma_{xz} + \sigma_x w_{,x} + \sigma_{xy} w_{,y})_{,x} + (\sigma_{yz} + \sigma_{xy} w_{,x} + \sigma_y w_{,y})_{,y}$$

$$+ (\sigma_z + \sigma_{zx} w_{,x} + \sigma_{zy} w_{,y})_{,z} + f_z = \rho_0 w_{,tt} \tag{1-46}$$

These simplified equations of motion with the rotatory inertia terms $\rho_0\, zw_{,xtt}$ and $\rho_0\, zw_{,ytt}$ to be neglected, can be directly obtained from equations (1-17) by the ad hoc assumption that the nonlinear terms involving products of stresses and plate slopes are retained in these equations. The corresponding simplified version of strain-displacement relations in the approximate sense are given by equations (1-41).

The type of plate under consideration is constructed of an arbitrary number of homogeneous orthotropic layers perfectly bonded together. Each layer has arbitrary elastic properties and orientation of orthotropic axes with respect to the plate axes. The geometry of the kth layer is defined by two planes $z = f_{k-1}(x, y)$ and $z = f_k(x, y)$, and the upper and lower boundary planes are defined by $z = -h_1(x, y)$ and $z = h_2(x, y)$ from the reference plane. The total thickness of the laminate given by $h = h_1 + h_2$, however, is small compared to its smallest lateral dimension. The plate materials are continuous everywhere and each layer obeys the generalized Hooke's law.

Under Kirchhoff's hypothesis the plate is in an approximate state of plane stress. By use of the plane-stress constitutive equation (1-34), we have for the kth layer (Ref. 1.5)

$$\begin{Bmatrix} \sigma_x^{(k)} \\ \sigma_y^{(k)} \\ \sigma_{xy}^{(k)} \end{Bmatrix} = \begin{bmatrix} C_{11}^{(k)} & C_{12}^{(k)} & C_{16}^{(k)} \\ C_{12}^{(k)} & C_{22}^{(k)} & C_{26}^{(k)} \\ C_{16}^{(k)} & C_{26}^{(k)} & C_{66}^{(k)} \end{bmatrix} \begin{Bmatrix} \varepsilon_x \\ \varepsilon_y \\ \varepsilon_{xy} \end{Bmatrix} \tag{1-47}$$

in which $C_{ij}^{(k)}$ are the reduced stiffnesses of the kth layer.

As in the classical plate theory, the stress resultants and couples are defined by

$$[N_x, N_y, N_{xy}] = \int_{-h_1}^{h_2} [\sigma_x^{(k)}, \sigma_y^{(k)}, \sigma_{xy}^{(k)}]\, dz \tag{1-48}$$

$$[Q_x, Q_y] = \int_{-h_1}^{h_2} [\sigma_{xz}^{(k)}, \sigma_{yz}^{(k)}]\, dz \tag{1-49}$$

$$[M_x, M_y, M_{xy}] = \int_{-h_1}^{h_2} [\sigma_x^{(k)}, \sigma_y^{(k)}, \sigma_{xy}^{(k)}] z\, dz \tag{1-50}$$

in which N_x, N_y, N_{xy} are membrane forces, Q_x, Q_y are transverse shear forces, and M_x, M_y, M_{xy} are bending and twisting moments, all per unit length. These forces and moments are shown in Fig. 1.4. Substituting equation (1-47) into equations (1-48) and (1-50), and taking equations (1-41) into account, yields the constitutive relations of the plate

$$\begin{Bmatrix} N \\ M \end{Bmatrix} = \begin{bmatrix} A & B \\ B & D \end{bmatrix} \begin{Bmatrix} \varepsilon^\circ \\ \kappa \end{Bmatrix} \tag{1-51}$$

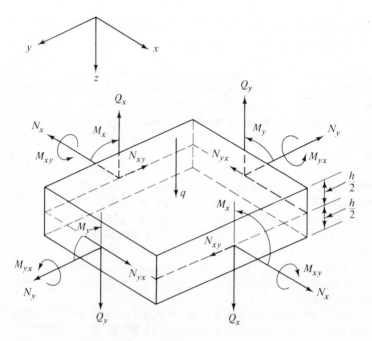

Figure 1.4 Senses of positive stress resultants and couples in rectangular cartesian coordinates.

where

$$\mathbf{N} = \begin{Bmatrix} N_x \\ N_y \\ N_{xy} \end{Bmatrix} \qquad \mathbf{M} = \begin{Bmatrix} M_x \\ M_y \\ M_{xy} \end{Bmatrix} \qquad \mathbf{A} = \begin{bmatrix} A_{11} & A_{12} & A_{16} \\ A_{12} & A_{22} & A_{26} \\ A_{16} & A_{26} & A_{66} \end{bmatrix}$$

$$\mathbf{B} = \begin{bmatrix} B_{11} & B_{12} & B_{16} \\ B_{12} & B_{22} & B_{26} \\ B_{16} & B_{26} & B_{66} \end{bmatrix} \qquad \mathbf{D} = \begin{bmatrix} D_{11} & D_{12} & D_{16} \\ D_{12} & D_{22} & D_{26} \\ D_{16} & D_{26} & D_{66} \end{bmatrix} \qquad (1\text{-}52)$$

$$\boldsymbol{\varepsilon}^{\circ} = \begin{Bmatrix} \varepsilon_x^{\circ} \\ \varepsilon_y^{\circ} \\ \varepsilon_{xy}^{\circ} \end{Bmatrix} \qquad \boldsymbol{\kappa} = \begin{Bmatrix} \kappa_x \\ \kappa_y \\ \kappa_{xy} \end{Bmatrix}$$

The elements A_{ij}, B_{ij}, and D_{ij} in equations (1-52) are given by

$$(A_{ij}, B_{ij}, D_{ij}) = \int_{-h_1}^{h_2} C_{ij}^{(k)}(1, z, z^2)\, dz \qquad (1\text{-}53)$$

which vary generally as functions of x and y and in which A_{ij}, B_{ij}, and D_{ij} are, respectively, the membrane rigidities, coupling rigidities, and flexural rigidities of the plate. The rigidities B_{ij} display coupling between transverse bending and inplane stretching. The coupling will disappear when $C_{ij}^{(k)}$ is an even function of z for the plate with $h_1 = h_2$.

The equations of motion of the plate are obtained by applying equations (1-44) to (1-46) to the kth layer and integrating with respect to z over the plate thickness, three equations can be obtained. Multiplying each of equations (1-44) and (1-45) by z and integrating in a similar manner leads to the other two equations. The resulting system of plate equations of motion (Ref. 1.6) is of the form

$$N_{x,x} + N_{xy,y} + q_x = \rho u^\circ_{,tt} - I w_{,xtt} \tag{1-54}$$

$$N_{xy,x} + N_{y,y} + q_y = \rho v^\circ_{,tt} - I w_{,ytt} \tag{1-55}$$

$$N_x w_{,xx} + 2 N_{xy} w_{,xy} + N_y w_{,yy} + Q_{x,x} + Q_{y,y}$$
$$+ w_{,x}(N_{x,x} + N_{xy,y}) + w_{,y}(N_{xy,x} + N_{y,y}) + q_z = \rho w_{,tt} \tag{1-56}$$

$$M_{x,x} + M_{xy,y} - Q_x + m_x = I u^\circ_{,tt} - J w_{,xtt} \tag{1-57}$$

$$M_{xy,x} + M_{y,y} - Q_y + m_y = I v^\circ_{,tt} - J w_{,ytt} \tag{1-58}$$

where

$$q_\alpha = p_\alpha^+ - p_\alpha^- + \int_{-h_1}^{h_2} f_\alpha^{(k)} \, dz \qquad (\alpha = x, y)$$

$$q_z = \left(\sigma_{zx}^{(k)} w_{,x} + \sigma_{zy}^{(k)} w_{,y}\right)\bigg|_{z=-h_1}^{z=h_2} + p_z^+ - p_z^- + \int_{-h_1}^{h_2} f_z \, dz$$

$$m_\alpha = h_2 p_\alpha^+ + h_1 p_\alpha^- + \int_{-h_1}^{h_2} f_\alpha^{(k)} z \, dz \tag{1-59}$$

$$(\rho, I, J) = \int_{-h_1}^{h_2} \rho_0^{(k)}(1, z, z^2) \, dz$$

In these equations the loading components per unit area in the x, y, and z directions have been represented by p_x^+, p_y^+, p_z^+ on the upper boundary plane and by p_x^-, p_y^-, p_z^- on the lower boundary plane.

In equations (1-54) to (1-58) the terms containing $u^\circ_{,tt}$ and $v^\circ_{,tt}$ arise from the inplane inertia forces, $\rho w_{,tt}$ is the transverse inertia term of the classical plate theory, the terms containing $w_{,xtt}$ and $w_{,ytt}$ are caused by the rotatory inertia effects, q_i ($i = x$, y, z) is the sum of the external forces, and m_α is the sum of the external moments. In equation (1-56) the terms of the type $N_x w_{,xx}$ originated from the change of direction of an element due to curvature are curvature terms (Ref. 1.7) while the terms of the type $w_{,x} N_{x,x}$ are buoyancy terms (Ref. 1.8) because they arise from some kind of buoyancy due to the deformation of an element in its own stress field and depend on the stress gradient. It is observed from the coefficient I defined in equations (1-59) that the rotatory inertia terms in equations (1-54) and (1-55) will disappear when $\rho_0^{(k)}$ is an even function of z for the plate with $h_1 = h_2$. Thus these terms do not appear in the homogeneous plate theory.

Eliminating Q_x and Q_y from equations (1-56) to (1-58) and taking into account equations (1-54) and (1-55) result in

$$M_{x,xx} + 2M_{xy,xy} + M_{y,yy} + N_x w_{,xx} + 2N_{xy} w_{,xy} + N_y w_{,yy}$$
$$+ w_{,x}(\rho u^\circ_{,tt} - I w_{,xtt} - q_x)$$
$$+ w_{,y}(\rho v^\circ_{,tt} - I w_{,ytt} - q_y) + q_z + m_{x,x} + m_{y,y}$$
$$= \rho w_{,tt} + I(u^\circ_{,x} + v^\circ_{,y})_{,tt} - J(w_{,xx} + w_{,yy})_{,tt} \tag{1-60}$$

Equations (1-54), (1-55), and (1-60) constitute a system of equations of motion for the plate. The first two equations describe motions in the plane of the plate and the last describes the transverse motion of the plate.

In most engineering applications of thin plates, body force and rotatory and inplane inertia effects can be neglected, and two boundary planes are free from shear stresses with the upper boundary plane subjected to the transverse normal stress $q(x, y)$. Under these conditions, from equations (1-57) and (1-58) the transverse shear forces yield

$$Q_x = M_{x,x} + M_{xy,y} \qquad Q_y = M_{xy,x} + M_{y,y} \tag{1-61}$$

and equations (1-54), (1-55), and (1-60) become

$$N_{x,x} + N_{xy,y} = 0 \tag{1-62}$$

$$N_{xy,x} + N_{y,y} = 0 \tag{1-63}$$

$$M_{x,xx} + 2M_{xy,xy} + M_{y,yy} + N_x w_{,xx} + 2N_{xy} w_{,xy}$$
$$+ N_y w_{,yy} + q = \rho w_{,tt} \tag{1-64}$$

In the future discussion the plate thickness is assumed to be constant and the reference plane is taken at the midplane of the undeformed plate. Thus

$$h_1 = h_2 = \frac{h}{2} \tag{1-65}$$

and the plate rigidities defined by equations (1-53) are constant.

In the formulation of a plate theory, the material properties of the plate can be taken into account at the final stage. Thus it has been expected that the static version of equations (1-62) to (1-64) are those of the von Kármán plate theory, since the displacement functions given by equations (1-39) have been defined for the entire laminate as a whole rather than different displacement functions have been defined for different layers (Refs. 1.9, 1.10).

In the derivation of the foregoing plate equations of motion, the basic assumption is the Kirchhoff hypothesis implying that the effect of the transverse shear deformation is neglected. The thinner the plate, the more accurate the hypothesis. It is expected that the shear effect on composite plates, especially highly anisotropic materials, is greater than that on homogeneous isotropic plates. In order to gain some idea regarding the range of applicability of the present plate theory, we first examine the classical laminated plate theory, a special case of the present theory which includes the bending-stretching coupling in unsymmetric laminates. This linear plate theory is also adopted in a text (Ref. 1.11). Solutions obtained from the classical laminated plate theory for bending, buckling, and vibration of symmetric and unsymmetric rectangular laminates of high modulus fiber-reinforced composite materials have been compared in literature (Refs. 1.12–1.20) with experimental data, elasticity solution, and those given by more accurate plate theories with the transverse shear included. The latter results asymptotically approach the solutions of the classical laminated plate theory when appropriate parameters in maximum deflection, edge compression, and fundamental frequency are plotted against the span-to-thickness ratio. The effect of shear deformation depends upon plate dimensions, lamination geometry, material properties, and boundary conditions (Ref. 1.21). In general, the classical laminated plate theory underestimates the maximum deflection and overestimates the buckling load and fundamental frequency of a composite plate. The theory yields more reliable results in unsymmetric laminates than in symmetric laminates. The stresses obtained from the theory converge more rapidly than the deflection. That is, the error in stresses is negligibly small although the shear deflections may be as high as 20 percent. The transverse shear effect on deflection, buckling load, and fundamental frequency of composite plates is generally significant at the span-to-thickness ratio of 20. In homogeneous isotropic plates the shear deflection at this span-to-thickness ratio is very small and can be neglected.

The effects of transverse shear and rotatory inertia on the geometrically nonlinear behavior of composite plates have been discussed by several investigators. Based on Berger's approach (see the following paragraph and Prob. 2.6 at the end of Chap. 2) the results for moderately large amplitude vibrations of these plates indicate that the effect of the transverse shear deformation decreases with increasing amplitude (Refs. 1.22–1.24), and that the rotatory inertia effect is small compared with the shear effect (Refs. 1.25, 1.26). A more accurate theory extending the von Kármán plate theory to inclusion of these effects and material anisotropy (Refs. 1.27–1.29) also leads to the same conclusion. To gain some quantitative idea of these influences, let us consider the nonlinear free flexural vibration of a clamped square boron-epoxy plate (Ref. 1.29) whose coordinate axes are at an angle of 40° with the principal axes of elasticity. At the span-to-thickness ratio of 20 the transverse shear effects on the nonlinear period are approximately 10 and 4 percent for the relative amplitude, the ratio of the amplitude to thickness, being 0.5 and 2.0 respectively. The effect of rotatory inertia on the nonlinear period is approximately 0.3 percent for the amplitudes considered. At the span-to-thickness ratio of 30, the transverse shear effect on the linear period is less than 6 percent. Including the effects of transverse shear and rotatory inertia, the nonlinear period increases with the angle of orientation from 0 to 45° for the plate.

In the case of moderately large deflections of symmetric and unsymmetric laminates under transverse load, the results based on the present nonlinear equations agree fairly with the experimental values (Refs. 1.30, 1.31). In order that the present nonlinear plate theory yields reasonable accuracy, roughly speaking the span-to-thickness ratio of a plate based on the foregoing information should not be less than 15 for homogeneous isotropic plates and 25 for composite plates, although the concept of thickness for laminates depends upon material properties as well as lamination geometry. Therefore, the use of the present nonlinear theory of laminated plates in the elastic design of composite skin as in aircraft structures is perfectly adequate.

The assumption imposed on bending curvatures given by equation (1-43) requires that the plate slopes or rotations should be less than 0.2. The limitations in the maximum deflection of a plate depend on the type of loading, boundary conditions, etc. Except for cylindrical bending, the ratio of maximum deflection to thickness generally may not be greater than 2 for rigidly clamped edges and 3 for simply supported edges. In certain cases the present theory, however, agrees closely with the experiment up to the deflection-to-thickness ratio of 6 (Fig. 2.16).

A brief review is herein made regarding the use of Berger equations for nonlinear analysis of elastic plates. Inasmuch as the von Kármán equations of isotropic plates are nonlinear and coupled, their solution is intricate and is known only in simple cases. To avoid difficulties Berger (Ref. 1.32) in 1955 proposed an alternative formulation for the static nonlinear theory of isotropic plates. According to Berger's hypothesis the elastic energy due to the second invariant of the membrane strain may be disregarded as compared to the square of the first invariant without appreciably impairing the accuracy of the results. The Euler-Lagrange equations so derived from the variational equation turn out to be much simpler than those of von Kármán. These differential equations may be treated as linear and uncoupled in the sense that it is possible to find separately the deflection from one equation linear in the deflection, and then the inplane displacement from the remaining equation linear in the displacement. Berger compared his results for large deflections of circular and rectangular plates with available solutions and found good agreement in all cases in which an exact solution was known. Berger's method was favorably accepted by the workers in the field. Consequently this method was applied to large deflections of rectangular plates (Refs. 1.33, 1.34) and nonrectangular plates (Refs. 1.34–1.45) and to postbuckling of circular plates (Ref. 1.46), and was extended to large deflections of orthotropic plates (Refs. 1.47–1.50), to nonlinear vibrations of rectangular plates (Refs. 1.51–1.58), circular plates (Refs. 1.59–1.63), and plates with other shapes (Refs. 1.64–1.70), and also to plate analysis including transverse shear and rotatory inertia (Refs. 1.22–1.26). However, it has not been possible so far to find a convincing mechanical justification of the underlying hypothesis of the vanishing of the second strain invariant in the middle plane of the plate. Most publications on the application of this method report a satisfactory accuracy with reference to a more exact theory. Curiously enough, most of the investigations use an immovable edge condition for the inplane motion. Recently the results in axisymmetric nonlinear bending of circular plates with various edge conditions (Ref. 1.41) revealed that the Berger method of linearizing nonlinear plate equations may lead to grave inaccuracies, and even become meaningless if the edge of the plate is free to move in the inplane directions. A very recent investigation of the variationally derived inplane boundary conditions (Ref. 1.71) revealed that the Berger equations imply zero nonlinearity in the case of plates with edges free from the inplane stress resultants, when the inplane inertia terms are neglected and the material is rectilinearly orthotropic. An extensive study of nonlinear flexural vibrations of rectangular, triangular, and circular plates with all-clamped and all-simply-supported immovable edges was also made in the same reference. The numerical results revealed that the Berger equations do not yield consistently accurate results, and do lead to an entirely different pattern of deformation compared to the von Kármán equations. The foregoing observations may justify certain reservations regarding general applications of the Berger equations.

1.6 EQUATIONS IN TERMS OF THREE DISPLACEMENTS

By virtue of equations (1-51) in conjunction with (1-42) and (1-43), equations (1-62) to (1-64) are reduced to the following system of three equations of order eight for three displacements $u°$, $v°$, and w.

$$L_1 u° + L_2 v° - L_3 w = -w_{,x} L_1 w - w_{,y} L_2 w \tag{1-66}$$

$$L_2 u° + L_4 v° - L_5 w = -w_{,x} L_2 w - w_{,y} L_4 w \tag{1-67}$$

$$L_3 u° + L_5 v° - L_6 w - \rho w_{,tt} = -q - [u°_{,x} + \tfrac{1}{2} w^2_{,x}] L_7 w$$

$$\qquad - [v°_{,y} + \tfrac{1}{2} w^2_{,y}] L_8 w - (u°_{,y} + v°_{,x} + w_{,x} w_{,y}) L_9 w$$

$$\qquad - w_{,x} L_3 w - w_{,y} L_5 w - 2(B_{12} - B_{66})[w^2_{,xy} - w_{,xx} w_{,yy}] \tag{1-68}$$

where L_i are the linear differential operators defined by

$$
\begin{aligned}
L_1 &= A_{11}(\ )_{,xx} + 2A_{16}(\ )_{,xy} + A_{66}(\ )_{,yy} \\
L_2 &= A_{16}(\ )_{,xx} + (A_{12} + A_{66})(\ )_{,xy} + A_{26}(\ )_{,yy} \\
L_3 &= B_{11}(\ )_{,xxx} + 3B_{16}(\ )_{,xxy} + (B_{12} + 2B_{66})(\ )_{,xyy} + B_{26}(\ )_{,yyy} \\
L_4 &= A_{66}(\ )_{,xx} + 2A_{26}(\ )_{,xy} + A_{22}(\ )_{,yy} \\
L_5 &= B_{16}(\ )_{,xxx} + (B_{12} + 2B_{66})(\ )_{,xxy} + 3B_{26}(\ )_{,xyy} + B_{22}(\ )_{,yyy} \\
L_6 &= D_{11}(\ )_{,xxxx} + 4D_{16}(\ )_{,xxxy} + 2(D_{12} + 2D_{66})(\ )_{,xxyy} \\
&\qquad + 4D_{26}(\ )_{,xyyy} + D_{22}(\ )_{,yyyy} \\
L_7 &= A_{11}(\ )_{,xx} + 2A_{16}(\ )_{,xy} + A_{12}(\ )_{,yy} \\
L_8 &= A_{12}(\ )_{,xx} + 2A_{26}(\ )_{,xy} + A_{22}(\ )_{,yy} \\
L_9 &= A_{16}(\ )_{,xx} + 2A_{66}(\ )_{,xy} + A_{26}(\ )_{,yy}
\end{aligned}
\tag{1-69}
$$

The system of equations (1-66) to (1-68) governs the transverse motion of unsymmetrically laminated anisotropic plates.

In view of equations (1-42) and (1-43), equations (1-51) and (1-61) lead to the membrane forces in terms of three displacements

$$N_x = J_{11}(A, u^\circ, v^\circ) - J_{21}(B, w) + J_{31}(A, w)$$
$$N_y = J_{12}(A, u^\circ, v^\circ) - J_{22}(B, w) + J_{32}(A, w) \qquad (1\text{-}70)$$
$$N_{xy} = J_{13}(A, u^\circ, v^\circ) - J_{23}(B, w) + J_{33}(A, w)$$

the bending and twisting moments

$$M_x = J_{11}(B, u^\circ, v^\circ) - J_{21}(D, w) + J_{31}(B, w)$$
$$M_y = J_{12}(B, u^\circ, v^\circ) - J_{22}(D, w) + J_{32}(B, w) \qquad (1\text{-}71)$$
$$M_{xy} = J_{13}(B, u^\circ, v^\circ) - J_{23}(D, w) + J_{33}(B, w)$$

and the transverse shear forces

$$Q_x = \{J_{11}(B, u^\circ, v^\circ) - J_{21}(D, w) + J_{31}(B, w)\}_{,x}$$
$$+ \{J_{13}(B, u^\circ, v^\circ) - J_{23}(D, w) + J_{33}(B, w)\}_{,y}$$
$$Q_y = \{J_{13}(B, u^\circ, v^\circ) - J_{23}(D, w) + J_{33}(B, w)\}_{,x} \qquad (1\text{-}72)$$
$$+ \{J_{12}(B, u^\circ, v^\circ) - J_{22}(D, w) + J_{32}(B, w)\}_{,y}$$

in which the operators J_{ij} are defined by

$$J_{11}((\ ), u^\circ, v^\circ) = (\ )_{11} u^\circ_{,x} + (\ )_{16}(u^\circ_{,y} + v^\circ_{,x}) + (\ )_{12} v^\circ_{,y}$$
$$J_{12}((\ ), u^\circ, v^\circ) = (\ )_{12} u^\circ_{,x} + (\ )_{26}(u^\circ_{,y} + v^\circ_{,x}) + (\ )_{22} v^\circ_{,y}$$
$$J_{13}((\ ), u^\circ, v^\circ) = (\ )_{16} u^\circ_{,x} + (\ )_{66}(u^\circ_{,y} + v^\circ_{,x}) + (\ )_{26} v^\circ_{,y}$$
$$J_{21}((\ ), w) = (\ )_{11} w_{,xx} + 2(\ )_{16} w_{,xy} + (\ )_{12} w_{,yy}$$
$$J_{22}((\ ), w) = (\ )_{12} w_{,xx} + 2(\ )_{26} w_{,xy} + (\ )_{22} w_{,yy} \qquad (1\text{-}73)$$
$$J_{23}((\ ), w) = (\ )_{16} w_{,xx} + 2(\ )_{66} w_{,xy} + (\ )_{26} w_{,yy}$$
$$J_{31}((\ ), w) = \tfrac{1}{2}[(\ )_{11} w^2_{,x} + 2(\ )_{16} w_{,x} w_{,y} + (\ )_{12} w^2_{,y}]$$
$$J_{32}((\ ), w) = \tfrac{1}{2}[(\ )_{12} w^2_{,x} + 2(\ )_{26} w_{,x} w_{,y} + (\ )_{22} w^2_{,y}]$$
$$J_{33}((\ ), w) = \tfrac{1}{2}[(\ )_{16} w^2_{,x} + 2(\ )_{66} w_{,x} w_{,y} + (\ )_{26} w^2_{,y}]$$

Using equations (1-41) to (1-43), the stresses in the kth layer given by the constitutive equation (1-47) are also expressed in terms of three displacements as follows

$$\sigma_x^{(k)} = C_{11}^{(k)}(u^\circ_{,x} + \tfrac{1}{2} w^2_{,x}) + C_{12}^{(k)}(v^\circ_{,y} + \tfrac{1}{2} w^2_{,y}) + C_{16}^{(k)}(u^\circ_{,y} + v^\circ_{,x} + w_{,x} w_{,y})$$
$$- z(C_{11}^{(k)} w_{,xx} + C_{12}^{(k)} w_{,yy} + 2C_{16}^{(k)} w_{,xy})$$
$$\sigma_y^{(k)} = C_{12}^{(k)}(u^\circ_{,x} + \tfrac{1}{2} w^2_{,x}) + C_{22}^{(k)}(v^\circ_{,y} + \tfrac{1}{2} w^2_{,y}) + C_{26}^{(k)}(u^\circ_{,y} + v^\circ_{,x} + w_{,x} w_{,y}) \qquad (1\text{-}74)$$
$$- z(C_{12}^{(k)} w_{,xx} + C_{22}^{(k)} w_{,yy} + 2C_{26}^{(k)} w_{,yy})$$

▼

▼

$$\sigma_{xy}^{(k)} = C_{16}^{(k)}(u^{\circ}_{,x} + \tfrac{1}{2}w^{2}_{,x}) + C_{26}^{(k)}(v^{\circ}_{,y} + \tfrac{1}{2}w^{2}_{,y}) + C_{66}^{(k)}(u^{\circ}_{,y} + v^{\circ}_{,x} + w_{,x}w_{,y}) \quad \blacktriangle$$
$$- z(C_{16}^{(k)}w_{,xx} + C_{26}^{(k)}w_{,yy} + 2C_{66}^{(k)}w_{,xy})$$

Introduction of these expressions in equilibrium equations (1-44) and (1-45) and integration of the resulting equations with respect to z yield

$$\sigma_{zx}^{(k)} = \tfrac{1}{2}z^{2}\{C_{11}^{(k)}w_{,xxx} + 3C_{16}^{(k)}w_{,xxy} + (C_{12}^{(k)} + 2C_{66}^{(k)})w_{,xyy}$$
$$+ C_{26}^{(k)}w_{,yyy}\} - z\{C_{11}^{(k)}u^{\circ}_{,xx} + 2C_{16}^{(k)}u^{\circ}_{,xy} + C_{66}^{(k)}u^{\circ}_{,yy}$$
$$+ C_{16}^{(k)}v^{\circ}_{,xx} + (C_{12}^{(k)} + C_{66}^{(k)})v^{\circ}_{,xy} + C_{26}^{(k)}v^{\circ}_{,yy}$$
$$+ w_{,x}[C_{11}^{(k)}w_{,xx} + 2C_{16}^{(k)}w_{,xy} + C_{66}^{(k)}w_{,yy}]$$
$$+ w_{,y}[C_{16}^{(k)}w_{,xx} + (C_{12}^{(k)} + C_{66}^{(k)})w_{,xy} + C_{26}^{(k)}w_{,yy}]\}$$
$$+ f^{(k)}(x,\ y) \tag{1-75}$$
$$\sigma_{zy}^{(k)} = \tfrac{1}{2}z^{2}\{C_{16}^{(k)}w_{,xxx} + (C_{12}^{(k)} + 2C_{66}^{(k)})w_{,xxy} + 3C_{26}^{(k)}w_{,xyy}$$
$$+ C_{22}^{(k)}w_{,yyy}\} - z\{C_{16}^{(k)}u^{\circ}_{,xx} + (C_{12}^{(k)} + C_{66}^{(k)})u^{\circ}_{,xy}$$
$$+ C_{26}^{(k)}u^{\circ}_{,yy} + C_{66}^{(k)}v^{\circ}_{,xx} + 2C_{26}^{(k)}v^{\circ}_{,xy} + C_{22}^{(k)}v^{\circ}_{,yy}$$
$$+ w_{,x}[C_{16}^{(k)}w_{,xx} + (C_{12}^{(k)} + C_{66}^{(k)})w_{,xy} + C_{26}^{(k)}w_{,yy}]$$
$$+ w_{,y}[C_{66}^{(k)}w_{,xx} + 2C_{26}^{(k)}w_{,xy} + C_{22}^{(k)}w_{,yy}]\} + g^{(k)}(x,\ y)$$

in which the body force and inplane and rotatory inertia terms have been neglected, and in which $f^{(k)}$ and $g^{(k)}$ are functions of integration to be determined by plane boundary conditions, $\sigma_{zx} = \sigma_{zy} = 0$ at $z = \pm h/2$, and by conditions of continuity between layers.

Now the governing equations (1-66) to (1-68) and stress resultants and couples given by equations (1-70) to (1-72) are specified for some particular cases.

a Unsymmetric Angle-Ply Plates

A laminated composite is usually assembled by bonding together undirectional layers of identical mechanical properties (Ref. 1.72). Unsymmetric angle-ply plates consist of an even number of orthotropic plies, all of the same thickness. The orthotropic axes of symmetry are oriented at an angle $-\theta$ with the x axis for odd plies and at an angle $+\theta$ for even plies. In this case it can be shown by a straightforward but laborious process that

$$A_{16} = A_{26} = 0$$
$$B_{11} = B_{12} = B_{22} = B_{66} = 0$$
$$D_{16} = D_{26} = 0 \tag{1-76}$$
$$(A_{11},\ A_{12},\ A_{22},\ A_{66}) = h(C_{11},\ C_{12},\ C_{22},\ C_{66})$$

$$(B_{16}, B_{26}) = -\frac{h^2}{2n}(C_{16}, C_{26})$$

$$(D_{11}, D_{12}, D_{22}, D_{66}) = \frac{h^3}{12}(C_{11}, C_{12}, C_{22}, C_{66})$$

in which the C_{ij} is the reduced stiffness matrix with $-\theta$ orientation and n is the total number of layers. The C_{ij} for $+\theta$ orientation is equal to that of the $-\theta$ orientation, except that the sign for C_{16} and C_{26} is changed. Introduction of equations (1-76) into equations (1-66) to (1-68) results in the following system of governing equations

$$
\begin{aligned}
A_{11}u^{\circ}_{,xx} &+ A_{66}u^{\circ}_{,yy} + (A_{12} + A_{66})v^{\circ}_{,xy} - 3B_{16}w_{,xxy} - B_{26}w_{,yyy} \\
&= -w_{,x}(A_{11}w_{,xx} + A_{66}w_{,yy}) - (A_{12} + A_{66})w_{,y}w_{,xy}
\end{aligned}
\tag{1-77}
$$

$$
\begin{aligned}
(A_{12} + A_{66})u^{\circ}_{,xy} &+ A_{66}v^{\circ}_{,xx} + A_{22}v^{\circ}_{,yy} - B_{16}w_{,xxx} - 3B_{26}w_{,xyy} \\
&= -(A_{12} + A_{66})w_{,x}w_{,xy} - w_{,y}(A_{66}w_{,xx} + A_{22}w_{,yy})
\end{aligned}
\tag{1-78}
$$

$$
\begin{aligned}
3B_{16}u^{\circ}_{,xxy} &+ B_{26}u^{\circ}_{,yyy} + B_{16}v^{\circ}_{,xxx} + 3B_{26}v^{\circ}_{,xyy} - D_{11}w_{,xxxx} \\
&- 2(D_{12} + 2D_{66})w_{,xxyy} - D_{22}w_{,yyyy} - \rho w_{,tt} \\
&= -q - (u^{\circ}_{,x} + \tfrac{1}{2}w^2_{,x})(A_{11}w_{,xx} + A_{12}w_{,yy}) \\
&- (v^{\circ}_{,y} + \tfrac{1}{2}w^2_{,y})(A_{12}w_{,xx} + A_{22}w_{,yy}) - 2A_{66}w_{,xy}(u^{\circ}_{,y} + v^{\circ}_{,x} + w_{,x}w_{,y}) \\
&- w_{,x}(3B_{16}w_{,xxy} + B_{26}w_{,yyy}) - w_{,y}(B_{16}w_{,xxx} + 3B_{26}w_{,xyy})
\end{aligned}
\tag{1-79}
$$

In a similar manner equations (1-70) to (1-72) result in the membrane forces

$$
\begin{aligned}
N_x &= A_{11}u^{\circ}_{,x} + A_{12}v^{\circ}_{,y} - 2B_{16}w_{,xy} + \tfrac{1}{2}(A_{11}w^2_{,x} + A_{12}w^2_{,y}) \\
N_y &= A_{12}u^{\circ}_{,x} + A_{22}v^{\circ}_{,y} - 2B_{26}w_{,xy} + \tfrac{1}{2}(A_{12}w^2_{,x} + A_{22}w^2_{,y}) \\
N_{xy} &= A_{66}(u^{\circ}_{,y} + v^{\circ}_{,x}) - B_{16}w_{,xx} - B_{26}w_{,yy} + A_{66}w_{,x}w_{,y}
\end{aligned}
\tag{1-80}
$$

the bending and twisting moments

$$
\begin{aligned}
M_x &= B_{16}(u^{\circ}_{,y} + v^{\circ}_{,x}) - D_{11}w_{,xx} - D_{12}w_{,yy} + B_{16}w_{,x}w_{,y} \\
M_y &= B_{26}(u^{\circ}_{,y} + v^{\circ}_{,x}) - D_{12}w_{,xx} - D_{22}w_{,yy} + B_{26}w_{,x}w_{,y} \\
M_{xy} &= B_{16}u^{\circ}_{,x} + B_{26}v^{\circ}_{,y} - 2D_{66}w_{,xy} + \tfrac{1}{2}(B_{16}w^2_{,x} + B_{26}w^2_{,y})
\end{aligned}
\tag{1-81}
$$

and the transverse shear forces

$$
\begin{aligned}
Q_x &= 2B_{16}u^{\circ}_{,xy} + B_{16}v^{\circ}_{,xx} + B_{26}v^{\circ}_{,yy} - D_{11}w_{,xxx} \\
&- (D_{12} + 2D_{66})w_{,xyy} \\
&+ w_{,y}(B_{16}w_{,xx} + B_{26}w_{,yy}) + 2B_{16}w_{,x}w_{,xy}
\end{aligned}
\tag{1-82}
$$

$$Q_y = B_{16} u^\circ_{,xx} + B_{26} u^\circ_{,yy} + 2B_{26} v^\circ_{,xy} \qquad \blacktriangle$$
$$- (D_{12} + 2D_{66})w_{,xxy} - D_{22} w_{,yyy}$$
$$+ w_{,x}(B_{16} w_{,xx} + B_{26} w_{,yy}) + 2B_{26} w_{,y} w_{,xy}$$

b Unsymmetric Cross-Ply Plates

Unsymmetric cross-ply laminates are constructed of an even number of orthotropic layers with orthotropic axes of symmetry in each layer alternately oriented at angles of 0 and 90° with the plate axes (Ref. 1.72). The fiber direction of the odd layers coincides with the x axis and of the even layers with the y axis. All the odd layers have the same thickness. The even layers also have the same thickness which may be different from that of the odd layers. In this case the plate rigidities are given by

$$A_{16} = A_{26} = D_{16} = D_{26} = 0$$

$$B_{12} = B_{16} = B_{26} = B_{66} = 0$$

$$A_{11} = \frac{\gamma + R}{1 + \gamma} C_{11} h \qquad A_{12} = C_{12} h$$

$$A_{22} = \frac{1 + \gamma R}{1 + \gamma} C_{11} h \qquad A_{66} = C_{66} h$$

$$B_{11} = \frac{\gamma(R - 1)}{n(1 + \gamma)^2} C_{11} h^2 \qquad B_{22} = -B_{11} \qquad (1\text{-}83)$$

$$D_{11} = [1 + k(R - 1)]\frac{C_{11} h^3}{12} \qquad D_{12} = \frac{C_{12} h^3}{12}$$

$$D_{22} = [R + k(1 - R)]\frac{C_{11} h^3}{12} \qquad D_{66} = \frac{C_{66} h^3}{12}$$

$$R = \frac{E_T}{E_L} \qquad k = \frac{1}{1 + \gamma} + \frac{8\gamma(\gamma - 1)}{n^2(1 + \gamma)^3}$$

in which γ is the cross-ply ratio defined as the ratio of the total thickness of the odd layers to that of the even layers, n is the total number of layers, and E_L and E_T are Young's moduli in the principal directions (L, T) of elasticity.

Correspondingly, governing equations (1-66) to (1-68) become

$$A_{11} u^\circ_{,xx} + A_{66} u^\circ_{,yy} + (A_{12} + A_{66})v^\circ_{,xy} - B_{11} w_{,xxx}$$
$$= -w_{,x}(A_{11} w_{,xx} + A_{66} w_{,yy}) - (A_{12} + A_{66})w_{,y} w_{,xy} \qquad (1\text{-}84)$$

$$(A_{12} + A_{66})u^\circ_{,xy} + A_{66} v^\circ_{,xx} + A_{22} v^\circ_{,yy} + B_{11} w_{,yyy}$$
$$= -(A_{12} + A_{66})w_{,x} w_{,xy} - w_{,y}(A_{66} w_{,xx} + A_{22} w_{,yy}) \qquad (1\text{-}85)$$

$$
\begin{aligned}
B_{11} u^\circ_{,xxx} &- B_{11} v^\circ_{,yyy} - D_{11} w_{,xxxx} - 2(D_{12} + 2D_{66})w_{,xxyy} \\
&- D_{22} w_{,yyyy} - \rho w_{,tt} = -q - (u^\circ_{,x} + \tfrac{1}{2} w^2_{,x}) \\
&\cdot (A_{11} w_{,xx} + A_{12} w_{,yy}) - (v^\circ_{,y} + \tfrac{1}{2} w^2_{,y}) \\
&\cdot (A_{12} w_{,xx} + A_{22} w_{,yy}) \\
&- 2A_{66} w_{,xy}(u^\circ_{,y} + v^\circ_{,x} + w_{,x} w_{,y}) - B_{11} w_{,x} w_{,xxx} \\
&+ B_{11} w_{,y} w_{,yyy}
\end{aligned}
\tag{1-86}
$$

By virtue of equations (1-70) to (1-72) and (1-83) membrane forces can be written as

$$
\begin{aligned}
N_x &= A_{11} u^\circ_{,x} + A_{12} v^\circ_{,y} - B_{11} w_{,xx} + \tfrac{1}{2}(A_{11} w^2_{,x} + A_{12} w^2_{,y}) \\
N_y &= A_{12} u^\circ_{,x} + A_{22} v^\circ_{,y} + B_{11} w_{,yy} + \tfrac{1}{2}(A_{12} w^2_{,x} + A_{22} w^2_{,y}) \\
N_{xy} &= A_{66}(u^\circ_{,y} + v^\circ_{,x} + w_{,x} w_{,y})
\end{aligned}
\tag{1-87}
$$

bending and twisting moments as

$$
\begin{aligned}
M_x &= B_{11} u^\circ_{,x} - D_{11} w_{,xx} - D_{12} w_{,yy} + \tfrac{1}{2} B_{11} w^2_{,x} \\
M_y &= -(B_{11} v^\circ_{,y} + D_{12} w_{,xx} + D_{22} w_{,yy} + \tfrac{1}{2} B_{11} w^2_{,y}) \\
M_{xy} &= -2D_{66} w_{,xy}
\end{aligned}
\tag{1-88}
$$

and transverse shear forces as

$$
\begin{aligned}
Q_x &= B_{11} u^\circ_{,xx} - D_{11} w_{,xxx} - (D_{12} + 2D_{66})w_{,xyy} + B_{11} w_{,x} w_{,xx} \\
Q_y &= -B_{11} v^\circ_{,yy} - (D_{12} + 2D_{66})w_{,xxy} - D_{22} w_{,yyy} - B_{11} w_{,y} w_{,yy}
\end{aligned}
\tag{1-89}
$$

c Unsymmetric Isotropic Laminates

In the case of an unsymmetric laminate composed of isotropic plies with different elastic properties, it requires that

$$
\begin{aligned}
A_{16} = A_{26} &= B_{16} = B_{26} = D_{16} = D_{26} = 0 \qquad A_{22} = A_{11} \\
A_{66} = \tfrac{1}{2}(A_{11} - A_{12}) \qquad B_{22} &= B_{11} \qquad B_{66} = \tfrac{1}{2}(B_{11} - B_{12}) \\
D_{22} = D_{11} \qquad D_{66} &= \tfrac{1}{2}(D_{11} - D_{12})
\end{aligned}
\tag{1-90}
$$

Thus the governing equations (1-66) to (1-68) are simplified to yield

$$
\begin{aligned}
A_{11} u^\circ_{,xx} &+ A_{66} u^\circ_{,yy} + (A_{12} + A_{66})v^\circ_{,xy} - B_{11}(w_{,xxx} + w_{,xyy}) \\
&= -w_{,x}(A_{11} w_{,xx} + A_{66} w_{,yy}) - (A_{12} + A_{66})w_{,y} w_{,xy}
\end{aligned}
\tag{1-91}
$$

$$
\begin{aligned}
(A_{12} + A_{66})u^\circ_{,xy} &+ A_{66} v^\circ_{,xx} + A_{11} v^\circ_{,yy} - B_{11}(w_{,xxy} + w_{,yyy}) \\
&= -(A_{12} + A_{66})w_{,x} w_{,xy} - w_{,y}(A_{66} w_{,xx} + A_{11} w_{,yy})
\end{aligned}
\tag{1-92}
$$

$$B_{11}(u^\circ_{,xxx} + u^\circ_{,xyy} + v^\circ_{,xxy} + v^\circ_{,yyy})$$

$$- D_{11}(w_{,xxxx} + 2w_{,xxyy} + w_{,yyyy}) - \rho w_{,tt}$$

$$= -q - (u^\circ_{,x} + \tfrac{1}{2}w^2_{,x})(A_{11}w_{,xx} + A_{12}w_{,yy})$$

$$+ (v^\circ_{,y} + \tfrac{1}{2}w^2_{,y})(A_{12}w_{,xx} + A_{11}w_{,yy})$$

$$+ 2A_{66}w_{,xy}(u^\circ_{,y} + v^\circ_{,x} + w_{,x}w_{,y})$$

$$- B_{11}[w_{,x}(w_{,xxx} + w_{,xyy}) + w_{,y}(w_{,xxy} + w_{,yyy})]$$

$$- 2(B_{12} - B_{66})(w^2_{,xy} - w_{,xx}w_{,yy}) \tag{1-93}$$

Similarly, equations (1-70) to (1-72) lead to the present membrane forces

$$N_x = A_{11}u^\circ_{,x} + A_{12}v^\circ_{,y} - B_{11}w_{,xx} - B_{12}w_{,yy} + \tfrac{1}{2}(A_{11}w^2_{,x} + A_{12}w^2_{,y})$$

$$N_y = A_{12}u^\circ_{,x} + A_{11}v^\circ_{,y} - B_{12}w_{,xx} - B_{11}w_{,yy} + \tfrac{1}{2}(A_{12}w^2_{,x} + A_{11}w^2_{,y}) \tag{1-94}$$

$$N_{xy} = A_{66}(u^\circ_{,y} + v^\circ_{,x}) - 2B_{66}w_{,xy} + A_{66}w_{,x}w_{,y}$$

bending and twisting moments

$$M_x = B_{11}u^\circ_{,x} + B_{12}v^\circ_{,y} - D_{11}w_{,xx} - D_{12}w_{,yy} + \tfrac{1}{2}(B_{11}w^2_{,x} + B_{12}w^2_{,y})$$

$$M_y = B_{12}u^\circ_{,x} + B_{11}v^\circ_{,y} - D_{12}w_{,xx} - D_{11}w_{,yy} + \tfrac{1}{2}(B_{12}w^2_{,x} + B_{11}w^2_{,y}) \tag{1-95}$$

$$M_{xy} = B_{66}(u^\circ_{,y} + v^\circ_{,x}) - 2D_{66}w_{,xy} + B_{66}w_{,x}w_{,y}$$

and transverse shear forces

$$Q_x = B_{11}u^\circ_{,xx} + B_{66}u^\circ_{,yy} + (B_{12} + B_{66})v^\circ_{,xy} - D_{11}w_{,xxx}$$

$$- (D_{12} + 2D_{66})w_{,xyy} + w_{,x}(B_{11}w_{,xx} + B_{66}w_{,yy})$$

$$+ (B_{12} + B_{66})w_{,y}w_{,xy}$$

$$Q_y = (B_{12} + B_{66})u^\circ_{,xy} + B_{66}v^\circ_{,xx} + B_{11}v^\circ_{,yy} \tag{1-96}$$

$$- (D_{12} + 2D_{66})w_{,xxy} - D_{11}w_{,yyy} + (B_{12} + B_{66})w_{,x}w_{,xy}$$

$$+ w_{,y}(B_{66}w_{,xx} + B_{11}w_{,yy})$$

d Symmetric Anisotropic Laminates

The layers of a symmetric laminate are so arranged that a midplane elastic symmetry exists. That is, for each layer above the midplane, there is a corresponding layer identical in thickness, elastic properties, and orientation of filaments located at the same distance below the midplane. In the present case the material coupling does not occur between transverse bending and inplane stretching, namely,

$$B_{ij} = 0 \qquad (i, j = 1, 2, 6) \tag{1-97}$$

The governing equations (1-66) to (1-68) thus read as

$$L_1 u^\circ + L_2 v^\circ = -w_{,x} L_1 w - w_{,y} L_2 w \tag{1-98}$$

$$L_2 u^\circ + L_4 v^\circ = -w_{,x} L_2 w - w_{,y} L_4 w \tag{1-99}$$

$$L_6 w + \rho w_{,tt} = q + (u^\circ_{,x} + \tfrac{1}{2} w^2_{,x}) L_7 w$$

$$+ (v^\circ_{,y} + \tfrac{1}{2} w^2_{,y}) L_8 w + (u^\circ_{,y} + v^\circ_{,x} + w_{,x} w_{,y}) L_9 w \tag{1-100}$$

in which the differential operators L_i are given by equations (1-69).

Equations (1-70) to (1-72) are simplified to the membrane forces

$$N_x = A_{11} u^\circ_{,x} + A_{16}(u^\circ_{,y} + v^\circ_{,x}) + A_{12} v^\circ_{,y}$$

$$+ \tfrac{1}{2}(A_{11} w^2_{,x} + 2A_{16} w_{,x} w_{,y} + A_{12} w^2_{,y})$$

$$N_y = A_{12} u^\circ_{,x} + A_{26}(u^\circ_{,y} + v^\circ_{,x}) + A_{22} v^\circ_{,y}$$

$$+ \tfrac{1}{2}(A_{12} w^2_{,x} + 2A_{26} w_{,x} w_{,y} + A_{22} w^2_{,y}) \tag{1-101}$$

$$N_{xy} = A_{16} u^\circ_{,x} + A_{66}(u^\circ_{,y} + v^\circ_{,x}) + A_{26} v^\circ_{,y}$$

$$+ \tfrac{1}{2}(A_{16} w^2_{,x} + 2A_{66} w_{,x} w_{,y} + A_{26} w^2_{,y})$$

the bending and twisting moments

$$M_x = -(D_{11} w_{,xx} + 2D_{16} w_{,xy} + D_{12} w_{,yy})$$

$$M_y = -(D_{12} w_{,xx} + 2D_{26} w_{,xy} + D_{22} w_{,yy}) \tag{1-102}$$

$$M_{xy} = -(D_{16} w_{,xx} + 2D_{66} w_{,xy} + D_{26} w_{,yy})$$

and the transverse shear forces

$$Q_x = -[D_{11} w_{,xxx} + 3D_{16} w_{,xxy} + (D_{12} + 2D_{66}) w_{,xyy} + D_{26} w_{,yyy}]$$

$$Q_y = -[D_{16} w_{,xxx} + (D_{12} + 2D_{66}) w_{,xxy} + 3D_{26} w_{,xyy} + D_{22} w_{,yyy}] \tag{1-103}$$

e Anisotropic Plates

For material homogeneity, equations (1-53) and (1-65) become

$$A_{ij} = hC_{ij} \qquad B_{ij} = 0 \qquad D_{ij} = \tfrac{1}{12} h^3 C_{ij} \qquad (i, j = 1, 2, 6) \tag{1-104}$$

which lead to

$$D_{ij} = \tfrac{1}{12} A_{ij} h^2 \tag{1-105}$$

In this case the governing equations and constitutive relations for these plates are the same as equations (1-98) to (1-103) for symmetric anisotropic laminates except for coefficients A_{ij} and D_{ij} in these equations.

f Orthotropic Plates

For an orthotropic plate with its material axes of symmetry parallel to the coordinate axes of the plate, the reduced stiffnesses in terms of engineering constants are given by

$$C_{11} = \frac{E_1}{\mu} \qquad C_{12} = \frac{v_{12} E_2}{\mu} \qquad C_{16} = 0$$

$$C_{22} = \frac{E_2}{\mu} \qquad C_{26} = 0 \qquad C_{66} = G_{12}$$

(1-106)

where

$$\mu = 1 - v_{12} v_{21}$$

(1-107)

In these equations E_1 and E_2 are moduli of elasticity along the principal material axes x and y respectively, G_{12} is the modulus of rigidity characterizing the change of the angle between the principal material directions, and v_{12} and v_{21} are Poisson's ratios with the first subscript indicating the direction of the tensile force and the second indicating the direction of contraction. These elastic constants satisfy the condition of elastic symmetry

$$v_{12} E_2 = v_{21} E_1$$

(1-108)

On account of equations (1-104) to (1-108) the governing equations (1-98) to (1-100) become

$$E_1 u^\circ_{,xx} + \mu G_{12} u^\circ_{,yy} + C v^\circ_{,xy} = -w_{,x}(E_1 w_{,xx} + \mu G_{12} w_{,yy}) - C w_{,y} w_{,xy}$$

(1-109)

$$C u^\circ_{,xy} + \mu G_{12} v^\circ_{,xx} + E_2 v^\circ_{,yy} = -C w_{,x} w_{,xy} - w_{,y}(\mu G_{12} w_{,xx} + E_2 w_{,yy})$$

(1-110)

$$D_1 w_{,xxxx} + 2D_3 w_{,xxyy} + D_2 w_{,yyyy} + \rho w_{,tt}$$

$$= q + \frac{h}{\mu} [(u^\circ_{,x} + \tfrac{1}{2} w^2_{,x})(E_1 w_{,xx} + v_{12} E_2 w_{,yy})$$

$$+ (v^\circ_{,y} + \tfrac{1}{2} w^2_{,y})(v_{12} E_2 w_{,xx} + E_2 w_{,yy})$$

$$+ 2\mu G_{12} w_{,xy}(u^\circ_{,y} + v^\circ_{,x} + w_{,x} w_{,y})]$$

(1-111)

where

$$C = v_{12} E_2 + \mu G_{12} \qquad D_1 = \frac{E_1 h^3}{12\mu} \qquad D_2 = \frac{E_2 h^3}{12\mu}$$

$$D_3 = v_{12} D_2 + 2D_4 \qquad D_4 = \frac{G_{12} h^3}{12}$$

(1-112)

In these equations D_1, D_2, and D_4 are the principal bending and twisting rigidities. In view of equations (1-101) to (1-103), the membrane forces are given by

$$N_x = \frac{E_1 h}{\mu} [u^\circ_{,x} + v_{21} v^\circ_{,y} + \tfrac{1}{2}(w^2_{,x} + v_{21} w^2_{,y})]$$

$$N_y = \frac{E_2 h}{\mu} [v_{12} u^\circ_{,x} + v^\circ_{,y} + \tfrac{1}{2}(v_{12} w^2_{,x} + w^2_{,y})]$$

(1-113)

$$N_{xy} = G_{12} h [u^\circ_{,y} + v^\circ_{,x} + w_{,x} w_{,y}]$$

with $E_1 h/\mu$ and $E_2 h/\mu$ being the principal extensional rigidities, the bending and twisting moments by

$$M_x = -D_1(w_{,xx} + v_{21} w_{,yy})$$

$$M_y = -D_2(v_{12} w_{,xx} + w_{,yy}) \tag{1-114}$$

$$M_{xy} = -2D_4 w_{,xy}$$

and the transverse shear forces by

$$Q_x = -D_1 w_{,xxx} - (v_{12} D_2 + 2D_4)w_{,xyy}$$

$$Q_y = -D_2 w_{,yyy} - (v_{12} D_2 + 2\mu D_4)w_{,xxy} \tag{1-115}$$

g Isotropic Plates

In the case of an isotropic plate

$$E_1 = E_2 = E \qquad v_{12} = v_{21} = v \qquad G_{12} = \frac{E}{2(1 + v)} \tag{1-116}$$

Thus the governing equations (1-109) to (1-111) are simplified to

$$u^\circ_{,xx} + d_1 u^\circ_{,yy} + d_2 v^\circ_{,xy}$$

$$= -w_{,x}(w_{,xx} + d_1 w_{,yy}) - d_2 w_{,y} w_{xy} \tag{1-117}$$

$$v^\circ_{,yy} + d_1 v^\circ_{,xx} + d_2 u^\circ_{,xy}$$

$$= -w_{,y}(w_{,yy} + d_1 w_{,xx}) - d_2 w_{,x} w_{,xy} \tag{1-118}$$

$$DV^4 w + \rho w_{,tt} = q + \frac{Eh}{1 - v^2}[(u^\circ_{,x} + \tfrac{1}{2}w^2_{,x})(w_{,xx} + v w_{,yy})$$

$$+ (v^\circ_{,y} + \tfrac{1}{2}w^2_{,y})(w_{,yy} + v w_{,xx})$$

$$+ (1 - v)w_{,xy}(u^\circ_{,y} + v^\circ_{,x} + w_{,x} w_{,y})] \tag{1-119}$$

where

$$V^4 w = w_{,xxxx} + 2w_{,xxyy} + w_{,yyyy}$$

$$d_1 = \frac{1 - v}{2} \qquad d_2 = \frac{1 + v}{2} \qquad D = \frac{Eh^3}{12(1 - v^2)} \tag{1-120}$$

Similarly, from equations (1-113) to (1-115) the membrane forces can be written as

$$N_x = \frac{Eh}{1 - v^2}[u^\circ_{,x} + v v^\circ_{,y} + \tfrac{1}{2}(w^2_{,x} + v w^2_{,y})]$$

$$N_y = \frac{Eh}{1 - v^2}[v^\circ_{,y} + v u^\circ_{,x} + \tfrac{1}{2}(w^2_{,y} + v w^2_{,x})] \tag{1-121}$$

$$N_{xy} = \frac{Eh}{2(1 + v)}[u^\circ_{,y} + v^\circ_{,x} + w_{,x} w_{,y}]$$

the bending and twisting moments as

$$M_x = -D[w_{,xx} + vw_{,yy}]$$
$$M_y = -D[w_{,yy} + vw_{,xx}] \tag{1-122}$$
$$M_{xy} = -D(1-v)w_{,xy}$$

and the transverse shear forces as

$$Q_x = -D(\nabla^2 w)_{,x} \qquad Q_y = -D(\nabla^2 w)_{,y} \tag{1-123}$$

Equations (1-117) to (1-123) can be obtained also by taking

$$A_{11} = A_{22} = \frac{Eh}{1-v^2} \qquad A_{12} = vA_{11} \qquad A_{66} = \frac{1-v}{2}A_{11}$$

$$B_{ij} = 0 \tag{1-124}$$

$$D_{11} = D_{22} = D \qquad D_{12} = vD \qquad D_{66} = \frac{1-v}{2}D$$

in equations (1-91) to (1-96).

It is observed that in the static case equations (1-117) to (1-119) are those of the von Kármán plate theory in terms of three displacements.

1.7 EQUATIONS IN TERMS OF TRANSVERSE DEFLECTION AND FORCE FUNCTION

In the previous section the equations of motion and constitutive relations for a plate are expressed in terms of three displacements at the midplane ($z = 0$). Sometimes, it is convenient to introduce a force function as one of the dependent variables for certain boundary-value problems. As usual a force function ψ is defined by

$$N_x = \psi_{,yy} \qquad N_y = \psi_{,xx} \qquad N_{xy} = -\psi_{,xy} \tag{1-125}$$

The force function thus satisfies equations (1-62) and (1-63) exactly.

A partial inverse of equation (1-51) yields

$$\begin{vmatrix} \varepsilon^\circ \\ \mathbf{M} \end{vmatrix} = \begin{bmatrix} \mathbf{A}^* & \mathbf{B}^* \\ -(\mathbf{B}^*)^T & \mathbf{D}^* \end{bmatrix} \begin{vmatrix} \mathbf{N} \\ \kappa \end{vmatrix} \tag{1-126}$$

in which the superscript T represents the matrix transpose and in which

$$\mathbf{A}^* = \mathbf{A}^{-1} \qquad \mathbf{B}^* = -\mathbf{A}^{-1}\mathbf{B} \qquad \mathbf{D}^* = \mathbf{D} - \mathbf{B}\mathbf{A}^{-1}\mathbf{B} \tag{1-127}$$

In general $\mathbf{A}^*$ and $\mathbf{D}^*$ are symmetric matrices but $\mathbf{B}^*$ is not a symmetric matrix.

In view of equations (1-43), (1-125), and (1-126), the bending moments can be written in the form

$$M_x = -B_{11}^* \psi_{,yy} - B_{21}^* \psi_{,xx} + B_{61}^* \psi_{,xy}$$
$$- D_{11}^* w_{,xx} - D_{12}^* w_{,yy} - 2D_{16}^* w_{,xy} \qquad \blacktriangledown$$

$$M_y = -B_{12}^* \psi_{,yy} - B_{22}^* \psi_{,xx} + B_{62}^* \psi_{,xy}$$

$$-D_{12}^* w_{,xx} - D_{22}^* w_{,yy} - 2D_{26}^* w_{,xy}$$

$$M_{xy} = -B_{16}^* \psi_{,yy} - B_{26}^* \psi_{,xx} + B_{66}^* \psi_{,xy}$$

$$-D_{16}^* w_{,xx} - D_{26}^* w_{,yy} - 2D_{66}^* w_{,xy}$$

(1-128)

Substituting equations (1-125) and (1-128) in (1-64), the equation of transverse motion in terms of w and ψ is obtained in the following

$$D_{11}^* w_{,xxxx} + 4D_{16}^* w_{,xxxy} + 2(D_{12}^* + 2D_{66}^*)w_{,xxyy}$$

$$+ 4D_{26}^* w_{,xyyy} + D_{22}^* w_{,yyyy} + B_{21}^* \psi_{,xxxx}$$

$$+ (2B_{26}^* - B_{61}^*)\psi_{,xxxy}$$

$$+ (B_{11}^* + B_{22}^* - 2B_{66}^*)\psi_{,xxyy} + (2B_{16}^* - B_{62}^*)\psi_{,xyyy}$$

$$+ B_{12}^* \psi_{,yyyy} + \rho w_{,tt} = q + w_{,xx}\psi_{,yy} + w_{,yy}\psi_{,xx}$$

$$- 2\psi_{,xy} w_{,xy}$$

(1-129)

The second equation is derived from the condition of compatibility

$$\varepsilon_{x,\,yy}^{\circ} + \varepsilon_{y,\,xx}^{\circ} - \varepsilon_{xy,\,xy}^{\circ} = w_{,xy}^2 - w_{,xx}w_{,yy}$$

(1-130)

which is satisfied by equations (1-42). Making use of equation (1-126) in conjunction with (1-43) and (1-125), the condition of compatibility is also expressed in terms of w and ψ

$$A_{22}^* \psi_{,xxxx} - 2A_{26}^* \psi_{,xxxy} + (2A_{12}^* + A_{66}^*)\psi_{,xxyy} - 2A_{16}^* \psi_{,xyyy}$$

$$+ A_{11}^* \psi_{,yyyy} - B_{21}^* w_{,xxxx} - (2B_{26}^* - B_{61}^*)w_{,xxxy}$$

$$- (B_{11}^* + B_{22}^* - 2B_{66}^*)w_{,xxyy} - (2B_{16}^* - B_{62}^*)w_{,xyyy}$$

$$- B_{12}^* w_{,yyyy} = w_{,xy}^2 - w_{,xx}w_{,yy}$$

(1-131)

Equations (1-129) and (1-131) constitute an eighth-order system of two equations for transverse deflection w and force function ψ.

With w and ψ determined, the membrane forces are found from equations (1-125), and the bending moments from equations (1-128). The transverse shear forces are obtained from equations (1-61) and (1-128) as follows

$$Q_x = -[B_{21}^* \psi_{,xxx} + (B_{26}^* - B_{61}^*)\psi_{,xxy} + (B_{11}^* - B_{66}^*)\psi_{,xyy}$$

$$+ B_{16}^* \psi_{,yyy} + D_{11}^* w_{,xxx} + 3D_{16}^* w_{,xxy}$$

$$+ (D_{12}^* + 2D_{66}^*)w_{,xyy} + D_{26}^* w_{,yyy}]$$

$$Q_y = -[B_{26}^* \psi_{,xxx} + (B_{22}^* - B_{66}^*)\psi_{,xxy} + (B_{16}^* - B_{62}^*)\psi_{,xyy}$$

$$+ B_{12}^* \psi_{,yyy} + D_{16}^* w_{,xxx} + (D_{12}^* + 2D_{66}^*)w_{,xxy}$$

$$+ 3D_{26}^* w_{,xyy} + D_{22}^* w_{,yyy}]$$

(1-132)

The inplane displacements are determined by introducing equations (1-42) into the first two constitutive relations in equation (1-126), and integrating with respect to x and y, respectively. The result is

$$u^\circ = A_{11}^* \int \psi_{,yy}\, dx + A_{12}^* \psi_{,x} - A_{16}^* \psi_{,y} - B_{11}^* w_{,x}$$

$$- B_{12}^* \int w_{,yy}\, dx - 2B_{16}^* w_{,y} - \tfrac{1}{2} \int w_{,x}^2\, dx$$

$$v^\circ = A_{22}^* \int \psi_{,xx}\, dy + A_{12}^* \psi_{,y} - A_{26}^* \psi_{,x} - B_{22}^* w_{,y}$$

$$- B_{12}^* \int w_{,xx}\, dy - 2B_{26}^* w_{,x} - \tfrac{1}{2} \int w_{,y}^2\, dy$$

(1-133)

in which the two arbitrary functions of integration representing a rigid-body displacement have been discarded. The stresses in each layer thus can be calculated from equations (1-74) and (1-75).

The governing equations (1-129) and (1-131), bending moments (1-128), and transverse shear forces (1-132), for unsymmetrically laminated anisotropic plates expressed in terms of the transverse deflection and a force function are specified for some particular cases. The membrane forces are always obtained from equations (1-125) in the present formulation.

a Unsymmetric Angle-Ply Plates

In this case equations (1-76) hold and hence equations (1-127) lead to

$$A_{16}^* = A_{26}^* = B_{11}^* = B_{12}^* = B_{21}^* = B_{22}^* = B_{66}^* = D_{16}^* = D_{26}^* = 0 \quad (1\text{-}134)$$

The governing equations are obtained from equations (1-129) and (1-131) in conjunction with equations (1-134).

$$L_1^* w + L_3^* \psi - L^*(w, \psi) - q + \rho w_{,tt} = 0 \qquad (1\text{-}135)$$

$$L_2^* \psi - L_3^* w + \tfrac{1}{2} L^*(w, w) = 0 \qquad (1\text{-}136)$$

where

$$L_1^*(\ ) = D_{11}^*(\ )_{,xxxx} + 2(D_{12}^* + 2D_{66}^*)(\ )_{,xxyy} + D_{22}^*(\ )_{,yyyy}$$

$$L_2^*(\ ) = A_{22}^*(\ )_{,xxxx} + (2A_{12}^* + A_{66}^*)(\ )_{,xxyy} + A_{11}^*(\ )_{,yyyy}$$

$$L_3^*(\ ) = (2B_{26}^* - B_{61}^*)(\ )_{,xxxy} + (2B_{16}^* - B_{62}^*)(\ )_{,xyyy}$$

$$L^*(w, \psi) = w_{,xx}\psi_{,yy} + w_{,yy}\psi_{,xx} - 2w_{,xy}\psi_{,xy}$$

(1-137)

In view of equations (1-128), (1-132), and (1-134), the bending and twisting moments assume in the form as

$$M_x = B_{61}^* \psi_{,xy} - D_{11}^* w_{,xx} - D_{12}^* w_{,yy}$$

$$M_y = B_{62}^* \psi_{,xy} - D_{12}^* w_{,xx} - D_{22}^* w_{,yy}$$

$$M_{xy} = -B_{26}^* \psi_{,xx} - B_{16}^* \psi_{,yy} - 2D_{66}^* w_{,xy}$$

(1-138)

and the transverse shear forces as

$$Q_x = -[(B_{26}^* - B_{61}^*)\psi_{,xxy} + B_{16}^* \psi_{,yyy} + D_{11}^* w_{,xxx} + (D_{12}^* + 2D_{66}^*)w_{,xyy}]$$
$$Q_y = -[B_{26}^* \psi_{,xxx} + (B_{16}^* - B_{62}^*)\psi_{,xyy} + (D_{12}^* + 2D_{66}^*)w_{,xxy} + D_{22}^* w_{,yyy}]$$ (1-139)

b Unsymmetric Cross-Ply Plates

Substitution of equations (1-83) into (1-127) leads to

$$A_{16}^* = A_{26}^* = B_{16}^* = B_{26}^* = B_{61}^* = B_{62}^* = B_{66}^* = D_{16}^* = D_{26}^* = 0 \quad (1\text{-}140)$$

Consequently, the governing equations (1-129) and (1-131) transform to

$$L_1^* w + L_4^* \psi - L^*(w, \psi) - q + \rho w_{,tt} = 0 \tag{1-141}$$

$$L_2^* \psi - L_4^* w + \tfrac{1}{2}L^*(w, w) = 0 \tag{1-142}$$

where

$$L_4^*(\ ) = B_{21}^*(\ )_{,xxxx} + (B_{11}^* + B_{22}^*)(\ )_{,xxyy} + B_{12}^*(\ )_{,yyyy} \tag{1-143}$$

The bending and twisting moments (1-128) reduce to

$$M_x = -B_{11}^* \psi_{,yy} - B_{21}^* \psi_{,xx} - D_{11}^* w_{,xx} - D_{12}^* w_{,yy}$$
$$M_y = -B_{12}^* \psi_{,yy} - B_{22}^* \psi_{,xx} - D_{12}^* w_{,xx} - D_{22}^* w_{,yy} \tag{1-144}$$
$$M_{xy} = -2D_{66}^* w_{,xy}$$

and the transverse shear forces (1-132) to

$$Q_x = -[B_{21}^* \psi_{,xxx} + B_{11}^* \psi_{,xyy} + D_{11}^* w_{,xxx} + (D_{12}^* + 2D_{66}^*)w_{,xyy}]$$
$$Q_y = -[B_{22}^* \psi_{,xxy} + B_{12}^* \psi_{,yyy} + (D_{12}^* + 2D_{66}^*)w_{,xxy} + D_{22}^* w_{,yyy}]$$ (1-145)

c Unsymmetric Isotropic Laminates

From equations (1-90) and (1-127) it is found that

$$A_{16}^* = A_{26}^* = 0 \qquad A_{22}^* = A_{11}^* \qquad A_{66}^* = 2(A_{11}^* - A_{12}^*)$$
$$B_{16}^* = B_{26}^* = B_{61}^* = B_{62}^* = 0 \qquad B_{21}^* = B_{12}^* \qquad B_{22}^* = B_{11}^*$$
$$B_{66}^* = B_{11}^* - B_{12}^* \qquad D_{16}^* = D_{26}^* = 0 \qquad D_{22}^* = D_{11}^* \tag{1-146}$$
$$D_{66}^* = \tfrac{1}{2}(D_{11}^* - D_{12}^*)$$

On account of these requirements the governing equations (1-129) and (1-131) take the following form

$$D_{11}^* \nabla^4 w + B_{12}^* \nabla^4 \psi - L^*(w, \psi) - q + \rho w_{,tt} = 0 \tag{1-147}$$

$$A_{11}^* \nabla^4 \psi - B_{12}^* \nabla^4 w + \tfrac{1}{2}L^*(w, w) = 0 \tag{1-148}$$

where $\qquad \nabla^4(\ ) = (\ )_{,xxxx} + 2(\ )_{,xxyy} + (\ )_{,yyyy} \tag{1-149}$

Using equations (1-128), (1-132), and (1-146) we obtain the bending and twisting moments

$$M_x = -B_{11}^* \psi_{,yy} - B_{12}^* \psi_{,xx} - D_{11}^* w_{,xx} - D_{12}^* w_{,yy}$$

$$M_y = -B_{12}^* \psi_{,yy} - B_{11}^* \psi_{xx} - D_{12}^* w_{,xx} - D_{11}^* w_{,yy} \tag{1-150}$$

$$M_{xy} = (B_{11}^* - B_{12}^*)\psi_{,xy} - (D_{11}^* - D_{12}^*)w_{,xy}$$

and the transverse shear forces

$$Q_x = -B_{12}^*(\psi_{,xxx} + \psi_{,xyy}) - D_{11}^*(w_{,xxx} + w_{,xyy})$$

$$Q_y = -B_{12}^*(\psi_{,xxy} + \psi_{,yyy}) - D_{11}^*(w_{,xxy} + w_{,yyy}) \tag{1-151}$$

d Symmetric Anisotropic Laminates

Introduction of equations (1-97) into (1-127) yields

$$B_{ij}^* = 0 \qquad D_{ij}^* = D_{ij} \qquad (i, j = 1, 2, 6) \tag{1-152}$$

In view of these requirements, the governing equations (1-129) and (1-131) read as

$$D_{11} w_{,xxxx} + 4D_{16} w_{,xxxy} + 2(D_{12} + 2D_{66})w_{,xxyy}$$

$$+ 4D_{26} w_{,xyyy} + D_{22} w_{,yyyy} + \rho w_{,tt}$$

$$= q + L^*(w, \psi) \tag{1-153}$$

$$A_{22}^* \psi_{,xxxx} - 2A_{26}^* \psi_{,xxxy} + (2A_{12}^* + A_{66}^*)\psi_{,xxyy} - 2A_{16}^* \psi_{,xyyy}$$

$$+ A_{11}^* \psi_{,yyyy} = -\tfrac{1}{2}L^*(w, w) \tag{1-154}$$

The bending and twisting moments are given by equations (1-102), and the transverse shear forces by equations (1-103).

e Anisotropic Plates

Substituting equations (1-104) into (1-127) leads to

$$A_{ij}^* = \frac{C_{ij}^*}{h} \qquad B_{ij}^* = 0 \qquad D_{ij}^* = D_{ij} = \frac{h^3 C_{ij}}{12} \tag{1-155}$$

where

$$C^* = C^{-1} \tag{1-156}$$

In the present case the governing equations and constitutive relations of the plate are of the same form as equations (1-153), (1-154), (1-102), and (1-103), but the coefficients A_{ij}^* and D_{ij} in these equations are given by equations (1-155).

A symmetrically laminated anisotropic plate will physically reduce to a homogeneous anisotropic plate when elastic properties and orientation of all the layers of the laminate are taken to be identical with one another.

f Orthotropic Plates

From equations (1-106) to (1-108) and (1-156)

$$C_{11}^* = \frac{1}{E_1} \qquad C_{12}^* = -\frac{v_{12}}{E_1} \qquad C_{16}^* = 0$$

$$C_{22}^* = \frac{1}{E_2} \qquad C_{26}^* = 0 \qquad C_{66}^* = \frac{1}{G_{12}} \tag{1-157}$$

Consequently the governing equations (1-153) and (1-154) are simplified to the following

$$D_1 w_{,xxxx} + 2D_3 w_{,xxyy} + D_2 w_{,yyyy}$$
$$- L^*(w, \psi) - q + \rho w_{,tt} = 0 \tag{1-158}$$

$$\delta_1 \psi_{,xxxx} + 2\delta_3 \psi_{,xxyy} + \delta_2 \psi_{,yyyy} + \frac{h}{2} L^*(w, w) = 0 \tag{1-159}$$

where

$$\delta_1 = \frac{1}{E_2} \qquad \delta_2 = \frac{1}{E_1} \qquad \delta_3 = \frac{1}{2G_{12}} - \frac{v_{12}}{E_1} \tag{1-160}$$

and D_1, D_2, and D_3 are given by equations (1-112). The bending and twisting are given by equations (1-114), and the transverse shear forces by equations (1-115).

g Isotropic Plates

Utilizing relations (1-107), (1-112), and (1-116) the governing equations (1-158) and (1-159) become

$$D\nabla^4 w - L^*(w, \psi) - q + \rho w_{,tt} = 0 \tag{1-161}$$

$$\nabla^4 \psi + \frac{Eh}{2} L^*(w, w) = 0 \tag{1-162}$$

The bending and twisting moments and transverse shear forces are given by equations (1-122) and (1-123), respectively. In the static case equations (1-161) and (1-162) are those of von Kármán plate theory.

In the case of a homogeneous plate, the bending and average membrane stresses are respectively related to the bending moments and membrane forces by the well-known formulas as

$$\sigma_x^b = \frac{12M_x}{h^3} z \qquad \sigma_y^b = \frac{12M_y}{h^3} z \qquad \sigma_{xy}^b = \frac{12M_{xy}}{h^3} z$$

$$\sigma_x^m = \frac{N_x}{h} \qquad \sigma_y^m = \frac{N_y}{h} \qquad \sigma_{xy}^m = \frac{N_{xy}}{h} \tag{1-163}$$

Thus the total stresses at a material point are

$$\sigma_x = \sigma_x^b + \sigma_x^m \qquad \sigma_y = \sigma_y^b + \sigma_y^m \qquad \sigma_{xy} = \sigma_{xy}^b + \sigma_{xy}^m \qquad (1\text{-}164)$$

In these expressions the superscripts b and m refer to the bending effect and membrane action. It is seen that $\sigma_x^b, \sigma_y^b, \sigma_{xy}^b$ vary linearly throughout the thickness of the plate. The relations between transverse shear stresses and forces are given by

$$\sigma_{zx} = \frac{3Q_x}{2h}\left[1 - \left(\frac{z}{h/2}\right)^2\right] \qquad \sigma_{zy} = \frac{3Q_y}{2h}\left[1 - \left(\frac{z}{h/2}\right)^2\right] \qquad (1\text{-}165)$$

in which the two boundary planes of the plate have been assumed to be free from shear stresses. As soon as forces and moments are determined, the stresses can be calculated by using these expressions rather than the general equations (1-74) and (1-75). Relations (1-163) to (1-165) hold true not only for isotropic plates but also for orthotropic and anisotropic plates.

1.8 BOUNDARY AND INITIAL CONDITIONS

In linear theory, satisfaction of appropriate initial and boundary conditions is necessary for a unique solution of a problem (Refs. 1.73, 1.74). In nonlinear theory the superposition principle does not hold and the prescription of boundary conditions ensures only that the principle of conservation of energy will not be violated (Ref. 1.7). In the present plate theory any system of nonlinear differential equations presented in Secs. 1.6 and 1.7 is of the eighth order. The four boundary conditions to be prescribed along each plate edge are those of von Kármán plate theory and can be any combination of the following displacements and stresses:

Geometrical condition		Statical condition
$u_n^\circ = \bar{u}_n^\circ$	or	$N_n = \bar{N}_n$
$u_s^\circ = \bar{u}_s^\circ$	or	$N_{ns} = \bar{N}_{ns}$
$w = \bar{w}$	or	$Q_n + M_{ns,\,s} = \bar{Q}_n + \bar{M}_{ns,\,s}$
$w_{,n} = \bar{w}_{,n}$	or	$M_n = \bar{M}_n$

$$(1\text{-}166)$$

where the subscripts n and s denote the outward normal and tangential directions at the boundary, respectively, and the barred quantities are prescribed.

The six initial conditions are the prescription of the initial values of u°, v°, w and their time derivatives throughout the plate.

$$u^\circ = \bar{u}^\circ(x, y, 0) \qquad u_{,t}^\circ = \bar{u}_{,t}^\circ(x, y, 0)$$

$$v^\circ = \bar{v}^\circ(x, y, 0) \qquad v_{,t}^\circ = \bar{v}_{,t}^\circ(x, y, 0) \qquad (1\text{-}167)$$

$$w = \bar{w}(x, y, 0) \qquad w_{,t} = \bar{w}_{,t}(x, y, 0)$$

Some boundary conditions usually encountered in engineering are presented in the following

1. Rigidly clamped edge

$$w = w_{,n} = u_n^\circ = u_s^\circ = 0 \tag{1-168}$$

2. Loosely clamped edge

$$w = w_{,n} = N_n = N_{ns} = 0 \tag{1-169}$$

3. Simply supported edge (movable in the plane of the plate)

$$w = M_n = N_n = N_{ns} = 0 \tag{1-170}$$

4. Hinged edge (or simply supported edge immovable in the plane of the plate)

$$w = M_n = u_n^\circ = u_s^\circ = 0 \tag{1-171}$$

5. Free edge

$$N_n = N_{ns} = M_n = M_{ns,\,s} + Q_n = 0 \tag{1-172}$$

6. Elastically supported (stress-free) edge against rotation

$$w = 0 \qquad M_n = \pm \xi w_{,n} \qquad N_n = N_{ns} = 0 \tag{1-173}$$

In these equations ξ is the rotational restraint coefficient at the plate edge and the values $\xi = 0, \infty$ correspond to simply supported and loosely clamped edges, respectively.

1.9 METHODS OF SOLUTION

Each set of the differential equations obtained in Secs. 1.6 and 1.7 is a system of nonlinear partial differential equations of the eighth order with constant coefficients. Exact and approximate solutions to these equations will be presented in this book for various geometrically nonlinear problems of thin elastic plates. The solution is said to be exact in the sense that an infinite set of nonlinear algebraic equations can be truncated to obtain any desired degree of accuracy. Exact solutions will be obtained by double Fourier series, generalized double Fourier series and a combination of these series for rectangular plates, and by power series for axisymmetric deformations of circular and annular plates. Approximate solutions will be presented by virtue of the principle of minimum potential energy, Ritz method, Galerkin's method, perturbation technique, finite-difference method, etc. Among these methods only those used often in this book are discussed.

a Double Fourier Series

The dependent variables and the loading function in governing differential equations are expressed as double Fourier series which may be double sine series, double sine-cosine series, or double cosine series. Let $f_1(x, y)$, $f_2(x, y)$ and $f_3(x, y)$ be piecewise continuous functions defined in the region $0 \leq x \leq a$ and $0 \leq y \leq b$, and represented by

$$f_1(x, y) = \sum_{m=1}^{\infty} \sum_{n=1}^{\infty} a_{mn} \sin \frac{m\pi x}{a} \sin \frac{n\pi y}{b}$$

$$f_2(x, y) = \sum_{m=1}^{\infty} \sum_{n=1}^{\infty} b_{mn} \sin \frac{m\pi x}{a} \cos \frac{n\pi y}{b} \qquad (1\text{-}174)$$

$$f_3(x, y) = \sum_{m=0}^{\infty} \sum_{n=0}^{\infty} c_{mn} \cos \frac{m\pi x}{a} \cos \frac{n\pi y}{b}$$

in which a_{mn}, b_{mn}, and c_{mn} are the Fourier coefficients of functions f_1, f_2, and f_3, respectively. In these series the trigonometric functions possess the following orthogonality properties

$$\int_0^a \sin \frac{m\pi x}{a} \sin \frac{i\pi x}{a} \, dx = \begin{cases} 0 & m \neq i \\ a/2 & m = i \end{cases}$$

$$\int_0^a \cos \frac{m\pi x}{a} \cos \frac{j\pi x}{a} \, dx = \begin{cases} 0 & m \neq j \\ a/2 & m = j \end{cases}$$

$$\int_0^a \sin \frac{m\pi x}{a} \cos \frac{k\pi x}{a} \, dx \qquad (1\text{-}175)$$

$$= \begin{cases} 0 & m = k \quad \text{or} \quad m \neq k \quad \text{with} \quad |m \pm k| = \text{even} \\ 2am/[\pi(m^2 - k^2)] & m \neq k \quad \text{with} \quad |m \pm k| = \text{odd} \end{cases}$$

For a given function, say $f_1(x, y)$, the Fourier coefficients a_{mn} can be determined if term-by-term integration of the corresponding series is permissible. In fact, the permissibility of the term-by-term integration of an infinite series is assured by the uniform convergence of the series (Ref. 1.75). It should be recalled that the criterion on the convergence of multiple Fourier series is analogous to that of single Fourier series (Ref. 1.76). Multiplying both sides of the first of equations (1-174) by $\sin (i\pi x/a) \sin (j\pi y/b)$ and integrating over their respective intervals, the coefficients a_{mn} are obtained as follows

$$a_{ij} = \frac{4}{ab} \int_0^a \int_0^b f_1(x, y) \sin \frac{i\pi x}{a} \sin \frac{j\pi y}{b} \, dx \, dy \qquad (1\text{-}176)$$

If f_2 and f_3 are the dependent functions of x and y to be determined in an analysis, their Fourier coefficients b_{mn} and c_{mn} in equations (1-174) are to be evaluated from the corresponding governing differential equations and boundary conditions.

In the case when functions of x and y are defined in the region $-a_0 \leq x \leq a_0$ and $-b_0 \leq y \leq b_0$, the double Fourier series representations of these functions can be obtained similarly. The application of these series to the plate problems can be found in Secs. 2.6, 2.7, and 5.4.

b Generalized Double Fourier Series

Owing to orthogonal functions involved in series (1-174), the calculation is simplified to some extent. In a similar manner dependent variables and loading function in a system of differential equations can be expressed in terms of any other orthogonal sets of functions. Let $f(x, y)$ be defined in the region $a \leq x \leq b$ and $c \leq y \leq d$, and be represented by any other two orthogonal sets of functions $X_m(x)$ and $Y_n(y)$ in the form

$$f(x, y) = \sum_{m=1}^{\infty} \sum_{n=1}^{\infty} f_{mn} X_m(x) Y_n(y) \tag{1-177}$$

which is called a generalized double Fourier series corresponding to the function $f(x, y)$. The coefficients f_{mn} in the series are called the Fourier constants of $f(x, y)$ with respect to these orthogonal sets of functions $X_m(x)$ and $Y_n(y)$. These functions possess the orthogonality properties as follows

$$\int_a^b X_m X_i \, dx = \begin{cases} 0 & m \neq i \\ \|X_i\|^2 & m = i \end{cases}$$
$$\int_c^d Y_n Y_j \, dy = \begin{cases} 0 & n \neq j \\ \|Y_j\|^2 & n = j \end{cases} \tag{1-178}$$

in which $\|X_i\|$ and $\|Y_j\|$ are the norms of X_i and Y_j, respectively.

It may be noticed that the base functions X_i and Y_j used throughout this book are beam eigenfunctions whose norms assume the same values for any i and j respectively. Consequently, the convergence of the generalized double Fourier series is practically the same as that of the double Fourier series.

If the series (1-177) does converge to $f(x, y)$, the Fourier constants f_{mn} for a given function $f(x, y)$ can be determined by multiplying both sides of expression (1-177) by $X_i X_j$ and integrating over their respective intervals provided that term-by-term integration is permissible. The result is

$$f_{mn} = \frac{1}{\|X_m\|^2 \|Y_n\|^2} \int_a^b \int_c^d f(x, y) X_m(x) Y_n(y) \, dx \, dy \tag{1-179}$$

In the case when the function $f(x, y)$ or dependent variables in a plate problem are to be determined, the generalized double Fourier series representations of these variables are generally chosen such that the prescribed boundary conditions are satisfied. The Fourier constants in these series are evaluated from the corresponding differential equations. It will be revealed from the numerical examples discussed later that these series converge more rapidly than a double Fourier series. The applications of the generalized double Fourier series to plate problems are given in Secs. 2.1, 2.4, 5.3, 5.10, 6.2, 6.6, 6.8, 7.3, 8.3, and 8.6.

c A Combination of Double Fourier Series and Generalized Double Fourier Series

In any system of differential equations given in Secs. 1.6 and 1.7 two or three dependent functions are involved. In a solution one of these functions is often represented by a double Fourier series and the other (or the others) by a generalized double Fourier series. These series are chosen such that the boundary conditions considered are satisfied. The coefficients in these series are determined from the corresponding differential equations, and examples of their use can be found in Secs. 2.3, 4.2, 5.5, 5.11, 6.3, 7.1, 7.2, 7.6, 8.1, 8.2, and 8.6.

d Ritz Method

The so-called Rayleigh-Ritz method or simply the Ritz method (Ref. 1.77) is a procedure for applying the principle of minimum potential energy to obtain approximate solutions of elastic problems. In the case when the three displacement components u°, v° and w are to be determined, the procedure consists essentially in assuming that the desired extremal of a given problem can be approximated by linear combinations of suitably chosen functions in the form

$$u^{\circ} = \sum_{m=1}^{M_1} \sum_{n=1}^{N_1} A_{mn} u_{mn}(x, y)$$

$$v^{\circ} = \sum_{m=1}^{M_2} \sum_{n=1}^{N_2} B_{mn} v_{mn}(x, y) \qquad (1\text{-}180)$$

$$w = \sum_{m=1}^{M_3} \sum_{n=1}^{N_3} C_{mn} w_{mn}(x, y)$$

In these expressions A_{mn}, B_{mn}, and C_{mn} are undetermined parameters and u_{mn}, v_{mn}, and w_{mn} are known functions, each of which may be expressed as $F_m(x)G_n(y)$. These functions are to be so chosen that they are continuous, satisfy at least the prescribed geometric or kinematic boundary conditions for any choice of these parameters, and are capable of representing the deformed shape of the elastic system. They should have at least the same order of continuous derivatives as are called for by the differential operators in the corresponding differential equations.

The total potential energy of the elastic system, denoted by Π, is

$$\Pi = V - W \qquad (1\text{-}181)$$

in which V is the strain energy and W is the potential energy of the external loads, both being functions of the displacement components. Substituting equations (1-180) into (1-181), the total potential energy Π becomes a function of the parameters A_{mn}, B_{mn}, and C_{mn}. These parameters are determined from the condition that the total potential energy of the system is a minimum with respect to them, namely,

$$\Pi_{,A_{mn}} = 0 \qquad \Pi_{,B_{mn}} = 0 \qquad \Pi_{,C_{mn}} = 0 \qquad (1\text{-}182)$$

These conditions state that the incremental energy due to a variation in any of these parameters be zero. Equations (1-182) give the same number of equations for A_{mn}, B_{mn}, and C_{mn} as the number of parameters taken. Evidently, the accuracy of the method depends upon the choice of the number of parameters and the approximating shape functions u_{mn}, v_{mn}, and w_{mn}. This method will be used in obtaining approximate solutions in Secs. 2.9 and 3.8.

e Galerkin's Method

In 1915 Galerkin (Ref. 1.78) developed a method of approximate solutions of the boundary-value problems. The method has been widely applied to both static and dynamic problems in the area of solid mechanics. The idea of the method is minimization of errors by orthogonalizing with respect to a set of given functions.

Let us consider a system of differential equations

$$L_i(u^\circ, v^\circ, w) = 0 \qquad i = 1, 2, 3 \tag{1-183}$$

subjected to appropriate boundary conditions. In these equations L_i are the nonlinear (or linear) differential operators. These equations physically represent the conditions of dynamic (or static) equilibrium of a differential element $h\, dx\, dy$ cut out from a thin plate under external forces. Let arbitrary virtual displacements δu°, δv°, δw be applied to the structural system. These displacements, however, are continuous functions of x, y, and t and satisfy the geometrical boundary conditions. The virtual work done on the element by these virtual displacements is

$$\{L_1(u^\circ, v^\circ, w)\, \delta u^\circ + L_2(u^\circ, v^\circ, w)\, \delta v^\circ + L_3(u^\circ, v^\circ, w)\, \delta w\} h\, dx\, dy$$

By the principle of virtual work the following is obtained

$$\iint_A \{L_1(u^\circ, v^\circ, w)\, \delta u^\circ + L_2(u^\circ, v^\circ, w)\, \delta v^\circ + L_3(u^\circ, v^\circ, w)\, \delta w\}\, dx\, dy = 0 \tag{1-184}$$

in which the integration is carried out over the entire plate area A.

An approximate solution of the problem is sought in the form

$$u^\circ = \sum_m \sum_n A_{mn}(t)\phi_{mn}(x, y)$$

$$v^\circ = \sum_m \sum_n B_{mn}(t)\chi_{mn}(x, y) \tag{1-185}$$

$$w = \sum_m \sum_n C_{mn}(t)\psi_{mn}(x, y)$$

in which A's, B's, C's are undetermined variable coefficients of time and ϕ's, χ's, ψ's are suitably chosen spatial functions satisfying the prescribed boundary conditions and capable of representing the mode of deformation. The assumed solution (1-185) is not required to satisfy equations (1-183) but the functions ϕ, χ, and ψ

should have at least the same order of derivatives as those in these differential equations. The virtual displacements are taken to be of the form

$$\delta u^\circ = \sum_m \sum_n \phi_{mn}(x, y) \, \delta A_{mn}(t)$$

$$\delta v^\circ = \sum_m \sum_n \chi_{mn}(x, y) \, \delta B_{mn}(t) \qquad (1\text{-}186)$$

$$\delta w = \sum_m \sum_n \psi_{mn}(x, y) \, \delta C_{mn}(t)$$

and substituted into the variational equation (1-184). Since A's, B's and C's can be varied independently, the only way that the resulting variational equation can be zero is that the coefficients of δA_{mn}, δB_{mn}, and δC_{mn} must vanish identically in the domain, namely,

$$\iint_A L_1(u^\circ, v^\circ, w)\phi_{mn}(x, y) \, dx \, dy = 0$$

$$\iint_A L_2(u^\circ, v^\circ, w)\chi_{mn}(x, y) \, dx \, dy = 0 \qquad (1\text{-}187)$$

$$\iint_A L_3(u^\circ, v^\circ, w)\psi_{mn}(x, y) \, dx \, dy = 0$$

which provide the same number of equations for the number of A_{mn}, B_{mn}, and C_{mn} taken. Introducing the approximate solution (1-185) into equations (1-187) and performing integration will lead either to a system of ordinary differential equations for $A_{mn}(t)$, $B_{mn}(t)$, and $C_{mn}(t)$ in the dynamic problem or to a system of algebraic equations for constant coefficients A_{mn}, B_{mn}, C_{mn} in the static problem. Unlike the Ritz method the Galerkin method does not require the formulation of an energy principle.

In the application of the foregoing technique to a system of equations as presented in Sec. 1.6, the one-term approximation for the inplane displacements, u° and v°, can differ considerably from the true solution for a given w in a single-mode analysis (Ref. 1.79). This method yields good approximations only after taking a few terms for u° and v° in expressions (1-185).

In the case of boundary conditions expressed in terms of w and F, it is convenient to use the system of differential equations as presented in Sec. 1.7.

$$L(w, F) = 0 \qquad (1\text{-}188)$$

$$J(w, F) = (w_{,xy})^2 - w_{,xx}w_{,yy} \qquad (1\text{-}189)$$

in which L and J are differential operators, and in which the first equation is the equation of motion in the transverse direction and the second is the equation of compatibility in the analysis. For the trial function being

$$w = \sum_m \sum_n C_{mn}(t)\psi_{mn}(x, y) \qquad (1\text{-}190)$$

equation (1-189) can be solved for F in conjunction with the prescribed membrane boundary conditions. The error in the approximate deflection function (1-190) is then minimized by the Galerkin procedure. In this case equations (1-187) take the following form

$$\iint_A L(w, F)\psi_{mn}(x, y) \, dx \, dy = 0 \tag{1-191}$$

in which F is a known function of x and y and the integration is carried out over the entire area of the plate. This equation implies that the virtual work, as a whole, vanishes at any instant. Taking into account equation (1-190) and performing integration, a set of nonlinear ordinary differential equations will be obtained for time-dependent coefficients $C_{mn}(t)$ in the vibration analysis. In the static case C_{mn} are constant coefficients in expression (1-190) and the final equations become a set of algebraic equations. Evidently the accuracy of this procedure is very sensitive to the choice of the trial functions. The use of Galerkin's method in obtaining approximate solutions can be found in Secs. 2.2, 2.3, 2.6, 3.7, 4.3, 4.8 to 4.12, 5.2, 5.7, 6.7, 6.9, 8.4, and 8.5.

f Perturbation Method

The perturbation or small parameter method (Ref. 1.80) is a common analytical method in obtaining approximate solutions to nonlinear problems of applied mechanics. It consists in developing the solution of a boundary (or initial) value problem in powers of a parameter which either appears explicitly in the original problem or is introduced artificially. The perturbation is generated in the neighborhood of the solution of the linearized equations such that the known properties of the linear system can be utilized for the solution to the perturbed system.

Developing the perturbation method, Poincaré (Ref. 1.81) has demonstrated that for some classes of ordinary differential equations the expansions, called asymptotic, converge uniformly in any finite interval of the independent variable if the absolute value of the parameter, denoted by ε, is sufficiently small. The scope of the systematic search of Poincaré and subsequent investigators was mainly confined to the equation

$$\ddot{x} + \alpha^2 x = \varepsilon f(\dot{x}, x, t) \tag{1-192}$$

in which x is a function of t (usually of time) and the solution sought is of periodic character. In spite of this and the fact that the question of convergence has not been fully clarified, the method has been successfully applied to more complex problems, systems of partial differential equations, and so on. This arises mainly from the fact that in practical applications only the first few terms of the perturbation series are used. The respective series may be even ultimately divergent without being inefficient (Ref. 1.82). Furthermore the perturbation series may be considered as a semiconvergence or convergently beginning expansion (Ref. 1.83). Thus the perturbation series are not regarded as power series in the parameter involved but as series asymptotic in nature. This dispenses with an investigation of the convergence of the procedure. It may be observed that a proof of convergence can be furnished only rarely for other analytical methods such as those due to Ritz, Galerkin, and others. In fact, similar difficulties are encountered in most formal solutions of mathematical problems sought in the form of infinite series.

The perturbation expansions generally are expressed in terms of a single parameter. The standard procedure is well known and not described herein. A generalization of the perturbation method (Ref. 1.80), however, is now considered. Let us suppose that the boundary, or initial, value problem under investigation includes N parameters ε_i $(i = 1, \ldots, N, N > 1)$ intrinsically independent of each other. It is natural to develop the solution $f(x, \varepsilon)$ in powers of N parameters as follows

$$f(x, \varepsilon) = \sum_{p, q, \ldots, s = 0}^{\infty} \sum_{i, j, \ldots, m = 1}^{N} (\varepsilon_i)^p (\varepsilon_j)^q \cdots (\varepsilon_m)^s \beta_{ij\ldots m}^{pq\ldots s}(x) \qquad (1\text{-}193)$$

Further procedure follows essentially the standard line. Apparently, the parameters involved may be of different character, for instance some describing the material properties, some geometrical or dynamical features of the problem, and so forth.

It may be of interest to note that, in contrast to the Ritz method and to the Galerkin procedure in which the solution is sought in the form of series of pre-assigned functions with unknown coefficients, the perturbation method, especially in the multiparameter form, consists in development of the solution in terms of unknown functions with preassigned coefficients.

The application of the perturbation method to geometrically nonlinear problems of plates can be found in Secs. 2.5, 3.2 to 3.5, 3.9, 4.7, 4.9, 5.1, 5.6, 5.8, 5.9, 7.4, 7.5, and 8.4. It may be noticed that the multiparameter perturbation method is used only in Secs. 3.5 and 5.8.

PROBLEMS

1.1 Using the strain-displacement relations (1-42) and Hamilton's principle, derive the equations of flexural motion and the associated boundary conditions for the moderately large-amplitude vibrations of isotropic plates. Compare the equations thus obtained with equations (1-117) to (1-119).

1.2 If an isotropic rectangular plate of constant thickness is subjected to aerodynamic heating and undergoes moderately large-amplitude vibrations, show that the dynamic von Kármán nonlinear equations of the plate, including the thermal effect, can be expressed as

$$D\nabla^4 w + \rho w_{,tt} = h(w_{,xx} F_{,yy} + w_{,yy} F_{,xx} - 2w_{,xy} F_{,xy}) + q - \frac{E}{1-v} \alpha \nabla^2 T_1$$

$$\nabla^4 F = E(w_{,xy}^2 - w_{,xx} w_{,yy}) - \frac{E}{h} \alpha \nabla^2 T_2$$

where F is the stress function and α is the coefficient of thermal expansion and where

$$T_1 = \int_{-h/2}^{h/2} T(x, y, z)z\, dz \qquad T_2 = \int_{-h/2}^{h/2} T(x, y, z)\, dz$$

with T being the temperature change from the initial state.

1.3 Let (L, T) represent the principal axes of elasticity of an orthotropic rectangular plate and (x, y) represent the chosen axes parallel to the plate edges. The x axis forms an angle θ with the L axis. If the stress-strain relations in the system of coordinates x, y are given by equation (1-34), and those in the system of coordinates L, T by

$$\begin{Bmatrix} \sigma_L \\ \sigma_T \\ \sigma_{LT} \end{Bmatrix} = \begin{bmatrix} C_L & C_{LT} & 0 \\ C_{LT} & C_T & 0 \\ 0 & 0 & C_S \end{bmatrix} \begin{Bmatrix} \varepsilon_L \\ \varepsilon_T \\ \varepsilon_{LT} \end{Bmatrix}$$

show that the two sets of elastic stiffnesses are related by equation (1-38).

1.4 Verify that the differential equations governing the moderately large-amplitude vibrations of orthotropic skew plates of variable thickness $h = h(\alpha, \beta)$ as shown in Fig. 3.12 are given by

$$F_{,\alpha\alpha\alpha\alpha} + k_1 F_{,\alpha\alpha\alpha\beta} + k_2 F_{,\alpha\alpha\beta\beta} + k_3 F_{,\alpha\beta\beta\beta} + k_4 F_{,\beta\beta\beta\beta} = cE_y(w_{,\alpha\beta}^2 - w_{,\alpha\alpha} w_{,\beta\beta})$$

$$w_{,\alpha\alpha\alpha\alpha} + k_5 w_{,\alpha\alpha\alpha\beta} + k_6 w_{,\alpha\alpha\beta\beta} + k_7 w_{,\alpha\beta\beta\beta} + k_8 w_{,\beta\beta\beta\beta}$$

$$+ \frac{3}{h^2} [(hh_{,\alpha\alpha} + 2h_{,\alpha}^2)(w_{,\alpha\alpha} + k_9 w_{,\beta\beta} + \tfrac{1}{2}k_5 w_{,\alpha\beta})$$

$$+ (hh_{,\beta\beta} + 2h_{,\beta}^2)(k_9 w_{,\alpha\alpha} + k_8 w_{,\beta\beta} + \tfrac{1}{2}k_7 w_{,\alpha\beta})$$

$$+ (hh_{,\alpha\beta} + 2h_{,\alpha} h_{,\beta})(\tfrac{1}{2}k_5 w_{,\alpha\alpha} + \tfrac{1}{2}k_7 w_{,\beta\beta} + k_{10} w_{,\alpha\beta})]$$

$$= \frac{12(1 - v_{xy} v_{yx})c^3}{E_x h^3} [cq - c\rho_0 w_{,tt} + h(w_{,\alpha\alpha} F_{,\beta\beta} + w_{,\beta\beta} F_{,\alpha\alpha} - 2w_{,\alpha\beta} F_{,\alpha\beta})]$$

where F is the Airy stress function and where

$$c = \cos\theta \qquad s = \sin\theta \qquad r = \frac{s}{c}$$

$$k^2 = \frac{E_y}{E_x} \qquad p^2 = \frac{G_{xy}}{E_x}(1 - v_{xy} v_{yx})$$

$$m^2 = \frac{1}{p^2}(k^2 - v_{yx}^2 - 2v_{yx}p^2) \qquad k_1 = -4s$$

$$k_2 = 6s^2 + c^2 m^2 \qquad k_3 = -2s(2s^2 + c^2 m^2)$$

$$k_4 = c^4(k^2 + m^2 r^2 + r^4) \qquad k_5 = -4s$$

$$k_6 = 2c^2(2p^2 + 3r^2 + v_{yx}) \qquad k_7 = -4c^2 s(2p^2 + r^2 + v_{yx})$$

$$k_8 = c^4[k^2 + r^4 + 2r^2(2p^2 + v_{yx})] \qquad k_9 = c^2(r^2 + v_{yx})$$

$$k_{10} = 4c^2(p^2 + r^2)$$

It may be noticed that in the isotropic case

$$E_x = E_y = E \qquad v_{xy} = v_{yx} = v$$

$$k^2 = 1 \qquad m^2 = 2 \qquad p^2 = \tfrac{1}{2}(1 - v)$$

1.5 From statics consideration, derive the von Kármán-type nonlinear equations for generally laminated anisotropic plates, which are the static version of equations (1-129) and (1-131).

1.6 To include the transverse shear deformation in the orthotropic plate analysis, the displacement components for a point off the midsurface may be assumed in the form

$$u(x, y, z, t) = u^\circ(x, y, t) + z\alpha(x, y, t)$$

$$v(x, y, z, t) = v^\circ(x, y, t) + z\beta(x, y, t)$$

$$w(x, y, z, t) = w(x, y, t)$$

where α and β are two functions to be determined. Assuming zero normal stress ($\sigma_z = 0$) the stress-strain relations for an orthotropic material may be expressed as

$$
\begin{Bmatrix} \sigma_x \\ \sigma_y \\ \sigma_{yz} \\ \sigma_{zx} \\ \sigma_{xy} \end{Bmatrix} =
\begin{bmatrix}
s_{11} & s_{12} & 0 & 0 & s_{16} \\
s_{12} & s_{22} & 0 & 0 & s_{26} \\
0 & 0 & s_{44} & s_{45} & 0 \\
0 & 0 & s_{45} & s_{55} & 0 \\
s_{16} & s_{26} & 0 & 0 & s_{66}
\end{bmatrix}
\begin{Bmatrix} \varepsilon_x \\ \varepsilon_y \\ \varepsilon_{yz} \\ \varepsilon_{zx} \\ \varepsilon_{xy} \end{Bmatrix}
$$

where s's are elastic stiffnesses.

Obtain the expressions for membrane forces, bending moments, and transverse shearing forces. Using equations (1-20) and (1-21) as well as the classical method of integration, formulate the nonlinear equations of transverse motion for the orthotropic plate.

1.7 Based on the assumptions made in Prob. 1.6, the strain energies of the orthotropic plate due to stretching, bending, and transverse shear are, for moderately large deflections,

$$V_s = \frac{h}{2} \iint_A \left[s_{11}(\varepsilon_x^\circ)^2 + s_{22}(\varepsilon_y^\circ)^2 + s_{66}(\varepsilon_{xy}^\circ)^2 + 2s_{12}\,\varepsilon_x^\circ \varepsilon_y^\circ + 2s_{16}\,\varepsilon_x^\circ \varepsilon_{xy}^\circ + 2s_{26}\,\varepsilon_y^\circ \varepsilon_{xy}^\circ \right] dx\,dy$$

$$V_b = \iint_A \left[M_x \alpha_{,x} + M_y \beta_{,y} + M_{xy}(\alpha_{,y} + \beta_{,x}) \right] dx\,dy$$

$$V_t = \iint_A \left[Q_x(\alpha + w_{,x}) + Q_y(\beta + w_{,y}) \right] dx\,dy$$

and the kinetic energy of the plate is

$$T = \frac{\rho_0}{2} \iint_A \left[(u^\circ_{,t})^2 + (v^\circ_{,t})^2 + (w_{,t})^2 + \frac{h^2}{12}(\alpha^2_{,t} + \beta^2_{,t}) \right] dx\,dy$$

where ρ_0 is the mass density per unit area of the plate and A is the area of the plate.

Using these expressions and Hamilton's principle and taking variations of u°, v°, w, α, and β independently and simultaneously, derive the Euler-Lagrange equations and reduce them to a system of four equations in terms of α, β, w, and stress function F.

REFERENCES

1.1. Y. C. Fung: "Foundations of Solid Mechanics," Prentice-Hall, Inc., Englewood Cliffs, N.J., 1965.
1.2. Y. Y. Yu: Generalized Hamilton's Principle and Variational Equation of Motion in Nonlinear Elasticity Theory, with Application to Plate Theory, *J. Acoust. Soc. Am.*, vol. 36, pp. 111–120, 1964.
1.3. T. von Kármán: Festigkeitsprobleme im Mashinenbau, *Encykl. Math. Wiss.*, vol. 4, no. 4, pp. 348–352, 1910.

1.4. S. Timoshenko and S. Woinowsky-Krieger: "Theory of Plates and Shells," McGraw-Hill Book Co., New York, 1959.

1.5. Y. Stavsky: Bending and Stretching of Laminated Aeolotropic Plates, *J. Eng. Mech. Div., Proc. ASCE*, vol. 87, no. EM6, pp. 31–56, 1961.

1.6. J. M. Whitney and A. W. Leissa: Analysis of Heterogeneous Anisotropic Plates, *ASME J. Appl. Mech.*, vol. 36, pp. 261–266, 1969.

1.7. G. Hermann: Influence of Large Amplitudes on Flexural Motions of Elastic Plates, *Nat. Advis. Comm. Aeronaut. (U.S.A.), Tech. Note 3578*, May 1955.

1.8. M. A. Biot: Non-Linear Theory of Elasticity and the Linearized Case for a Body Under Initial Stress, *London, Dublin, and Edinburgh Philosoph. Mag. J. Sci.*, ser. 7, vol. 27, no. 183, pp. 468–489, 1939.

1.9. Y. Y. Yu: Application of Variational Equation of Motion to the Nonlinear Vibration Analysis of Homogeneous and Layered Plates and Shells, *ASME J. Appl. Mech.*, vol. 30, pp. 78–86, 1963.

1.10. N. Ren and Y. Y. Yu: Flexural and Extensional Vibrations of Two-Layered Plates, *AIAA J.*, vol. 5, pp. 797–799, 1967.

1.11. J. E. Ashton and J. M. Whitney: "Theory of Laminated Plates," Technomic Publishing Co., Inc., 1970.

1.12. N. J. Pagano: Exact Solutions of Composite Laminates in Cylindrical Bending, *J. Comp. Mater.*, vol. 3, pp. 398–411, 1969.

1.13. J. M. Whitney: The Effect of Transverse Shear Deformation on the Bending of Laminated Plates, *J. Comp. Mater.*, vol. 3, pp. 534–547, 1969.

1.14. N. J. Pagano: Exact Solutions for Rectangular Bidirectional Composites and Sandwich Plates, *J. Comp. Mater.*, vol. 4, pp. 20–34, 1970.

1.15. J. M. Whitney and N. J. Pagano: Shear Deformation in Heterogeneous Anisotropic plates, *ASME J. Appl. Mech.*, vol. 37, pp. 1031–1036, 1970.

1.16. S. Srinivas, C. V. Joga Rao, and A. K. Rao: An Exact Analysis for Vibration of Simply Supported Homogeneous and Laminated Thick Rectangular Plates, *J. Sound Vib.*, vol. 12, pp. 187–199, 1970.

1.17. S. Srinivas and A. K. Rao: Bending, Vibration and Buckling of Simply Supported Thick Orthotropic Rectangular Plates and Laminates, *Int. J. Solids Struct.*, vol. 6, pp. 1463–1481, 1970.

1.18. T. P. Kicher and J. F. Mandell: A Study of the Buckling of Laminated Composite Plates, *AIAA J.*, vol. 9, pp. 605–613, 1971.

1.19. J. M. Whitney: Shear Correction Factors for Orthotropic Laminates Under Static Load, *ASME J. Appl. Mech.*, vol. 40, pp. 302–304, 1973.

1.20. L. L. Durocher and R. Solecki: Bending and Vibration of Transversely Isotropic Two-Layer Plates, *AIAA J.*, vol. 13, pp. 1522–1524, 1975.

1.21. Y. Y. Yu and J. L. Lai: Influence of Transverse Shear and Edge Condition on Nonlinear Vibration and Dynamic Buckling of Homogeneous and Sandwich Plates, *ASME J. Appl. Mech.*, vol. 33, pp. 934–936, 1966.

1.22. C. I. Wu and J. R. Vinson: Influence of Large Amplitudes, Transverse Shear Deformation, And Rotatory Inertia on Lateral Vibrations of Transversely Isotropic Plates, *ASME J. Appl. Mech.*, vol. 36, pp. 254–260, 1969.

1.23. C. I. Wu and J. R. Vinson: On the Nonlinear Oscillations of Plates Composed of Composite Materials, *J. Comp. Mater.*, vol. 3, pp. 548–561, 1969.

1.24. C. I. Wu and J. R. Vinson: Nonlinear Oscillations of Laminated Specially Orthotropic Plates with Clamped and Simply Supported Edges, *J. Acoust. Soc. Am.*, vol. 49, pp. 1561–1567, 1971.

1.25. M. Sathyamoorthy: Shear and Rotatory Inertia Effects on Large Amplitude Vibration of Skew Plates, *J. Sound Vib.*, vol. 52, pp. 155–163, 1977.

1.26. M. Sathyamoorthy: Vibration of Plates Considering Shear and Rotatory Inertia, *AIAA J.*, vol. 16, pp. 285–286, 1978.

1.27. M. Sathyamoorthy: Shear and Rotatory Inertia Effects on the Large Amplitude Vibration of Plates, *J. Eng. Mech. Div., Proc. ASCE*, vol. 104, no. EM5, pp. 1288–1293, 1978.

1.28. M. Sathyamoorthy: Shear Effects on Vibration of Plates, *J. Sound Vib.*, vol. 60, pp. 308–311, 1978.

1.29. M. Sathyamoorthy and C. Y. Chia: Effect of Transverse Shear and Rotatory Inertia on Large Amplitude Vibration of Anisotropic Skew Plates, I—Theory, and II—Numerical Results, *ASME J. Appl. Mech.* (in press).

1.30. S. A. Zaghloul and J. B. Kennedy: Nonlinear Behavior of Symmetrically Laminated Plates, *ASME J. Appl. Mech.*, vol. 42, pp. 234–236, 1975.

1.31. S. A. Zaghloul and J. B. Kennedy: Nonlinear Analysis of Unsymmetrically Laminated Plates, *J. Eng. Mech. Div., Proc. ASCE*, vol. 101, no. EM3, pp. 169–186, 1975.

1.32. H. M. Berger: A New Approach to the Analysis of Large Deflections of Plates, *ASME J. Appl. Mech.*, vol. 22, pp. 465–472, 1955.

1.33. J. Nowinski: Note on the Nonlinear Analysis of Large Deflections of Rectangular Plates, *Appl. Sci. Res., Sec. A*, vol. 11, pp. 85–96, 1962.

1.34. S. N. Sinha: Large Deflections of Plates on Elastic Foundations, *J. Eng. Mech. Div., Proc. ASCE*, vol. 89, no. EM1, pp. 1–24, 1963.

1.35. S. Basuli: Note on the Large Deflection of a Circular Plate Under a Concentrated Load, *Z. Angew. Math. Phys.*, vol. 12, pp. 357–362, 1961.

1.36. S. Basuli: Note on the Large Deflection of a Circular Plate of Variable Thickness Under Lateral Loads, *Bul. Inst. Polit. Jasy.*, vol. 10, pp. 63–66, 1964.

1.37. B. Banerjee: Note on the Large Deflection of a Circular Plate with Clamped Edge Under Symmetrical Load, *Bul. Calcutta Math. Soc.*, vol. 59, pp. 175–179, 1967.

1.38. B. Banerjee: Large Deflection of a Semi-Circular Plate Under a Uniform Load, *Bul. Acad. Polonaise Sci. Ser. Sci. Tech.*, vol. 15, pp. 183–187, 1967.

1.39. M. C. Pal: Large Deflections of Heated Circular Plates, *Acta Mech.*, vol. 8, pp. 82–103, 1969.

1.40. R. Schmidt: A Remark on Berger's Method in the Nonlinear Theory of Plates, *J. Indust. Math. Soc.*, vol. 22, part 2, pp. 83–86, 1972.

1.41. J. L. Nowinski and H. Ohnabe: On Certain Inconsistencies in Berger Equations for Large Deflections of Elastic Plates, *Int. J. Mech. Sci.*, vol. 14, pp. 165–170, 1972.

1.42. R. Schmidt: On Berger's Method in the Nonlinear Theory of Plates, *ASME J. Appl. Mech.*, vol. 41, pp. 521–523, 1974.

1.43. R. Schmidt and D. A. DaDeppo: A New Approach to the Analysis of Shells, Plates, and Membranes with Finite Deflections, *Int. J. Non-Linear Mech.*, vol. 9, pp. 409–419, 1974.

1.44. S. Datta: Large Deflection of a Circular Plate on Elastic Foundation Under a Concentrated Load at the Center, *ASME J. Appl. Mech.*, vol. 42, pp. 503–505, 1975.

1.45. M. M. Banerjee: Note on the Large Deflections of Irregular Shaped Plates by the Method of Conformal Mapping, *ASME J. Appl. Mech.*, vol. 43, pp. 356–357, 1976.

1.46. R. Bera: A Note on the Buckling of Plates Due to Large Deflections, *J. Sci. Eng. Res.*, vol. 9, pp. 343–350, 1965.

1.47. T. Iwinski and J. Nowinski: The Problem of Large Deflections of Orthotropic Plates (I), *Arch. Mech. Stos.* vol. 9, pp. 593–603, 1957.

1.48. B. Banerjee: Large Deflection of an Orthotropic Circular Plate Under a Concentrated Load, *Bul. Acad. Polonaise Sci. Ser. Sci. Tech.*, vol. 15, pp. 699–704, 1967.

1.49. S. Datta: Large Deflection of a Triangular Orthotropic Plate on Elastic Foundation, *Def. Sci. J.*, vol. 25, pp. 115–120, 1975.

1.50. M. M. Banerjee: Note on the Large Deflection of an Orthotropic Circular Plate with Clamped Edge Under Symmetrical Load, *J. Indian Inst. Sci.*, vol. 58, pp. 175–180, 1976.

1.51. W. A. Nash and J. R. Modeer: Certain Approximate Analysis of the Nonlinear Behavior of Plates and Shells, *Proc. I.U.T.A.M. Symp. on the Theory of Thin Elastic Shells*, North-Holland Publishing Company, pp. 331–354, 1960.

1.52. T. Wah: Large Amplitude Flexural Vibrations of Rectangular Plates, *Int. J. Mech. Sci.*, vol. 5, pp. 425–438, 1963.

1.53. T. Wah: The Normal Modes of Vibration of Certain Nonlinear Continuous Systems, *ASME J. Appl. Mech.*, vol. 31, pp. 139–140, 1964.

1.54. N. Gajendar: Large Amplitude Vibrations of Plates on Elastic Foundations, *Int. J. Non-Linear Mech.*, vol. 2, pp. 163–172, 1967.

1.55. J. Ramachandran: Large Amplitude Vibrations of Elastically Restrained Rectangular Plates, *ASME J. Appl. Mech.*, vol. 40, pp. 811–813, 1973.

1.56. B. Kishor: Nonlinear Transverse Vibration Analysis of a Rectangular Plate with Lumped M-S-D Systems, *ASME J. Appl. Mech.*, vol. 40, pp. 825–826, 1973.

1.57. B. Kishor: Nonlinear Vibration Analysis of Rectangular Plate on a Viscoelastic Foundation, *Aeronaut. Q.*, vol. 25, pp. 37–46, 1974.

1.58. M. C. Pal: Large Amplitude Free Vibrations of Rectangular Plates Subjected to Aerodynamic Heating, *J. Eng. Math.*, vol. 4, pp. 39–49, 1970.

1.59. T. Wah: Vibration of Circular Plates at Large Amplitudes, *J. Eng. Mech. Div., Proc. ASCE*, vol. 89, no. EM5, pp. 1–15, Oct. 1963.

1.60. A. V. Srinivasan: Large Amplitude Free Oscillations of Beams and Plates, *AIAA J.*, vol. 3, pp. 1951–1953, 1965.

1.61. A. V. Srinivasan: Nonlinear Vibrations of Beams and Plates, *Int. J. Non-Linear Mech.*, vol. 1, pp. 179–191, 1966.

1.62. M. C. Pal: Large Amplitude Free Vibration of Circular Plates Subjected to Aerodynamic Heating, *Int. J. Solids Struct.*, vol. 6, pp. 301–313, 1970.

1.63. D. C. Chiang and S. S. H. Chen: Large Amplitude Vibration of a Circular Plate With Concentrated Rigid Mass, *ASME J. Appl. Mech.*, vol. 39, pp. 1050–1054, 1972.

1.64. B. Banerjee: Large Amplitude Free Vibrations of Elliptic Plates, *J. Phys. Soc. Japan*, vol. 23, pp. 1169–1172, 1967.

1.65. M. C. Pal: Large Amplitude Free Vibrations of Recti-Linear Plates, *J. Sci. Eng. Res.*, vol. 11, pp. 317–326, 1967.

1.66. B. Banerjee: Large Amplitude Free Vibration of an Isosceles Right Angled Triangular Plate with Simply Supported Edges, *J. Sci. Eng. Res.*, vol. 12, pp. 45–49, 1968.

1.67. M. Sathyamoorthy and K. A. V. Pandalai: Vibration of Simply Supported Clamped Skew Plates at Large Amplitudes, *J. Sound Vib.*, vol. 27, pp. 37–46, 1973.

1.68. M. Sathyamoorthy and K. A. V. Pandalai: Large Amplitude Flexural Vibration of Simply Supported Skew Plates, *AIAA J.*, vol. 11, pp. 1279–1282, 1973.

1.69. M. Sathyamoorthy and K. A. V. Pandalai: Nonlinear Vibration of Elastic Skew Plates Exhibiting Rectilinear Orthotropy, *J. Franklin Inst.*, vol. 296, pp. 359–369, 1973.

1.70. M. Sathyamoorthy and K. A. V. Pandalai: Large Amplitude Vibration of Variable Thickness Skew Plates, *Proc. Conf. Noise, Shock and Vibration*, Monash University, Austrialia, pp. 99–106, 1974.

1.71. C. P. Vendhan: A Study of Berger Equations Applied to Nonlinear Vibration of Elastic Plates, *Int. J. Mech. Sci.*, vol. 17, pp. 461–468, 1975.

1.72. S. W. Tsai: Structural Behavior of Composite Materials, *NASA Contract Rep. No. 71, Nat. Aeronaut. Space Admin.*, Washington, D.C., 1964.

1.73. A. E. H. Love: "A Treatise on the Mathematical Theory of Elasticity," 4th ed., Dover Publications, p. 176, 1944.

1.74. R. D. Mindlin: Influence of Rotatory Inertia and Shear on Flexural Motions of Isotropic, Elastic Plates, *ASME J. Appl. Mech.*, vol. 18, pp. 31–38, 1951.

1.75. C. Lanczos: "Discourse on Fourier Series," Oliver & Boyd, London, 1966.

1.76. A. Zygmund: "Trigonometric Series," vol. 1, 2d ed., Cambridge University Press, p. 301, 1959.

1.77. W. Ritz: Über Eine Neue Methode zur Lösung Gewissen Variations-Problems der Mathematischen Physik, *J. Reine u. Angew. Math.*, vol. 135, pp. 1–61, 1908.

1.78. B. G. Galerkin: *Vestn. Inzh. Tekh.*, vol. 1, pp. 879–903, 1915.

1.79. C. P. Vendhan and Y. C. Das: Application of Rayleigh-Ritz and Galerkin Methods to Nonlinear Vibration of Plates, *J. Sound Vib.*, vol. 39, pp. 147–157, 1975.

1.80. J. L. Nowinski and I. A. Ismail: Application of a Multi-Parameter Perturbation Method to Elastostatics, *Dev. Theor. Appl. Mech.*, vol. 2, Pergamon Press, pp. 35–45, 1965.

1.81. H. Poincaré: "New Methods in Celestial Mechanics" (in French), Gauthier-Villars, 1892.

1.82. T. Kato: On the Convergence of the Perturbation Method, *Prog. Theor. Phys.*, vol. 5, pp. 95–101, 1950.

1.83. A. Erdelyi: "Asymptotic Expansions," Dover Publications.

ADDITIONAL REFERENCES

Allen, H. G.: "Analysis and Design of Structural Sandwich Panels," Pergamon Press, 1969.

Ambartsumyan, S. A.: "Theory of Anisotropic Plates," Translated from Russian, edited by J. E. Ashton and T. Cheron, Technomic Publishing Co., 1969.

Alwan, A. M.: Large Deflection of Sandwich Plates With Orthotropic Cores, *AIAA J.*, vol. 2, pp. 1820–1822, 1964.

————: Bending of Sandwich Plates with Large Deflections, *J. Eng. Mech. Div., Proc. ASCE*, vol. 93, no. EM3, pp. 83–93, 1967.

Alwar, R. S. and N. K. Adimurthy: Nonlinear Dynamic Response of Sandwich Panels Under Pulse and Shock Type Excitations, *J. Sound Vib.*, vol. 39, pp. 43–54, 1975.

Bernstein, E. L.: On Large Deflection Theories of Plates, *ASME J. Appl. Mech.*, vol. 32, pp. 695–697, 1965.

Bleich, H.: Buckling Strength of Metal Structures, McGraw-Hill Book Company, New York, 1952.

Brush, D. O. and B. O. Almroth: "Buckling of Bars, Plates and Shells," McGraw-Hill Book Company, New York, 1975.

Bulson, P. S.: "The Stability of Flat Plates," American Elsevier Publishing Co. 1970.

Calcote, L. R.: "The Analysis of Laminated Composite Structures," Van Nostrand-Reinhold, 1969.

Cheng, S.: On the Theory of Bending of Sandwich Plates, Proc. 4th U.S. Nat. Cong. Appl. Mech., pp. 511–518, 1962.

Chia, C. Y.: Nonlinear Theory of Heterogeneous Anisotropic Plates, *Proc. 3d Australasian Conf. Mech. Struct. Mater.*, vol. 2 (Auckland), pp. 1-25, 1971.

Cox, H. L.: "The Buckling of Plates and Shells," Pergamon Press, 1963.

Donnell, L. H.: "Beams, Plates, and Shells," McGraw-Hill Book Company, New York, 1976.

Dowell, E. H.: "Aeroelasticity of Plates and Shells," Noordhoff International Publishing, 1975.

Ebcioglu, I. K.: A Large-Deflection Theory of Anisotropic Plates, *Ing.-Arch.*, vol. 33, pp. 396–403, 1964.

————: On the Theory of Sandwich Panels in the Reference State, *Int. J. Eng. Sci.*, vol. 2, pp. 549–563, 1965.

Eringen, A. C.: On the Nonlinear Oscillations of Viscoelastic Plates, *ASME J. Appl. Mech.*, vol. 22, pp. 563–567, 1955.

Evan-Iwanowski, R. M.: "Resonance Oscillations in Mechanical Systems," Elsevier Scientific Publishing Co., 1976.

Flügge, W. (ed.): "Handbook of Engineering Mechanics," McGraw-Hill Book Company, New York, 1962.

Girkmann, K.: "Flächentragwerke", Springer-Verlag, New York, 1956.

Glockner, P. G. and T. Vishwanath: On the Analysis of Nonlinear Membranes, *Int. J. Non-Linear Mech.*, vol. 7, pp. 361–394, 1972.

Habip, L. M.: A Review of Recent Russian Work on Sandwich Structures, *Int. J. Mech. Sci.*, vol. 6, pp. 483–487, 1964.

————: Theory of Elastic Plates in the Reference State, *Int. J. Solids Struct.*, vol. 2, pp. 157–166, 1966.

Hearmon, R. F. S.: "An Introduction to Applied Anisotropic Elasticity," Oxford University Press, London, 1961.

Herrmann, G., and A. E. Armenakas: Vibrations and Stability of Plates Under Initial Stress, *J. Eng. Mech. Div., Proc., ASCE*, vol. 86, no. EM3, pp. 65–94, 1960.

Jaeger, L. G.: "Elementary Theory of Plates," Pergamon Press, 1964.

Jones, R. M.: "Mechanics of Composite Materials," Scripta Book Co., 1975.

Kalnins, A. and C. L. Dym: "Vibration: Beams, Plates and Shells," Hutchinson and Ross Inc., 1976.

Kamiya, N.: Governing Equation for Large Deflections of Sandwich Plates, *AIAA J.*, vol. 14, pp. 250–253, 1976.

Karmakar, B. M.: Amplitude-Frequency Characteristics of Large-Amplitude Vibrations of Sandwich Plates, *ASME J. Appl. Mech.*, vol. 46, 1979, pp. 230–231.

Kaul, R. K.: Finite Thermal Oscillations of Thin Plates, *Int. J. Solids Struct.*, vol. 2, pp. 337–350, 1966.

Kirchhoff, G.: "Vorlesungen uber Mathematisch Physik, Mechanik," 3d ed., B. G. Teubner (Leipzig), 1883.

Kovarik, V.: Finite-Deflection Theory of Sandwich Plates, *Arch. Mech. Stos.*, vol. 17, pp. 563–576, 1965.

Leissa, A. W.: Vibration of Plates, *NASA Spec. Publ. 160*, 1969.

Lekhnitskii, S. G.: "Anisotropic Plates," Translated from Russian (2d ed.) by S. W. Tsai and T. Cheron, Gordon and Breach Science Publishers, 1968.

McFarland, D., B. L. Smith, and W. D. Bernhart: "Analysis of Plates," Spartan Books, 1972.

Mansfield, E. H.: "The Bending and Stretching of Plates," Pergamon Press, 1964.

——— and P. W. Kleeman: A Large Deflection Theory for Thin Plates, *Aircr. Eng.*, vol. 27, pp. 102–108, 1955.

Marguerre, K. and H. T. Woernle: "Elastic Plates," Blaisdell Publishing Co., a division of Ginn and Co., 1969.

Medwadowski, S. J.: A Refined Theory of Elastic, Orthotropic Plates, *ASME J. Appl. Mech.*, vol. 25, pp. 437–443, 1958.

Morley, L. S. D.: "Skew Plates and Structures," Pergamon Press, 1963.

Morozov, N. F.: Nonlinear Vibrations of Thin Plates Including the Rotatory Inertia (in Russian), *Dokl. Akad. Nauk SSSR*, vol. 176, pp. 522–525, 1967.

Nádai, A.: "Die Elastischen Platten," Julius Springer, 1968.

Nowinski, J. L. and H. Ohnabe: Fundamental Equations for Large Deflections of Sandwich Plates with Orthotropic Core and Faces, *Proc. 10th Int. Symp. Space Tech. Sci.*, Tokyo, pp. 311–318, 1973.

Panc, V.: "Theories of Elastic Plates" (in English), Noordhoff International Publishing, 1975.

Pister, K. S. and S. B. Dong: Elastic Bending of Layered Plates, *J. Eng. Mech. Div., Proc. ASCE*, vol. 85, no. EM4, pp. 1–10, 1959.

Plantema, F. J.: "Sandwich Constructions," John Wiley & Sons, New York, 1966.

Reissner, E.: On Finite Deflections of Circular Plates, *Proc. 1st Symp. Appl. Math.*, vol. 1, pp. 213–219, 1947.

———: Finite Deflections of Sandwich Plates, *J. Aeronaut. Sci.*, vol. 15, pp. 435–440, 1948.

Sathyamoorthy, M.: Vibration of Skew Plates at Large Amplitudes Including Shear and Rotatory Inertia Effects, *Int. J. Solids Struct.*, vol. 14, pp. 869–880, 1978.

Sathyamoorthy, M. and K. A. V. Pandalai: Large Amplitude Vibration of Certain Deformable Bodies, Part II—Plates and Shells, *J. Aeronaut. Soc. India*, vol. 25, pp. 1–10, 1973.

Savin, G. N. and N. P. Fleishman: Rib-Reinforced Plates and Shells (Translated from Russian), *NASA Tech. Transl. F-427*, 1967.

Schmidt, G.: Nonlinear Parametric Vibrations of Sandwich Plates, *Pol. Akad. Nauk, Proc. Vibr. Prob.*, vol. 6, pp. 209–228, 1965.

Schmidt, R.: Refined Nonlinear Theory of Plates with Transverse Shear Deformation, *J. Indust. Math. Soc.*, vol. 27, part 1, 1977, pp. 23–38.

Shahin, R. M.: Nonlinear Vibrations of Multi-Layer Sandwich Plates, *43rd Shock and Vib. Symp.*, Pacific Grove, California, 1972.

———: Nonlinear Vibrations of Multi-Layer Orthotropic Sandwich Plates, *J. Sound Vib.*, vol. 36, pp. 361–374, 1974.

Shen, M. K.: On the Nonlinear Differential Equations of Cylindrical Anisotropic Plates, *Acta Mech.*, vol. 2, pp. 209–216, 1966.

Singh, P. N., Y. C. Das, and V. Sundararajan: Large Amplitude Vibration of Rectangular Plates, *J. Sound Vib.*, vol. 17, pp. 235–240, 1971.

Stavsky, Y.: Finite Deformations of a Class of Aeolotropic Plates with Material Heterogeneity, *Israel J. Technol.*, vol. 1, pp. 69–74, 1963.

———: On the General Theory of Heterogeneous Aeolotropic Plates, *Aeronaut. Q.*, vol. 15, pp. 29–38, 1964.

Sun, C. T. and N. A. Shaefy: Wave Propagation in Heterogeneous Anisotropic Plates Involving Large Deflection, *Int. J. Solids Struct.*, vol. 11, pp. 99–114, 1975.

Szilard, R.: "Theory and Analysis of Plates," Prentice-Hall Inc., Englewood Cliffs, N.J., 1974.

Tadjbaklsh, I. and E. Saibel: On the Large Elastic Deflections of Plates, *ZAMM*, vol. 40, pp. 259–268, 1960.

Timoshenko, S. and J. M. Gere: "Theory of Elastic Stability," McGraw-Hill Book Company, New York, 1961.

Turner, C. E.: "Introduction to Plate and Shell Theory," American Elsevier Publishing Co., 1965.

Ueng, C. E. S. and Y. J. Lin: A Note on a Nonlinear Theory of Bending of Orthotropic Sandwich Plates, *Aeronaut. Q.*, vol. 19, pp. 127–134, 1968.

Vendhan, C. P.: An Investigation into Nonlinear Vibrations of Thin Plates, *Int. J. Non-Linear Mech.*, vol. 2, pp. 209–221, 1977.

Vinson, J. R., "Structural Mechanics: The Behavior of Plates and Shells," John Wiley & Sons, New York, 1974.

—— and T. W. Chou: "Composite Materials and their Use in Structures," Halsted Press, 1975.

Vlasov, V. Z. and N. N. Leontév: Beams, Plates and Shells on Elastic Foundation (Translated from Russian), *NASA Tech. Transl. F-357*, or *65-50135*, 1966.

Vol'mir, A. S.: "Flexible Plates and Shells" (in Russian), Moscow, 1956, or (German translation), Veb Verlag für Bauwesen, 1961.

Wang, C. T.: Principle and Application of Complementary Energy Method for Thin Homogeneous and Sandwich Plates and Shells with Finite Deflections, *NASA Tech. Note 2620*, 1952.

Wempner, G.: "Mechanics of Solids with Application to Thin Bodies," McGraw-Hill Book Company, New York, 1973.

Wempner, G. A.: General Theory of Sandwich Plates with Dissimilar Facings, *Int. J. Solids Struct.*, vol. 1, pp. 157–177, 1965.

Widera, O. E.: An Asymptotic Theory for the Moderately Large Deflections of Anisotropic Plates, *J. Eng. Math.*, vol. 3, pp. 239–244, 1969.

Wood, R. N.: "Plastic and Elastic Design of Plates," Renald Press, 1961.

Yu, Y. Y.: Nonlinear Flexural Vibrations of Sandwich Plates, *J. Acoust. Soc. Am.*, vol. 34, pp. 1176–1183, 1962.

——: Application of Variational Equation of Motion to the Nonlinear Analysis of Dynamic Buckling, *Proc. 9th Midwest. Mech. Conf.*, pp. 105–113, 1965.

TWO

MODERATELY LARGE DEFLECTIONS OF ISOTROPIC RECTANGULAR PLATES

The von Kármán nonlinear equations of isotropic plates have been obtained as a special case of the laminated plate theory presented in the previous chapter. It will be recalled that the formulation of this theory is based on the fundamental assumption that strains and square of rotations are small compared to unity. As is well known, the von Kármán plate theory predicts deflections and stresses in a thin plate with reasonable accuracy for deflections having the order of the plate thickness. Thus the present plate theory, which is restricted to small strains but moderately large rotations, is termed as the moderately large deflection theory but, customarily, as the large deflection theory.

Solutions for the moderately large deflection behavior of rectangular isotropic plates under external loads are presented in this chapter. The types of load under consideration are uniformly or nonuniformly distributed transverse load over the entire or partial region of the plate, a single concentrated load, and a combined lateral and inplane load with the latter being not greater than the buckling load. The boundary conditions of the plate are mostly all-clamped and all-simply-supported along the four movable or immovable edges. The mixed boundary conditions of the plate with clamped and simply supported edges are treated as a special case of Sec. 2.7. A variety of the inplane, or membrane, boundary conditions is also considered. The methods of solution may be classified into double Fourier series, generalized Fourier series, perturbation technique, Galerkin's method, Ritz method, finite-difference technique, and method of similarity. The results obtained by different techniques are compared with one another for the same or similar boundary-value problems. Theoretical results are also compared in Sec. 2.8 with experimental values. In addition, solutions for orthotropic, anisotropic, and laminated plates discussed in Chaps. 5 and 7 can be specified for an isotropic plate, and the static large deflection of the plate can be treated as a special case of the nonlinear plate vibration. Attention should be paid to the solutions in Sec. 5.2 for an orthotropic plate resting on elastic foundation, in Secs. 5.3 and 5.4 for an elastically supported orthotropic plate against rotation, and in Sec. 7.7 for a laminate under uniform edge moment.

Taking into account the initial curvatures of isotropic plates Marguerre equations are derived by use of the principle of minimum potential energy. These equations can reduce those of von Kármán and are applied to nonlinear bending of initially deflected isotropic rectangular plates.

2.1 LOOSELY CLAMPED PLATE UNDER TRANSVERSE LOAD

In the static case the governing equations (1-161) and (1-162) reduce to the von Kármán equations for large deflections of isotropic plates

$$D\,\nabla^4 w = q + h(w_{,xx}F_{,yy} + w_{,yy}F_{,xx} - 2w_{,xy}F_{,xy}) \qquad (2\text{-}1)$$

$$\nabla^4 F = E[w_{,xy}^2 - w_{,xx}\,w_{,yy}] \qquad (2\text{-}2)$$

in which ψ has been replaced by hF with F being the Airy stress function. If a clamped rectangular plate (Fig. 2.1) is free from boundary stresses, the appropriate boundary conditions are

$$w = w_{,x} = F_{,yy} = F_{,xy} = 0 \qquad \text{at} \quad x = \pm\frac{a}{2}$$

$$\qquad\qquad (2\text{-}3)$$

$$w = w_{,y} = F_{,xx} = F_{,xy} = 0 \qquad \text{at} \quad y = \pm\frac{b}{2}$$

in which $a = 2a_0$ and $b = 2b_0$ are the width and length of the plate, respectively. Equations (2-1) and (2-2) are to be solved in conjunction with boundary conditions (2-3).

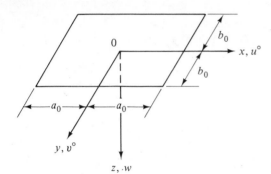

Figure 2.1 Geometry of rectangular plate.

A solution is sought in the form of generalized double Fourier series (Ref. 2.1)

$$w = \sum_{m=1}^{\infty} \sum_{n=1}^{\infty} w_{mn} X_m(x) Y_n(y)$$

$$F = \sum_{p=1}^{\infty} \sum_{q=1}^{\infty} F_{pq} X_p(x) Y_q(y)$$

(2-4)

where w_{mn} and F_{pq} are constant coefficients to be determined and X_m and Y_n are beam eigenfunctions given by

$$X_m = \frac{\cosh \alpha_m x}{\cosh \alpha_m a_0} - \frac{\cos \alpha_m x}{\cos \alpha_m a_0}$$

$$Y_n = \frac{\cosh \beta_n y}{\cosh \beta_n b_0} - \frac{\cos \beta_n y}{\cos \beta_n b_0}$$

(2-5)

All the boundary conditions (2-3) are satisfied if the values of α_m and β_n are the roots of the transcendental equation

$$\tanh \lambda_m + \tan \lambda_m = 0$$

(2-6)

where

$$\lambda_m = \alpha_m a_0 \quad \text{or} \quad \beta_n b_0$$

(2-7)

The roots of equation (2-6) are given in Table 2.1. The functions $X_m(x)$ and $Y_n(y)$ satisfy the following orthogonality relations

$$\int_{-a_0}^{a_0} X_i X_j \, dx = \begin{cases} 0 & i \neq j \\ 2a_0 & i = j \end{cases}$$

$$\int_{-b_0}^{b_0} Y_i Y_j \, dy = \begin{cases} 0 & i \neq j \\ 2b_0 & i = j \end{cases}$$

(2-8)

The transverse load $q(x, y)$ is expanded into a double series

$$q(x, y) = \sum_{m=1}^{\infty} \sum_{n=1}^{\infty} q_{mn} X_m(x) Y_n(y)$$

(2-9)

where

$$q_{mn} = \frac{1}{ab} \int_{-a_0}^{a_0} \int_{-b_0}^{b_0} q(x, y) X_m(x) Y_n(y) \, dx \, dy$$

(2-10)

Table 2.1 Roots of equation (2-6)

m	1	2	3	4	$m > 4$
λ_m	2.3650	5.4978	8.6394	11.7810	$\pi(m - 0.25)$

Substituting equations (2-4) and (2-9) into (2-1) and (2-2) we obtain

$$\sum_{m=1}^{\infty} \sum_{n=1}^{\infty} w_{mn}[(\alpha_m^4 + \beta_n^4)X_m Y_n + 2X_m'' Y_n'']$$

$$= \frac{1}{D} \sum_{m=1}^{\infty} \sum_{n=1}^{\infty} q_{mn} X_m Y_n + \frac{h}{D} \sum_{p=1}^{\infty} \sum_{q=1}^{\infty} \sum_{r=1}^{\infty} \sum_{s=1}^{\infty} w_{pq} F_{rs}$$

$$\cdot (X_r X_p'' Y_q Y_s'' + X_p X_r'' Y_s Y_q'' - 2X_p' X_r' Y_q' Y_s') \qquad (2\text{-}11)$$

$$\sum_{p=1}^{\infty} \sum_{q=1}^{\infty} F_{pq}[(\alpha_p^4 + \beta_q^4)X_p Y_q + 2X_p'' Y_q'']$$

$$= E \sum_{m=1}^{\infty} \sum_{n=1}^{\infty} \sum_{r=1}^{\infty} \sum_{s=1}^{\infty} w_{mn} w_{rs}(X_m' X_r' Y_n' Y_s' - X_r X_m'' Y_n Y_s'') \qquad (2\text{-}12)$$

in which primes denote differentiation with respect to the corresponding coordinates.

Multiplying each of equations (2-11) and (2-12) by $X_i(x)Y_j(y)$, integrating with respect to x and y over their respective intervals, and using equations (2-7) and (2-8) leads to a system of nonlinear algebraic equations (Ref. 2.2)

$$w_{ij}\left(\frac{b^2}{a^2}\lambda_i^4 + \frac{a^2}{b^2}\lambda_j^4\right) + 2\sum_{m=1}^{\infty}\sum_{n=1}^{\infty} w_{mn}\lambda_m^2\lambda_n^2 K_1^{im}L_1^{jn}$$

$$= \frac{a^2 b^2}{16D} q_{ij} + \frac{h}{D} \sum_{p=1}^{\infty}\sum_{q=1}^{\infty}\sum_{r=1}^{\infty}\sum_{s=1}^{\infty} w_{pq} F_{rs}$$

$$\cdot (\lambda_p^2\lambda_s^2 K_2^{irp}L_2^{jqs} + \lambda_q^2\lambda_r^2 K_2^{ipr}L_2^{jsq} - 2\lambda_p\lambda_q\lambda_r\lambda_s K_3^{ipr}L_3^{jqs})$$

$$i, j = 1, 2, 3, \dots \qquad (2\text{-}13)$$

$$F_{ij}\left(\frac{b^2}{a^2}\lambda_i^4 + \frac{a^2}{b^2}\lambda_j^4\right) + 2\sum_{p=1}^{\infty}\sum_{q=1}^{\infty} F_{pq}\lambda_p^2\lambda_q^2 K_1^{ip}L_1^{jq}$$

$$= E \sum_{m=1}^{\infty}\sum_{n=1}^{\infty}\sum_{r=1}^{\infty}\sum_{s=1}^{\infty} w_{mn} w_{rs}$$

$$\cdot (\lambda_m\lambda_n\lambda_r\lambda_s K_3^{imr}L_3^{jns} - \lambda_m^2\lambda_s^2 K_2^{irm}L_2^{jns})$$

$$i, j = 1, 2, 3, \dots \qquad (2\text{-}14)$$

where

$$K_1^{im} = \frac{1}{a\alpha_m^2}\int_{-a_0}^{a_0} X_i X_m'' \, dx \qquad L_1^{jn} = \frac{1}{b\beta_n^2}\int_{-b_0}^{b_0} Y_j Y_n'' \, dy$$

$$K_2^{irp} = \frac{1}{a\alpha_p^2}\int_{-a_0}^{a_0} X_i X_r X_p'' \, dx \qquad L_2^{jqs} = \frac{1}{b\beta_s^2}\int_{-b_0}^{b_0} Y_j Y_q Y_s'' \, dy \qquad (2\text{-}15)$$

$$K_3^{ipr} = \frac{1}{a\alpha_p\alpha_r}\int_{-a_0}^{a_0} X_i X_p' X_r' \, dx \qquad L_3^{jqs} = \frac{1}{b\beta_q\beta_s}\int_{-b_0}^{b_0} Y_j Y_q' Y_s' \, dy$$

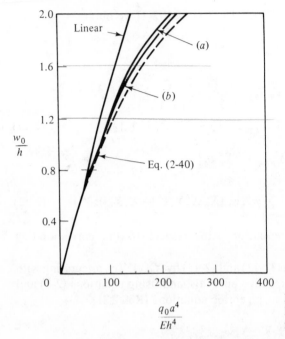

$$\frac{q_0 a^4}{E h^4}$$

Figure 2.2 Load-deflection curves for loosely clamped square plate under uniform lateral load.

For various values of i and j the conditions (2-13) and (2-14) give the same number of equations for w_{ij} and F_{ij} as the number of terms taken in the series (2-4). After solving these algebraic equations simultaneously for these coefficients, the transverse deflection, membrane forces, bending moments, and transverse shear forces everywhere in the plate can be found from equations (2-4), (1-125), (1-122), and (1-123), respectively. It may be observed that the solution (2-4) is exact in the sense that an infinite set of equations (2-13) and (2-14) can be truncated to obtain any desired degree of accuracy.

Numerical results are presented by taking (a) only the first term† in each of the series for W and F, and (b) the first term in the series for W and the first four terms in the series for F. The central deflection w_0 of a square plate ($v = 0.316$) subjected to uniformly distributed transverse load q_0 per unit area is plotted in Fig. 2.2 against the load. The two solid curves which represent these approximations show that the maximum difference between these two approximations is about 5 percent. The dashed curve is obtained from the one-term approximation of the Galerkin method which will be discussed in the next section.

Let $q(x, y)$ be a concentrated load P uniformly distributed over a portion of the plate surface as shown in Fig. 2.3. The load coefficients (2-10) in this case become

---

† In calculation of a series a few terms at least should be taken into account.

$$q_{mn} = \frac{P}{\alpha\beta\lambda_m\lambda_n}\left[\frac{\cosh \alpha_m x_1}{\cosh \lambda_m}\sinh \frac{\lambda_m \alpha}{a} - \frac{\cos \alpha_m x_1}{\cos \lambda_m}\sin \frac{\lambda_m \alpha}{a}\right]$$

$$\cdot \left[\frac{\cosh \beta_n y_1}{\cosh \lambda_n}\sinh \frac{\lambda_n \beta}{b} - \frac{\cos \beta_n y_1}{\cos \lambda_n}\sin \frac{\lambda_n \beta}{b}\right] \tag{2-16}$$

where $\alpha \times \beta$ and (x_1, y_1) are the loading area and center, respectively. Inserting equation (2-16) into (2-13), the deflection and stress resultants in a partially loaded plate can be calculated as in the case of a fully loaded plate.

If $x_1 = y_1 = 0$, $\alpha = a$ and $\beta = b$, equation (2-16) reduces to that for the fully loaded plate. If P is a single concentrated load at the point (x_1, y_1), then equation (2-16) yields

$$q_{mn} = \frac{P}{ab}\left(\frac{\cosh \alpha_m x_1}{\cosh \lambda_m} - \frac{\cos \alpha_m x_1}{\cos \lambda_m}\right)\left(\frac{\cosh \beta_n y_1}{\cosh \lambda_n} - \frac{\cos \beta_n y_1}{\cos \lambda_n}\right) \tag{2-17}$$

With these values of q_{mn} the geometrically nonlinear behavior of a rectangular plate under a single concentrated load P can be investigated by the foregoing series solution. In a similar manner the solution can be applied to the other types of transverse loading such as hydrostatic pressure and a load in the form of a triangular prism.

It is observed that even a large number of terms in the truncated series (2-4) may not give a good approximation if the loading function $q(x, y)$ is not an even function of x and y. This arises from the fact that each term in these series is even in x and y. Such difficulties may be avoided by choosing the origin of the coordinate system at one corner of the plate and the appropriate beam eigenfunctions $X_i(x)$ and $Y_j(y)$ as given in Refs. 2.2 and 2.3.

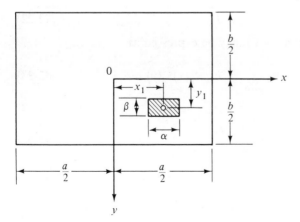

Figure 2.3 Partially loaded plate.

2.2 GALERKIN'S METHOD FOR LOOSELY CLAMPED PLATE

The large deflection problem of a loosely clamped rectangular plate under distributed load q is reconsidered by making use of the one-term approximation of the Galerkin method (Ref. 2.4). The equilibrium equation (2-1) is rewritten as

$$L(w, F) \equiv D \nabla^4 w - q - h(w_{,xx} F_{,yy} + w_{,yy} F_{,xx} - 2w_{,xy} F_{,xy}) = 0 \quad (2\text{-}18)$$

The compatibility relation (2-2) and boundary conditions (2-3) remain unchanged.

The transverse deflection is assumed to be of the form

$$w = hW_m \cos^2\left(\frac{\pi x}{a}\right) \cos^2\left(\frac{\pi y}{b}\right) \quad (2\text{-}19)$$

in which W_m is the nondimensional maximum deflection at the plate center given by w_0/h, and w_0 denotes the central deflection. This approximated deflection obviously satisfies the geometrical boundary conditions in equation (2-3). Upon substitution equation (2-2) may be expressed as

$$\nabla^4 F = -\frac{\pi^4 E h^2 W_m^2}{a^2 b^2} \sum_{p=0}^{\infty} \sum_{q=0}^{\infty} a_{pq} R_p(x) S_q(y) \quad (2\text{-}20)$$

where

$$R_p(x) = \cos\frac{2p\pi x}{a} \qquad S_q(y) = \cos\frac{2q\pi y}{b}$$

$$a_{01} = a_{10} = a_{02} = a_{20} = a_{12} = a_{21} = \tfrac{1}{2}$$

$$a_{11} = 1 \quad \text{and all other} \quad a_{pq} = 0$$

$$(2\text{-}21)$$

The general solution of equation (2-20) is the sum of the complementary function F_c and a particular integral F_p, i.e.,

$$F = F_c + F_p \quad (2\text{-}22)$$

A particular integral of equation (2-20) may be expressed as

$$F_p = E h^2 W_m^2 \sum_{p=0}^{\infty} \sum_{q=0}^{\infty} b_{pq} R_p(x) S_q(y) \quad (2\text{-}23)$$

where

$$b_{pq} = -\frac{\lambda^2 a_{pq}}{16(p^2 + \lambda^2 q^2)^2} \quad (2\text{-}24)$$

In equation (2-24) λ is the aspect ratio or the length-to-width ratio of the rectangular plate defined by

$$\lambda = \frac{a}{b} \quad (2\text{-}25)$$

It is easily seen that F_p given by expression (2-23) is an even function of x and y with the vanishing shear stresses along the boundaries. With the same properties the complementary function may be expressed in the form

$$F_c = \frac{1}{2} W_m^2 (C_1 x^2 + C_2 y^2) + Eh^2 W_m^2 \sum_{n=1}^{\infty} \left\{ \frac{A_n}{n^2 [\sinh(n\pi/\lambda)\cosh(n\pi/\lambda) + n\pi/\lambda]} \right.$$

$$\cdot \left[\left(\sinh \frac{n\pi}{\lambda} + \frac{n\pi}{\lambda} \cosh \frac{n\pi}{\lambda} \right) \cosh \frac{2n\pi}{a} y - \frac{2n\pi}{a} y \sinh \frac{n\pi}{\lambda} \sinh \frac{2n\pi}{a} y \right]$$

$$\cdot \cos \frac{2n\pi}{a} x + \frac{B_n}{n^2 \lambda^2 (\sinh n\pi\lambda \cosh n\pi\lambda + n\pi\lambda)}$$

$$\cdot \left[(\sinh n\pi\lambda + n\pi\lambda \cosh n\pi\lambda) \cosh \frac{2n\pi}{b} x \right.$$

$$\left. - \frac{2n\pi}{b} x \sinh n\pi\lambda \sinh \frac{2n\pi}{b} x \right] \cos \frac{2n\pi}{b} y \right\} \tag{2-26}$$

in which C_1, C_2, A_n and B_n are arbitrary constants. On the determination of these constants it is observed that

$$[F_{c,\,yy}]_{x=\pm a/2} = W_m^2 C_2 - \frac{4\pi^2 Eh^2 W_m^2}{a^2} \sum_{n=1}^{\infty} \left[(-1)^n A_n \phi\left(\frac{n}{\lambda}, \frac{2y}{b}\right) + B_n S_n(y) \right]$$

$$[F_{c,\,xx}]_{y=\pm b/2} = W_m^2 C_1 - \frac{4\pi^2 Eh^2 W_m^2}{a^2} \sum_{n=1}^{\infty} \left[A_n R_n(x) + (-1)^n B_n \phi\left(n\lambda, \frac{2x}{a}\right) \right] \tag{2-27}$$

where

$$\phi(\gamma, \xi) = \frac{(\sinh \gamma\pi - \gamma\pi \cosh \gamma\pi)\cosh \gamma\pi\xi + \gamma\pi\xi \sinh \gamma\pi \sinh \gamma\pi\xi}{\gamma\pi + \sinh \gamma\pi \cosh \gamma\pi} \tag{2-28}$$

The function $\phi(\gamma, \xi)$ is expanded into a Fourier series in the interval, $-1 \le \xi \le 1$,

$$\phi(\gamma, \xi) = \sum_{m=1}^{\infty} g(\gamma, m) \cos m\pi\xi \tag{2-29}$$

where

$$g(\gamma, m) = \frac{4(-1)^m \gamma m^2}{\pi(\gamma^2 + m^2)^2} \cdot \frac{\sinh^2 \gamma\pi}{\gamma\pi + \sinh \gamma\pi \cosh \gamma\pi} \tag{2-30}$$

Upon substitution equations (2-27) become

$$[F_{c,\,yy}]_{x=\pm a/2} = W_m^2 C_2 - \frac{4\pi^2 Eh^2 W_m^2}{a^2} \sum_{n=1}^{\infty} \left[B_n + \sum_{p=1}^{\infty} (-1)^p A_p g\left(\frac{p}{\lambda}, n\right) \right] S_n(y)$$

$$[F_{c,\,xx}]_{y=\pm b/2} = W_m^2 C_1 - \frac{4\pi^2 Eh^2 W_m^2}{a^2} \sum_{n=1}^{\infty} \left[A_n + \sum_{p=1}^{\infty} (-1)^p B_p g(p\lambda, n) \right] R_n(x) \tag{2-31}$$

Introducing equation (2-22) into the boundary conditions (2-3) and taking into account equations (2-23) and (2-31), we obtain the conditions $C_1 = C_2 = 0$ together with the following relations

$$B_n + \sum_{p=1}^{\infty} (-1)^p A_p g\left(\frac{p}{\lambda}, n\right) = -n^2 \lambda^2 \sum_{q=0}^{\infty} (-1)^q b_{qn}$$

$$A_n + \sum_{p=1}^{\infty} (-1)^p B_p g(p\lambda, n) = -n^2 \sum_{q=0}^{\infty} (-1)^q b_{nq} \tag{2-32}$$

which can be solved for A_n and B_n $(n = 1, 2, 3, \ldots)$.

For convenience the complementary function F_c is also represented by a double cosine series

$$F_c = Eh^2 W_m^2 \sum_{p=0}^{\infty} \sum_{q=0}^{\infty} c_{pq} R_p(x) S_q(y) \tag{2-33}$$

The Fourier coefficients c_{mn} in the series are given by

$$c_{mn} = \frac{4\lambda}{\pi(m^2 + \lambda^2 n^2)^2}$$

$$\left[\frac{m(-1)^n \varepsilon_n \sinh^2 (m\pi/\lambda)}{(m\pi/\lambda) + \sinh (m\pi/\lambda) \cosh (m\pi/\lambda)} A_m + \frac{n(-1)^m \varepsilon_m \sinh^2 n\pi\lambda}{n\pi\lambda + \sinh n\pi\lambda \cosh n\pi\lambda} B_n\right]$$

$$m, n = 0, 1, 2, \ldots \tag{2-34}$$

where

$$\varepsilon_0 = \tfrac{1}{2} \qquad \varepsilon_1 = \varepsilon_2 = \cdots = 1 \tag{2-35}$$

By substitution equation (2-22) yields

$$F = Eh^2 W_m^2 \sum_{p=0}^{\infty} \sum_{q=0}^{\infty} d_{pq} R_p(x) S_q(y) \tag{2-36}$$

where

$$d_{pq} = b_{pq} + c_{pq} \tag{2-37}$$

Functions (2-19) for w and (2-26) for F satisfy all the boundary conditions (2-3) as well as the compatibility condition (2-2). With these expressions, however, the equilibrium equation (2-1) generally cannot be exactly satisfied. Instead of satisfaction of this equation we apply the Galerkin method to minimize the error function which is obtained by inserting equations (2-19) and (2-36) into (2-18), i.e.,

$$\int_0^{a_0} \int_0^{b_0} L(w, F) w \, dx \, dy = 0 \tag{2-38}$$

For simplicity the loading is assumed to be uniform with intensity q_0.

An integration leads to the following algebraic equation

$$\frac{\pi^4 Dh}{a^4} (3 + 2\lambda^2 + 3\lambda^4) W_m - \frac{2\pi^4 Eh^4}{a^2 b^2}$$

$$\cdot (d_{01} + d_{10} + d_{11} + \tfrac{1}{2}d_{12} + \tfrac{1}{2}d_{21} + d_{02} + d_{20}) W_m^3 = q_0 \tag{2-39}$$

In the case of a square plate ($\lambda = 1$), equation (2-39) reduces to

$$\frac{q_0 a^4}{Eh^4} = \pi^4 \left[\frac{2}{3(1 - v^2)} W_m + 0.14903 W_m^3 \right] \tag{2-40}$$

in which the multiplying factor 0.14903 was obtained by taking n from 1 to 8 in calculating A_n and B_n by equation (2-32). The relationship between the maximum deflection and uniform load for a square plate with $v = 0.316$ is shown in Fig. 2.2 by the dashed line. The result is in good agreement with that obtained by taking one term for w and four terms for F in the truncated series (2-4).

2.3 SIMPLY SUPPORTED PLATE SUBJECTED TO TRANSVERSE LOAD

Consider a rectangular plate subjected to transverse load $q(x, y)$. The four edges of the plate are all simply supported and free from boundary stresses. The boundary conditions for these edges can be written in the form

$$w = w_{,xx} = F_{,yy} = F_{,xy} = 0 \qquad \text{at} \quad x = \pm \frac{a}{2}$$

$$\tag{2-41}$$

$$w = w_{,yy} = F_{,xx} = F_{,xy} = 0 \qquad \text{at} \quad y = \pm \frac{b}{2}$$

All these boundary conditions are satisfied by taking (Ref. 2.1)

$$w = \sum_{m=1, 3, \ldots}^{\infty} \sum_{n=1, 3, \ldots}^{\infty} w_{mn} \cos \frac{m\pi x}{a} \cos \frac{n\pi y}{b}$$

$$\tag{2-42}$$

$$F = \sum_{p=1}^{\infty} \sum_{q=1}^{\infty} F_{pq} X_p(x) Y_q(y)$$

in which X_p and Y_q are defined by equation (2-5) with the values of α_p and β_q given in Table 2.1.

Inserting expressions (2-42) into governing equations (2-1) and (2-2), multiplying the first of the resulting equations by $\cos(i\pi x/a) \cos(j\pi y/b)$ and the second by $X_i(x) Y_j(y)$, and integrating with respect to their respective intervals as in Sec. 2.1, we obtain the following system of algebraic equations for coefficients w_{mn} and F_{pq}

$$w_{mn} \left(\frac{m^2}{a^2} + \frac{n^2}{b^2} \right)^2 = \frac{q_{mn}}{\pi^4 D} - \frac{4}{\pi^2 abD} \sum_{p=1, 3, \ldots}^{\infty} \sum_{q=1, 3, \ldots}^{\infty} \sum_{r=1}^{\infty} \sum_{s=1}^{\infty} w_{pq} F_{rs}$$

$$\cdot \left[\frac{p^2}{a^2} M_1^{rmp} N_2^{snq} + \frac{q^2}{b^2} M_2^{rmp} N_1^{snq} + 2 \frac{pq}{ab} M_3^{rpm} N_3^{sqn} \right]$$

$$m, n = 1, 3, 5, \ldots \tag{2-43}$$

$$F_{ij}\left(\frac{b^2}{a^2}\lambda_i^4 + \frac{a^2}{b^2}\lambda_j^4\right) + 2\sum_{p=1}^{\infty}\sum_{q=1}^{\infty}F_{pq}\lambda_p^2\lambda_q^2 K_1^{ip}L_1^{jq}$$

$$= \frac{\pi^4 E}{16ab}\sum_{m=1,3,\ldots}^{\infty}\sum_{n=1,3,\ldots}^{\infty}\sum_{r=1,3,\ldots}^{\infty}\sum_{s=1,3,\ldots}^{\infty}w_{mn}w_{rs}$$

$$\cdot\left(mnrs M_4^{imr}N_4^{jns} - m^2s^2 M_1^{imr}N_1^{jns}\right)$$

$$i, j = 1, 2, 3, \ldots \quad (2\text{-}44)$$

where K_1 and L_1 are given by equation (2-15) and where

$$q(x, y) = \sum_{m=1,3,\ldots}^{\infty}\sum_{n=1,3,\ldots}^{\infty}q_{mn}\cos\frac{m\pi x}{a}\cos\frac{n\pi y}{b}$$

$$M_1^{rmp} = \int_{-a_0}^{a_0}X_r\cos\frac{m\pi x}{a}\cos\frac{p\pi x}{a}\,dx$$

$$M_2^{rmp} = \int_{-a_0}^{a_0}X_r''\cos\frac{m\pi x}{a}\cos\frac{p\pi x}{a}\,dx \qquad (2\text{-}45)$$

$$M_3^{rpm} = \int_{-a_0}^{a_0}X_r'\sin\frac{p\pi x}{a}\cos\frac{m\pi x}{a}\,dx$$

$$M_4^{imr} = \int_{-a_0}^{a_0}X_i\sin\frac{m\pi x}{a}\sin\frac{r\pi x}{a}\,dx$$

The constants N_1 to N_4 in equations (2-43) and (2-44) are obtained by replacing M, X, x, a, m, p, and r by N, Y, y, b, n, q, and s, respectively.

By taking only the first terms in series (2-42) and $v = 0.316$, for a square plate under uniform transverse load q_0, we obtain

$$\left(\frac{w_0}{h}\right)^3 + 5.8595\frac{w_0}{h} = 0.26335\frac{q_0 a^4}{Eh^4} \qquad (2\text{-}46)$$

in which w_0 is the deflection at the center of the plate.

The Galerkin method has been previously applied to the problem of a clamped plate under uniform transverse load. An approximate solution for a simply supported and uniformly loaded rectangular plate also can be obtained by the use of this method as well as the equations given in Sec. 2.2. The geometrical boundary conditions in equations (2-41) are satisfied if the deflection function is taken to be

$$w = hW_m\cos\frac{\pi x}{a}\cos\frac{\pi y}{b} \qquad (2\text{-}47)$$

With this approximate deflection the nonzero Fourier coefficients a_{pq} in equation (2-20) are given by

$$a_{01} = a_{10} = \tfrac{1}{2} \qquad (2\text{-}48)$$

In both cases the statical boundary conditions are the same and hence equations (2-22) to (2-38) can be used in the present case without any modification. Substi-

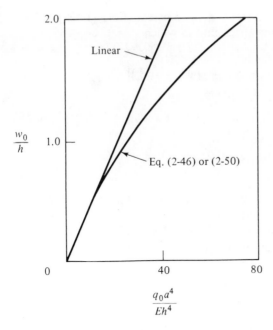

Figure 2.4 Central deflection versus uniform lateral pressure for simply supported square plate with stress-free edges.

tuting equations (2-47) and (2-36) into (2-38) and performing the integration, we obtain

$$\frac{\pi^6 Dh}{a^4}(1 + \lambda^2)^2 W_m - \frac{2\pi^6 Eh^4}{a^2 b^2}(d_{01} + d_{10})W_m^3 = q_0 \qquad (2\text{-}49)$$

In the case of a square plate, equation (2-49) yields

$$\frac{q_0 a^4}{Eh^4} = \frac{\pi^6}{16}\left[\frac{1}{3(1 - v^2)}W_m + 0.06492 W_m^3\right] \qquad (2\text{-}50)$$

The numerical results obtained from formulas (2-46) and (2-50) by taking $v = 0.316$ coincide with each other and are shown in Fig. 2.4. It is noticed that the multiplying factor 0.06492 was obtained by taking n from 1 to 8 in calculating A_n and B_n by equation (2-32). These results are in good agreement with experimental data shown in Fig. 2.14 later.

2.4 RIGIDLY CLAMPED PLATE UNDER TRANSVERSE LOAD

In the static case the governing equations (1-117) to (1-119) become

$$u^{\circ}_{,xx} + d_1 u^{\circ}_{,yy} + d_2 v^{\circ}_{,xy} = -w_{,x}(w_{,xx} + d_1 w_{,yy}) - d_2 w_{,y} w_{,xy} \qquad (2\text{-}51)$$

$$v^{\circ}_{,yy} + d_1 v^{\circ}_{,xx} + d_2 u^{\circ}_{,xy} = -w_{,y}(w_{,yy} + d_1 w_{,xx}) - d_2 w_{,x} w_{,xy} \qquad (2\text{-}52)$$

$$\nabla^4 w = \frac{q}{D} + \frac{h}{D}(\sigma^m_x w_{,xx} + \sigma^m_y w_{,yy} + 2\sigma^m_{xy} w_{,xy}) \qquad (2\text{-}53)$$

in which d_1, d_2 and D are material constants defined by equations (1-120) and the superscript m denotes the membrane effect, and in which

$$\sigma_x^m = \frac{E}{1 - v^2} [u^\circ{}_{,x} + vv^\circ{}_{,y} + \tfrac{1}{2}(w^2{}_{,x} + vw^2{}_{,y})]$$

$$\sigma_y^m = \frac{E}{1 - v^2} [v^\circ{}_{,y} + vu^\circ{}_{,x} + \tfrac{1}{2}(w^2{}_{,y} + vw^2{}_{,x})] \tag{2-54}$$

$$\sigma_{xy}^m = \frac{E}{2(1 + v)} [u^\circ{}_{,y} + v^\circ{}_{,x} + w_{,x} w_{,y}]$$

Equations (2-51) to (2-53) are those of the von Kármán nonlinear plate theory in terms of three displacements at the middle surface.

If a rectangular plate under transverse load $q(x, y)$ is rigidly clamped along its edges, the appropriate boundary conditions are

$$u^\circ = v^\circ = w = w_{,x} = 0 \qquad \text{at} \quad x = \pm \frac{a}{2}$$

$$\tag{2-55}$$

$$u^\circ = v^\circ = w = w_{,y} = 0 \qquad \text{at} \quad y = \pm \frac{b}{2}$$

The governing equations (2-51) to (2-53) are to be solved with boundary conditions (2-55).

A solution for three displacements is taken as double series in the form (Ref. 2.1)

$$u^\circ = \sum_{m=1}^{\infty} \sum_{n=1}^{\infty} u_{mn} R_m(x) Y_n(y)$$

$$v^\circ = \sum_{m=1}^{\infty} \sum_{n=1}^{\infty} v_{mn} X_m(x) S_n(y) \tag{2-56}$$

$$w = \sum_{m=1}^{\infty} \sum_{n=1}^{\infty} w_{mn} X_m(x) Y_n(y)$$

in which functions X_m and Y_n are defined by equations (2-5) and in which

$$R_m(x) = \sin \frac{2m\pi x}{a} \qquad S_n(y) = \sin \frac{2n\pi y}{b} \tag{2-57}$$

All the boundary conditions (2-55) are satisfied if the values of α_m and β_n in X_m and Y_n, respectively, satisfy equation (2-6).

Substituting expressions (2-56) into (2-51) and (2-52), and using the orthogonality properties of $R_i(x)$, $S_i(y)$, $X_i(x)$, and $Y_i(y)$, the following functions in the resulting equations are expanded into series

$$X_i' = \frac{2\lambda_i}{a} \sum_{m=1}^{\infty} P_1^{mi} R_m \qquad X_i'' = \frac{4\lambda_i^2}{a^2} \sum_{m=1}^{\infty} P_2^{mi} X_m$$

$$R_i' = \frac{2i\pi}{a} \sum_{m=1}^{\infty} P_3^{mi} X_m \qquad X_i X_r = \sum_{m=1}^{\infty} P_4^{mir} X_m$$

$$X_i X_r'' = \frac{4\lambda_r^2}{a^2} \sum_{m=1}^{\infty} P_5^{mir} X_m \qquad X_i' X_r' = \frac{4\lambda_i \lambda_r}{a^2} \sum_{m=1}^{\infty} P_6^{mir} X_m$$

$$X_i' X_r = \frac{2\lambda_i}{a} \sum_{m=1}^{\infty} P_7^{mir} R_m \qquad X_i' X_r'' = \frac{8\lambda_i \lambda_r^2}{a^3} \sum_{m=1}^{\infty} P_8^{mir} R_m$$

(2-58)

in which the values of λ_i are given in Table 2.1. Fourier coefficients Q_1 to Q_8 in series representation of functions of y in the above resulting equations can be similarly defined and obtained by replacing a, i, m, r, P, R, and X in equations (2-58) by b, j, n, s, Q, S, and Y, respectively. Thus, equations (2-51) and (2-52) after substitution and some manipulation can be expressed in the form

$$\sum_{m=1}^{\infty} \sum_{n=1}^{\infty} \alpha_{mn} R_m(x) Y_n(y) = \sum_{m=1}^{\infty} \sum_{n=1}^{\infty} \beta_{mn} R_m(x) Y_n(y)$$

$$\sum_{m=1}^{\infty} \sum_{n=1}^{\infty} \gamma_{mn} X_m(x) S_n(y) = \sum_{m=1}^{\infty} \sum_{n=1}^{\infty} \delta_{mn} X_m(x) S_n(y)$$

(2-59)

Equating the corresponding coefficients in each of these equations, we obtain

$$\frac{\pi^2}{a^2} m^2 u_{mn} - \frac{d_1}{b^2} \sum_{j=1}^{\infty} \lambda_j^2 Q_2^{nj} u_{mj} - \frac{\pi d_2}{ab} \sum_{i=1}^{\infty} \sum_{j=1}^{\infty} \lambda_i j P_1^{mi} Q_3^{nj} v_{ij}$$

$$= \sum_{i=1}^{\infty} \sum_{j=1}^{\infty} \sum_{r=1}^{\infty} \sum_{s=1}^{\infty} w_{ij} w_{rs}$$

$$\cdot \left(\frac{2\lambda_i \lambda_r^2}{a^3} P_8^{mir} Q_4^{njs} + \frac{2d_1 \lambda_i \lambda_s^2}{ab^2} P_7^{mir} Q_5^{njs} + \frac{2d_2 \lambda_r \lambda_j \lambda_s}{ab^2} P_7^{mri} Q_6^{njs} \right)$$

$$n, m = 1, 2, 3, \dots \quad (2\text{-}60)$$

$$\frac{\pi^2}{b^2} n^2 v_{mn} - \frac{d_1}{a^2} \sum_{i=1}^{\infty} \lambda_i^2 P_2^{mi} v_{in} - \frac{\pi d_2}{ab} \sum_{i=1}^{\infty} \sum_{j=1}^{\infty} i\lambda_j P_3^{mi} Q_1^{nj} u_{ij}$$

$$= \sum_{i=1}^{\infty} \sum_{j=1}^{\infty} \sum_{r=1}^{\infty} \sum_{s=1}^{\infty} w_{ij} w_{rs}$$

$$\cdot \left(\frac{2\lambda_j \lambda_s^2}{b^3} P_4^{mir} Q_8^{njs} + \frac{2d_1 \lambda_j \lambda_r^2}{a^2 b} P_5^{mir} Q_7^{njs} + \frac{2d_2 \lambda_i \lambda_r \lambda_s}{a^2 b} P_6^{mir} Q_7^{nsj} \right)$$

$$n, m = 1, 2, 3, \dots \quad (2\text{-}61)$$

By virtue of equations (2-56) and (2-58), equations (2-54) yield

$$\sigma_x^m = \frac{E}{1-v^2} \sum_{m=1}^{\infty} \sum_{n=1}^{\infty} F_{mn} X_m Y_n$$

$$\sigma_y^m = \frac{E}{1-v^2} \sum_{m=1}^{\infty} \sum_{n=1}^{\infty} G_{mn} X_m Y_n \qquad (2\text{-}62)$$

$$\sigma_{xy}^m = \frac{E}{2(1+v)} \sum_{m=1}^{\infty} \sum_{n=1}^{\infty} H_{mn} R_m S_n$$

where

$$F_{mn} = \frac{2\pi}{a} \sum_{i=1}^{\infty} i P_3^{mi} u_{in} + \frac{2v\pi}{b} \sum_{j=1}^{\infty} j Q_3^{nj} v_{mj}$$
$$+ 2\sum_{i=1}^{\infty} \sum_{j=1}^{\infty} \sum_{r=1}^{\infty} \sum_{s=1}^{\infty} \left(\frac{\lambda_i \lambda_r}{a^2} P_6^{mir} Q_4^{njs} + \frac{v\lambda_j \lambda_s}{b^2} P_4^{mir} Q_6^{njs} \right) w_{ij} w_{rs}$$

$$G_{mn} = \frac{2v\pi}{a} \sum_{i=1}^{\infty} i P_3^{mi} u_{in} + \frac{2\pi}{b} \sum_{j=1}^{\infty} j Q_3^{nj} v_{mj}$$
$$+ 2\sum_{i=1}^{\infty} \sum_{j=1}^{\infty} \sum_{r=1}^{\infty} \sum_{s=1}^{\infty} w_{ij} w_{rs} \left(\frac{v\lambda_i \lambda_r}{a^2} P_6^{mir} Q_4^{njs} + \frac{\lambda_i \lambda_s}{b^2} P_4^{mir} Q_6^{njs} \right) \qquad (2\text{-}63)$$

$$H_{mn} = \frac{2}{b} \sum_{j=1}^{\infty} \lambda_j Q_1^{nj} u_{mj} + \frac{2}{a} \sum_{i=1}^{\infty} \lambda_i Q_1^{mi} v_{in}$$
$$+ \frac{4}{ab} \sum_{i=1}^{\infty} \sum_{j=1}^{\infty} \sum_{r=1}^{\infty} \sum_{s=1}^{\infty} w_{ij} w_{rs} \lambda_i \lambda_j P_7^{mir} Q_7^{njs}$$

Equations (2-9), (2-56), and (2-62) are substituted into (2-53) and functions $R_i(x) X_r'(x)$ and $S_j(y) Y_s'(y)$ are represented by

$$R_i X_r' = \frac{2\lambda_r}{a} \sum_{m=1}^{\infty} P_9^{mir} X_m \qquad S_j Y_s' = \frac{2\lambda s}{b} \sum_{n=1}^{\infty} Q_9^{njs} Y_n \qquad (2\text{-}64)$$

Equating coefficients in the resulting equation, we obtain

$$w_{mn} \left(\frac{\lambda_m^4}{a^4} + \frac{\lambda_n^4}{b^4} \right) + 2 \sum_{i=1}^{\infty} \sum_{j=1}^{\infty} w_{ij} \frac{\lambda_i^2 \lambda_j^2}{a^2 b^2} P_2^{mi} Q_2^{nj}$$

$$= \frac{q_{mn}}{16D} + \frac{h}{4D} \sum_{i=1}^{\infty} \sum_{j=1}^{\infty} \sum_{r=1}^{\infty} \sum_{s=1}^{\infty}$$

$$\cdot \left[\frac{E}{1-v^2} w_{rs} \left(\frac{\lambda_r^2}{a^2} P_5^{mir} Q_4^{njs} F_{ij} + \frac{\lambda_s^2}{b^2} P_4^{mir} Q_5^{njs} G_{ij} \right) \right.$$

$$\left. + \frac{E}{1+v} w_{rs} \frac{\lambda_r \lambda_s}{ab} P_9^{mir} Q_9^{njs} H_{ij} \right] \qquad m, n = 1, 2, 3, \ldots \quad (2\text{-}65)$$

The system of differential equations (2-51) to (2-53) thus is reduced to a set of nonlinear algebraic equations (2-60), (2-61), and (2-65). The Fourier coefficients P_i and Q_i defined by equations (2-58) and (2-64) can be determined by use of the orthogonality properties of functions $R_m(x)$, $S_n(y)$, $X_m(x)$, and $Y_n(y)$. It is observed that the set of algebraic equations can be obtained also by substituting equations (2-9) and (2-56) into (2-51) to (2-53), multiplying each of the resulting equations by these appropriate functions of x and y, integrating with respect to x and y over their respective intervals, and using the orthogonality properties as in Sec. 2.1.

In practice only a finite number of terms are taken in each series given by equation (2-56). Coefficients u_{mn} and v_{mn} can be expressed in terms of w_{mn} by virtue of equations (2-60) and (2-61). Substituting these values of u and v coefficients into equations (2-63), coefficients F_{mn}, G_{mn}, and H_{mn} can be determined in terms of w_{mn}. A final substitution of these coefficients in equation (2-65) leads to a set of simultaneous cubic equations which can be solved for w_{mn}.

Let us consider again the case of a square plate under uniform transverse load q_0. Taking only the first term in each series and $v = 0.316$, we obtain

$$\left(\frac{w_{11}}{h}\right)^3 + 0.2522 \frac{w_{11}}{h} = 0.0001333 \frac{q_0 a^4}{Dh} \tag{2-66}$$

$$w_0 = 2.5223 w_{11}$$

This result will be compared with the other solutions in Fig. 2.7.

2.5 PERTURBATION METHOD FOR RIGIDLY CLAMPED, UNIFORMLY LOADED PLATE

Based on the perturbation technique an approximate solution is presented for the large deflection of a rigidly clamped plate under uniform transverse load (Ref. 2.5). Firstly the nondimensional parameters are introduced as follows

$$\lambda = \frac{a_0}{b_0} \qquad \zeta = \frac{x}{a_0} \qquad \eta = \frac{y}{b_0} \qquad Q = 2\sqrt{3}\frac{q_0 a_0^4}{Dh}$$

$$U = \frac{12 a_0 u^0}{h^2} \qquad V = \frac{12 a_0 v^0}{h^2} \qquad W = 2\sqrt{3}\frac{w}{h} \tag{2-67}$$

in which a_0 and b_0 are half-length and half-width of the plate. Substituting equations (2-67) into (2-51) to (2-53) leads to the nondimensional governing equations

$$U_{,\zeta\zeta} + d_1 \lambda^2 U_{,\eta\eta} + d_2 \lambda V_{,\zeta\eta}$$
$$= -W_{,\zeta}(W_{,\zeta\zeta} + d_1 \lambda^2 W_{,\eta\eta}) - d_2 \lambda^2 W_{,\eta} W_{,\zeta\eta} \tag{2-68}$$

$$\lambda^2 V_{,\eta\eta} + d_1 V_{,\zeta\zeta} + d_2 \lambda U_{,\zeta\eta}$$
$$= -\lambda W_{,\eta}(\lambda^2 W_{,\eta\eta} + d_1 W_{,\zeta\zeta}) - d_2 \lambda W_{,\zeta} W_{,\zeta\eta} \tag{2-69}$$

$$W_{,\zeta\zeta\zeta\zeta} + 2\lambda^2 W_{,\zeta\zeta\eta\eta} + \lambda^4 W_{,\eta\eta\eta\eta}$$

$$= Q + (U_{,\zeta} + v\lambda V_{,\eta})W_{,\zeta\zeta} + \lambda^2(\lambda V_{,\eta} + vU_{,\zeta})W_{,\eta\eta}$$

$$+ \lambda(1 - v)(\lambda U_{,\eta} + V_{,\zeta})W_{,\zeta\eta} + \tfrac{1}{2}[W_{,\zeta}^2 + v\lambda^2 W_{,\eta}^2]W_{,\zeta\zeta}$$

$$+ \frac{\lambda^2}{2}[\lambda^2 W_{,\eta}^2 + v W_{,\zeta}^2]W_{,\eta\eta}$$

$$+ \lambda^2(1 - v)W_{,\zeta} W_{,\eta} W_{,\zeta\eta} \tag{2-70}$$

Similarly, the boundary conditions (2-55) for a rigidly clamped plate can be written in the nondimensional form

$$U = V = W = W_{,\zeta} = 0 \quad \text{at} \quad \zeta = \pm 1$$

$$U = V = W = W_{,\eta} = 0 \quad \text{at} \quad \eta = \pm 1 \tag{2-71}$$

The perturbation procedure used here to solve equations (2-68) to (2-70) in conjunction with boundary conditions (2-71) is briefly outlined. Let the non-dimensional center deflection $W(0, 0)$ be denoted by W_0. The parameters Q, U, V, and W are developed into ascending perturbation series with respect to W_0. Because of the plate with twofold symmetry, these parameters may be expressed in the form

$$Q = \sum_{n=1, 3, \ldots}^{\infty} q_n W_0^n \qquad W = \sum_{n=1, 3, \ldots}^{\infty} w_n(\zeta, \eta)W_0^n$$

$$U = \sum_{n=2, 4, \ldots}^{\infty} u_n(\zeta, \eta)W_0^n \qquad V = \sum_{n=2, 4, \ldots}^{\infty} v_n(\zeta, \eta)W_0^n \tag{2-72}$$

in which Q and W are direction-dependent and U and V are independent of the sign of Q, and in which the definition of W_0 requires that

$$w_1(0, 0) = 1 \qquad w_3(0, 0) = w_5(0, 0) = \cdots = 0 \tag{2-73}$$

Substituting equations (2-72) into (2-68) to (2-71) and equating like powers of W_0 leads to a series of linear differential equations and boundary conditions. In the first approximation the terms in the first power of W_0 are equated and we obtain the small deflection equation

$$w_{1,\zeta\zeta\zeta\zeta} + 2\lambda^2 w_{1,\zeta\zeta\eta\eta} + \lambda^4 w_{1,\eta\eta\eta\eta} = q_1 \tag{2-74}$$

and the boundary conditions

$$w_1 = w_{1,\zeta} = 0 \quad \text{at} \quad \zeta = \pm 1$$

$$w_1 = w_{1,\eta} = 0 \quad \text{at} \quad \eta = \pm 1 \tag{2-75}$$

When the terms in W_0^2 are equated, the following differential equations are obtained

$$u_{2,\zeta\zeta} + d_1\lambda^2 u_{2,\eta\eta} + d_2\lambda v_{2,\zeta\eta}$$
$$= -w_{1,\zeta}(w_{1,\zeta\zeta} + d_1\lambda^2 w_{1,\eta\eta}) - d_2\lambda^2 w_{1,\eta} w_{1,\zeta\eta}$$

$$\lambda^2 v_{2,\eta\eta} + d_1 v_{2,\zeta\zeta} + d_2\lambda u_{2,\zeta\eta}$$
$$= -\lambda w_{1,\eta}(\lambda^2 w_{1,\eta\eta} + d_1 w_{1,\zeta\zeta}) - d_2\lambda w_{1,\zeta} w_{1,\zeta\eta}$$

$$(2\text{-}76)$$

The associated boundary conditions which are to be satisfied are given by

$$u_2 = v_2 = 0 \quad\quad \text{at} \quad \zeta = \pm 1 \quad \text{and} \quad \eta = \pm 1 \quad\quad (2\text{-}77)$$

The third approximation leads to the differential equation

$$w_{3,\zeta\zeta\zeta\zeta} + 2\lambda^2 w_{3,\zeta\zeta\eta\eta} + \lambda^4 w_{3,\eta\eta\eta\eta} = q_3 + (u_{2,\zeta} + v\lambda v_{2,\eta})w_{1,\zeta\zeta}$$
$$+ \lambda^2(\lambda v_{2,\eta} + vu_{2,\zeta})w_{1,\eta\eta} + \lambda(1-v)(\lambda u_{2,\eta} + v_{2,\zeta})w_{1,\zeta\eta}$$
$$+ \tfrac{1}{2}(w_{1,\zeta}^2 + v\lambda^2 w_{1,\eta}^2)w_{1,\zeta\zeta} + \tfrac{1}{2}\lambda^2(\lambda^2 w_{1,\eta}^2 + vw_{1,\zeta}^2)w_{1,\eta\eta}$$
$$+ \lambda^2(1-v)w_{1,\zeta} w_{1,\eta} w_{1,\zeta\eta}$$

$$(2\text{-}78)$$

and the boundary conditions

$$w_3 = w_{3,\zeta} = 0 \quad\quad \text{at} \quad \zeta = \pm 1$$
$$w_3 = w_{3,\eta} = 0 \quad\quad \text{at} \quad \eta = \pm 1$$

$$(2\text{-}79)$$

If necessary, the fourth- and higher-order approximations can be obtained in a similar manner.

Approximate solutions to equations (2-74), (2-76), and (2-78) are sought in the form of polynomials. A solution of equation (2-74) is assumed to be

$$w_1 = (1 - \zeta^2)^2(1 - \eta^2)^2(1 + A_1\zeta^2 + A_2\eta^2 + A_3\zeta^4 + A_4\eta^4 + A_5\zeta^2\eta^2) \quad (2\text{-}80)$$

which satisfies the boundary conditions (2-75), the requirements of plate symmetry, and equation (2-73). Introducing equation (2-80) into (2-74), six algebraic equations are generated by equating the constant term to q_1 and the terms in ζ^2, η^2, ζ^4, η^4, and $\zeta^2\eta^2$ to zero. The last five equations are then solved for A_i. The substitution of these constants into the first of these equations leads to the solution for q_1. The numerical results are presented in Table A.1 in Appendix A for different values of the aspect ratio λ (Ref. 2.6). In calculation Poisson's ratio was taken to be $\tfrac{1}{3}$.

The boundary conditions (2-77), and the direction dependency of the inplane displacements are satisfied by taking

$$u_2 = \zeta(1 - \zeta^2)(1 - \eta^2)$$
$$\cdot (B_1 + B_2\zeta^2 + B_3\eta^2 + B_4\zeta^4 + B_5\eta^4 + B_6\zeta^2\eta^2)$$
$$v_2 = \eta(1 - \zeta^2)(1 - \eta^2)$$
$$\cdot (C_1 + C_2\zeta^2 + C_3\eta^2 + C_4\zeta^4 + C_5\eta^4 + C_6\zeta^2\eta^2)$$

$$(2\text{-}81)$$

When equations (2-80) and (2-81) are substituted in (2-76), six algebraic equations from each of equations (2-76) are generated by equating like powers of ζ and η. These algebraic equations are solved simultaneously for B_i and C_i with the results given in Tables A.2 and A.3.

A solution of equation (2-78) satisfying (2-73), boundary conditions (2-79), and the requirements of plate symmetry is taken to be

$$w_3 = (1 - \zeta^2)^2(1 - \eta^2)^2(H_1\zeta^2 + H_2\eta^2 + H_3\zeta^4 + H_4\eta^4 + H_5\zeta^2\eta^2) \quad (2\text{-}82)$$

The procedure of the determination of H_i and q_3 is the same as in the first approximation. The results for various values of λ are shown in Table A.4 (Ref. 2.7).

As usual the perturbation series (2-72) is approximated by

$$Q = q_1 W_0 + q_3 W_0^3 \qquad W = w_1(\zeta, \eta)W_0 + w_3(\zeta, \eta)W_0^3$$
$$U = u_2(\zeta, \eta)W_0^2 \qquad V = v_2(\zeta, \eta)W_0^2 \quad (2\text{-}83)$$

In the first of these expressions the first term gives the corresponding linear solution and the second term takes into account the effect of stretching of the middle surface. By use of functions (2-80) to (2-82) in conjunction with Tables A.1 to A.4, the solution (2-83) can be easily calculated for a given λ.

The total stress at a material point within the plate is the sum of membrane and bending stresses given by equations (1-164) and (1-165). By virtue of equations (1-121), (1-122), and (2-67), the membrane stresses can be written in the nondimensional form (Ref. 2.6) as

$$\sigma_\zeta^m = U_{,\zeta} + \lambda v V_{,\eta} + \tfrac{1}{2}[W_{,\zeta}^2 + \lambda^2 v W_{,\eta}^2]$$
$$\sigma_\eta^m = \lambda V_{,\eta} + v U_{,\zeta} + \tfrac{1}{2}[\lambda^2 W_{,\eta}^2 + v W_{,\zeta}^2] \quad (2\text{-}84)$$
$$\sigma_{\zeta\eta}^m = \frac{1 - v}{2}[\lambda U_{,\eta} + V_{,\zeta} + \lambda W_{,\zeta} W_{,\eta}]$$

and the extreme-fiber bending stresses as

$$\sigma_\zeta^b = \pm\sqrt{3}(W_{,\zeta\zeta} + \lambda^2 v W_{,\eta\eta})$$
$$\sigma_\eta^b = \pm\sqrt{3}(\lambda^2 W_{,\eta\eta} + v W_{,\zeta\zeta}) \quad (2\text{-}85)$$
$$\sigma_{\zeta\eta}^b = \pm\sqrt{3}(1 - v)\lambda W_{,\zeta\eta}$$

where

$$(\sigma_\zeta^m, \sigma_\eta^m, \sigma_{\zeta\eta}^m) = \frac{a_0^2 h}{D}(\sigma_x^m, \sigma_y^m, \sigma_{xy}^m)$$

$$(\sigma_\zeta^b, \sigma_\eta^b, \sigma_{\zeta\eta}^b) = \frac{a_0^2 h}{D}(\sigma_x^b, \sigma_y^b, \sigma_{xy}^b) \quad (2\text{-}86)$$

The stresses which are of most interest are the normal stresses at the center of the plate and that in the ζ direction at the middle of the long side. The latter is the

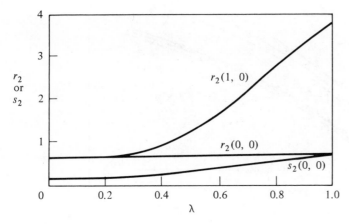

Figure 2.5 Membrane stress coefficients in Eq. (2-87).

maximum stress. In view of equations (2-80) to (2-82) one may write

$$\sigma_\zeta^m(\zeta, 0) = r_2(\zeta, 0)W_0^2$$
$$\sigma_\eta^m(0, \eta) = s_2(0, \eta)W_0^2$$
$$\sigma_\zeta^b(\zeta, 0) = \alpha_1(\zeta, 0)W_0 + \alpha_3(\zeta, 0)W_0^3 \qquad (2\text{-}87)$$
$$\sigma_\eta^b(0, \eta) = \beta_1(0, \eta)W_0 + \beta_3(0, \eta)W_0^3$$

in which the coefficients r_2, s_2, α_1, α_3, β_1, and β_3 are plotted in Figs. 2.5 and 2.6.

A comparison of the transverse deflection, membrane strain, and extreme-fiber bending strains at the center of the rectangular plate predicted by the

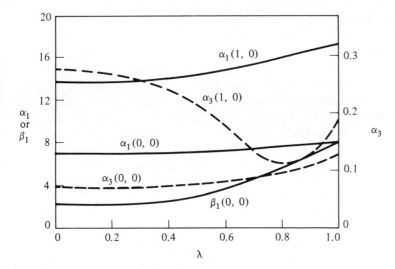

Figure 2.6 Bending stress coefficients in Eq. (2-87).

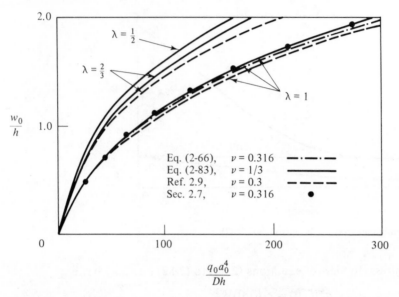

Figure 2.7 Load-deflection curves for rigidly clamped rectangular plate under uniform lateral load.

approximate solution (2-83) with the experimental results in Ref. 2.8 for various values of the aspect ratio shows that a good agreement is found between theory and experiment. For a given central deflection the theoretical values are generally higher than the experimental data. In the case when $\lambda = \frac{1}{3}$, a theoretical result for the central membrane strain in the transverse direction agrees fairly with the experimental result, but that in the longitudinal direction does not. It should be observed that the former strain is much greater than the latter.

The central deflection w_0 is plotted against uniform normal pressure q_0 in Fig. 2.7 for various values of the aspect ratio λ. The solid load-deflection curves are given by solution (2-83). The results obtained by Way (Ref. 2.9) using the Ritz method, an exact solution discussed in Sec. 2.7, and the first term in the series solution (2-56) or equation (2-66) are also shown here for comparison. A good agreement is found among these solutions for a square plate. The inconsistencies of these approximate solutions based on the Ritz and perturbation methods can be found from a comparison of the load-deflection curves for different values of λ. The $\lambda = 0$ curve (not presented here) for an infinitely long plate predicted by the solution (2-83) approaches, and at high values of W_0 crosses over, the $\lambda = \frac{1}{2}$ curve. A similar inconsistency appears in Ref. 2.9 for the curves predicted when $\lambda = \frac{1}{2}$ and $\frac{2}{3}$ at the values of w_0/h close to 2. The maximum bending stress which occurs at the middle of the long side is shown in Fig. 2.8. The results obtained from the third of equations (2-87) are in fair agreement with Way's solution. Both solutions suffer from the same limitation that the stress for $\lambda = \frac{1}{2}$ exceeds that predicted when $\lambda = \frac{2}{3}$ for large values of W_0. The membrane stress at the middle of the long side is plotted in Fig. 2.9 against the central deflection. The trend of these

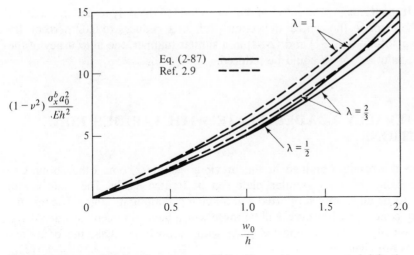

Figure 2.8 Extreme-fiber bending stress at middle of long side versus central deflection for rigidly clamped, uniformly loaded rectangular plate.

two approximate solutions is not the same. The results of a series of rectangular plate tests (Ref. 2.8) showed that the membrane stresses were reliably predicted by the present method. The inaccuracy of the present solution could be removed by taking the first three or more terms in series (2-72) for Q and W, and reduced by improving the polynomial solution (2-80) to (2-82). In the latter, the maximum deflection of a square plate obtained from the present linear solution $Q = q_0 W_0$ is different from the exact solution (Ref. 1.10) by the amount of approximately 2

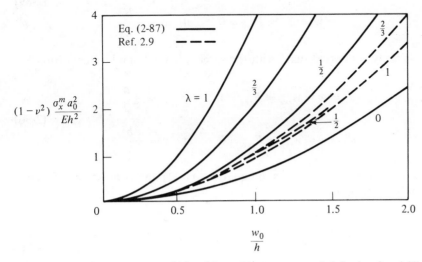

Figure 2.9 Membrane stress at middle of long side versus central deflection for rigidly clamped rectangular plate under uniform transverse load.

percent. If the terms $\zeta^6, \zeta^4\eta^2, \zeta^2\eta^4$, and η^6 are added to the polynomial in equation (2-80), the error in the central deflection (Ref. 2.10) reduces to 0.02 percent. By improving solutions (2-81) and (2-82) in a similar manner, the inaccuracy of the two-term solution for W could be reduced.

2.6 LATERALLY LOADED PLATE WITH VARIOUS EDGE CONDITIONS

Based on the results obtained in the previous sections, some other boundary value problems of a rectangular plate can be treated easily. The plate is still assumed to be all-simply-supported and all-clamped along its edges. The inplane boundary conditions, however, will be those which have not been considered yet. In the case of a simply supported plate with immovable edges, the boundary conditions are given by

$$u^0 = v^0 = w = w_{,xx} = 0 \qquad \text{at} \quad x = \pm\frac{a}{2}$$

$$u^0 = v^0 = w = w_{,yy} = 0 \qquad \text{at} \quad y = \pm\frac{b}{2}$$

$$(2\text{-}88)$$

The other two sets of boundary conditions under consideration are for a clamped plate with zero boundary normal displacement and tangential force

$$u^0 = w = w_{,x} = F_{,xy} = 0 \qquad \text{at} \quad x = \pm\frac{a}{2}$$

$$v^0 = w = w_{,y} = F_{,xy} = 0 \qquad \text{at} \quad y = \pm\frac{b}{2}$$

$$(2\text{-}89)$$

and for a simply supported plate with the same inplane boundary conditions

$$u^0 = w = w_{,xx} = F_{,xy} = 0 \qquad \text{at} \quad x = \pm\frac{a}{2}$$

$$v^0 = w = w_{,yy} = F_{,xy} = 0 \qquad \text{at} \quad y = \pm\frac{b}{2}$$

$$(2\text{-}90)$$

By virtue of the first two relations in equations (1-42), the two inplane displacements can be written as

$$u^0 = \int_0^x \left[\frac{1}{E}(F_{,yy} - vF_{,xx}) - \frac{1}{2}w_{,x}^2\right] dx$$

$$v^0 = \int_0^y \left[\frac{1}{E}(F_{,xx} - vF_{,yy}) - \frac{1}{2}w_{,y}^2\right] dy$$

$$(2\text{-}91)$$

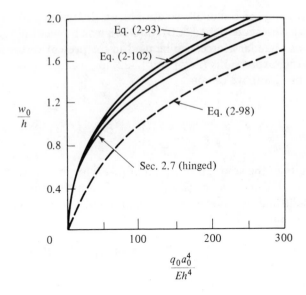

Figure 2.10 Load-deflection curves for uniformly loaded square plate with various edge conditions ($v = 0.316$).

Solutions to these problems are separately formulated. All the boundary conditions (2-88) are satisfied if we take (Ref. 2.1)

$$u^0 = \sum_{m=1}^{\infty} \sum_{n=1,\,3,\,\dots}^{\infty} u_{mn} \sin \frac{2m\pi x}{a} \cos \frac{n\pi y}{b}$$

$$v^0 = \sum_{m=1,\,3,\,\dots}^{\infty} \sum_{n=1}^{\infty} v_{mn} \cos \frac{m\pi x}{a} \sin \frac{2n\pi y}{b} \qquad (2\text{-}92)$$

$$w = \sum_{m=1,\,3,\,\dots}^{\infty} \sum_{n=1,\,3,\,\dots}^{\infty} w_{mn} \cos \frac{m\pi x}{a} \cos \frac{n\pi y}{b}$$

Substituting these expressions and the first of equations (2-45) into governing equations (2-51) to (2-53), following a similar calculation as in Sec. 2.4, and taking only the first terms in these series, we obtain, for a square plate with $v = 0.316$, the relation between the central deflection w_0 and the uniform transverse load of intensity q_0 given by

$$\left(\frac{w_0}{h}\right)^3 + 0.47 \frac{w_0}{h} = 0.03375 \frac{q_0 a^4}{Eh^4} \qquad (2\text{-}93)$$

which is shown in Fig. 2.10.

Approximate solutions for the other two problems are derived on the basis of the one-term approximation of the Galerkin method. For a clamped plate the deflection function is approximated by (Ref. 2.4)

$$w = h W_m \cos^2 \left(\frac{\pi x}{a}\right) \cos^2 \left(\frac{\pi y}{b}\right) \qquad (2\text{-}94)$$

which is expression (2-19) satisfying the boundary conditions for deflection and slope given in equations (2-89). Thus equations (2-20) to (2-26), which meet the requirement for zero tangential boundary force, can be used in the present case without any alternation. Inserting expressions (2-94) and (2-22) for w and F into the first of boundary conditions (2-89), we obtain

$$A_n = B_n = 0$$

$$C_1 = \frac{3(\lambda^2 + v)}{32(1 - v^2)} \cdot \frac{\pi^2 Eh^2}{a^2} \qquad C_2 = \frac{3(1 + v\lambda^2)}{32(1 - v^2)} \cdot \frac{\pi^2 Eh^2}{a^2} \qquad (2\text{-}95)$$

which are the required constants in the solution of equation (2-20) for the stress function F. Under conditions (2-95), expressions (2-94) and (2-22) exactly satisfy all the boundary conditions (2-89) and the compatibility equation (2-2). Introduction of equations (2-23), (2-26), and (2-95) in (2-22) yields

$$F = \tfrac{1}{2}W_m^2(C_1 x^2 + C_2 y^2) + Eh^2 W_m^2 \sum_{p=0}^{\infty} \sum_{q=0}^{\infty} b_{pq} R_p(x) S_q(y) \qquad (2\text{-}96)$$

in which b_{pq}, R_p, and S_q are given by equations (2-21) and (2-24). Instead of satisfaction of the equilibrium equation (2-1) we apply the Galerkin method to determine the unknown parameter W_m in the assumed solution (2-94). Equations (2-94) and (2-22) are substituted in (2-38) and an integration gives

$$\frac{\pi^4 Dh}{a^4}(3 + 2\lambda^2 + 3\lambda^4)W_m + \frac{3\pi^2 h^2}{4a^2}(\lambda^2 C_1 + C_2)W_m^3$$

$$- \frac{2\pi^4 Eh^4}{a^2 b^2}(b_{01} + b_{10} + b_{11} + \tfrac{1}{2}b_{12} + \tfrac{1}{2}b_{21} + b_{02} + b_{20})W_m^3 = q_0 \qquad (2\text{-}97)$$

In the case of a square plate ($\lambda = 1$), equation (2-97) becomes

$$\frac{q_0 a^4}{Eh^4} = \pi^4 \left[\frac{2}{3(1 - v^2)}W_m + \left(0.16656 + \frac{0.14063}{1 - v}\right)W_m^3 \right] \qquad (2\text{-}98)$$

The result of this cubic equation is shown in Fig. 2.10 by a dashed curve.

In a similar manner the boundary conditions for transverse deflection and bending moment in equation (2-90) are satisfied by taking

$$w = hW_m \cos\frac{\pi x}{a} \cos\frac{\pi y}{b} \qquad (2\text{-}99)$$

which is equation (2-47).

Introduction of equation (2-99) in the compatibility equation (2-2) leads to equation (2-20) with the nonzero Fourier coefficients a_{pq} given by equation (2-48). The stress function (2-22) obtained from equations (2-23) and (2-26) satisfies the last of boundary conditions (2-90). The boundary condition for inplane displacements is also satisfied if the integration constants in expression (2-22) are given by

$$A_n = B_n = 0$$

$$C_1 = \frac{\lambda^2 + v}{1 - v^2} \cdot \frac{\pi^2 Eh^2}{8a^2} \qquad C_2 = \frac{1 + v\lambda^2}{1 - v^2} \cdot \frac{\pi^2 Eh^2}{8a^2} \qquad (2\text{-}100)$$

Inserting equations (2-99) and (2-22) into (2-38) and performing integration result in

$$\frac{\pi^6 Dh}{a^4}(1+\lambda^2)^2 W_m + \frac{\pi^4 h^2}{a^2}(\lambda^2 C_1 + C_2)W_m^3 - \frac{\pi^6 Eh^4}{8a^2 b^2}(d_{01} + d_{10})W_m^3 = 16q_0$$

$$(2\text{-}101)$$

In the case of a square plate, equation (2-101) reads

$$\frac{q_0 a^4}{Eh^4} = \frac{\pi^6}{16}\left[\frac{1}{3(1-v^2)}W_m + \frac{3-v}{8(1+v)}W_m^3\right] \qquad (2\text{-}102)$$

This relation between central deflection and uniform transverse load is also presented in Fig. 2.10. Due to the fact that boundary conditions (2-90), are nearly the same as those given by equations (2-88), the load-deflection curve given by solution (2-102) approaches that obtained from solution (2-93). An exact solution for a hinged and uniformly loaded square plate which will be discussed in the next section is also shown in Fig. 2.10 for comparison with these two solutions. The curves indicate that these one-term solutions, especially in the series (2-92) do not give good approximations. For a better accuracy two or more terms in the truncated series should be taken into account.

2.7 CLAMPED PLATE WITH STIFFENED EDGES

Consider a rectangular plate with stiffened edges (Refs. 2.11, 2.12†) as in airplane structures. In this case all the edges must remain straight during deformation and the elongations of the plate, denoted by δ_x in the x direction and by δ_y in the y direction, must be independent of the position along the length or width at which they are measured. If the origin of the coordinate system is taken at the upper left corner of the plate (Fig. 2.11), the boundary conditions for clamped edges are given by

$$w(0, y) = w(a, y) = w(x, 0) = w(x, b) = 0 \qquad (2\text{-}103)$$

$$w_{,x}(0, y) = w_{,x}(a, y) = w_{,y}(x, 0) = w_{,y}(x, b) = 0 \qquad (2\text{-}104)$$

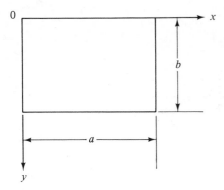

Figure 2.11 Coordinates of rectangular plate.

† Reprinted from the *Proceedings of Symposium in Applied Mechanics*, vol. 1, pp. 197–210, by permission of the American Mathematical Society. © 1974 by the American Mathematical Society.

and those for straight edges by

$$\int_0^a \left[\frac{1}{E} \left(F_{,yy} - \nu F_{,xx} \right) - \frac{1}{2} w_{,x}^2 \right] dx = \delta_x$$

$$\int_0^b \left[\frac{1}{E} \left(F_{,xx} - \nu F_{,yy} \right) - \frac{1}{2} w_{,y}^2 \right] dy = \delta_y \tag{2-105}$$

If the total inplane load is represented by P_x in the x direction and by P_y in the y direction, the corresponding boundary condition for each edge is

$$h \int_0^b F_{,yy} \, dy = P_x \qquad h \int_0^a F_{,xx} \, dx = P_y$$

which can be written as

$$F_{,y}(x, b) - F_{,y}(x, 0) = \frac{P_x}{h} \qquad F_{,x}(a, y) - F_{,x}(0, y) = \frac{P_y}{h} \tag{2-106}$$

In the analysis the required bending moments per unit length, denoted respectively by m_{xo} and m_{xa} along the edges $x = 0$, a and by m_{yo} and m_{yb} along the edges $y = 0$, b, are replaced by an equivalent lateral pressure distribution $q_e(x, y)$ near the edges of the plate as shown in Fig. 2.12. If this pressure distribution is ex-

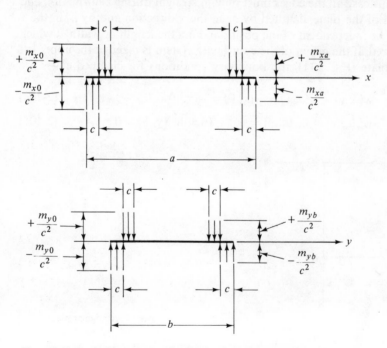

Figure 2.12 Equivalent pressure distribution $(c \to 0)$ for edge moments.

pressed by a Fourier series and the value of c approaches to zero, we have

$$q_e = \frac{2\pi}{a^2} \sum_{r=1}^{\infty} [m_{xo} - (-1)^r m_{xa}] r \sin \frac{r\pi x}{a}$$

$$+ \frac{2\pi}{b^2} \sum_{s=1}^{\infty} [m_{yo} - (-1)^s m_{yb}] s \sin \frac{s\pi y}{b} \qquad (2\text{-}107)$$

The edge moments are expanded into Fourier series

$$m_{xo} = \frac{a^2}{2\pi} \sum_{p=1}^{\infty} A_p \sin \frac{p\pi y}{b} \qquad \text{at} \quad x = 0$$

$$m_{xa} = \frac{a^2}{2\pi} \sum_{p=1}^{\infty} B_p \sin \frac{p\pi y}{b} \qquad \text{at} \quad x = a$$

$$(2\text{-}108)$$

$$m_{yo} = \frac{b^2}{2\pi} \sum_{q=1}^{\infty} C_q \sin \frac{q\pi x}{a} \qquad \text{at} \quad y = 0$$

$$m_{yb} = \frac{b^2}{2\pi} \sum_{q=1}^{\infty} H_q \sin \frac{q\pi x}{a} \qquad \text{at} \quad y = b$$

in which A_p, B_p, C_q, and H_q are coefficients to be determined.

Introduction of equations (2-108) in (2-107) yields

$$q_e = \sum_{m=1}^{\infty} \sum_{n=1}^{\infty} k_{mn} \sin \frac{m\pi x}{a} \sin \frac{n\pi y}{b} \qquad (2\text{-}109)$$

where

$$k_{mn} = n[C_m - (-1)^n H_m] + m[A_n - (-1)^m B_n] \qquad (2\text{-}110)$$

The transverse load may be also represented by a Fourier series

$$q = \sum_{m=1}^{\infty} \sum_{n=1}^{\infty} q_{mn} \sin \frac{m\pi x}{a} \sin \frac{n\pi y}{b} \qquad (2\text{-}111)$$

The sum of the transverse load and equivalent pressure distribution for edge moments, denoted by $p(x, y)$, is given by

$$p = \sum_{m=1}^{\infty} \sum_{n=1}^{\infty} p_{mn} \sin \frac{m\pi x}{a} \sin \frac{n\pi y}{b} \qquad (2\text{-}112)$$

where

$$p_{mn} = k_{mn} + q_{mn} \qquad (2\text{-}113)$$

A solution of equations (2-1) and (2-2), satisfying conditions (2-103) to (2-106) for a clamped plate, are formulated on the basis of the general solution for simply supported plates (Ref. 2.13). The boundary condition (2-103) for zero deflection is satisfied by taking

$$w = \sum_{m=1}^{\infty} \sum_{n=1}^{\infty} w_{mn} \sin \frac{m\pi x}{a} \sin \frac{n\pi y}{b} \qquad (2\text{-}114)$$

It can be shown that equation (2-114) also satisfies the boundary condition (2-104) for zero slope if the deflection coefficients w_{mn} satisfy the relations for any value of n

$$\sum_{m=1}^{\infty} m w_{mn} = 0 \qquad \sum_{m=1}^{\infty} (-1)^m m w_{mn} = 0$$

$$\sum_{n=1}^{\infty} n w_{mn} = 0 \qquad \sum_{n=1}^{\infty} (-1)^n n w_{mn} = 0 \tag{2-115}$$

The boundary condition (2-106) for constant inplane edge load is satisfied if the stress function is expressed as

$$F = \frac{P_x y^2}{2bh} + \frac{P_y x^2}{2ah} + \sum_{m=0}^{\infty} \sum_{n=0}^{\infty} F_{mn} \cos \frac{m\pi x}{a} \cos \frac{n\pi y}{b} \tag{2-116}$$

Introduction of expressions (2-114) and (2-116) in boundary condition (2-105) yields

$$\delta_x = \frac{1}{Eh}(\lambda P_x - \nu P_y) - \frac{\pi^2}{8a} \sum_{m=1}^{\infty} \sum_{n=1}^{\infty} m^2 w_{mn}^2$$

$$\delta_y = \frac{1}{Eh}\left(\frac{P_y}{\lambda} - \nu P_x\right) - \frac{\pi^2}{8a} \sum_{m=1}^{\infty} \sum_{n=1}^{\infty} n^2 w_{mn}^2 \tag{2-117}$$

where λ is the aspect ratio of the plate defined by equation (2-25). Since the right-hand sides of equations (2-117) are independent of x and y, the boundary conditions (2-105) for constant inplane edge displacement are satisfied by the series (2-114) and (2-116). In practice two of the constants δ_x, δ_y, P_x, and P_y will be prescribed and the other two must be determined by relations (2-117).

Inserting the solution (2-114) and (2-116) into the compatibility equation (2-2) and equating coefficients of like trigonometric terms lead to the relation between F_{mn} and w_{mn}

$$F_{mn} = \frac{E\lambda^2}{4(m^2 + n^2\lambda^2)^2}(b_1 + b_2 + b_3 + \cdots + b_9) \tag{2-118}$$

where

$$b_1 = \sum_{r=1}^{m-1} \sum_{s=1}^{n-1} [rs(m-r)(n-s) - r^2(n-s)^2] w_{rs} w_{(m-r)(n-s)}$$

$$\qquad\qquad\qquad\qquad\qquad\qquad \text{if } m \neq 0 \text{ and } n \neq 0$$

$$b_1 = 0 \qquad\qquad\qquad\qquad\qquad\qquad \text{if } m = 0 \text{ or } n = 0$$

$$b_2 = \sum_{r=1}^{\infty} \sum_{s=1}^{n-1} [rs(r+m)(n-s) + r^2(n-s)^2] w_{rs} w_{(r+m)(n-s)} \tag{2-119}$$

$$\qquad\qquad\qquad\qquad\qquad\qquad \text{if } n \neq 0$$

$$b_2 = 0 \qquad\qquad\qquad\qquad\qquad\qquad \text{if } n = 0$$

$\blacktriangledown$

$\blacktriangledown$

....

$$b_9 = \sum_{r=1}^{\infty} \sum_{s=1}^{\infty} [rs(r+m)(s+n) - s^2(r+m)^2] w_{rs} w_{(r+m)(s+n)}$$

$$\text{if} \quad m \neq 0$$

$$b_9 = 0 \qquad\qquad\qquad\qquad\qquad \text{if} \quad m = 0$$

The relation (2-118) can be simplified to

$$F_{mn} = \frac{E\lambda^2}{4(m^2 + n^2\lambda^2)^2} \sum f_{klrs} w_{kl} w_{rs} \tag{2-120}$$

In this equation the summation includes all products $w_{kl} w_{rs}$ for which m is equal to either the sum or difference of k and r and for which n is equal to either the sum or difference of l and s. The coefficients f_{klrs} are given by

$$f_{klrs} = 2klrs \pm (k^2s^2 + l^2r^2) \tag{2-121}$$

in which the sign before the parenthesis is positive either if m is the sum of k and r, and n is the difference of l and s, or if m is the difference of k and r, and n is the sum of l and s. In any other circumstances the sign is negative. For example, we obtain for a rectangular plate under general lateral loading

$$F_{02} = \frac{E}{64\lambda^2} (4w_{11}^2 - 4w_{11}w_{13} - 4w_{12}w_{14} + 16w_{21}^2 - 16w_{21}w_{23} + \cdots) \tag{2-122}$$

Similarly, substituting expressions (2-112), (2-114), and (2-116) into the equilibrium equation (2-1) and equating coefficients of like trigonometric terms, we obtain the relation between p_{rs}, w_{rs}, and F_{rs} as follows

$$p_{rs} = \left[D\pi^4 \left(\frac{r^2}{a^2} + \frac{s^2}{b^2} \right)^2 + \frac{\pi^2 r^2}{a^2 b} P_x + \frac{\pi^2 s^2}{ab^2} P_y \right] w_{rs}$$

$$+ \frac{h\pi^4}{4a^2 b^2} \left\{ - \sum_{k=1}^{r} \sum_{l=1}^{s} [(s-l)k - (r-k)l]^2 F_{(r-k)(s-l)} w_{kl} \right.$$

$$- \sum_{k=0}^{\infty} \sum_{l=0}^{\infty} [l(k+r) - k(l+s)]^2 F_{kl} w_{(k+r)(l+s)} + \cdots\cdots$$

$$+ \left. \sum_{k=1}^{\infty} \sum_{l=1}^{\infty} [(s-l)k + l(k+r)]^2 F_{(k+r)(s-l)} w_{kl} \right\} \tag{2-123}$$

in which the dots denote the other six similar double series.

This relation can be simplified to

$$p_{mn} = \left[D\pi^4 \left(\frac{m^2}{a^2} + \frac{n^2}{b^2} \right)^2 + \frac{\pi^2 m^2}{a^2 b} P_x + \frac{\pi^2 n^2}{ab^2} P_y \right] w_{mn}$$

$$+ \frac{h\pi^4}{4a^2 b^2} \sum d_{klrs} F_{kl} w_{rs} \tag{2-124}$$

in which the summation includes all products $F_{kl}w_{rs}$ for which m is equal to either the sum or difference of k and r and for which n is equal to either the sum or difference of l and s, and in which the coefficients d_{klrs} are given by

$$d_{klrs} = \pm(ks \pm lr)^2 \qquad \text{if} \quad k \neq 0 \quad \text{and} \quad l \neq 0 \qquad (2\text{-}125)$$

and are twice this value if either k or l is zero. In equation (2-125) the first sign is positive if either $k - r = m$ or $l - s = n$, but not if both conditions are true. It is negative in all other cases. The second sign is positive either if m is the sum of k and r, and n is the difference of l and s, or if m is the difference of k and r, and n is the sum of l and s. It is negative otherwise. In the case of a square plate under uniformly distributed lateral load, the terms in the series (2-112) and (2-114) vanish when the indices m and n are even numbers, and those in the series (2-116) vanish when m and n are odd numbers. Thus we obtain

$$p_{31} = \frac{\pi^2}{a^4}(100D\pi^2 + 9aP_x + aP_y)w_{31} + \frac{h\pi^4}{4a^4}(72F_{02}w_{31} - 72F_{02}w_{33}$$

$$- 8F_{20}w_{11} - 8F_{20}w_{51} + 16F_{22}w_{11} - 64F_{22}w_{13} + \cdots) \qquad (2\text{-}126)$$

Equations (2-115), (2-120), and (2-124) each represent infinite sets of equations. An exact solution should satisfy all of these equations. In practice only a finite number of terms different from zero in each truncated series (2-112), (2-114), and (2-116) is taken into account. Equation (2-120) is substituted in (2-124) and, in each of the resulting equations, the linear term in w_{mn} is expressed in terms of the cubic terms in w_{mn} and the linear terms in p_{mn}. The deflection coefficients w_{mn} thus obtained are now introduced in equation (2-115). In view of relations (2-110) and (2-113), the result will be a set of equations involving linear terms in the edge moment coefficients A_m, B_m, C_n and H_n, and cubic terms in the deflection coefficients w_{mn}. These simultaneous cubic equations can be solved by the Newton-Raphson method. The accuracy of the solution can be judged by observing the change in the answer as the number of the w_{mn} coefficients is gradually increased.

The solution given above for clamped edges can be reduced to that for simply supported edges by deleting equations (2-104) and (2-115) and setting the edge moment coefficients $A_m = B_m = C_m = H_m = 0$. Substituting equation (2-120) into (2-124) and solving the resulting simultaneous cubic equations for w_{mn} leads to the solution for simply supported plates.

Taking, for a numerical example, a uniformly loaded square plate with immovable edges, we obtain

$$\lambda = 1 \qquad q = q_0 \qquad \delta_x = \delta_y = 0 \qquad (2\text{-}127)$$

In this case the terms involving even summation indices vanish in equations (2-112) and (2-114) and those involving odd summation indices vanish in equation (2-116). The inplane force resultants P_x and P_y can be found from equations (2-117). The central deflection is given by

$$w_0 = - \sum_{m=1,3,\dots}^{\infty} \sum_{n=1,3,\dots}^{\infty} (-1)^{(m+n)/2}w_{mn} \qquad (2\text{-}128)$$

The load-deflection curve for the plate with rigidly clamped edges is shown in Fig. 2.7 and that with hinged edges in Fig. 2.10, both for comparison with other solutions.

In the case of uniformly loaded, simply supported $(P_x = P_y = 0)$ square plate, the load-deflection curve is presented in Fig. 2.17 also for comparison with other solutions.

A solution for a rectangular plate with one or more edges clamped and the other edges simply supported can be obtained by taking the moment coefficients of the corresponding simply supported edges equal to zero. Either the postbuckling behavior of a rectangular plate under edge compression, or the combined action of lateral and inplane loads with the inplane load beyond the corresponding buckling load, can be also treated by the present method with numerical examples given in Chap. 4.

2.8 FINITE-DIFFERENCE METHOD FOR PLATE UNDER LATERAL PRESSURE AND EDGE COMPRESSION

Making the resulting solution more general, the following nondimensional parameters are introduced

$$\zeta = \frac{x}{b} \qquad \eta = \frac{y}{b} \qquad W = \frac{w}{h} \qquad \Psi = \frac{F}{Eh^2} \qquad (2\text{-}129)$$

in which b is the plate width in the y direction and in which ζ, η and W are defined differently from those in equations (2-67).

Upon substitution, the governing differential equations (2-1) and (2-2) for a rectangular plate under uniform lateral pressure q_0 are transformed to the nondimensional form

$$\Psi_{,\zeta\zeta\zeta\zeta} + 2\Psi_{,\zeta\zeta\eta\eta} + \Psi_{,\eta\eta\eta\eta} = W^2_{,\zeta\eta} - W_{,\zeta\zeta} W_{,\eta\eta} \qquad (2\text{-}130)$$

$$W_{,\zeta\zeta\zeta\zeta} + 2W_{,\zeta\zeta\eta\eta} + W_{,\eta\eta\eta\eta} = 12(1 - v^2)$$

$$\cdot \left[\frac{q_0 b^4}{Eh^4} + W_{,\zeta\zeta} \Psi_{,\eta\eta} + W_{,\eta\eta} \Psi_{,\zeta\zeta} - 2W_{,\zeta\eta} \Psi_{,\zeta\eta} \right] \qquad (2\text{-}131)$$

If the laterally loaded plate is simply supported and subjected to uniform inplane compression P_x in the x direction, and if the loaded edges are free from shear stress and the unloaded edges are stress-free, the boundary conditions can be written in the nondimensional form as

$$W = W_{,\zeta\zeta} = \Psi_{,\zeta\eta} = 0 \qquad \Psi_{,\eta\eta} = -\frac{P_x b}{Eh^3} \qquad \text{at} \quad \zeta = \pm\frac{\lambda}{2}$$

$$\qquad (2\text{-}132)$$

$$W = W_{,\eta\eta} = \psi_{,\zeta\eta} = \psi_{,\zeta\zeta} = 0 \qquad \text{at} \quad \eta = \pm\frac{1}{2}$$

where λ is the aspect ratio of the plate given by equation (2-25).

Now the problem as stated above is solved by the finite-difference method (Ref. 2.14). Replacing the partial derivatives in equations (2-130) and (2-131) by central finite-difference approximations, we obtain

$$\frac{\delta_\zeta^4 \Psi}{(\Delta\zeta)^4} + 2\frac{\delta_{\zeta\eta}^2 \Psi}{(\Delta\zeta)^2(\Delta\eta)^2} + \frac{\delta_\eta^4 \Psi}{(\Delta\eta)^4} = \left(\frac{\delta_{\zeta\eta} W}{4\Delta\zeta\,\Delta\eta}\right)^2 - \frac{\delta_\zeta^2 W}{(\Delta\zeta)^2}\frac{\delta_\eta^2 W}{(\Delta\eta)^2} \qquad (2\text{-}133)$$

$$\frac{\delta_\zeta^4 W}{(\Delta\zeta)^4} + 2\frac{\delta_{\zeta\eta}^2 W}{(\Delta\zeta)^2(\Delta\eta)^2} + \frac{\delta_\eta^4 W}{(\Delta\eta)^4} = 12(1 - v^2)$$

$$\cdot \left[\frac{q_0 b^4}{Eh^4} + \frac{\delta_\zeta^2 W}{(\Delta\zeta)^2}\frac{\delta_\eta^2 \Psi}{(\Delta\eta)^2} + \frac{\delta_\eta^2 W}{(\Delta\eta)^2}\frac{\delta_\zeta^2 \Psi}{(\Delta\zeta)^2} - \frac{1}{8}\,2\frac{\delta_{\zeta\eta} W}{\Delta\zeta\,\Delta\eta}\frac{\delta_{\zeta\eta} \Psi}{\Delta\zeta\,\Delta\eta}\right] \qquad (2\text{-}134)$$

Since loading and deformation are symmetrical, only one quarter of the plate need be considered. Thus the domain of the problem is

$$0 \le \zeta \le \lambda/2 \qquad 0 \le \eta \le \tfrac{1}{2}$$

Now the domain is divided by rectangular mesh into $m \times n$ divisions as shown in Fig. 2.13. The three second central finite differences of W at the meshing point

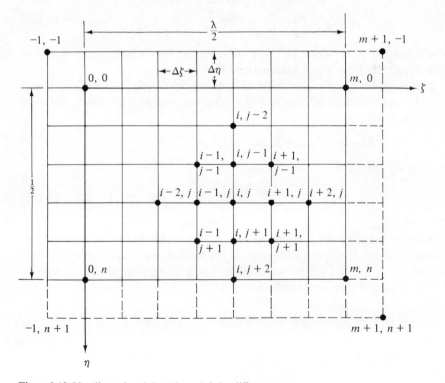

Figure 2.13 Nondimensional domain and finite difference set.

(i, j) are given by

$$\delta_\zeta^2 W_{i,j} = W_{i+1,j} - 2W_{i,j} + W_{i-1,j}$$
$$\delta_\eta^2 W_{i,j} = W_{i,j+1} - 2W_{i,j} + W_{i,j-1} \qquad (2\text{-}135)$$
$$\delta_{\zeta\eta} W_{i,j} = W_{i+1,j+1} - W_{i-1,j+1} + W_{i-1,j-1} - W_{i+1,j-1}$$

and the three fourth central finite differences by

$$\delta_\zeta^4 W_{i,j} = W_{i+2,j} - 4W_{i+1,j} + 6W_{i,j} - 4W_{i-1,j} + W_{i-2,j}$$
$$\delta_\eta^4 W_{i,j} = W_{i,j+2} - 4W_{i,j+1} + 6W_{i,j} - 4W_{i,j-1} + W_{i,j-2}$$
$$\delta_{\zeta\eta}^2 W_{i,j} = 4W_{ij} - 2(W_{i+1,j} + W_{i,j+1} + W_{i-1,j} + W_{i,j-1}) \qquad (2\text{-}136)$$
$$\qquad + W_{i+1,j+1} + W_{i-1,j+1} + W_{i-1,j-1} + W_{i+1,j-1}$$

The second and fourth central finite differences of Ψ can be similarly obtained. By substitution, equations (2-133) and (2-134) at the meshing point (i, j) yield for a square mesh $(\Delta\zeta = \Delta\eta = \Delta l)$

$$20\Psi_{i,j} - 8(\Psi_{i+1,j} + \Psi_{i,j+1} + \Psi_{i-1,j} + \Psi_{i,j-1})$$
$$\qquad + 2(\Psi_{i+1,j+1} + \Psi_{i-1,j+1} + \Psi_{i-1,j-1} + \Psi_{i+1,j-1})$$
$$\qquad + \Psi_{i+2,j} + \Psi_{i,j+2} + \Psi_{i-2,j} + \Psi_{i,j-2}$$
$$= \tfrac{1}{16}(W_{i+1,j+1} - W_{i-1,j+1} + W_{i-1,j-1} - W_{i+1,j-1})^2$$
$$\qquad - (W_{i+1,j} - 2W_{i,j} + W_{i-1,j})(W_{i,j+1} - 2W_{i,j} + W_{i,j-1}) \qquad (2\text{-}137)$$

$$20W_{i,j} - 8(W_{i+1,j} + W_{i,j+1} + W_{i-1,j} + W_{i,j-1})$$
$$\qquad + 2(W_{i+1,j+1} + W_{i-1,j+1} + W_{i-1,j-1} + W_{i+1,j-1})$$
$$\qquad + W_{i+2,j} + W_{i,j+2} + W_{i-2,j} + W_{i,j-2} = 12(1 - v^2)$$
$$\qquad \cdot \left[\frac{q_0 b^4}{Eh^4}(\Delta l)^4 + (W_{i+1,j} - 2W_{i,j} + W_{i-1,j})\right.$$
$$\qquad \cdot (\Psi_{i,j+1} - 2\Psi_{i,j} + \Psi_{i,j-1})$$
$$\qquad + (W_{i,j+1} - 2W_{i,j} + W_{i,j-1})(\Psi_{i+1,j} - 2\Psi_{i,j} + \Psi_{i-1,j})$$
$$\qquad - \tfrac{1}{8}(W_{i+1,j+1} - W_{i-1,j+1} + W_{i-1,j-1} - W_{i+1,j-1})$$
$$\qquad \left. \cdot (\Psi_{i+1,j+1} - \Psi_{i-1,j+1} + \Psi_{i-1,j-1} - \Psi_{i+1,j-1})\right] \qquad (2\text{-}138)$$

Referring to Fig. 2.13, the points along the edges $\zeta = \lambda/2$ and $\eta = \tfrac{1}{2}$ are represented by (m, j) and (i, n), respectively, and the points along the dashed lines are fictitious points placed outside the plate in order to give a better approximation to the boundary conditions. In terms of the central finite differences, the supporting conditions in equations (2-132) become

$$W_{m,j} = 0 \qquad W_{i,n} = 0$$
$$W_{m+1,j} + W_{m-1,j} = 0 \qquad W_{i,n+1} + W_{i,n-1} = 0 \tag{2-139}$$

in which the first two conditions have been used in the last two. The inplane or membrane boundary conditions transform to

$$\Psi_{m+1,j+1} - \Psi_{m-1,j+1} + \Psi_{m-1,j-1} - \Psi_{m+1,j-1} = 0$$

$$\Psi_{m,j+1} - 2\Psi_{m,j} + \Psi_{m,j-1} = -\frac{P_x b(\Delta l)^2}{Eh^3}$$

$$\Psi_{i+1,n+1} - \Psi_{i-1,n+1} + \Psi_{i-1,n-1} - \Psi_{i+1,n-1} = 0 \tag{2-140}$$

$$\Psi_{i+1,n} - 2\Psi_{i,n} + \Psi_{i-1,n} = 0$$

Examination of the finite-difference equations reveals that the number of unknown W's is equal to the number of equations in W and hence these equations will yield a unique solution for W. The number of unknown Ψ's, however, is one greater than that of equations in Ψ, and this defines the values of Ψ to within an unknown constant. Since the solution is affected only by the derivatives of Ψ, the actual values of Ψ are irrelevant. Thus the unknown constant may be defined by setting $\Psi_{m,n} = 0$ without affecting the solution in any way.

The membrane boundary conditions (2-140) are not in a convenient form and are reformulated. The boundary condition (2-132) for edge loading is integrated twice with respect to η along the loaded edge and the integration constants are evaluated from the condition of symmetry, $\partial\Psi/\partial\eta = 0$ at $\eta = 0$, and the definition, $\Psi_{m,n} = 0$ or $\Psi(\lambda/2, 1/2) = 0$. The result is

$$\Psi = -\frac{P_x b}{2Eh^3}(\eta^2 - \tfrac{1}{4}) \qquad \text{at} \quad \zeta = \frac{\lambda}{2}$$

which is the equation of a parabola. In terms of the finite differences this equation becomes

$$\Psi_{m,j} = -\frac{P_x b}{2Eh^3}(\Delta l)^2[j^2 - n^2] \tag{2-141a}$$

In the case of zero edge loading this boundary condition reduces to

$$\Psi_{m,j} = 0$$

From symmetry the condition for zero normal stress along the edge, $\eta = \tfrac{1}{2}$ in equation (2-132), transforms to

$$\Psi_{i,n} = 0 \tag{2-141b}$$

After integration and evaluation of the arbitrary constants, the condition $\partial^2 \Psi / \partial \zeta \, \partial \eta = 0$ along edges $\zeta = \lambda/2$ and $\eta = 1/2$ can be written as

$$\Psi_{m+1, j} = \Psi_{m-1, j} \tag{2-141c}$$

$$\Psi_{i, n+1} = \Psi_{i, n-1} + \Psi_{m, n+1} - \Psi_{m, n-1} \tag{2-141d}$$

In the analysis the membrane boundary conditions (2-140) are replaced by (2-141).

If equations (2-137) and (2-138) are written for each nodal point in the domain shown in Fig. 2.13, then, utilizing boundary and symmetry conditions, this results in two sets of $(m \times n)$ simultaneous linear equations each in $(m \times n)$ unknowns. In matrix notation the resulting set of equations corresponding to (2-137) can be written as

$$\mathbf{H}\Psi = \mathbf{G} \tag{2-142}$$

in which $\mathbf{H}$ is an $(m \times n)$ by $(m \times n)$ matrix of coefficients, Ψ is an $(m \times n)$ column vector of the unknown Ψ's, and $\mathbf{G}$ is an $(m \times n)$ column vector dependent on W. By treating the unknown Ψ's on the right-hand side of equation (2-138) as known quantities and transposing them to the left-hand side, the resulting set of these equations is given by

$$\mathbf{KW} = 12(1 - v^2)(\Delta l)^4 \frac{q_0 b^4}{Eh^4} \tag{2-143}$$

where $\mathbf{K}$ is an $(m \times n)$ by $(m \times n)$ matrix of coefficients depending on Ψ, and $\mathbf{W}$ is an $(m \times n)$ column vector of the unknown deflections. A solution of equations (2-142) and (2-143) is obtained by an iterative procedure. Setting the values of Ψ equal to zero reduces equation (2-143) to the small deflection equation which is, for some small value of $q_0 b^4 / Eh^4$, solved for $\mathbf{W}$. With the linear solution $\mathbf{W}^{(0)}$, equation (2-142) is solved for Ψ and the first approximation $\mathbf{W}^{(1)}$ to the nonlinear problem is computed from equation (2-143). The process is repeated until a desired accuracy would be achieved. Unfortunately, in this case convergence does not necessarily occur and an acceleration factor γ has to be employed to ensure convergence. The value of γ lies between 0 and 1. Thus we substitute $\mathbf{W} = \gamma \mathbf{W}^{(0)} + (1 - \gamma)\mathbf{W}^{(1)}$ in equation (2-142) instead of $\mathbf{W}^{(1)}$ and solve the resulting equation for Ψ, and then equation (2-143) for $\mathbf{W}$. If the old and new values of $\mathbf{W}$, denoted by $\mathbf{W}^{(n)}$ and $\mathbf{W}^{(n+1)}$ respectively, do not agree to the desired accuracy, then set $\mathbf{W} = \gamma \mathbf{W}^{(n)} + (1 - \gamma)\mathbf{W}^{(n+1)}$ in the iterative process. Once a convergent solution is obtained, we can calculate the stresses, increase pressure, extrapolate to obtain approximate values of $\mathbf{W}$, and substitute them in equation (2-142).

The value of γ requires some care in selection, especially when edge load is applied. For plates subjected to lateral load only, it was found that satisfactory convergence was obtained by taking $\gamma = 0.5$. The introduction of edge loading into the problem resulted in a failure of the solution to converge. The range of pressure over which convergence could be obtained decreased with increasing edge loading. Increasing the value of γ to 0.6 resulted in an increase in the range to some extent. It was also found necessary to use relatively small increments of edge loading to obtain convergence of the solution.

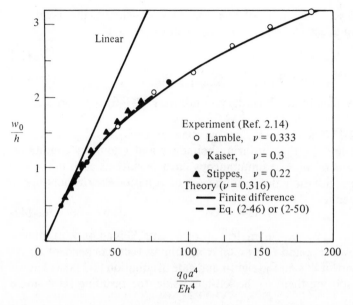

Figure 2.14 Central deflection of simply supported square plate versus uniform lateral pressure.

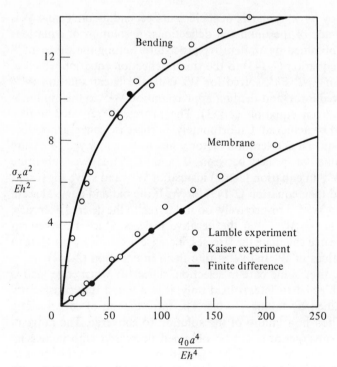

Figure 2.15 Bending and membrane stresses at center of simply supported square plate versus uniform lateral pressure.

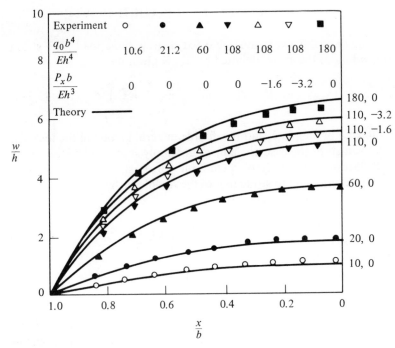

Figure 2.16 Deflection profiles along longitudinal center line of one symmetrical half rectangular plate for various pressures and edge compressions ($\lambda = 2$).

In the case of the finite-difference solution for laterally loaded plates (Ref. 2.15), it was found that the solutions converged rapidly with reducing mesh size. In the present case the same rapid convergence did not occur but the rate of convergence with reducing mesh size was considerably improved when a modification was made to the right-hand side of equation (2-142). The reasoning may be due to the fact that the computation of $\partial^2 W/\partial\zeta^2$ and $\partial^2 W/\partial\eta^2$ is made with a grid length Δl (Fig. 2.13) while that of $\partial^2 W/\partial\zeta\,\partial\eta$ is made with a grid length $2\,\Delta l$. This leads to an underestimate of $\partial^2 W/\partial\zeta\,\partial\eta$ compared with that of $\partial^2 W/\partial\zeta^2$ and $\partial^2 W/\partial\eta^2$ and a consequent lowering of the value of W. The systematic error in W may be removed by computing these three derivatives with a grid of length $\sqrt{2}\,\Delta l$.

Numerical results are presented for a square plate by dividing one symmetrical quarter of the plate into 25 square meshes, and for a rectangular plate with $\lambda = 2$ into 32 square meshes. The load-deflection curve for the square plate under uniform lateral pressure only is shown in Fig. 2.14 with experimental and previous theoretical results. The variations of membrane and bending stresses at the center of the square plate with increasing pressure are shown in Fig. 2.15 with experimental values. The deflection profiles along the longitudinal center line of the rectangular plate for various pressures and edge loadings (less than the corresponding buckling value) are compared in Fig. 2.16 with experimental results. In general a good agreement is found between theory and experiment.

2.9 RITZ METHOD FOR LATERALLY LOADED PLATE

Consider a rectangular isotropic plate subjected to transverse load. The strain energy due to bending of the plate, denoted by V_b, is given by

$$V_b = \frac{D}{2} \iint_A \{(w_{,xx} + w_{,yy})^2 - 2(1 - v)[w_{,xx}w_{,yy} - w_{,xy}^2]\} \, dx \, dy \qquad (2\text{-}144)$$

in which A is the area of the plate, and the double integral involving the terms in the brackets will vanish in the case of clamped or simply supported edges. In the case of large deflections the effect of membrane forces should be taken into account. The strain energy due to stretching of the middle surface, denoted by V_s, may be expressed in terms of displacements

$$V_s = \frac{Eh}{4(1 - v^2)} \iint_A \{2(u_{,x}^\circ + \tfrac{1}{2}w_{,x}^2)^2 + 2(v_{,y}^\circ + \tfrac{1}{2}w_{,y}^2)^2$$

$$+ 4v(u_{,x}^\circ + \tfrac{1}{2}w_{,x}^2)(v_{,y}^\circ + \tfrac{1}{2}w_{,y}^2)$$

$$+ (1 - v)(u_{,y}^\circ + v_{,x}^\circ + w_{,x}w_{,y})^2\} \, dx \, dy \qquad (2\text{-}145)$$

This strain energy can be also expressed in terms of the transverse deflection and a stress function as in Sec. 4.4 if desired. The potential energy of the total lateral load is

$$W = \iint_A qw \, dx \, dy \qquad (2\text{-}146)$$

The total potential energy of the elastic system is

$$\Pi = V_b + V_s - W \qquad (2\text{-}147)$$

When this energy expression is minimized with respect to the variations in the three-displacement functions, the equilibrium equations (2-51) to (2-53) can be obtained. Now the Ritz method is used in obtaining approximate solutions for nonlinear bending of a uniformly loaded plate with two sets of boundary conditions.

a Simply Supported Square Plate with Zero Boundary Normal Stress and Tangential Displacement

In such case the boundary conditions can be written as

$$v^\circ = w = w_{,xx} = 0 \qquad \varepsilon_x^\circ = \varepsilon_y^\circ = 0 \qquad \text{at} \quad x = 0, a$$

$$u^\circ = w = w_{,yy} = 0 \qquad \varepsilon_y^\circ = \varepsilon_x^\circ = 0 \qquad \text{at} \quad y = 0, a \qquad (2\text{-}148)$$

in which the two midsurface strains are related to two inplane displacements u° and v° and transverse deflection w by equations (1-42).

The boundary conditions (2-148) are satisfied if we take (Ref. 2.16)

$$w = \sum_{m=1,3}^{\infty} \sum_{n=1,3}^{\infty} A_{mn} \sin \frac{m\pi x}{a} \sin \frac{n\pi y}{a}$$

$$u^{\circ} = -\frac{a}{2\pi} g(y) \sin \frac{2\pi x}{a}$$

$$+ \sum_{m=1,3}^{\infty} \sum_{n=1,3}^{\infty} B_{mn} \cos \frac{m\pi x}{a} \sin \frac{n\pi y}{a} \qquad (2\text{-}149)$$

$$v^{\circ} = -\frac{a}{2\pi} f(x) \sin \frac{2\pi y}{a}$$

$$+ \sum_{m=1,3}^{\infty} \sum_{n=1,3}^{\infty} B_{nm} \sin \frac{m\pi x}{a} \cos \frac{n\pi y}{a}$$

In these expressions $f(x)$ and $g(y)$ are defined by

$$f(x) = \tfrac{1}{2} w_{,y}^2 \qquad \text{along} \quad y = 0 \quad \text{and} \quad y = a$$
$$g(y) = \tfrac{1}{2} w_{,x}^2 \qquad \text{along} \quad x = 0 \quad \text{and} \quad x = a \qquad (2\text{-}150)$$

which are added to the expressions for u° and v°, respectively, in order to satisfy the last second boundary condition along each edge.

It is observed that expressions (2-149) also satisfy the condition of symmetry, $w(x, y) = w(y, x)$ and $u^{\circ}(x, y) = v^{\circ}(y, x)$. Taking the first four terms in each truncated series we have

$$w = A_{11} \sin \frac{\pi x}{a} \sin \frac{\pi y}{a} + A_{13}\left(\sin \frac{\pi x}{a} \sin \frac{3\pi y}{a} + \sin \frac{3\pi x}{a} \sin \frac{\pi y}{a} \right)$$

$$+ A_{33} \sin \frac{3\pi x}{a} \sin \frac{3\pi y}{a}$$

$$u^{\circ} = B_{11} \cos \frac{\pi x}{a} \sin \frac{\pi y}{a} + B_{13} \cos \frac{\pi x}{a} \sin \frac{3\pi y}{a} + B_{31} \cos \frac{3\pi x}{a} \sin \frac{\pi y}{a}$$

$$+ B_{33} \cos \frac{3\pi x}{a} \sin \frac{3\pi y}{a}$$

$$- \frac{\pi}{4a} \sin \frac{2\pi x}{a} \left[\alpha^2 \sin^2 \frac{\pi y}{a} + \alpha\beta\left(\cos \frac{2\pi y}{a} - \cos \frac{4\pi y}{a} \right) + \beta^2 \sin^2 \frac{3\pi y}{a} \right]$$

$$\qquad (2\text{-}151)$$

$$v^{\circ} = B_{11} \sin \frac{\pi x}{a} \cos \frac{\pi y}{a} + B_{13} \sin \frac{3\pi x}{a} \cos \frac{\pi y}{a} + B_{31} \sin \frac{\pi x}{a} \cos \frac{3\pi y}{a}$$

$$+ B_{33} \sin \frac{3\pi x}{a} \cos \frac{3\pi y}{a} - \frac{\pi}{4a} \sin \frac{2\pi y}{a}$$

$$\cdot \left[\alpha^2 \sin^2 \frac{\pi x}{a} + \alpha\beta\left(\cos \frac{2\pi x}{a} - \cos \frac{4\pi x}{a} \right) + \beta^2 \sin^2 \frac{3\pi x}{a} \right]$$

where

$$\alpha = A_{11} + 3A_{13} \qquad \beta = A_{13} + 3A_{33} \qquad (2\text{-}152)$$

Substituting equations (2-151) into (2-147) and performing the integration, we then minimize the resulting energy expression by setting

$$\Pi_{,A_{mn}} = 0 \quad \text{and} \quad \Pi_{,B_{mn}} = 0 \qquad (2\text{-}153)$$

Equations (2-153) yield a set of simultaneous algebraic equations which are linear in the B's and cubic in the A's. Elimination of the B coefficients and the parameter $q_0 a_0^4/Dh$ in which a_0 is the half-length of the plate leads to a set of simultaneous cubic equations for the A coefficients. The number of equations in this set is one less than the number of the A coefficients. Thus the values of the A's can be obtained by the Newton-Raphson method for arbitrarily selecting values for one of the A's, say A_{11}. The corresponding values of $q_0 a_0^4/Dh$ and the B coefficients could have been already obtained by substituting back into the original equations. Stress resultants and couples can be calculated from equations (1-121) to (1-123).

Three solutions were carried out, first, with $A_{13} = A_{33} = B_{13} = B_{31} = B_{33} = 0$; second, with $A_{33} = B_{33} = 0$; and third, with all of the terms in equations (2-151). The result in the load-deflection curve obtained from the four-term solution is not substantially different from the one-term and three-term solutions. The curve obtained from the three-term solution for a square plate with $v = 0.3$ is shown in Fig. 2.17 for comparison with the solution ($v = 0.316$) given in Sec. 2.7

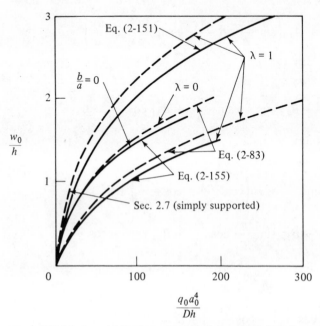

Figure 2.17 Maximum deflections of square plate and infinite strip versus uniform transverse pressure.

for a simply supported square plate with constant edge displacement. The difference between these two curves partially arises from different inplane boundary conditions.

b Rigidly Clamped Rectangular Plate with Immovable Edges

The appropriate boundary conditions for the plate are given by

$$u^\circ = v^\circ = w = w_{,x} = 0 \qquad \text{at} \quad x = \pm \frac{a}{2}$$

$$u^\circ = v^\circ = w = w_{,y} = 0 \qquad \text{at} \quad y = \pm \frac{b}{2}$$

(2-154)

For the determination of three displacements satisfying these conditions in the Ritz method, polynomials (Ref. 2.9) may be employed. On the other hand, the following functions (Ref. 2.17) are equally admissible

$$u^\circ = \sum_{m=2,4}^{\infty} \sum_{n=1,3}^{\infty} A_{mn} \sin \frac{m\pi x}{a} \cos \frac{n\pi y}{b}$$

$$v^\circ = \sum_{m=1,3}^{\infty} \sum_{n=2,4}^{\infty} B_{mn} \cos \frac{m\pi x}{a} \sin \frac{n\pi y}{b}$$

(2-155)

$$w = \sum_{m=2,4}^{\infty} \sum_{n=2,4}^{\infty} C_{mn} \left[\cos \frac{m\pi x}{a} - (-1)^{m/2} \right] \left[\cos \frac{n\pi y}{b} - (-1)^{n/2} \right]$$

Owing to some orthogonal functions involved, such a representation simplifies the calculation of total potential energy to some extent. Following a similar calculation in the foregoing case, the Fourier coefficients A_{mn}, B_{mn}, and C_{mn} in these truncated series (2-155) can be determined.

Numerical results are obtained for the two extreme cases of a square plate with $b/a = 1$ and the infinite strip with $b/a = 0$. The Poisson ratio is taken to be $v = 0.3$. For the square plate, the four terms with the coefficients $A_{21} = B_{12}$, $A_{23} = B_{32}$, $A_{41} = B_{14}$, and $A_{43} = B_{43}$ in u° and v°, and the three terms with C_{22}, $C_{24} = C_{42}$ in w are considered. For the infinite strip, $u^\circ = 0$, and the two terms with B_2, B_4 in v° and C_2, C_4 in w of the following series are retained

$$v^\circ = \sum_{m=2,4}^{\infty} B_m \sin \frac{m\pi y}{b}$$

$$w = \sum_{m=2,4}^{\infty} C_m \left[\cos \frac{m\pi y}{b} - (-1)^{m/2} \right]$$

(2-156)

The nondimensional maximum deflection is plotted in Fig. 2.17 against the load parameter, for $b/a = 1$ and 0. A comparison of these results with those obtained by the method of perturbation such as solution (2-83) shows that a fair agreement is found between these results. It may be noted that solution (2-83) is in good agreement with experimental data (Ref. 2.8) and that the theoretical values are generally higher than the experimental values. Thus the experimental values will fall between the corresponding load-deflection curves obtained from the Ritz method and the perturbation technique for a clamped plate.

2.10 MARGUERRE EQUATIONS FOR INITIALLY DEFLECTED PLATES

The nonlinear theory of curved plates due to initial curvatures is much more complicated than the corresponding theory of flat plates. In 1938 Marguerre (Ref. 2.18) developed an approximate nonlinear theory of isotropic plates with initially slight curvatures or generally shallow shells by use of the energy method. This approximate theory has been used extensively in the nonlinear analysis of shallow shells as the von Kármán nonlinear theory of flat plates used in the plate analysis.

Let us consider a volume element $h\,dx\,dy$ cut out of an initially deflected plate (Fig. 2.18). If the shape of the middle surface of the undeformed plate is defined by $\xi(x, y)$ and if the vertical distance of an arbitrary point measured from the middle surface is denoted by $z(x, y)$, the position vector of the point in the undeformed state is

$$\mathbf{r}_0 = x\mathbf{i} + y\mathbf{j} + (\xi + z)\mathbf{k} \tag{2-157}$$

in which $\mathbf{i}$, $\mathbf{j}$, $\mathbf{k}$ are unit vectors along three cartesian coordinate axes x, y, z. To relate the displacements u, v, w of the point to the displacements u°, v° and w° in the middle surface, we adopt Kirchhoff's hypothesis that during bending, straight fibers initially normal to the middle surface remain straight and normal to that surface. Consequently

$$u = u^\circ - zw_{,x} \qquad v = v^\circ - zw_{,y} \qquad w = w^\circ \tag{2-158}$$

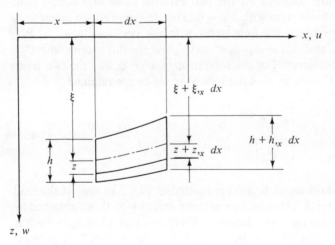

z, w

Figure 2.18 Geometry of curved plate element.

which are the von Kármán displacement assumptions for flat plates given by equations (1-39). The position vector (2-157) in the deformed state is thus given by

$$\mathbf{r} = (x + u^\circ - zw_{,x})\mathbf{i} + (y + v^\circ - zw_{,y})\mathbf{j} + (\xi + z + w)\mathbf{k} \qquad (2\text{-}159)$$

In the formulation of the strain energy of the curved plate, we consider a differential linear element ds_0. By virtue of equations (2-157) and (2-158) the square of the length of the element before deformation is given by

$$
\begin{aligned}
ds_0^2 = d\mathbf{r}_0 \cdot d\mathbf{r}_0 = {} & \{1 + [(\xi + z)_{,x}]^2\} \, dx^2 \\
& + 2(\xi + z)_{,x}(\xi + z)_{,y} \, dx \, dy \\
& + \{1 + [(\xi + z)_{,y}]^2\} \, dy^2 \qquad (2\text{-}160)
\end{aligned}
$$

and after deformation by

$$
\begin{aligned}
ds^2 = d\mathbf{r} \cdot d\mathbf{r} = {} & [\{1 + u^\circ_{,x} - (zw_{,x})_{,x}\}^2 + \{v^\circ_{,x} - (zw_{,y})_{,x}\}^2 \\
& + (\xi + z + w)_{,x}^2] \, dx^2 + 2[\{1 + u^\circ_{,x} - (zw_{,x})_{,x}\} \\
& \cdot \{u^\circ_{,y} - (zw_{,x})_{,y}\} + \{v^\circ_{,x} - (zw_{,y})_{,x}\} \\
& \cdot \{1 - v^\circ_{,y} - (zw_{,y})_{,y}\} \\
& + (\xi + z + w)_{,x}(\xi + z + w)_{,y}] \, dx \, dy \\
& + [\{u^\circ_{,y} - (zw_{,x})_{,y}\}^2 \\
& + \{1 + v^\circ_{,y} - (zw_{,y})_{,y}\}^2 + (\xi + z + w)_{,y}^2] \, dy^2 \qquad (2\text{-}161)
\end{aligned}
$$

As a measure of strain we write as in equation (1-4)

$$ds^2 - ds_0^2 = 2(\varepsilon_x \, dx^2 + \varepsilon_{xy} \, dx \, dy + \varepsilon_y \, dy^2) \qquad (2\text{-}162)$$

where

$$
\begin{aligned}
\varepsilon_x &= u^\circ_{,x} + \tfrac{1}{2}[(u^\circ_{,x})^2 + (v^\circ_{,x})^2 + w_{,x}^2] + \xi_{,x} w_{,x} - zw_{,xx} + \ldots \ldots \\
\varepsilon_{xy} &= u^\circ_{,y} + v^\circ_{,x} + u^\circ_{,x} u^\circ_{,y} + v^\circ_{,x} v^\circ_{,y} + w_{,x} w_{,y} + \xi_{,y} w_{,x} \\
&\quad + \xi_{,x} w_{,y} - 2zw_{,xy} + \ldots \ldots \\
\varepsilon_y &= v^\circ_{,y} + \tfrac{1}{2}[(u^\circ_{,y})^2 + (v^\circ_{,y})^2 + w_{,y}^2] + \xi_{,y} w_{,y} - zw_{,yy} + \ldots \ldots
\end{aligned}
\qquad (2\text{-}163)
$$

In these expressions the dots denote the terms of the type $u^\circ_{,x}(zw_{,x})_{,x}$ and $(zw_{,x})_{,x}^2$ which are usually neglected as small quantities of higher order, and the terms such as $z_{,x}$ varying with variable thickness of the plate have been dropped out by the assumption of constant thickness. It is seen that ε_{ij} represent components of the strain. The total strain energy of the curved plate denoted by V is then given by

$$V = \frac{E}{2(1 - v^2)} \iint_A \left\{ \int_{-h/2}^{h/2} [(\varepsilon_x + \varepsilon_y)^2 - 2(1 - v)(\varepsilon_x \varepsilon_y - \tfrac{1}{4}\varepsilon_{xy}^2)] \, dz \right\} dx \, dy$$

$$(2\text{-}164)$$

where A is the area of the plate. Using expressions (2-163) and performing integration with respect to z we obtain

$$V = \frac{Eh}{2(1 - v^2)} \iint\limits_A [(\varepsilon_x^\circ + \varepsilon_y^\circ)^2 - 2(1 - v)\{\varepsilon_x^\circ \varepsilon_y^\circ - \tfrac{1}{4}(\varepsilon_{xy}^\circ)^2\}] \, dx \, dy$$

$$+ \frac{D}{2} \iint\limits_A [(w_{,xx} + w_{,yy})^2 - 2(1 - v)(w_{,xx} w_{,yy} - w_{,xy}^2)] \, dx \, dy \quad (2\text{-}165)$$

where

$$\varepsilon_x^\circ = u_{,x}^\circ + \tfrac{1}{2}[(u_{,x}^\circ)^2 + (v_{,x}^\circ)^2 + (w_{,x})^2] + \xi_{,x} w_{,x}$$

$$\varepsilon_y^\circ = v_{,y}^\circ + \tfrac{1}{2}[(u_{,y}^\circ)^2 + (v_{,y}^\circ)^2 + (w_{,y})^2] + \xi_{,y} w_{,y} \quad (2\text{-}166)$$

$$\varepsilon_{xy}^\circ = u_{,y}^\circ + v_{,x}^\circ + u_{,x}^\circ u_{,y}^\circ + v_{,x}^\circ v_{,y}^\circ + w_{,x} w_{,y} + \xi_{,y} w_{,x} + \xi_{,x} w_{,y}$$

In expression (2-165), the second part represents the strain energy due to bending as a result of Kirchhoff's hypothesis (2-158), and the first the strain energy due to stretching of the middle surface.

It may be observed that the terms quadratic in displacements u° and v° in expressions (2-166) are small compared to the other terms in the case of a plate with sufficiently slight curvature. This arises from the fact that the behavior of a slightly curved plate is considerably similar to that of a flat plate. Equations (2-166) thus may be simplified to yield

$$\varepsilon_x^\circ = u_{,x}^\circ + \tfrac{1}{2}w_{,x}^2 + \xi_{,x} w_{,x}$$

$$\varepsilon_y^\circ = v_{,y}^\circ + \tfrac{1}{2}w_{,y}^2 + \xi_{,y} w_{,y} \quad (2\text{-}167)$$

$$\varepsilon_{xy}^\circ = u_{,y}^\circ + v_{,x}^\circ + w_{,x} w_{,y} + \xi_{,y} w_{,x} + \xi_{,x} w_{,y}$$

Three equations of equilibrium are obtained from the principle of minimum potential energy

$$\delta(V - W) = 0 \quad (2\text{-}168)$$

where W is the potential energy of the external forces. If, for simplicity, the displacements are prescribed along the boundary, then δu°, δv°, δw, and hence δW vanish at the boundary. The potential energy of the applied transverse load of intensity $q(x, y)$ is given by

$$W = \iint\limits_A q(x, y)w \, dx \, dy \quad (2\text{-}169)$$

By virtue of equations (2-165) and Hooke's law, the total potential energy of the system is, in the absence of body forces,

$$V - W = \frac{h}{2} \iint\limits_A (\sigma_x^m \varepsilon_x^\circ + \sigma_y^m \varepsilon_y^\circ + \sigma_{xy}^m \varepsilon_{xy}^\circ) \, dx \, dy$$

$$+ \frac{D}{2} \iint\limits_A [(w_{,xx} + w_{,yy})^2 - 2(1 - v)(w_{,xx} w_{,yy} - w_{,xy}^2)] \, dx \, dy$$

$$- \iint\limits_A qw \, dx \, dy \quad (2\text{-}170)$$

Inserting equations (2-170) in (2-168), taking variations of displacements u°, v° and w, and integrating by parts, the three Euler equations are obtained in the form

$$\sigma^m_{x,x} + \sigma^m_{xy,y} = 0 \tag{2-171}$$

$$\sigma^m_{xy,x} + \sigma^m_{y,y} = 0 \tag{2-172}$$

$$\frac{D}{h}\nabla^2\nabla^2 w - \sigma^m_x(\xi_{,xx} + w_{,xx}) - \sigma^m_y(\xi_{,yy} + w_{,yy}) - 2\sigma^m_{xy}(\xi_{,xy} + w_{,xy}) = q(x, y) \tag{2-173}$$

Equations (2-171) and (2-172) are identically satisfied by introduction of the Airy stress function F

$$\sigma^m_x = F_{,yy} \qquad \sigma^m_y = F_{,xx} \qquad \sigma^m_{xy} = -F_{,xy} \tag{2-174}$$

Introducing the condition of compatibility and substituting equations (2-167) and (2-174) into this condition and equation (2-173), we obtain the following system of equations

$$\nabla^4 F = E[(w_{,xy})^2 - w_{,xx}w_{,yy} + 2\xi_{,xy}w_{,xy} - \xi_{,xx}w_{,yy} - \xi_{,yy}w_{,xx}] \tag{2-175}$$

$$\nabla^4 w = \frac{h}{D}\left[\frac{q}{h} + F_{,yy}(\xi_{,xx} + w_{,xx}) + F_{,xx}(\xi_{,yy} + w_{,yy})\right.$$

$$\left. - 2F_{,xy}(\xi_{,xy} + w_{,xy})\right] \tag{2-176}$$

These equations, which constitute an eighth-order system of differential equations, are a generalization of the von Kármán plate equations (2-1) and (2-2). They are applicable to thin plates or shells which do not differ greatly in shape from a plane before and after loading.

2.11 INITIALLY DEFLECTED PLATE UNDER TRANSVERSE LOAD

An initially deflected rectangular plate under transverse load is essentially a large deflection problem in which the membrane stresses cannot be neglected. In a system of cartesian coordinates coinciding with those of an initially flat plate, the shape of the middle surface of the initially deflected plate when unstressed is defined by ξ, some function of x and y. The differential equations governing the large deflection behavior of the plate are given by equations (2-175) and (2-176). In this analysis we are interested in developing a method such that the solutions for flat plates discussed previously can be applied to initially deflected plates. In other words, the method of solution (Refs. 2.19, 2.20) consists of determining the conditions under which equations (2-175) and (2-176) for the initially deflected plate, and equations (2-1) and (2-2) for the initially flat plate (having the same material properties as for the initially deflected plate), are similar such that a solution of the flat plate equations is also a solution of the initially deflected plate equations.

Let us assume that the initial deflection ξ is proportional to the deflection w under loading and can be defined by

$$\xi = kw \tag{2-177}$$

in which k is a constant. Upon substitution equations (2-175) and (2-176) become

$$\nabla^4 F = E(1 + 2k)[w_{,xy}^2 - w_{,xx} w_{,yy}] \tag{2-178}$$

$$\nabla^4 w = \frac{q}{D} + \frac{h}{D}(1 + k)[w_{,xx} F_{,yy} + w_{,yy} F_{,xx} - 2w_{,xy} F_{,xy}] \tag{2-179}$$

A comparison of equations (2-178) and (2-179) for the initially deflected plate with equations (2-1) and (2-2) for the initially flat plate shows that under certain circumstances the two sets of equations are similar. Therefore, we shall determine the conditions which must be fulfilled in order that the following relations hold:

$$F_f = C_1 F \qquad w_f = C_2 w \tag{2-180}$$

in which C_1 and C_2 are constants and the subscript f refers to the initially flat plate. These variables are substituted into equations (2-1) and (2-2), and then comparison with equations (2-178) and (2-179) shows that relations (2-180) hold if

$$\frac{C_2^2}{C_1} = 1 + 2k \qquad \frac{h_f}{h} = \sqrt{\frac{C_1}{1 + k}}$$

$$\frac{1}{C_2} \frac{q_f a_0^4}{D_f h_f} \frac{h_f}{h} = \frac{q a_0^4}{Dh} \tag{2-181}$$

in which a_0 is the half-width of the plate and the last expression has been expressed in nondimensional form for the latter use. If relations (2-181) are satisfied by an appropriate choice of the quantities C_1, C_2, h_f/h, and q_f/q, the two sets of governing equations are identically equal. In that case a solution of the governing equations of the initially flat plate also involves that of the initially deflected plate. The fact that the governing equations are satisfied implies that the conditions for equilibrium and continuity are fulfilled. On the other hand it is not certain beforehand that the boundary conditions for the initially deflected plate are satisfied if they are fulfilled for the initially flat plate. This question should therefore be examined separately in each particular case.

If the plates are rigidly clamped along their edges, the boundary conditions given by equations (2-55) are associated with the inplane displacements u° and v° and deflection w. In view of equations (1-42) we have, for an initially flat plate,

$$E[u_{f,x}^\circ + \tfrac{1}{2}(w_{f,x})^2] = \sigma_{xf}^m - v\sigma_{yf}^m$$

$$E[v_{f,y}^\circ + \tfrac{1}{2}(w_{f,y})^2] = \sigma_{yf}^m - v\sigma_{xf}^m \tag{2-182}$$

$$G(u_{f,y}^\circ + v_{f,x}^\circ + w_{f,x} w_{f,y}) = \sigma_{xyf}^m$$

The corresponding relations for the initially deflected plate are, from equation (2-167) and (2-177),

$$E[u^\circ_{,x} + \tfrac{1}{2}w^2_{,x}(1 + 2k)] = \sigma^m_x - v\sigma^m_y$$
$$E[v^\circ_{,y} + \tfrac{1}{2}w^2_{,y}(1 + 2k)] = \sigma^m_y - v\sigma^m_x \qquad (2\text{-}183)$$
$$G[u^\circ_{,y} + v^\circ_{,x} + w_{,x}w_{,y}(1 + 2k)] = \sigma^m_{xy}$$

Integrating equations (2-182) and (2-183) and taking into account equations (2-180) and (2-181) leads to

$$u^\circ = \frac{u^\circ_f}{C_1} \qquad v^\circ = \frac{v^\circ_f}{C_1} \qquad (2\text{-}184)$$

in which the two arbitrary functions of integration representing rigid-body displacements have been discarded and which indicate that the two inplane displacements in the initially deflected plate are conformable to those in the initially flat plate. Consequently, the boundary conditions (2-55), for the initially deflected plate are likewise satisfied if those for the initially flat plate are satisfied.

Introduction of the first two of equations (2-181) into the last yields

$$\frac{qa_0^4}{Dh} = \left(\frac{qa_0^4}{Dh}\right)_f \cdot \frac{1}{\sqrt{(1 + k)(1 + 2k)}} \qquad (2\text{-}185)$$

By virtue of the second equations of (2-180) and (2-181), the relation between two central deflections is

$$\frac{w_0}{h} = \left(\frac{w_0}{h}\right)_f \cdot \frac{1}{\sqrt{(1 + k)(1 + 2k)}} \qquad (2\text{-}186)$$

On the determination of constant k, the initial central deflection ξ_0 is expressed in terms of the plate thickness, by constant α, i.e.,

$$\xi_0 = \alpha h = kw_0 \qquad (2\text{-}187)$$

From equations (2-186) and (2-187)

$$k = \alpha\sqrt{(1 + k)(1 + 2k)} \Big/ \left(\frac{w_0}{h}\right)_f \qquad (2\text{-}188)$$

from which k can be determined. Hence the relationship between qa_0^4/Dh and w_0/h can be determined in relation to that between $(qa_0^4/Dh)_f$ and $(w_0/h)_f$ from equations (2-185) and (2-186).

The membrane and extreme-fiber bending stresses in the x direction are for the initially flat plate

$$(\sigma^m_x)_f = F_{f,yy}$$
$$(\sigma^b_x)_f = \frac{Eh_f}{2(1 - v^2)}(w_{,xx} + vw_{,yy})_f \qquad (2\text{-}189)$$

Using equations (2-180) and (2-181) the corresponding stresses for the initially deflected plate can be written in the nondimensional form

$$\frac{\sigma_x^m a_0^2}{Eh^2} = \left(\frac{\sigma_x^m a_0^2}{Eh^2}\right)_f \frac{1}{1+k}$$

$$\frac{\sigma_x^b a_0^2}{Eh^2} = \left(\frac{\sigma_x^b a_0^2}{Eh^2}\right)_f \frac{1}{\sqrt{(1+k)(1+2k)}}$$

(2-190)

The load-deflection curve and bending and membrane stresses for the plate having an initial central deflection αh can be determined provided that the corresponding flat plate solution is found.

If the perturbation technique is used in obtaining a solution for the initially flat plate under uniform pressure q_0, as given in Sec. 2.5, the series solution is approximated by

$$\left(\frac{q_0 a_0^4}{Dh}\right)_f = p_1 \left(\frac{w_0}{h}\right)_f + p_3 \left(\frac{w_0}{h}\right)_f^3$$

$$\left(\frac{\sigma_x^b a_0^2}{Eh^2}\right)_f = b_1 \left(\frac{w_0}{h}\right)_f + b_3 \left(\frac{w_0}{h}\right)_f^3 \qquad \text{at} \quad y = 0 \qquad (2\text{-}191)$$

$$\left(\frac{\sigma_x^m a_0^2}{Eh^2}\right)_f = c_2 \left(\frac{w_0}{h}\right)_f^2 \qquad \text{at} \quad y = 0$$

in which the values of coefficients p_1, p_3, b_1, b_3 and c_2 needed in the solution are given in Table 2.2 for Poisson's ratio $v = \frac{1}{3}$. The results for $\lambda < 0.5$ are not shown because plates having $\lambda \leq 0.5$ could be regarded as behaving as infinitely long plates. Figure 2.19 shows the load-deflection curves for an initially deflected rectangular plate having the initial central deflection $\alpha = 0$, 1.0, 2.5 and the aspect ratio $\lambda = 0.5, 0.8, 1.0$.

If the generalized Fourier series solution given in Sec. 2.4 is used in obtaining a solution for the initially flat plate, then a solution for the initially deflected plate under partial loading, hydrostatic pressure, or single concentrated load can be obtained from equations (2-185), (2-186), (2-188), and (2-190). The present method is quite general. Any solution for the initially flat plate can be used in obtaining

Table 2.2 Coefficients in equations (2-191)

λ	p_1	p_3	b_1	b_3	c_2
1.0	50.3815	24.3772	5.5161	0.7182	4.2435
0.9	41.5860	20.1804	5.3608	0.4914	3.6893
0.8	35.0452	17.2136	5.1138	0.4374	3.0667
0.7	30.3550	15.3521	4.9090	0.5184	2.4336
0.6	27.1842	14.4770	4.7461	0.7452	1.8427
0.5	25.2606	14.3645	4.6246	0.8370	1.3462
0.0	24.0000	17.5543	4.5000	1.0962	0.6857

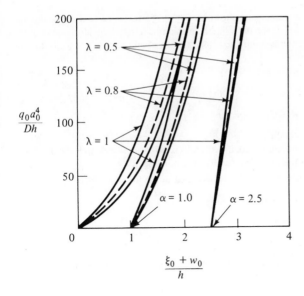

$\dfrac{q_0 a_0^4}{Dh}$

$\lambda = 0.5$

$\lambda = 0.8$

$\lambda = 1$

$\alpha = 1.0$

$\alpha = 2.5$

$\dfrac{\xi_0 + w_0}{h}$

Figure 2.19 Total central deflection of initially deflected plate for various aspect ratios and initial central deflections.

the corresponding solutions for the initially deflected plate as soon as the stresses and displacements in a curved plate are in proportion to those for the corresponding flat plate.

PROBLEMS

2.1 Derive the complementary function F_c given by equation (2-26).

2.2 Consider the set of equations (2-1) to (2-5). Taking $v = 0.316$, $\lambda = 1.0$ and $m = n = p = q = 1$ in equations (2-4) and (2-5) and applying Galerkin's method to equations (2-1) and (2-2), obtain an approximate relationship between uniform lateral pressure q_0 and central deflection w_0, and compare the numerical results with those given by curve (a) of Fig. 2.2.

2.3 A simply supported isotropic rectangular plate shown in Fig. 2.11 is subjected to a concentrated load P at its center. If the central deflection is denoted by w_0, it can be shown that the displacement functions

$$u^\circ = \frac{\pi w_0^2}{16a}\left(\cos\frac{2\pi y}{b} - 1 + v\lambda^2\right)\sin\frac{2\pi x}{a}$$

$$v^\circ = \frac{\pi w_0^2}{16b}\left(\cos\frac{2\pi x}{a} - 1 + \frac{v}{\lambda^2}\right)\sin\frac{2\pi y}{b}$$

$$w = w_0 \sin\frac{\pi x}{a}\sin\frac{\pi y}{b}$$

satisfy the two inplane equilibrium equations (2-51) and (2-52) and the following boundary conditions

$$w = w_{,xx} = u^\circ = \sigma_{xy}^m = 0 \qquad \text{at} \quad x = 0, a$$

$$w = w_{,yy} = v^\circ = \sigma_{xy}^m = 0 \qquad \text{at} \quad y = 0, b$$

where σ_{xy}^m is the membrane shear stress.

Find an approximate relationship between concentrated load and central deflection for moderately large deflections of the plate.

2.4 A rigidly clamped isotropic rectangular plate shown in Fig. 2.1 is subjected to a uniformly distributed load of intensity q_0. As an approximate solution to the moderately large deflections of the plate, the transverse deflection w and the two inplane displacements u° and v° may be assumed in the form

$$u^\circ = Ax(a_0^2 - x^2)(b_0^2 - y^2)$$

$$v^\circ = By(a_0^2 - x^2)(b_0^2 - y^2)$$

$$w = C(a_0^2 - x^2)^2(b_0^2 - y^2)^2$$

which satisfy the required boundary conditions.

Use the Ritz energy method to obtain the load-deflection relation for $\lambda = 1$ and $v = 0.316$ and compare the result so obtained with the graphical results shown in Fig. 2.7.

2.5 In Prob. 2.4 the displacement components are now assumed in the following form

$$u^\circ = Ax(a_0^2 - x^2)(b_0^2 - y^2)^2$$

$$v^\circ = By(a_0^2 - x^2)^2(b_0^2 - y^2)$$

$$w = C(a_0^2 - x^2)^2(b_0^2 - y^2)^2$$

(*a*) Verify that these displacement functions satisfy the following boundary conditions:

$$w = w_{,x} = u^\circ = \sigma_{xy}^m = 0 \qquad \text{at} \quad x = \pm a_0$$

$$w = w_{,y} = v^\circ = \sigma_{xy}^m = 0 \qquad \text{at} \quad y = \pm b_0$$

(*b*) Solve this boundary-value problem and compare the numerical results with those obtained in Prob. 2.4.

2.6 In view of equations (1-42) and (2-147), the total potential energy of a laterally loaded isotropic plate with moderately large deflections can be written as

$$\Pi = \frac{D}{2} \iint_A \left\{ (w_{,xx} + w_{,yy})^2 + \frac{12}{h} e_1^2 - 2(1 - v) \right.$$

$$\left. \cdot \left[w_{,xx} w_{,yy} - w_{,xy}^2 + \frac{12}{h^2} e_2 \right] \right\} dx\, dy - \iint_A qw\, dx\, dy$$

where

$$e_1 = \varepsilon_x^\circ + \varepsilon_y^\circ \qquad e_2 = \varepsilon_x^\circ \varepsilon_y^\circ - \tfrac{1}{4}(\varepsilon_{xy}^\circ)^2$$

According to Berger's hypothesis (Ref. 1.32), the second strain invariant e_2 may be disregarded as compared to the square of the first strain invariant e_1 without appreciably impairing the accuracy of the results. The Euler-Lagrange equations thus derived from the variational equation are given by

$$e_{1,x} = 0 \qquad e_{1,y} = 0$$

$$\nabla^4 w - \frac{12}{h^2}[(e_1 w_{,x})_{,x} + (e_1 w_{,y})_{,y}] = \frac{q}{D}$$

in which the first two equations require e_1 to be a constant. Thus the last equation becomes

$$\nabla^4 w - \xi^2 \nabla^2 w = \frac{q}{D} \qquad\qquad (a)$$

$$\xi^2 = \frac{12}{h^2}\left(u_{,x}^\circ + v_{,y}^\circ + \tfrac{1}{2}w_{,x}^2 + \tfrac{1}{2}w_{,y}^2\right) \qquad\qquad (b)$$

Equations (*a*) and (*b*) are the approximate equations due to Berger. Once w is determined from these equations, the inplane displacements u° and v° can be determined from equations (1-117) and (1-118).

Use Berger's approach to solve the boundary-value problem in Prob. 2.4 and compare the load-deflection relation thus obtained for $v = 0.316$ and $\lambda = 1$ with the graphical results shown in Fig. 2.7.

2.7 A loosely clamped isotropic rectangular plate (Fig. 2.1) under uniform lateral load is subjected to a nonuniform temperature distribution as follows

$$T = \left[C_1 + C_2 \left(\frac{a_0^2 - x_0^2}{a_0^2} \right) \left(\frac{b_0^2 - y_0^2}{b_0^2} \right) \right] \left(1 + \frac{2z}{3h} \right)$$

where T is the temperature change from the initial state and where C_1 and C_2 are two known constants. The governing equations can be obtained from Prob. 1.2. An approximate solution is assumed in the form

$$w = w_{11} X_1(x) Y_1(y)$$

$$F = F_{11} X_1(x) Y_1(y)$$

where X_1 and Y_1 are defined in equations (2-5).

Evaluate the coefficients w_{11} and F_{11} and also the thermal effect on the static large deflection behavior of the plate.

REFERENCES

2.1. K. T. Sundara Raja Iyengar and M. M. Naqvi: Large Deflections of Rectangular Plates, *Int. J. Non-Linear Mech.*, vol. 1, Pergamon Press, pp. 109–122, 1966.

2.2. C. Y. Chia and M. K. Prabhakara: Postbuckling Behaviour of Unsymmetrically Layered Aniso-tropic Rectangular Plates, *ASME J. Appl. Mech.*, vol. 41, pp. 155–162, 1974.

2.3. M. K. Prabhakara and C. Y. Chia: Finite Deflections of Unsymmetrically Layered Anisotropic Rectangular Plates Subjected to the Combined Action of Transverse and In-Plane Loads, *ASME J. Appl. Mech.*, vol. 42, pp. 517–518, 1975.

2.4. N. Yamaki: Influence of Large Amplitudes on Flexural Vibrations of Elastic Plates, *Z. Angew. Math. Mech.*, vol. 41, Akademie-Verlag (Berlin), pp. 501–510, 1961.

2.5. W. Z. Chien and K. Y. Yeh: On the Large Deflection of Rectangular Plate, *Proc. 9th Int. Cong. Appl. Mech.*, vol. 6, University of Brussels (Belgium), pp. 403–412, 1957.

2.6. R. Hooke: Approximate Analysis of the Large Deflection Elastic Behavior of Clamped, Uni-formly Loaded, Rectangular Plates, *J. Mech. Eng. Sci.*, vol. 11, Institution of Mechanical Engin-eers (London), pp. 256–268, 1969.

2.7. C. Y. Chia: Large Deflection of Rectangular Orthotropic Plates, *Res. Rep.*, CE 71-11, Depart-ment of Civil Engineering, University of Calgary, June 1971 (or *J. Eng. Mech. Div., Proc. ASCE*, vol. 98, no. EM5, pp. 1285–1298, 1972).

2.8. R. Hooke and B. Rawlings: An Experimental Investigation of the Behaviour of Clamped, Rec-tangular, Mild Steel Plates Subjected to Uniform Transverse Pressure, *Proc. Inst. Civ. Eng.*, vol. 42, pp. 75–103, 1969.

2.9. S. Way: Uniformly Loaded, Clamped, Rectangular Plates with Large Deflection, *Proc. 5th Int. Cong. Appl. Mech.*, John Wiley & Sons, Inc., New York, pp. 123–128, 1938.

2.10. C. Y. Chia: Finite Deflections of Uniformly Loaded Clamped, Rectangular, Anisotropic Plates, *AIAA J.*, vol. 10, pp. 1339–1340, 1972.

2.11. S. Levy: Square Plate with Clamped Edges Under Normal Pressure Producing Large Deflections, *Nat. Advis. Comm. Aeronaut. (U.S.A.), Rep. 740*, 1942.

2.12. S. Levy: Large Deflection Theory For Rectangular Plates, *Proc. 1st Symp. Appl. Math.*, vol. 1, pp. 197–210, 1947.

2.13. S. Levy: Bending of Rectangular Plates with Large Deflections, *Nat. Advis. Comm. Aeronaut. (U.S.A.), Rep. 737*, 1942.

2.14. J. C. Brown and J. M. Harvey: Large Deflections of Rectangular Plates Subjected to Uniform Lateral Pressure and Compressive Edge Loading, *J. Mech. Eng. Sci.*, vol. 11, Institution of Mechanical Engineers (London), pp. 305–317, 1969.

2.15. C. T. Wang: Nonlinear Large-Deflection Boundary-Value Problems of Rectangular Plates, *Nat. Advis. Comm. Aeronaut. (U.S.A.), Tech. Note 1425*, 1948.

2.16. F. J. Stanek: Uniformly Loaded Square Plate with No Lateral or Tangential Edge Displacements, *Proc. 3d U.S. Nat. Cong. Appl. Mech., ASME*, pp. 461–466, 1958.

2.17. M. Balachandra and S. Golpalacharyulu: Large Deflections of Clamped Plate by Modified Fourier Series, *ASME J. Appl. Mech.*, vol. 32, p. 943, 1965.

2.18. K. Marguerre: Zur Theorie Der Gekrummten Platte Grosser Formanderung, *Proc. 5th Int. Cong. Appl. Mech.*, John Wiley & Sons, Inc., New York, pp. 93–101, 1938.

2.19. H. Nylander: Initially Deflected Thin Plate with Initial Deflection Affine to Additional Deflection, *Int. Assoc. Bridge Struct. Eng.*, vol. 11, pp. 347–374, 1951.

2.20. R. Hooke: Post-Elastic Deflection Prediction of Plates, *J. Struct. Div., Proc. ASCE*, vol. 96, no. ST4, pp. 757–771, 1970.

ADDITIONAL REFERENCES

Aalami, B.: Large Deflection of Plates Under Hydrostatic Pressure, *J. Ship Res.*, vol. 16, pp. 261–270, 1972.

————: Large Deflection of Elastic Plates Under Patch Loading, *J. Struct. Div., Proc. ASCE*, vol. 98, no. ST11, pp. 2567–2586, 1972.

————, and J. C. Chapman: Large-Deflexion Behaviour of Ship Plate Panels Under Normal Pressure and In-plane Loading. *Trans. Roy. Inst. Nav. Architects*, vol. 114, pp. 155–181, 1972.

Bauer, F., L. Bauer, W. Becker, and E. L. Reiss: Bending of Rectangular Plates with Finite Deflections, *ASME J. Appl. Mech.*, vol. 32, pp. 821–825, 1965.

Berger, H. M.: A New Approach to the Analysis of Large Deflections of Plates, *ASME J. Appl. Mech.*, vol. 22, pp. 465–472, 1955.

Bernstein, E. L.: On Large Deflection Theories of Plates, *ASME J. Appl. Mech.*, vol. 32, pp. 695–697, 1965.

Clarkson, J.: Strength of Approximately Flat Long Rectangular Plates Under Lateral Pressure, *Trans. N.E. Cst. Inst. Eng. Shipbuild.*, vol. 74, p. 21, 1957–58.

Federhofer, K.: Die Grundgleichung für elastische Platten veränderlicher Dicke und grosser Ausbiegung, *ZAMM*, vol. 25/27, pp. 17–21, 1947.

Foppl, A., and L. Fopple: Drang and Zwang, R. Oldenbourg, pp. 230–232, 1920.

Fung, Y. C., and W. H. Wittrick: A Boundary Layer Phenomenon in the Large Deflexion of Thin Plates, *Q. J. Mech. Appl. Math.*, vol. 8, part 2, pp. 191–210, 1955.

Gajendar, N.: Deformation and Thermal Stress in a Rectangular Plate Having a Pair of Opposite Edges Simply Supported and the Remaining Two Edges are Clamped and Subjected to Aerodynamic Heating, *Arch. Mech. Stos.*, vol. 2, pp. 197–209, 1965.

Ghosh, P. K.: Large Deflection of a Rectangular Plate Resting on a Pasternak-Type Elastic Foundation, *ASME J. Appl. Mech.*, vol. 44, pp. 509–511, 1977.

Green, J. R., and R. V. Southwell: Relaxation Methods Applied to the Engineering Problems, VIII A. Problems Relating to Large Transverse Displacements of Thin Elastic Plates, *Phil. Trans. Roy. Soc., Ser. A*, vol. 239, pp. 539–578, 1945.

Hencky, H.: Die Berechnung dünner recheckiger Platten mit verschwindender Biegungsteifigkeit, *ZAMM*, vol. 1, pp. 81–89, 1921.

Kaiser, R.: Rechnerische und experimentelle Ermittlung der Durchbiegungen und Spannungen von quadratischen Platten bei freier Auflagerung an den Rändern, gleichmässig verteilter Last und grossen Ausbiegungen, *ZAMM*, vol. 16, pp. 73–98, 1936.

Levy, S., and S. Greenman: Bending with Large Deflection of a Clamped Rectangular Plate with Length-Width Ratio of 1.5 Under Normal Pressure, *NACA Tech. Note 853*, 1942.

————, D. Goldenberg, and G. Zibritosky: Simply Supported Long Rectangular Plate under Combined Axial Load and Normal Pressure, *NACA Tech. Note 949*, 1944.

Murray, D. W., and E. L. Wilson: Finite-Element Large Deflection Analysis of Plates, *J. Eng. Mech. Div., Proc. ASCE*, vol. 95, no. EM1, pp. 143–165, 1969.

Nowinski, J.: Note on an Analysis of Large Deflections of Rectangular Plates, *Appl. Sci. Res.*, sec. A, vol. 11, pp. 85–96, 1962.

Reissner, E.: Finite Twisting and Bending of Thin Rectangular Elastic Plates, *ASME J. Appl. Mech.*, vol. 24, pp. 391–396, 1957.

Rushton, K. R.: Large Deflexion of Variable-Thickness Plates, *Int. J. Mech. Sci.*, vol. 10, pp. 723–735, 1968.

————: Dynamic-Relaxation Solution of the Large Deflection of Plates with Specified Boundary Stresses, *J. Strain Anal.*, vol. 4, pp. 75–80, 1969.

————: Large Deflexion of Plates with Initial Curvature, *Int. J. Mech. Sci.*, vol. 12, pp. 1037–1051, 1970.

Shaw, F. S., and N. Perrone: A Numerical Solution for the Nonlinear Deflection of Membranes, *ASME J. Appl. Mech.*, vol. 21, pp. 117–128, 1954.

Sinha, S. N.: Large Deflections of Plates on Elastic Foundations, *J. Eng. Mech. Div., Proc. ASCE*, vol. 89, no. EM1, pp. 1–24, 1965.

Stippes, M.: Large Deflections of Rectangular Plates, *Proc. 1st U.S. Nat. Cong. Appl. Mech.*, pp. 339–345, 1951.

Tezcan, S. S.: Nonlinear Analysis of Thin Plates by Framework Method, *AIAA J.*, vol. 5, pp. 1890–1892, 1967.

Wang, C. T.: Bending of Rectangular Plates with Large Deflections, *NACA Tech. Note 1462*, 1948.

Woolley, R. M., J. N. Corrick, and S. Levy: Clamped Long Rectangular Plate Under Combined Axial Load and Normal Pressure, *NACA Tech. Note 1047*, 1946.

THREE

NONLINEAR BENDING OF ISOTROPIC NONRECTANGULAR PLATES

In the previous chapter different techniques were used in obtaining solutions of various boundary-value problems. The shape and the material of the plate in discussion, however, were restricted to rectangular and isotropic. In this chapter we are still confining ourselves to the isotropic material, but solutions to moderately large deflection problems are presented for circular, annular, elliptical, and skew plates, and circular plates on elastic foundation. The types of loads under consideration are uniform transverse load, uniform edge moment, and a concentrated load acting at the center of a circular plate or uniformly distributed along the inner edge of an annular plate. The boundary conditions are those for simply supported and clamped plates with movable and immovable edges. The methods of solution used for these boundary-value problems are single-parameter and multiparameter perturbation method, power series, Galerkin's procedure, and Ritz method. Solutions of the same boundary-value problem obtained by different techniques are compared with one another. The moderately large deflection problem of a triangular isotropic plate, a special case of the corresponding orthotropic problem, will be discussed in Sec. 5.7, and the application of the finite-difference method and the Galerkin method to laterally or partially loaded plates with various edge conditions in Secs. 4.6, 4.10, and 4.11.

3.1 EQUATIONS OF MOTION OF ISOTROPIC PLATES IN CYLINDRICAL POLAR COORDINATES

In the discussion of elastic behavior of circular or annular plates, it will be much more convenient to use cylindrical coordinates than rectangular cartesian coordinates. Consider an element cut out of the plate by two adjacent radial planes

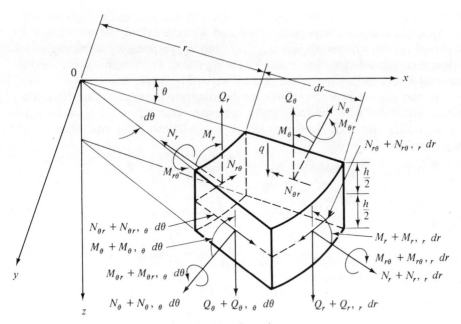

Figure 3.1 Plate element with stress resultants and couples.

and by two adjacent cylindrical surfaces as shown in Fig. 3.1. The polar coordinates r and θ lie in the plate midsurface before deformation and the z axis in the thickness direction. By use of equations of transformation and the chain rule of partial differentiation, the following relations hold

$$(\ )_{,x} = (\ )_{,r} \qquad (\ )_{,y} = \frac{1}{r}(\ )_{,\theta}$$

$$(\ )_{,xx} = (\ )_{,rr} \qquad (\ )_{,yy} = \frac{1}{r}(\ )_{,r} + \frac{1}{r^2}(\ )_{,\theta\theta} \qquad (3\text{-}1)$$

$$(\ )_{,xy} = \frac{1}{r}(\ )_{,r\theta} - \frac{1}{r^2}(\ )_{,\theta}$$

in which the polar angle θ has been taken to be zero. Since the position of the x axis is arbitrary, the result so obtained applies to any radial line of the plate.

As in the case of rectangular coordinates, the inplane forces, bending moments, and transverse shear forces in polar coordinates are defined by

$$[N_r, N_\theta, N_{r\theta}] = \int_{-h/2}^{h/2} [\sigma_r, \sigma_\theta, \sigma_{r\theta}] \, dz$$

$$[Q_r, Q_\theta] = \int_{-h/2}^{h/2} [\sigma_{zr}, \sigma_{z\theta}] \, dz \qquad (3\text{-}2)$$

$$[M_r, M_\theta, M_{r\theta}] = \int_{-h/2}^{h/2} [\sigma_r, \sigma_\theta, \sigma_{r\theta}]z \, dz$$

in which σ_r and σ_θ are the normal stresses and $\sigma_{r\theta}$, σ_{zr}, and $\sigma_{z\theta}$ are the shear stresses. These stress components associated with the cylindrical coordinates are identical to the stresses σ_x, σ_y, σ_{xy}, σ_{zx}, and σ_{zy} respectively if the radius r is allowed to coincide with the x axis by letting $\theta = 0$. The positive senses of these internal forces and moments are also shown in Fig. 3.1.

In the case of isotropic plates the bending moments and transverse shear forces associated with the rectangular cartesian coordinates are given by equations (1-122) and (1-123) respectively. Using relations (3-1), equations (1-122) transform to

$$M_r = -D\left(w_{,rr} + \frac{v}{r}w_{,r} + \frac{v}{r^2}w_{,\theta\theta}\right)$$

$$M_\theta = -D\left(\frac{1}{r}w_{,r} + \frac{1}{r^2}w_{,\theta\theta} + vw_{,rr}\right) \qquad (3\text{-}3)$$

$$M_{r\theta} = -D(1-v)\left(\frac{1}{r}w_{,r\theta} - \frac{1}{r^2}w_{,\theta}\right)$$

and equations (1-123) to

$$Q_r = -D(\nabla^2 w)_{,r}$$

$$Q_\theta = -\frac{D}{r}(\nabla^2 w)_{,\theta} \qquad (3\text{-}4)$$

where

$$\nabla^2(\ ) = (\ )_{,rr} + \frac{1}{r}(\ )_{,r} + \frac{1}{r^2}(\ )_{,\theta\theta} \qquad (3\text{-}5)$$

is the harmonic or Laplace operator in polar coordinates.

Similarly, the inplane forces (1-125) expressed in terms of the stress function transform to

$$N_r = \frac{h}{r}F_{,r} + \frac{h}{r^2}F_{,\theta\theta}$$

$$N_\theta = hF_{,rr} \qquad (3\text{-}6)$$

$$N_{r\theta} = \frac{h}{r^2}F_{,\theta} - \frac{h}{r}F_{,r\theta} = -h\left(\frac{1}{r}F_{,\theta}\right)_{,r}$$

in which the force function ψ has been replaced by hF with F being the Airy stress function as in equations (2-1) and (2-2). Thus the dynamic von Kármán nonlinear plate equations (1-161) and (1-162) are transformed to

$$\nabla^2\nabla^2 w + \frac{\rho}{D}w_{,tt} = \frac{q(r,\theta,t)}{D} + \frac{h}{D}\left[w_{,rr}\left(\frac{1}{r}F_{,r} + \frac{1}{r^2}F_{,\theta\theta}\right)\right.$$

$$\left. + F_{,rr}\left(\frac{1}{r}w_{,r} + \frac{1}{r^2}w_{,\theta\theta}\right) - 2\left(\frac{1}{r}w_{,\theta}\right)_{,r}\left(\frac{1}{r}F_{,\theta}\right)_{,r}\right] \qquad (3\text{-}7)$$

$$\nabla^2\nabla^2 F = E\left[\left(\frac{1}{r}w_{,r\theta} - \frac{1}{r^2}w_{,\theta}\right)^2 - w_{,rr}\left(\frac{1}{r}w_{,r} + \frac{1}{r^2}w_{,\theta\theta}\right)\right] \qquad (3\text{-}8)$$

Once a solution of these equations is obtained, the bending moments and shear and membrane forces can be found from equations (3-3) to (3-6), and the stresses at a general point within the plate, from the relations similar to equations (1-163) to (1-165)

$$\sigma_r = \frac{N_r}{h} + \frac{12M_r}{h^3} z$$

$$\sigma_\theta = \frac{N_\theta}{h} + \frac{12M_\theta}{h^3} z$$

$$\sigma_{r\theta} = \frac{N_{r\theta}}{h} + \frac{12M_{r\theta}}{h^3} z \qquad (3\text{-}9)$$

$$\sigma_{zr} = \frac{3Q_r}{2h} \left[1 - \left(\frac{z}{h/2} \right)^2 \right]$$

$$\sigma_{z\theta} = \frac{3Q_\theta}{2h} \left[1 - \left(\frac{z}{h/2} \right)^2 \right]$$

Noting that

$$u^\circ_{,x} = u_{r,r} \qquad u^\circ_{,y} = \frac{1}{r} \left(u_{r,\theta} - u_\theta \right)$$

$$v^\circ_{,x} = u_{\theta,r} \qquad v^\circ_{,y} = \frac{1}{r} \left(u_r + u_{\theta,\theta} \right)$$

the nonlinear strain-displacement relations (1-42) transform to

$$\varepsilon^\circ_r = u_{r,r} + \tfrac{1}{2} w^2_{,r}$$

$$\varepsilon^\circ_\theta = \frac{1}{r} \left(u_r + u_{\theta,\theta} \right) + \frac{1}{2r^2} w^2_{,\theta} \qquad (3\text{-}10)$$

$$\varepsilon^\circ_{r\theta} = \frac{1}{r} \left(u_{r,\theta} - u_\theta \right) + u_{\theta,r} + \frac{1}{r} w_{,r} w_{,\theta}$$

in which ε°_r, ε°_θ, $\varepsilon^\circ_{r\theta}$, u_r, and u_θ are reference-surface strains and displacements at $z = 0$ in the system of cylindrical coordinates. By virtue of relations (3-10) and Hooke's law these two inplane displacements can be expressed in terms of F and w as in equations (1-133).

A complete solution of equations (3-7) and (3-8) depends upon the boundary conditions along the edge of the plate and the initial conditions throughout the plate. The boundary conditions usually encountered are given below

1. Simply supported edge (movable in the plane of plate)

$$w = M_r = N_r = N_{r\theta} = 0 \qquad (3\text{-}11)$$

2. Hinged edge (or simply supported edge immovable in the plane of plate)

$$w = M_r = u_r = u_\theta = 0 \tag{3-12}$$

3. Rigidly clamped edge

$$w = w_{,r} = u_r = u_\theta = 0 \tag{3-13}$$

4. Loosely clamped edge

$$w = w_{,r} = N_r = N_{r\theta} = 0 \tag{3-14}$$

5. Free edge

$$N_r = N_{r\theta} = M_r = \frac{1}{r} M_{r\theta,\theta} + Q_r = 0 \tag{3-15}$$

The six initial conditions are the prescribed values of u_r, u_θ, w and their time derivatives.

3.2 UNIFORMLY LOADED CIRCULAR PLATE WITH VARIOUS EDGE CONDITIONS

In the case when a circular plate is deformed axisymmetrically with respect to the axis of the plate, stresses and displacements are independent of the polar angle θ and all derivatives with respect to θ vanish. Equations (3-7) and (3-8) in the static case are simplified to

$$\left\{ r \left[\frac{1}{r} (r w_{,r})_{,r} \right]_{,r} \right\}_{,r} = \frac{r q(r)}{D} + \frac{h}{D} (w_{,r} F_{,r})_{,r} \tag{3-16}$$

$$\left\{ r \left[\frac{1}{r} (r F_{,r})_{,r} \right]_{,r} \right\}_{,r} = -\frac{E}{2} (w_{,r}^2)_{,r} \tag{3-17}$$

Integrating once and using equation (3-6) leads to

$$r \left[\frac{1}{r} (r w_{,r})_{,r} \right]_{,r} = \frac{1}{D} \int_0^r \xi q(\xi)\, d\xi + \frac{r}{D} N_r w_{,r} \tag{3-18}$$

$$r \left[\frac{1}{r} (r^2 N_r)_{,r} \right]_{,r} = -\frac{Eh}{2} w_{,r}^2 \tag{3-19}$$

In view of equations (3-6) the circumferential force N_θ is related to the radial force N_r by

$$N_\theta = (r N_r)_{,r} \tag{3-20}$$

Using the second of equations (3-10), Hooke's law, and relation (3-20), the radial displacement u_r can be expressed as

$$u_r = \frac{1}{Eh} [r N_{r,r} + (1 - v) N_r] \tag{3-21}$$

Consider a circular plate of radius a and thickness h subjected to uniform lateral pressure q_0. The power series solution of this problem can be found in literature such as Refs. 1.4, 3.1, 3.2. Now an approximate solution is formulated by the perturbation method (Ref. 3.3). Let us introduce the following nondimensional parameters

$$\xi = 1 - \frac{r^2}{a^2} \qquad W = \frac{w}{h} \qquad S = \frac{N_r a^2}{Eh^3}$$

$$Q = \frac{q_0 a^4}{Eh^4}(1 - v^2)$$

(3-22)

With these quantities equations (3-18) and (3-19) become

$$[(1 - \xi)W,_\xi],_{\xi\xi} = -\tfrac{3}{4}Q + 3(1 - v^2)SW,_\xi$$

$$[(1 - \xi)S],_{\xi\xi} = -\tfrac{1}{2}W^2,_\xi$$

(3-23)

The nondimensional boundary conditions for a rigidly clamped edge are

$$W = W,_\xi = 2S,_\xi - (1 - v)S = 0 \qquad \text{at edge} \quad \xi = 0$$

(3-24)

and $W,_\xi$ and S remain finite at the plate center ($\xi = 1$).

A solution of equations (3-23) and (3-24) is then obtained by expanding Q, S, and W into the perturbation series with respect to the nondimensional maximum deflection $W(1)$, denoted by W_m.

$$Q = \frac{16}{3} \sum_{n=1, 3, \ldots}^{\infty} q_n W_m^n \qquad W = \sum_{n=1, 3, \ldots}^{\infty} w_n(\xi)W_m^n$$

$$S = \sum_{n=2, 4, \ldots}^{\infty} s_n(\xi)W_m^n$$

(3-25)

in which only odd powers of W_m occur in the series for Q and W because a change in sign of Q produces a change in sign of W. Only even powers of W_m for S are required because a change in sign of Q does not affect the radial force S.

By definition it follows that

$$w_1(1) = 1 \qquad w_3(1) = w_5(1) = \cdots = 0$$

(3-26)

A standard procedure yields a sequence of linear differential equations for q_n, w_n, s_n in conjunction with the corresponding boundary conditions. These can be solved directly by integration. The first approximation requires the coefficients of W_m to be zero and yields the differential equation and boundary conditions

$$[(1 - \xi)w_{1,\xi}],_{\xi\xi} = -4q_1$$

$$w_1(0) = w_{1,\xi}(0) = 0$$

(3-27)

and $w_{1,\xi}(1)$ remains finite.

The solution of this linear boundary-value problem is

$$w_1(\xi) = \xi^2 \qquad q_1 = 1$$

(3-28)

which also satisfy the first of conditions (3-26). This is the well-known solution for small deflections of a clamped plate (Ref. 1.4).

The second approximation requires the coefficients of W_m^2 to be zero. The corresponding differential equation and boundary conditions are

$$[(1 - \xi)s_2]_{,\xi\xi} = -\tfrac{1}{2}(w_{1,\,\xi})^2$$
$$2s_{2,\,\xi}(0) - (1 - v)s_2(0) = 0 \tag{3-29}$$

and $s_2(1)$ remains finite. The solution of this problem is

$$s_2(\xi) = \frac{1}{6}\left(\frac{2}{1 - v} + \xi + \xi^2 + \xi^3\right) \tag{3-30}$$

The third approximation gives

$$[(1 - \xi)w_{3,\,\xi}]_{,\xi\xi} = -4q_3 + 3(1 - v^2)s_2 w_{1,\,\xi}$$
$$w_3(0) = w_{3,\,\xi}(0) = 0 \tag{3-31}$$

and $w_3(1)$ remains finite. The solution is

$$q_3 = \frac{1}{360}(1 + v)(173 - 73v)$$

$$w_3(\xi) = \frac{1}{360}(1 - v^2)\xi^2(1 - \xi)\left(\frac{83 - 43v}{1 - v} + 23\xi + 8\xi^2 + 2\xi^3\right) \tag{3-32}$$

which also satisfies the second of conditions (3-26).

The next approximation yields

$$[(1 - \xi)s_4]_{,\xi\xi} = -w_{1,\,\xi}w_{3,\,\xi}$$
$$2s_{4,\,\xi}(0) - (1 - v)s_4(0) = 0 \tag{3-33}$$

and $s_4(1)$ remains finite with the solution

$$s_4(\xi) = \frac{1}{7560}(1 - v^2)\left[\frac{160 - 104v}{(1 - v)^2} + \frac{80 - 52v}{1 - v}(\xi + \xi^2 + \xi^3)\right.$$
$$\left. - \frac{501 - 249v}{1 - v}\xi^4 - 123\xi^5 - 39\xi^6 - 9\xi^7\right] \tag{3-34}$$

If necessary, the higher-order approximations can be obtained in a similar manner. Now the perturbation series (3-25) is approximated by

$$\tfrac{3}{16}Q = q_1 W_m + q_3 W_m^3 \qquad W = w_1(\xi)W_m + w_3(\xi)W_m^3$$
$$S = s_2(\xi)W_m^2 + s_4(\xi)W_m^4 \tag{3-35}$$

in which q_1, q_3, w_1, w_3, s_2, and s_4 are given by equations (3-28), (3-30), (3-32), and (3-34). The circumferential force N_θ and radial displacement u_r can be found from equations (3-20) and (3-21), and the bending moments and stresses from the simplified version of equations (3-3) and (3-9).

Numerical formulas for the load-deflection relation and radial membrane and bending stresses are presented. The relationship between uniform transverse pressure q_0 and central deflection w_0 is given by

$$\frac{q_0 a^4}{Eh^4} = \frac{16}{3(1 - v^2)}\left[\frac{w_0}{h} + \frac{1}{360}(1 + v)(173 - 73v)\left(\frac{w_0}{h}\right)^3\right] \qquad (3\text{-}36)$$

The radial membrane and extreme-fiber bending stresses are at the edge of the plate

$$\frac{\sigma_r^m a^2}{Eh^2} = \frac{1}{3(1 - v)}\left(\frac{w_0}{h}\right)^2\left[1 + \frac{1}{360}(1 + v)(40 - 26v)\left(\frac{w_0}{h}\right)^2\right]$$

$$\frac{\sigma_r^b a^2}{Eh^2} = \frac{4}{1 - v^2}\left[\frac{w_0}{h} + \frac{1}{360}(1 + v)(83 - 43v)\left(\frac{w_0}{h}\right)^4\right] \qquad (3\text{-}37)$$

and at the center

$$\frac{\sigma_r^m a^2}{Eh^2} = \frac{1}{6(1 - v)}\left(\frac{w_0}{h}\right)^3\left[(5 - 3v) - \frac{1}{315}(1 + v)(68 - 148v + 66v^2)\left(\frac{w_0}{h}\right)^2\right]$$

$$\frac{\sigma_r^b a^2}{Eh^2} = \frac{2}{1 - v}\left[\frac{w_0}{h} - \frac{1}{180}(1 + v)(29 - 19v)\left(\frac{w_0}{h}\right)^3\right] \qquad (3\text{-}38)$$

These stresses for the case $v = 0.3$ are shown in Fig. 3.2. They are numerically in full agreement with those obtained by the series solution due to Way (Ref. 3.4 or 1.4). The central deflection given by equation (3-36) is subjected to a maximum error of less than 2 percent for the numerical values shown in Fig. 203 of Ref. 1.4.

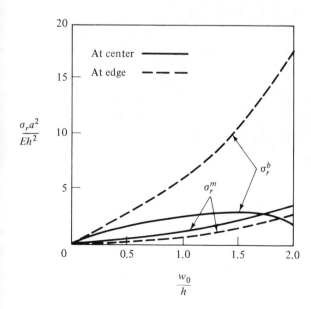

Figure 3.2 Variation of stresses with central deflection of a clamped circular plate under uniform pressure.

Following a similar calculation as above, it is possible to derive solutions for large deflections of the uniformly loaded circular plate with other edge conditions. Numerical formulas ($v = 0.3$) for the load-deflection relation, membrane stresses, and extreme-fiber bending stresses are given for the following cases (Ref. 3.5):

(*a*) Simply supported edge

$$w = M_r = N_r = 0 \qquad \text{at} \quad r = a$$
$$w_{,r} \quad \text{and} \quad N_r \text{ finite} \qquad \text{at } r = 0 \tag{3-39}$$

The corresponding formulas are given by

$$\frac{q_0 a^4}{E h^4} = 1.4375 \frac{w_0}{h} + 0.4128\left(\frac{w_0}{h}\right)^3$$

$$\frac{\sigma_r^m a^2}{E h^2} = 0.2959\left(\frac{w_0}{h}\right)^2 - 0.01451\left(\frac{w_0}{h}\right)^4 \qquad \text{at center} \tag{3-40}$$

$$\frac{\sigma_r^b a^2}{E h^2} = 1.7790 \frac{w_0}{h} - 0.1460\left(\frac{w_0}{h}\right)^3 \qquad \text{at center}$$

(*b*) Hinged edge

$$w = M_r = u_r = 0 \qquad \text{at} \quad r = a$$
$$w_{,r} \quad \text{and} \quad N_r \text{ finite} \qquad \text{at} \quad r = 0 \tag{3-41}$$

The formulas associated with these boundary conditions are

$$\frac{q_0 a^4}{E h^4} = 1.4375 \frac{w_0}{h} + 2.7252\left(\frac{w_0}{h}\right)^3$$

$$\frac{\sigma_r^m a^2}{E h^2} = 0.6118\left(\frac{w_0}{h}\right)^2 + 0.04731\left(\frac{w_0}{h}\right)^4 \qquad \text{at edge}$$

$$\frac{\sigma_r^m a^2}{E h^2} = 0.9077\left(\frac{w_0}{h}\right)^2 + 0.2057\left(\frac{w_0}{h}\right)^4 \qquad \text{at center} \tag{3-42}$$

$$\frac{\sigma_r^b a^2}{E h^2} = 1.7790 \frac{w_0}{h} - 0.2601\left(\frac{w_0}{h}\right)^3 \qquad \text{at center}$$

(*c*) Loosely clamped edge

$$w = w_{,r} = N_r = 0 \qquad \text{at} \quad r = a$$
$$w_{,r} \quad \text{and} \quad N_r \text{ finite} \qquad \text{at} \quad r = 0 \tag{3-43}$$

In this case the approximate formulas are

$$\frac{q_0 a^4}{E h^4} = 5.8608 \frac{w_0}{h} + 1.0816\left(\frac{w_0}{h}\right)^3$$

▼

$$\frac{\sigma_r^m a^2}{Eh^2} = 0.50\left(\frac{w_0}{h}\right)^2 - 0.03164\left(\frac{w_0}{h}\right)^4 \qquad \text{at center} \qquad \blacktriangle$$

$$\frac{\sigma_r^b a^2}{Eh^2} = -4.3956\frac{w_0}{h} - 0.4779\left(\frac{w_0}{h}\right)^3 \qquad \text{at edge} \qquad \blacktriangle \qquad (3\text{-}44)$$

$$\frac{\sigma_r^b a^2}{Eh^2} = 2.8571\frac{w_0}{h} - 0.2744\left(\frac{w_0}{h}\right)^3 \qquad \text{at center}$$

A solution for various elastically supported edges is also given in the above reference but the edge restraint coefficients are not specified.

3.3 CIRCULAR PLATE LOADED AT ITS CENTER WITH VARIOUS EDGE CONDITIONS

In the case of a single concentrated load P applied at the center of a circular plate, equations (3-18) and (3-19) for axisymmetrical deformation of the plate can be written in the following form

$$\left[\frac{1}{r}(r\beta)_{,r}\right]_{,r} = \frac{1}{D}\left(\frac{P}{2\pi r} + \beta N_r\right) \qquad (3\text{-}45)$$

$$(r^3 N_{r,r})_{,r} = -\tfrac{1}{2}Ehr\beta^2 \qquad (3\text{-}46)$$

where

$$\beta = w_{,r} \qquad (3\text{-}47)$$

is the rotation of a radial line element of the middle plane.

Introduce the nondimensional parameters

$$\rho = \left(\frac{r}{a}\right)^2 \qquad \zeta = \frac{kr\beta}{h} \qquad \eta = \frac{r^2 N_r}{4D}$$

$$p = \frac{4a^2 k^3 P}{\pi Eh^4} \qquad k = \left[\frac{3(1-v^2)}{8}\right]^{1/2} \qquad (3\text{-}48)$$

where a is the radius of the plate. With these notations equations (3-45) and (3-46) become

$$\eta_{,\rho\rho} = -\frac{\zeta^2}{\rho^2} \qquad \zeta_{,\rho\rho} = \frac{\zeta\eta}{\rho^2} + \frac{p}{\rho} \qquad (3\text{-}49)$$

From equations (3-3) and (3-20) the circumferential force and bending moments are given by

$$N_\theta = \frac{8D}{a^2}\left(\eta_{,\rho} - \frac{\eta}{2\rho}\right) \qquad \blacktriangledown$$

$$M_r = -\frac{Dh}{a^2 k}\left[2\zeta_{,\rho} - (1-v)\frac{\zeta}{\rho}\right]$$

▲
▲
(3-50)

$$M_\theta = -\frac{Dh}{a^2 k}\left[2v\zeta_{,\rho} + (1-v)\frac{\zeta}{\rho}\right]$$

and the radial and transverse displacements by

$$u_r = \frac{4D}{Eha}\rho^{-1/2}[2\rho\eta_{,\rho} - (1+v)\eta] \qquad w_{,\rho} = \frac{h\zeta}{2k\rho} \tag{3-51}$$

Approximate solutions of equations (3-49) satisfying different sets of boundary conditions will be formulated by use of the perturbation technique.

Case (*a*). Rigidly clamped edge

The appropriate boundary conditions in this case are

$$\zeta = 0 \qquad \eta_{,\rho} - \tfrac{1}{2}(1+v)\eta = 0 \qquad \text{at } \rho = 1$$
$$\zeta = 0 \qquad \eta = 0 \qquad \text{at } \rho = 0 \tag{3-52}$$

and $w = 0$ at $\rho = 1$. In these expressions $\eta = 0$ at $\rho = 0$ requires that N_r be finite at the center of the plate.

A solution of equations (3-49) is expressed as the perturbation series in the central deflection w_0 (Ref. 3.6)

$$p = \sum_{i=1}^{\infty} P_{2i-1} W_m^{2i-1} \qquad \zeta = \sum_{i=1}^{\infty} \zeta_{2i-1}(\rho)W_m^{2i-1}$$

$$\eta = \sum_{i=1}^{\infty} \eta_{2i}(\rho)W_m^{2i} \tag{3-53}$$

where $W_m = w_0/h$ is a nondimensional maximum deflection at the center of the plate. Inserting equations (3-53) into (3-49) and (3-52), and equating the coefficients of the like powers of W_m, we obtain a series of linear differential equations

$$\rho\zeta_{1,\rho\rho} = P_1 \qquad \rho^2\zeta_{2i+1,\rho\rho} = \rho P_{2i+1} + \sum_{j=1}^{i} \eta_{2(i-j+1)}\zeta_{2j-1}$$

$$\rho^2\eta_{2i,\rho\rho} = -\sum_{j=1}^{i} \zeta_{2j-1}\zeta_{2i-2j+1} \tag{3-54}$$

and the corresponding boundary conditions

$$\zeta_{2i-1} = 0 \qquad \eta_{2i,\rho} - \tfrac{1}{2}(1+v)\eta_{2i} = 0 \qquad \text{at} \quad \rho = 1$$

$$\zeta_{2i-1} = 0 \qquad \eta_{2i} = 0 \qquad \text{at} \quad \rho = 0 \tag{3-55}$$

in which the subscript i takes on the values of 1, 2, 3, ...

Equations (3-54) can be solved successively, by direct integration, in conjunction with the corresponding boundary conditions (3-55). The constants p_{2i-1} are determined from the condition on w. Substituting the series for ζ into the last of equations (3-51) and integrating, leads to

$$\frac{w}{h} = \sum_{i=1}^{\infty} w_{2i-1} W_m^{2i-1} \qquad (3\text{-}56)$$

where

$$w_1 = 1 + \frac{1}{2k} \int_0^\rho \frac{\zeta_1}{\rho}\, d\rho$$

$$\qquad (3\text{-}57)$$

$$w_{2i+1} = \frac{1}{2k} \int_0^\rho \frac{\zeta_{2i+1}}{\rho}\, d\rho$$

It is observed that series (3-56) meets the requirements

$$w_1(0) = 1 \qquad w_3(0) = w_5(0) = \cdots = 0 \qquad (3\text{-}58)$$

For the first approximation we have

$$\rho \zeta_{1,\rho\rho} = p_1 \qquad \zeta_1(1) = 0 \qquad \zeta_1(0) = 0 \qquad (3\text{-}59)$$

whose solution is

$$\zeta_1 = p_1 \rho \log \rho \qquad (3\text{-}60)$$

Introducing this solution in the first of equations (3-57) and using the condition $w_{2i-1} = 0$ at $\rho = 0$, we find

$$p_1 = 2k \qquad (3\text{-}61)$$

Similarly, solutions for η_2, ζ_3, η_4, ζ_5, etc., can be obtained.

The truncated series expressions obtained for functions $\zeta(\rho)$ and $\eta(\rho)$ are of great length and will not be presented herein. Only certain numerical formulas are given for $v = 0.3$. At the center of the plate

$$\frac{Pa^2}{Eh^4} = 4.603 W_m + 2.048 W_m^3 - 0.1112 W_m^5 + 0.02009 W_m^7 + \cdots$$

$$\qquad (3\text{-}62)$$

$$\frac{a^2 N_r}{Eh^3} = 1.232 W_m^2 + 0.05046 W_m^4 - 0.001139 W_m^6 + \cdots$$

and at the edge

$$\frac{a^2 N_r}{Eh^3} = 0.3571 W_m^2 - 0.01464 W_m^4 + 0.002788 W_m^6 + \cdots$$

$$\frac{a^2 M_r}{Eh^4} = -0.3363 W_m - 0.02623 W_m^3 + 0.001214 W_m^5$$

$$\qquad (3\text{-}63)$$

$$- 0.00002656 W_m^7 + \cdots$$

These formulas are sufficiently accurate for $w_0/h \le 1$. It is of interest to note that the first two terms in the first of formulas (3-62) are equivalent to equation (y) on page 415 of Ref. 1.4.

Case (b). Loosely clamped edge

The present boundary conditions are taken to be

$$\zeta = \eta = 0 \quad \text{at} \quad \rho = 0, 1 \tag{3-64}$$

and $w = 0$ at $\rho = 1$.

A solution of equations (3-49) is expressed as the perturbation series in the loading parameter p (Ref. 3.7)

$$\zeta = \sum_{n=1}^{\infty} \zeta_{2n-1}(\rho)p^{2n-1} \qquad \eta = \sum_{n=1}^{\infty} \eta_{2n}(\rho)p^{2n} \tag{3-65}$$

The solution, of course, also can be assumed in the form of power series in the central deflection as in equations (3-53). Inserting series (3-65) into equations (3-49) and boundary conditions (3-64) and collecting terms of the same degree in p, we obtain an infinite system of linear differential equations

$$\zeta_{1,\,\rho\rho} = \frac{1}{\rho} \qquad \eta_{2,\,\rho\rho} = -\frac{\zeta_1^2}{\rho^2} \qquad \zeta_{3,\,\rho\rho} = \frac{1}{\rho^2}\zeta_1\eta_2$$

$$\eta_{4,\,\rho\rho} = -\frac{2}{\rho^2}\zeta_1\zeta_3 \qquad \zeta_{5,\,\rho\rho} = \frac{1}{\rho^2}(\zeta_1\eta_4 + \zeta_3\eta_2) \cdots \tag{3-66}$$

and associated boundary conditions

$$\zeta_{2n-1} = 0 \qquad \eta_{2n} = 0 \qquad \text{at} \quad \rho = 0, 1 \tag{3-67}$$

Equations (3-66) can be solved successively for ζ_i and η_i, by direct integration, if these functions individually satisfy the corresponding boundary conditions (3-67). The deflection w is then determined with the aid of equations (3-51) and (3-65).

Numerical formulas for central deflection, inplane forces, and radial bending moment are presented for $\nu = 0.3$. At the center of the plate

$$\frac{w_0}{h} = 0.21725p_0 - 0.0020626p_0^3 + 0.000062328p_0^5 + \cdots$$

$$\frac{a^2N_r}{Eh^3} = \frac{a^2N_\theta}{Eh^3} = 0.041297p_0^2 - 0.00078496p_0^4 + 0.000027594p_0^6 + \cdots \tag{3-68}$$

and at the edge

$$\frac{a^2N_\theta}{Eh^3} = -(0.011799p_0^2 - 0.00022676p_0^4 + 0.0000079509p_0^6 + \cdots)$$

$$\frac{a^2M_r}{Eh^4} = -(0.079577p_0 - 0.00048655p_0^3 + 0.000014459p_0^5 + \cdots) \tag{3-69}$$

where

$$p_0 = \frac{Pa^2}{Eh^4} \tag{3-70}$$

It is noticed that the circumferential membrane force N_θ is compressive near the edge and, therefore, there exists danger of local buckling (Ref. 3.8).

Using the same approach as in Sec. 3.2 and taking $v = 0.3$, numerical formulas for the load-deflection relation and radial stresses in a circular plate loaded at its center are also presented for the following cases (Ref. 3.5).

Case (c). Simply supported edge

The numerical results corresponding to the edge conditions, equation (3-39), are

$$\frac{Pa^2}{Eh^4} = 1.8132\,\frac{w_0}{h} + 0.4939\left(\frac{w_0}{h}\right)^3$$

$$\frac{\sigma_r^m a^2}{Eh^2} = 0.4067\left(\frac{w_0}{h}\right)^2 + 0.007213\left(\frac{w_0}{h}\right)^4 \qquad \text{at center}$$

(3-71)

Case (d). Hinged edge

The approximate formulas for the edge conditions (3-41) are

$$\frac{Pa^2}{Eh^4} = 1.8132\,\frac{w_0}{h} + 2.5912\left(\frac{w_0}{h}\right)^2$$

$$\frac{\sigma_r^m a^2}{Eh^2} = 0.4883\left(\frac{w_0}{h}\right)^2 - 0.1001\left(\frac{w_0}{h}\right)^4 \qquad \text{at edge} \qquad (3\text{-}72)$$

$$\frac{\sigma_r^m a^2}{Eh^2} = 0.8950\left(\frac{w_0}{h}\right)^2 - 0.04212\left(\frac{w_0}{h}\right)^4 \qquad \text{at center}$$

3.4 CIRCULAR PLATE BENT BY UNIFORM EDGE MOMENT

Consider a sliding simply supported plate subjected to uniformly distributed couple $M = -M_r(a)$, along its edge. By setting $\beta = w_{,r}$ the boundary conditions are

$$\beta_{,r} + \frac{v}{a}\beta = \frac{M}{D} \qquad N_r = 0 \qquad w = 0 \qquad \text{at} \quad r = a$$

$$\beta = 0 \qquad N_r = \text{finite} \qquad\qquad\qquad \text{at} \quad r = 0$$

(3-73)

In the case of axisymmetrical deformation equations (3-45) to (3-47) for $P = 0$ are used. A solution is expressed as the perturbation series in the angle of rotation (Ref. 3.9).

$$\beta = \sum_{i=1}^{\infty} \beta_{2i-1}(r)\gamma^{2i-1} \qquad N_r = \sum_{i=1}^{\infty} N_{2i}(r)\gamma^{2i}$$

$$M = \sum_{i=1}^{\infty} M_{2i-1}\gamma^{2i-1}$$

(3-74)

in which $\gamma = \beta(a)$ is the angle of rotation at the edge with the requirements

$$\beta_1(a) = 1 \qquad \beta_3(a) = \beta_5(a) = \beta_7(a) = \cdots = 0 \tag{3-75}$$

Substituting equations (3-74) into (3-45) to (3-47), and equating coefficients of equal powers of γ, we obtain the following infinite system of successively integrable differential equations

$$\left[\frac{1}{r}(r\beta_1)_{,r}\right]_{,r} = 0 \qquad (r^3 N_{2,r})_{,r} = -\tfrac{1}{2}Ehr\beta_1^2$$

$$\left[\frac{1}{r}(r\beta_3)_{,r}\right]_{,r} = \frac{1}{D}\beta_1 N_2 \qquad (r^3 N_{4,r})_{,r} = -Ehr\beta_1\beta_3$$

$$\left[\frac{1}{r}(r\beta_5)_{,r}\right]_{,r} = \frac{1}{D}(\beta_1 N_4 + \beta_3 N_2) \qquad (r^3 N_{6,r})_{,r} = -\tfrac{1}{2}Ehr(\beta_3^2 + 2\beta_1\beta_5) \tag{3-76}$$

$$\left[\frac{1}{r}(r\beta_7)_{,r}\right]_{,r} = \frac{1}{D}(\beta_1 N_6 + \beta_5 N_2) \qquad \cdots\cdots$$

$$w_{i,r} = \beta_i \qquad i = 1, 3, 5, \ldots$$

From equations (3-73) and (3-74) the following boundary conditions are obtained

$$\beta_{i,r} + \frac{v}{a}\beta_i = \frac{M_i}{D} \qquad N_i = w_i = 0 \qquad \text{at} \quad r = a$$

$$\beta_i = 0 \qquad N_i = \text{finite} \qquad \text{at} \quad r = 0 \tag{3-77}$$

Integrating equations (3-76) successively and satisfying conditions (3-75) and (3-77), coefficients β_i, w_i, N_i, and M_i can be determined. Next, we calculate

$$W_c \equiv \frac{1}{h}[w(a) - w(0)] = \frac{1}{2}\left(\frac{a\gamma}{h}\right)$$

$$\cdot \left[1 - \frac{5(1 - v^2)}{192}\left(\frac{a\gamma}{h}\right)^2 + \frac{243(1 - v^2)^2}{102400}\left(\frac{a\gamma}{h}\right)^4\right.$$

$$\left. - \frac{283823(1 - v^2)^3}{963379200}\left(\frac{a\gamma}{h}\right)^6 + \cdots\right] \tag{3-78}$$

Reversion of this series yields

$$\frac{a\gamma}{h} = 2W_c + \frac{5(1 - v^2)}{24}W_c^3 - \frac{13(1 - v^2)^2}{1200}W_c^5 + \frac{35129(1 - v^2)^3}{22579200}W_c^7 + \cdots \tag{3-79}$$

The other physical quantities M, $M_\theta(a)$, $M_r(0)$, $N_\theta(a)$ and $N_r(0)$ can be expressed in the form similar to equation (3-78). Taking into account equation (3-79), these quantities assume in the form

$$\frac{a^2 M}{Eh^4} = \frac{1}{6(1-v)} W_c + \frac{17+5v}{288} W_c^3 - \frac{(11+26v)(1-v^2)}{28800} W_c^5$$

$$+ \frac{(47813 + 35129v)(1-v^2)^2}{270950400} W_c^7 + \cdots$$

$$\frac{a^2 M_\theta(a)}{Eh^4} = \frac{1}{6(1-v)} W_c + \frac{5+17v}{288} W_c^3 - \frac{(26+11v)(1-v^2)}{28800} W_c^5$$

$$+ \frac{(35129 + 47813v)(1-v^2)^2}{270950400} W_c^7 + \cdots$$

$$\frac{a^2 M_r(0)}{Eh^4} = \frac{1}{6(1-v)} W_c - \frac{7(1+v)}{288} W_c^3 + \frac{47(1+v)(1-v^2)}{14400} W_c^5 \qquad (3\text{-}80)$$

$$- \frac{140809(1+v)(1-v^2)^2}{270950400} W_c^7 + \cdots$$

$$\frac{a^2 N_\theta(a)}{Eh^3} = -\tfrac{1}{2}W_c^2 - \frac{1-v^2}{24} W_c^4 + \frac{149(1-v^2)^2}{115200} W_c^6 + \cdots$$

$$\frac{a^2 N_r(0)}{Eh^3} = \tfrac{1}{4}W_c^2 - \frac{1-v^2}{48} W_c^4 + \frac{253(1-v^2)^2}{76800} W_c^6 + \cdots$$

$$u_r(a) = \frac{a}{Eh} N_\theta(a)$$

For $v = 0.3$, $a = 23h$, and $W_c = 0.55$, the first of equations (3-80) yields $M = 0.002923D/h$ which is very close to the result obtained by numerical integration on page 399 of Ref. 1.4.

Equations (3-80) can be also obtained by developing M, β, N_r into the perturbation series with respect to the central deflection w_0.

3.5 SIMPLY SUPPORTED CIRCULAR PLATE UNDER COMBINED LATERAL LOADING

In the previous sections the perturbation or small parameter method of Poincaré has been used in obtaining approximate solutions of some boundary-value problems by developing a solution in ascending powers of a single parameter in central deflection, applied load, or angle of rotation. It is noted that the method is still valid even for values of the parameter in the central deflection greater than unity. Now the generalized perturbation method including several parameters discussed in Sec. 1.9 is applied to the following boundary-value problem.

Let us consider a circular plate of radius a under the combined action of uniformly distributed load q_0 and a concentrated load P applied at its center. In this case the governing equations (3-18) and (3-19), for axisymmetrical deformation, can be used and written as

$$x\left[\frac{1}{x}(xW_{,x})_{,x}\right]_{,x} = x^2Q + p + x\eta W_{,x} \tag{3-81}$$

$$[x(x\eta)_{,x}]_{,x} - \eta = -m^2 W_{,x}^2 \tag{3-82}$$

where

$$x = \frac{r}{a} \qquad W = \frac{w}{h} \qquad \eta = \frac{a^2}{D}N_r$$

$$\tag{3-83}$$

$$Q = \frac{q_0 a^4}{2hD} \qquad p = \frac{Pa^2}{2\pi hD} \qquad m^2 = 6(1 - v^2)$$

If the edge of the plate is simply supported and free from the radial force, the corresponding boundary conditions can be written in the nondimensional form

$$W = \eta = 0 \qquad W_{,xx} + \frac{v}{x}W_{,x} = 0 \qquad \text{at} \quad x = 1 \tag{3-84}$$

and all functions involved remain bounded at $x = 0$.

In this problem the nondimensional quantities Q and p characterizing both the applied loads are taken to be the perturbation parameters (Ref. 1.80). The functions W and η are thus expanded into the asymptotic series as†

$$W = \phi_1(x)Q + \psi_1(x)p + \phi_3(x)Q^3 + \psi_3(x)p^3 + \phi_{21}(x)Q^2p$$
$$+ \psi_{21}(x)Qp^2 + \cdots \tag{3-85}$$
$$\eta = \alpha_2(x)Q^2 + \beta_2(x)p^2 + \alpha_{12}(x)Qp + \alpha_4(x)Q^4 + \cdots$$

A standard procedure furnishes a sequence of linear differential equations and boundary conditions. The first approximation is associated with the terms linear in Q and p, the second with the terms bilinear in Q and p, and so forth. The boundary and the regularity conditions for each approximation which are the same, and identical with conditions (3-84), will not be recorded herein. The first approximation is supplied by the solution of the set of two boundary-value problems

$$\left[\frac{1}{x}(x\phi_{1,x})_{,x}\right]_{,x} = x$$

$$\tag{3-86}$$

$$\left[\frac{1}{x}(x\psi_{1,x})_{,x}\right]_{,x} = \frac{1}{x}$$

---

† Instead of the multiparameter form one may use a linear combination of the two external loads, $k_1 q_0 + k_2 P$, as a perturbation parameter. This procedure reduces simply to equations (3-82) because the values of the constants k_1 and k_2 may be chosen arbitrarily without affecting the result.

The corresponding solution is

$$\phi_1 = \tfrac{1}{32}(x^4 - 2Ax^2 + B)$$
$$\psi_1 = \tfrac{1}{8}(2x^2 \log x - Aa^2 + A)$$

(3-87)

in which A and B are constants given by

$$A = \frac{3 + v}{1 + v} \qquad B = \frac{5 + v}{1 + v}$$

(3-88)

For the second approximation we obtain three governing equations

$$[x(x\alpha_2)_{,x}]_{,x} - \alpha_2 = -m^2(\phi_{1,\,x})^2$$
$$[x(x\beta_2)_{,x}]_{,x} - \beta_2 = -m^2(\psi_{1,\,x})^2 \cdot$$
$$[x(x\alpha_{12})_{,x}]_{,x} - \alpha_{12} = -m^2\phi_{1,\,x}\psi_{1,\,x}$$

(3-89)

The solution of the above system becomes

$$\alpha_2 = \frac{m^2}{3072}[6A^2(1 - x^2) - 4A(1 - x^4) + 1 - x^6]$$

$$\beta_2 = \frac{m^2}{256}\{2A^2 + 2A + 3$$

(3-90)

$$- [8 \log^2 x - 4(1 + 2A) \log x + 2A^2 + 2A + 3]x^2\}$$

in which $\alpha_{12}(x)$ is not presented herein.

A similar argument leads to the set of four boundary-value problems related to the third approximation.

$$\left[\frac{1}{x}(x\phi_{3,\,x})_{,x}\right]_{,x} = \alpha_2\phi_{1,\,x}$$

$$\left[\frac{1}{x}(x\psi_{3,\,x})_{,x}\right]_{,x} = \beta_2\psi_{1,\,x}$$

(3-91)

$$\left[\frac{1}{x}(x\phi_{21,\,x})_{,x}\right]_{,x} = \alpha_2\psi_{1,\,x} + \alpha_{12}\phi_{1,\,x}$$

$$\left[\frac{1}{x}(x\psi_{21,\,x})_{,x}\right]_{,x} = \beta_2\phi_{1,\,x} + \alpha_{12}\psi_{1,\,x}$$

For conciseness we restrict ourselves to the first four terms in the series for W. The solutions of the foregoing first two boundary-value problems are given by

$$\phi_3 = \frac{m^2}{196,608}\left(-\frac{x^{12}}{180} + \frac{A}{20}x^{10} - \frac{5A}{24}x^8 + \frac{6A^3 + 6A^2 - 4A + 1}{18}x^6\right.$$

$$\left. -\frac{6A^3 - 4A^2 + A}{4}x^4 + 2C_1x^2 + 8C_2\right)$$

▼

$$\psi_3 = \frac{m^2}{1024}\left[-\frac{x^2}{9}\log^3 x + \frac{7+6A}{36}x^6 \log^2 x \right.$$

$$-\frac{3A^2+7A+6}{36}x^6\log x$$

$$+\frac{2A^2+2A+3}{16}x^4\log x + \frac{18A^3+63A^2+108A+49}{1296}x^6$$

$$\left. -\frac{(1+A)(2A^2+2A+3)}{32}x^4 + C_3\frac{x^2}{4} + C_4 \right] \tag{3-92}$$

where

$$C_1 = \frac{1}{1+v}\left[2A^3 - \tfrac{31}{12}A^2 + \tfrac{31}{24}A - \tfrac{7}{30} + v(A^3 - \tfrac{13}{12}A^2 + \tfrac{11}{24}A - \tfrac{1}{15})\right]$$

$$C_2 = \tfrac{1}{4}(\tfrac{7}{12}A^3 - \tfrac{41}{24}A^2 + \tfrac{19}{90}A - \tfrac{1}{40} - C_1)$$

$$C_3 = \frac{1}{2(1+v)}\left[-\frac{5+v}{54}(18A^3 + 45A^2 + 66A + 13) \right.$$

$$\left. + \tfrac{1}{4}(3+v)(1+2A)(2A^2+2A+3) - \tfrac{1}{3}(5-4A) \right] \tag{3-93}$$

$$C_4 = \tfrac{1}{4}[-\tfrac{1}{1296}(18A^3 + 63A^2 + 208A + 49)$$

$$+ \tfrac{1}{32}(1+A)(2A^2+2A+3) - C_3]$$

As mentioned above the nondimensional deflection given by the first of expressions (3-85) is approximated by

$$W = \phi_1(x)Q + \psi_1(x)p + \phi_3(x)Q^3 + \psi_3(x)p^3 \tag{3-94}$$

By taking $v = 0.3$ a simple calculation yields the deflection w_0 at the center of a circular plate subjected to a combined loading.

$$\frac{w_0}{h} = 0.127Q + 0.317p - 0.00059Q^3 - 0.00966p^3 \tag{3-95}$$

This result is now specified for a uniform pressure $(p = 0)$ and a centrally concentrated load $(Q = 0)$. Upon inverting the resulting equations we obtain for a uniform lateral pressure

$$\frac{q_0 a^4}{2hD} = 7.87\frac{w_0}{h} + 2.26\left(\frac{w_0}{h}\right)^3 \tag{3-96}$$

and for a concentrated force applied at the center of the plate

$$\frac{Pa^2}{2\pi hD} = 3.15\frac{w_0}{h} + 0.854\left(\frac{w_0}{h}\right)^3 \tag{3-97}$$

It is observed that for $v = 0.3$ and $w_0/h = 2.0$ the value of $q_0 a^4/Eh^4$ given by equation (3-96) is different from that obtained by equation (n) on page 412 of Ref. 1.4, by the amount of less than 5 percent. Equation (3-97) is identical with the solution given in Ref. 3.10.

3.6 ANNULAR PLATE SUBJECTED TO AXISYMMETRICAL LINE LOAD AROUND THE CENTRAL HOLE

Suppose that an annular plate of outer radius a and inner radius b is subjected to a concentrated load P uniformly distributed along the inner edge (Fig. 3.3). For axisymmetrical deformations the governing equations are given by equations (3-18) and (3-19) for $q = 0$, and may be expressed in the nondimensional form as

$$\eta_{r,\,zz} + 2k\eta_{r,\,z} = -\tfrac{1}{2}(1 - v^2)k^2\phi^2 \tag{3-98}$$

$$\phi_{,zz} - k^2\phi = 12\left(\frac{k}{C}\right)^2(-pe^{kz} + \eta_r\phi e^{2kz}) \tag{3-99}$$

where

$$\phi = \frac{d(w/a)}{d(r/a)} \qquad \eta_r = \frac{1 - v^2}{Eh}N_r \qquad k = \log\left(\frac{b}{a}\right)$$

$$z = \frac{1}{k}\log\left(\frac{r}{a}\right) \qquad p = \frac{(1 - v^2)P}{2\pi aEh} \qquad C = \frac{h}{a} \tag{3-100}$$

A solution of equations (3-98) and (3-99) is sought in the form of the series (Ref. 3.11)

$$\eta_r = e^{-2kz}\sum_{n=0}^{\infty} A_n z^n \qquad \phi = e^{-kz}\sum_{n=0}^{\infty} B_n z^n \tag{3-101}$$

which are assumed to be analytic in the annular region. The question of the domain of convergence is discussed in the above reference. Substituting expressions (3-101) into equations (3-98) and (3-99), and collecting terms of like powers of z yields the following recurrence formulas:

$$A_n = -\frac{c_1}{n}A_{n-1} - \frac{c_2}{n(n-1)}\sum_{i=0}^{n-2}B_i B_{n-2-i} \qquad (n \geq 2)$$

$$B_n = -\frac{c_1}{n}B_{n-1} - \frac{c_3(-c_1)^{n-2}}{n!} + \frac{c_4}{n(n-1)}\sum_{i=0}^{n-2}A_i B_{n-2-i} \quad (n \geq 2) \tag{3-102}$$

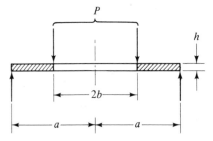

Figure 3.3 Simply supported annular plate under axisymmetrical line load.

in which c's are positive constants given by

$$c_1 = -2 \log\left(\frac{b}{a}\right) \qquad c_2 = \tfrac{1}{2}(1 - v^2) \log^2\left(\frac{b}{a}\right)$$

$$c_3 = \frac{12p}{C^2} \log^2\left(\frac{b}{a}\right) \qquad c_4 = \frac{c_3}{p}$$

(3-103)

These formulas determine all the coefficients A_n and B_n $(n \geq 2)$ in terms of the leading coefficients A_0, A_1, B_0, and B_1. These four constants are to be chosen so as to satisfy the prescribed boundary conditions. In the analysis only one set of boundary conditions is considered although the method is equally applicable to other boundary conditions. If the edges of the annular plate are free from radial forces and normal bending moments, by virtue of equations (3-3) and (3-100) the nondimensional boundary conditions are

$$\eta_r = \omega_r = 0 \qquad \text{at} \quad z = 0, 1$$

(3-104)

where

$$\omega_r = \frac{aM_r}{D} = -\left(\phi_{,x} + v\frac{\phi}{x}\right) \qquad x = \frac{r}{z}$$

(3-105)

The conditions at the outer edge, $z = 0$, and the inner edge, $z = 1$, require that

$$A_0 = 0 \qquad B_1 = k(1 - v)B_0 \qquad \sum_{n=0}^{\infty} A_n = 0$$

$$-k(1 - v)B_1 + \sum_{n=2}^{\infty}[n - k(1 - v)]B_n = 0$$

(3-106)

In calculation only a finite number of terms, say N, in the truncated series (3-101) are taken into account. Eliminating A_0 and B_1 from equations (3-106) and using relations (3-102), two simultaneous equations for A_1 and B_0 will be obtained. For any approximation to the coefficients A_1 and B_0, these equations generally will not be satisfied. In other words the approximation yields a residual tension and moment at the inner edge. Thus for any approximation we consider, instead of the last two of equations (3-106),

$$\sum_{n=0}^{N} A_n = R_A(A_1, B_0)$$

$$-k^2(1 - v)^2 B_1 + \sum_{n=2}^{N}[n - k(1 - v)]B_n = R_B(A_1, B_0)$$

(3-107)

The object is now to find A_1 and B_0 for which R_A and R_B vanish. This may be achieved by the Newton-Raphson process with the coefficients A_1 and B_0 regarded as two roots to be determined. The process is repeated until the improved values of A_1 and B_0 satisfy the boundary conditions to a desired degree

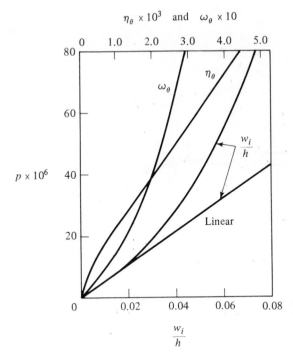

Figure 3.4 Variation of edge deflection and circumferential force and moment with axisymmetrical line load acting at inner edge of simply supported annular plate.

of accuracy. A numerical procedure for solving equations (3-107) is also given in Ref. 3.11.

The numerical results are graphically presented in Figs. 3.4 and 3.5 by taking

$$\frac{b}{a} = 0.5 \qquad \frac{h}{a} = 0.05 \qquad v = 0.3$$

In these figures w_i is the transverse deflection at the inner edge and η_θ and ω_θ are the nondimensional circumferential membrane force and bending moment defined by

$$\eta_\theta = \frac{1 - v^2}{Eh} N_\theta \qquad \omega_\theta = \frac{a M_\theta}{D} \tag{3-108}$$

The value of w_i was obtained by using the first of equations (3-100) and the condition $w = 0$ at the outer edge. For the particular load $p = 41.3 \times 10^{-6}$ shown in Fig. 3.5, the coefficients A_1 and B_0 are both positive and given by

$$A_1 = 0.8543 \times 10^{-3} \qquad B_0 = 0.9560 \times 10^{-1}$$

The convergence of the series solution is certainly dependent on the magnitudes of the ratios b/a and h/a and the load parameter p. In particular, small values of h/a can result in extremely slow convergence. A similar limitation exists for the series solutions of solid circular plates such as the solution presented in Ref. 3.2.

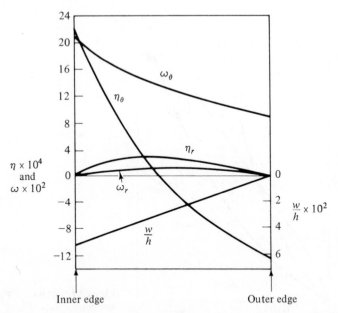

Figure 3.5 Membrane forces, bending moments, and transverse deflection of an annular plate under axisymmetrical line load ($p = 41.3 \times 10^{-6}$).

In the case of the annular plate with clamped edges shown in Fig. 3.6, the boundary conditions may be described by

$$w = w_{,r} = u_r = 0 \qquad \text{at} \quad r = a$$

$$w_{,r} = u_r = 0 \qquad \text{at} \quad r = b \tag{3-109}$$

An approximate solution of this boundary-value problem is formulated by the perturbation method (Ref. 3.12). In other words the nondimensional parameters in axisymmetrical line load P acting along the inner edge, transverse deflection, and radial force are expanded in the asymptotic series with respect to the non-

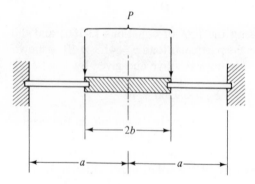

Figure 3.6 Clamped annular plate under axisymmetrical line load.

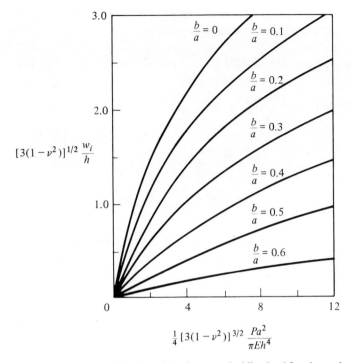

$$\frac{1}{4}[3(1-\nu^2)]^{3/2}\frac{Pa^2}{\pi Eh^4}$$

Figure 3.7 Variation of maximum deflection with axisymmetrical line load for clamped annular plate $(\nu = 0.3)$.

dimensional deflection at the inner edge. The standard procedure is not given herein, only the load-deflection curves obtained from the two-term approximation being presented in Fig. 3.7 for various values of the b/a ratio. In the special case of a solid plate $(b/a = 0)$ the present result is in good agreement with that obtained by the first two terms in equation (3-62). The maximum difference between the two sets of values is less than 3.5 percent for the values of w_0/h up to 1.82 shown in Fig. 3.7.

3.7 UNIFORMLY LOADED CIRCULAR PLATE ON ELASTIC FOUNDATION WITH VARIOUS EDGE CONDITIONS

Consider a circular plate of radius a and thickness h resting on a Winkler-type elastic foundation and subjected to a uniform lateral pressure q_0, and in which the intensity of the reaction of the plate is proportional to the deflection of the plate. The net load is thus equal to the difference, $q_0 - kw$, in which k is the foundation modulus. For axisymmetrical deflections the governing equations are obtained by setting $q = q_0 - kw$ in equations (3-16) and (3-17). Integrating the last equation once, the resulting equations can be written as

$$L(w, F) = \nabla^2 \nabla^2 w - h\left(Q - \frac{\alpha w}{h}\right) - \frac{h}{D\rho}(w_{,\rho\rho} F_{,\rho} + F_{,\rho\rho} w_{,\rho}) = 0 \quad (3\text{-}110)$$

$$(\nabla^2 F)_{,\rho} = -\frac{E}{2\rho} w_{,\rho}^2 \qquad (3\text{-}111)$$

where

$$\rho = \frac{r}{a} \qquad \nabla^2(\ ) = \frac{1}{\rho}[\rho(\ )_{,\rho}]_{,\rho}$$

$$Q = \frac{q_0 a^4}{Dh} \qquad \alpha = \frac{ka^4}{D} \qquad (3\text{-}112)$$

The radial force, bending moment, and displacement are given by

$$N_r = \frac{h}{a^2 \rho} F_{,\rho} \qquad M_r = -\frac{D}{a^2}\left(w_{,\rho\rho} + \frac{v}{\rho} w_{,\rho}\right) \qquad u_r = \frac{\rho}{Ea^2}\left(F_{,\rho\rho} - \frac{v}{\rho} F_{,\rho}\right)$$
$$(3\text{-}113)$$

An approximate solution of equations (3-110) and (3-111) is formulated by use of Galerkin's method (Ref. 3.13). The deflection function is assumed in the form

$$w = h \sum_{n=1}^{\infty} a_n w_n(\rho) \qquad (3\text{-}114)$$

In this expression w_n are eigenfunctions of the biharmonic operator in the polar coordinates given by

$$w_n = I_0^*(\lambda_n \rho) - J_0^*(\lambda_n \rho) \qquad (3\text{-}115)$$

in which

$$I_0^* = \frac{I_0(\lambda_n \rho)}{I_0(\lambda_n)} \qquad J_0^* = \frac{J_0(\lambda_n \rho)}{J_0(\lambda_n)} \qquad (3\text{-}116)$$

In these expressions λ_n are unknown coefficients. It is observed that functions w_n satisfy conditions $w_n(1) = 0$.

Equation (3-111) is integrated twice with the result

$$F_{,\rho} = -\frac{E}{2\rho}\int_0^\rho y\left[\int_0^y \frac{1}{x} w_{,x}^2 \, dx\right] dy + \tfrac{1}{2}C_1 \rho + \frac{C_2}{\rho} \qquad (3\text{-}117)$$

The finite conditions of the slope and membrane stress at the center of the plate require that $C_2 = 0$. The constant C_1 and coefficients λ_n are to be determined by the boundary conditions. Inserting expression (3-114) into (3-117) and performing the indicated integrations leads to

$$F_{,\rho} = -\tfrac{1}{8}Eh^2 \sum_{i=1}^{\infty} \sum_{j=1}^{\infty} a_i a_j f_{ij} + \tfrac{1}{2}C_1 \rho \qquad (3\text{-}118)$$

where

$$f_{ii} = 2\lambda_i^2 \rho \left\{ [I_0^*(\lambda_i\rho)]^2 - [I_1^*(\lambda_i\rho)]^2 - [J_0^*(\lambda_i\rho)]^2 \right.$$

$$- [J_1^*(\lambda_i\rho)]^2 + \frac{1}{\lambda_i\rho}[J_0^*(\lambda_i\rho)J_1^*(\lambda_i\rho) - I_0^*(\lambda_i\rho)I_1^*(\lambda_i\rho)]$$

$$\left. + \frac{1}{2}\left[\frac{1}{J_0^2(\lambda_i)} - \frac{1}{I_0^2(\lambda_i)}\right] + \frac{\xi_i}{\rho}\right\}$$

(3-119)

$$f_{ij} = \frac{8}{\rho}\int_0^\rho y\left[\int_0^y \frac{1}{x}w_i(x)w_j(x)\,dx\right]dy$$

In the last second expression

$$\xi_i = \frac{1}{\rho}\int_0^\rho \frac{4x^3}{I_0(\lambda_i)J_0(\lambda_i)}\sum_{k=0}^\infty \frac{(\lambda_k x/2)^{2k}\,_2F_1(-k, -k-1; 2; -1)}{k!(2k+2)(2)_k}\,dx$$

(3-120)

in which $(c)_k = c(c+1)\cdots(c+k-1)$ is Pochhammer's symbol and $_2F_1$ is the hypergeometric series defined by

$$_2F_1(c_1, c_2; d_1; z) = \sum_{k=0}^\infty \frac{(c_1)_k(c_2)_k z^k}{k!(d_1)_k}$$

(3-121)

which converges for all z if the parameters are integers. For conciseness the array f_{ij} is chosen to be triangular and can be obtained numerically or as an integral of four sums through the repeated use of integrals (Ref. 3.14) of the form

$$\int_0^\rho \frac{1}{x}J_1^*(\lambda_i x)J_1^*(\lambda_j x)\,dx = \frac{(\lambda_i\rho)(\lambda_j\rho)}{4J_0(\lambda_i)J_0(\lambda_j)}\sum_{n=0}^\infty$$

$$\cdot\frac{(-1)^n(\lambda_i\rho/2)^{2n}\,_2F_1[-n, -n-1; 2; (\lambda_j/\lambda_i)^2]}{n!(2n+2)(2)_n}$$

(3-122)

Differentiating equation (3-118) with respect to ρ yields

$$F_{,\rho\rho} = -\tfrac{1}{8}Eh^2\sum_{i=1}^\infty\sum_{j=1}^\infty a_i a_j f_{ij,\rho} + \frac{C_1}{2}$$

(3-123)

For convenience the constant C_1 is written in the form

$$C_1 = \frac{Eh^2}{4}\sum_{i=1}^\infty\sum_{j=1}^\infty d_{ij}a_i a_j$$

(3-124)

where d_{ij} are coefficients to be determined by the prescribed boundary conditions. Now let us consider the following sets of boundary conditions

(a) Rigidly clamped edge

$$w_n = w_{n,\rho} = 0 \qquad F_{,\rho\rho} - vF_{,\rho} = 0 \qquad \text{at} \quad \rho = 1$$

(3-125)

(*b*) Loosely clamped edge

$$w_n = w_{n,\,\rho} = F_{,\rho} = 0 \qquad \text{at} \quad \rho = 1 \tag{3-126}$$

(*c*) Simply supported edge

$$w_n = F_{,\rho} = 0 \qquad w_{n,\,\rho\rho} + v w_{n,\,\rho} = 0 \qquad \text{at} \quad \rho = 1 \tag{3-127}$$

(*d*) Hinged edge

$$w_n = 0 \qquad w_{n,\,\rho\rho} + v w_{n,\,\rho} = 0 \qquad F_{,\rho\rho} - v F_{,\rho} = 0 \tag{3-128}$$

In addition to the above conditions, $w_{,r}$ and N_r remain finite at the center of the plate ($\rho = 0$).

The condition $w_n(1) = 0$ is satisfied by each term of the series (3-114). For movable $(N_r|_{\rho=1} = 0)$ and immovable $(u_r|_{\rho=1} = 0)$ edges the following is obtained:

$$d_{ij} = f_{ij}(1) \tag{3-129}$$

$$d_{ij} = (1 - v)[f_{ij,\,\rho}(1) - v f_{ij}(1)] \tag{3-130}$$

The boundary conditions for the vanishing of slope and bending moment require

$$I_1(\lambda_n)J_0(\lambda_n) + I_0(\lambda_n)J_1(\lambda_n) = 0 \tag{3-131}$$

$$(1 - v)[I_0(\lambda_n)J_1(\lambda_n) + I_1(\lambda_n)J_0(\lambda_n)] - 2\lambda_n I_0(\lambda_n)J_0(\lambda_n) = 0 \tag{3-132}$$

The first three roots of equations (3-131) and (3-132) are given in Table 3.1. The values of d_{ij} and λ_n are thus given by equations (3-130) and (3-131) for a rigidly clamped edge, by equations (3-129) and (3-131) for a loosely clamped edge, by equations (3-129) and (3-132) for a movable simply supported edge, and by equations (3-130) and (3-132) for a hinged edge (or immovable simply supported edge).

The functions w and $F_{,\rho}$ constructed above satisfy the compatibility equation (3-111) and the prescribed boundary conditions but generally not the equilibrium equation (3-110). That is, the residual L will not vanish identically because of the assumed deflection function. Instead of satisfaction of equation (3-110), the Galerkin procedure is applied in obtaining an approximate solution. Upon substitution equation (3-110) can be put in the form

$$L(w_n, a_n) = \sum_{n=1}^{\infty} \left\{ (\lambda_n^4 + \alpha) w_n a_n + 1.5(1 - v^2) \right.$$

$$\left. \cdot \left[w_{n,\,\rho\rho} a_n \sum_{i=1}^{\infty} \sum_{j=1}^{\infty} (f_{ij} - d_{ij}\rho) a_i a_j + w_{n,\,\rho} a_n \sum_{i=1}^{\infty} \sum_{j=1}^{\infty} (f_{ij,\,\rho} - d_{ij}) a_i a_j \right] \right\}$$

$$- 10.92 \frac{q_0 a^4}{Eh^4} \tag{3-133}$$

Table 3.1 Roots of equations (3-131) and (3-132) for $v = 0.3$

n	Clamped	Simply supported
1	3.19622	2.22152
2	6.30644	5.45161
3	9.43950	8.61139

According to Galerkin, each of the weighted averages of the residual L over the plate area with respect to the weighting function w_n $(n = 1, 2, \ldots)$ should vanish, i.e.,

$$\int_0^1 L(w_n, a_n) w_n(\rho) \, d\rho = 0 \qquad n = 1, 2, 3, \ldots \qquad (3\text{-}134)$$

Performing integration and taking $v = 0.3$ equation (3-134) yields the following set of algebraic equations

$$(\lambda_n^4 + \alpha)\gamma_n + 1.365 w_n(0) \sum_{i=1}^{\infty} \sum_{j=1}^{\infty} \sum_{k=1}^{\infty} \delta_n ijk\gamma_i\gamma_j\gamma_k - \frac{\delta_n q_0 a^4}{Eh^4} = 0$$

$$n = 1, 2, 3, \ldots \qquad (3\text{-}135)$$

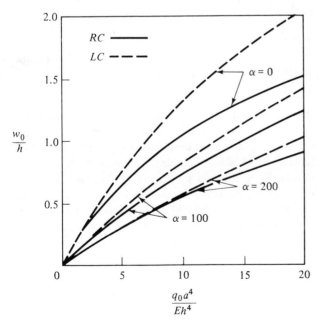

Figure 3.8 Central deflection of rigidly (RC) and loosely (LC) clamped plate on elastic foundation loaded by uniform lateral pressure ($v = 0.3$).

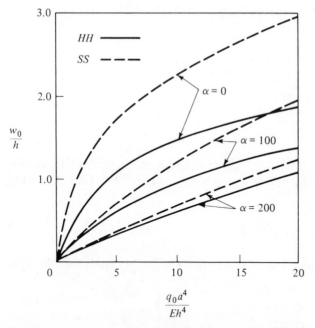

Figure 3.9 Central deflection of hinged (*HH*) and simply supported (*SS*) circular plates on elastic foundation loaded by uniform lateral pressure ($v = 0.3$).

where

$$\gamma_n = a_n w_n(0)$$

$$\delta_n = 10.92 w_n(0) \int_0^1 \frac{w_n \rho}{\int_0^1 w_n^2 \rho \, d\rho} \, d\rho \tag{3-136}$$

Taking the terms up to $n = 3$, equations (3-135) can be solved numerically. The resulting central deflection w_0 is plotted in Figs. 3.8 and 3.9 against uniform lateral load for various edge conditions and different values of the foundation modulus. These figures indicate that the effect of an elastic foundation is to reduce the deflection and is proportionally greater in plates with movable edges. The results for α or $k = 0$ are in good agreement with the load-deflection relations given by equations (3-36), (3-40), (3-42), and (3-44). The numerical results for radial membrane and bending stresses given in Ref. 3.13 are not presented herein. It was found that the third term γ_3 contributed significantly to the bending stress but only a small amount to the deflection and membrane stresses. Furthermore its relative importance increased with increasing foundation stiffness.

3.8 CLAMPED ELLIPTICAL PLATE SUBJECTED TO UNIFORM TRANSVERSE LOAD

An approximate solution for a uniformly loaded elliptical plate (Fig. 3.10) undergoing the moderately large deflection will be formulated by use of the Ritz method (Ref. 3.15). In the case of rigidly clamped edge the boundary conditions are

$$u^\circ = v^\circ = w = w_{,n} = 0 \quad \text{at the boundary} \quad \frac{x^2}{a^2} + \frac{y^2}{b^2} - 1 = 0 \quad (3\text{-}137)$$

in which n is the outward normal to the boundary and a and b are the semi-axes of the plate. The last condition implies that $w_{,x} = w_{,y} = 0$ along the boundary.

Let us introduce the new variables

$$W = \frac{w}{h} \qquad U = \frac{u^\circ}{h^2} \qquad V = \frac{v^\circ}{h^2} \qquad Q = \frac{2q_0}{Dh} \qquad (3\text{-}138)$$

where q_0 is the intensity of transverse uniform load. Upon substitution the total potential energy of the system given by equations (2-144) to (2-147) assumes the form for the clamped plate

$$\Pi = 24Dh^2 \int_0^b \int_0^{a\sqrt{1 - y^2/b^2}} \left\{ \frac{1}{3}[(W_{,xx} + W_{,yy})^2 - QW] \right.$$

$$+ U_{,x}^2 + U_{,x}W_{,x}^2 + V_{,y}^2 + V_{,y}W_{,y}^2 + \frac{1}{4}(W_{,x}^2 + W_{,y}^2)^2$$

$$+ v[2U_{,x}V_{,y} + U_{,x}W_{,y}^2 + V_{,y}W_{,x}^2]$$

$$\left. + \frac{1 - v}{2}[(U_{,y} + V_{,x})^2 + 2(U_{,y} + V_{,x})W_{,x}W_{,y}] \right\} dx\, dy \qquad (3\text{-}139)$$

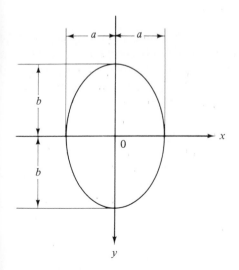

Figure 3.10 Geometry of elliptical plate.

The boundary conditions (3-137) can be written in the form

$$U = V = W = W_{,x} = W_{,y} = 0 \qquad \text{at the boundary} \qquad (3\text{-}140)$$

The boundary and symmetry conditions are satisfied by taking

$$W = \left(1 - \frac{x^2}{a^2} - \frac{y^2}{b^2}\right)^2 \sum_{m=0}^{\infty} \sum_{n=0}^{\infty} a_{2m,\,2n} x^{2m} y^{2n}$$

$$U = x\left(1 - \frac{x^2}{a^2} - \frac{y^2}{b^2}\right) \sum_{m=0}^{\infty} \sum_{n=0}^{\infty} b_{2m,\,2n} x^{2m} y^{2n} \qquad (3\text{-}141)$$

$$V = y\left(1 - \frac{x^2}{a^2} - \frac{y^2}{b^2}\right) \sum_{m=0}^{\infty} \sum_{n=0}^{\infty} c_{2m,\,2n} x^{2m} y^{2n}$$

Naturally it is impossible to determine all the coefficients a's, b's, and c's in these series (3-141) by the Ritz method. Thus we take as an approximate solution

$$W = \left(1 - \frac{x^2}{a^2} - \frac{y^2}{b^2}\right)^2 (a_{00} + a_{20} x^2 + a_{02} y^2)$$

$$U = x\left(1 - \frac{x^2}{a^2} - \frac{y^2}{b^2}\right)(b_{00} + b_{20} x^2 + b_{02} y^2 + b_{22} x^2 y^2) \qquad (3\text{-}142)$$

$$V = y\left(1 - \frac{x^2}{a^2} - \frac{y^2}{b^2}\right)(c_{00} + c_{20} x^2 + c_{02} y^2 + c_{22} x^2 y^2)$$

These expressions are now substituted into equation (3-139). Performing the integration, the resulting energy expression will be a function of the eleven coefficients whose numerical values can be determined from the condition that

$$\Pi_{,a_{00}} = \Pi_{,a_{20}} = \Pi_{,a_{02}} = 0$$

$$\Pi_{,b_{00}} = \Pi_{,b_{20}} = \Pi_{,b_{02}} = \Pi_{,b_{22}} = 0 \qquad (3\text{-}143)$$

$$\Pi_{,c_{00}} = \Pi_{,c_{20}} = \Pi_{,c_{02}} = \Pi_{,c_{22}} = 0$$

In equations (3-143) the first three equations will be cubic in the a_{mn} and linear in the b_{mn} and c_{mn}, and the other equations will contain only linear terms in the b_{mn} and c_{mn} along with the quadratic terms in the a_{mn}. In the numerical procedure the latter eight equations can be first solved for the eight b_{mn} and c_{mn} parameters and expressed in terms of the a_{mn}. On substitution the first three of equations (3-143) will result in three simultaneous cubic equations which can be solved by the Newton-Raphson method to yield the a_{mn} in terms of Q. As soon as the transverse deflection and two inplane displacements are determined, membrane forces, bending moments, and transverse shearing forces can be found from equations (1-121) to (1-123).

The present solution for elliptical plates is specified for the infinite strip by setting $b = \infty$, $a/b = 0$, so that neither transverse deflection nor inplane displacements can be a function of y. This condition is satisfied only if

$$a_{02} = b_{02} = b_{22} = c_{00} = c_{20} = c_{02} = c_{22} = 0$$

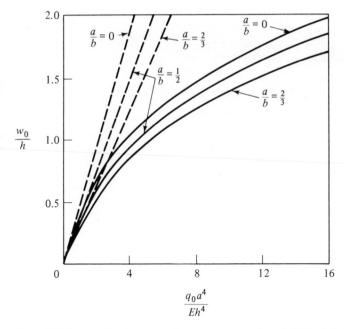

Figure 3.11 Load-deflection curves for various axes ratios of elliptical plate under uniform transverse load ($v = 0.3$).

The relationship between central deflection w_0 and uniformly distributed load q_0 is shown in Fig. 3.11 for various ratios of minor axis to major axis of an elliptical plate. The straight dash lines are obtained from the small-deflection theory such as given in Ref. 1.4. For a given load, the deflection increases as the axes ratio a/b decreases, holding the width of the plates constant as shown in Fig. 3.10. The deviation between the elementary and large-deflection solutions increases progressively with the magnitude of loading. In general the error involved in the elementary solution becomes significant when the central deflection of the plate exceeds 30 percent of the plate thickness. In the case of an infinite strip a good agreement for deflections is found between the present solution and the perturbation solution discussed in Sec. 2.5.

3.9 SKEW PLATE UNDER UNIFORM LATERAL PRESSURE

For skew plates it is more convenient to adopt a system of oblique coordinates α and β as shown in Fig. 3.12. Thus rectangular coordinates x, y are related to oblique coordinates by

$$x = \alpha \cos \theta \qquad y = \beta + \alpha \sin \theta \qquad (3\text{-}144)$$

in which θ is the skew angle.

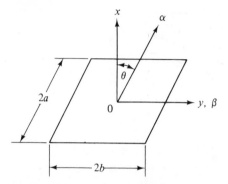

Figure 3.12 Geometry of skew plate.

If the oblique dimensions of the plate are denoted by $2a$ and $2b$, and if the following dimensionless quantities are introduced

$$R = \frac{b}{a} \qquad \zeta = \frac{\alpha}{a} \qquad \eta = \frac{\beta}{b} \qquad Q = \frac{q_0 b^4}{Dh}$$

$$U = \frac{u^\circ a}{h^2} \qquad V = \frac{v^\circ a}{h^2} \qquad W = \frac{w}{h} \tag{3-145}$$

equations (1-117) to (1-119) in the static case can be written in terms of dimensionless oblique coordinates as

$$
\begin{aligned}
&2R^3 c U_{,\zeta\zeta} - 4R^2 sc U_{,\zeta\eta} + R[2s^2 c + (1-v)c^3]U_{,\eta\eta} \\
&\quad + Rc^2(1+v)(RV_{,\zeta\eta} - sV_{,\eta\eta}) + 2R^2 W_{,\zeta\zeta}(RW_{,\zeta} - sW_{,\eta}) \\
&\quad - RW_{,\zeta\eta}\{4RsW_{,\zeta} - W_{,\eta}[4s^2 + (1+v)c^2]\} \\
&\quad + W_{,\eta\eta}[RW_{,\zeta}(1+s^2 - vc^2) - 2sW_{,\eta}] = 0
\end{aligned} \tag{3-146}
$$

$$
\begin{aligned}
&R(1 + c^2 - vs^2)V_{,\eta\eta} - 2R^2 s(1-v)V_{,\zeta\eta} + R^3(1-v)V_{,\zeta\zeta} \\
&\quad + (1+v)(R^2 c U_{,\zeta\eta} - Rsc U_{,\eta\eta}) + W_{,\eta\eta}[2W_{,\eta} - Rs(1+v)W_{,\zeta}] \\
&\quad - RW_{,\zeta\eta}[s(3-v)W_{,\eta} - R(1+v)W_{,\zeta}] + R^2(1-v)W_{,\zeta\zeta}W_{,\eta} = 0
\end{aligned} \tag{3-147}
$$

$$
\begin{aligned}
&R^4 W_{,\zeta\zeta\zeta\zeta} - 4Rs(R^2 W_{,\zeta\zeta\zeta\eta} + W_{,\zeta\eta\eta\eta}) + 2R^2(1 + 2s^2)W_{,\zeta\zeta\eta\eta} + W_{,\eta\eta\eta\eta} \\
&\quad = Qc^4 + 12\{Rc(RU_{,\zeta} - sU_{,\eta}) + \tfrac{1}{2}(RW_{,\zeta} - sW_{,\eta})^2 \\
&\qquad + vc^2[RV_{,\eta} + \tfrac{1}{2}W_{,\eta}^2]\} \\
&\quad \cdot (R^2 W_{,\zeta\zeta} - 2RsW_{,\zeta\eta} + s^2 W_{,\eta\eta}) + 12c^2 W_{,\eta\eta} \\
&\quad \cdot \{Rc^2 V_{,\eta} + \tfrac{1}{2}(cW_{,\eta})^2 + v[Rc^2 U_{,\zeta} - Rsc U_{,\eta} + \tfrac{1}{2}(RW_{,\zeta} - sW_{,\eta})^2]\} \\
&\quad + 12(1-v)[R^2 c V_{,\zeta} - Rsc V_{,\eta} \\
&\quad + W_{,\eta}(RcW_{,\zeta} - scW_{,\eta})] + Rc^2 U_{,\eta}](RcW_{,\zeta\eta} - scW_{,\eta\eta})
\end{aligned} \tag{3-148}
$$

where

$$s = \sin \theta \qquad c = \cos \theta \tag{3-149}$$

If the skew plate is rigidly clamped along the edges, the appropriate boundary conditions are

$$u^\circ = v^\circ = w = w_{,n} = 0 \qquad \text{at} \quad \beta = \pm b$$

$$u^\circ = v^\circ = w = w_{,x} = 0 \qquad \text{at} \quad \alpha = \pm a$$

or

$$U = V = W = W_{,n} = 0 \qquad \text{at} \quad \eta = \pm 1$$

$$U = V = W = W_{,x} = 0 \qquad \text{at} \quad \zeta = \pm 1 \tag{3-150}$$

Hence the problem of large deflections of the skew plate is reduced to finding a solution to equations (3-146) to (3-148) satisfying conditions (3-150).

The perturbation technique used in obtaining an approximate solution of the boundary-value problem (Ref. 3.16) requires the expansion of the dimensionless displacement components and load into the series of ascending powers of the dimensionless center deflection parameter W_0 $(= w_0/h)$.

$$Q = \sum_{n=1}^{\infty} q_{2n-1} W_0^{2n-1} \qquad W = \sum_{n=1}^{\infty} w_{2n-1}(\zeta, \eta) W_0^{2n-1}$$

$$U = \sum_{n=1}^{\infty} u_{2n}(\zeta, \eta) W_0^{2n} \qquad V = \sum_{n=1}^{\infty} v_{2n}(\zeta, \eta) W_0^{2n} \tag{3-151}$$

From the series for W, the deflection at the plate center requires

$$w_1(0, 0) = 1 \qquad \text{and} \qquad w_i(0, 0) = 0 \qquad i = 3, 5, 7, \dots \tag{3-152}$$

Substituting equations (3-151) into equations (3-146) to (3-148) and (3-150) and equating powers of W_0 yields a series of differential equations and boundary conditions. For the first-order approximation the differential equation for skewed plates with small deflections is given by

$$R^4 w_{1,\zeta\zeta\zeta\zeta} - 4R^3 s w_{1,\zeta\zeta\zeta\eta} - 4R s w_{1,\zeta\eta\eta\eta}$$
$$+ 2R^2(1 + 2s^2) w_{1,\zeta\zeta\eta\eta} + w_{1,\eta\eta\eta\eta} = q_1 c^4 \tag{3-153}$$

and the associated boundary conditions by

$$w_1 = w_{1,n} = 0 \qquad \text{at} \quad \eta = \pm 1$$

$$w_1 = w_{1,x} = 0 \qquad \text{at} \quad \zeta = \pm 1 \tag{3-154}$$

It can be readily verified that conditions (3-154) are identically satisfied when

$$w_1 = (1 - \eta^2)^2 (1 - \zeta^2)^2 (1 - \zeta\eta)(1 + A_1 \eta^2 + A_2 \zeta^2 + A_3 \eta^4 + A_4 \zeta^4 + A_5 \zeta^2 \eta^2) \tag{3-155}$$

which meets the first condition in equation (3-152) as well as the geometrical requirements

$$w_1(\zeta, \eta) = w_1(-\zeta, -\eta) \quad \text{and} \quad w_1(-\zeta, \eta) = w_1(\zeta, -\eta) \quad (3\text{-}156)$$

Inserting expression (3-155) into equation (3-153) and equating corresponding powers of ζ and η, we can generate six linear algebraic equations for coefficients $q_1, A_1, \ldots, A_5$. The solution of this matrix equation defines the value of the small deflection of the plate everywhere.

When the terms in powers of W_0^2 are equated, the following differential equations governing the two inplane-displacements functions are obtained

$$2R^3 cu_{2,\zeta\zeta} - 4R^2 scu_{2,\zeta\eta} + R[2s^2c + (1-v)c^3]u_{2,\eta\eta}$$
$$+ Rc^2(1+v)(Rv_{2,\zeta\eta} - sv_{2,\eta\eta}) + 2R^2 w_{1,\zeta\zeta}(Rw_{1,\zeta} - sw_{1,\eta})$$
$$- Rw_{1,\zeta\eta}\{4Rsw_{1,\zeta} - w_{1,\eta}[4s^2 + (1+v)c^2]\}$$
$$+ w_{1,\eta\eta}[Rw_{1,\zeta}(1 + s^2 - vc^2) - 2sw_{1,\eta}] = 0 \qquad (3\text{-}157)$$

$$R(1 + c^2 - vs^2)v_{2,\eta\eta} - 2R^2 s(1-v)v_{2,\zeta\eta} + R^3(1-v)v_{2,\zeta\zeta}$$
$$+ (1+v)(R^2 cu_{2,\zeta\eta} - Rscu_{2,\eta\eta}) + w_{1,\eta\eta}[2w_{1,\eta} - Rs(1+v)w_{1,\zeta}]$$
$$- Rw_{1,\zeta\eta}[s(3-v)w_{1,\eta} - R(1+v)w_{1,\zeta}] + R^2(1-v)w_{1,\zeta\zeta}w_{,\eta} = 0 \qquad (3\text{-}158)$$

The corresponding boundary conditions imposed on the inplane displacements are

$$u_2 = v_2 = 0 \quad \text{at} \quad \eta = \pm 1 \quad \text{and} \quad \zeta = \pm 1 \qquad (3\text{-}159)$$

These conditions are satisfied by taking

$$u_2 = (1 - \zeta^2)(1 - \eta^2)(B_1\zeta + B_2\eta + B_3\zeta^3 + B_4\eta^3 + B_5\zeta\eta^2$$
$$+ B_6\zeta^2\eta + B_7\zeta^3\eta^2 + B_8\zeta^2\eta^3)$$
$$v_2 = (1 - \zeta^2)(1 - \eta^2)(C_1\eta + C_2\zeta + C_3\eta^3 + C_4\zeta^3 + C_5\zeta^2\eta$$
$$+ C_6\zeta\eta^2 + C_7\zeta^2\eta^3 + C_8\zeta^3\eta^2) \qquad (3\text{-}160)$$

which also meet the physical requirements

$$u_2(\zeta, \eta) = -u_2(-\zeta, -\eta) \qquad u_2(-\zeta, \eta) = -u_2(\zeta, -\eta)$$
$$v_2(\zeta, \eta) = -v_2(-\zeta, -\eta) \qquad v_2(-\zeta, \eta) = -v_2(\zeta, -\eta) \qquad (3\text{-}161)$$

Substituting expressions (3-155) and (3-160) into equations (3-157) and (3-158) and equating powers of ζ and η leads to sufficient linear algebraic equations to determine the 16 undetermined coefficients B_i and C_i and hence the inplane displacements.

Collecting the coefficients of W_0^3-terms we obtain the differential equation

$$R^4 w_{3,\zeta\zeta\zeta\zeta} - 4Rs(R^2 w_{3,\zeta\zeta\zeta\eta} + w_{3,\zeta\eta\eta\eta}) + 2R^2(1 + 2s^2)w_{3,\zeta\zeta\eta\eta} + w_{3,\eta\eta\eta\eta}$$
$$= q_3 c^4 + 12\{Rc(Ru_{2,\zeta} - su_{2,\eta}) + \tfrac{1}{2}(Rw_{1,\zeta} - sw_{1,\eta})^2$$
$$+ vc^2[Rv_{2,\eta} + \tfrac{1}{2}(w_{1,\eta})^2]\}$$

▼

$\cdot (R^2 w_{1,\zeta\zeta} - 2Rs w_{1,\zeta\eta} + s^2 w_{1,\eta\eta}) + 12c^2 w_{1,\eta\eta}$

$\cdot \{Rc^2 v_{2,\eta} + \tfrac{1}{2}(cw_{1,\eta})^2 + v[Rc^2 u_{2,\zeta} - Rscu_{2,\eta} + \tfrac{1}{2}(Rw_{1,\zeta} - sw_{1,\eta})^2]\}$

$+ 12(1 - v)[R^2 cv_{2,\zeta} - Rscv_{2,\eta} + w_{1,\eta}(Rcw_{1,\zeta} - scw_{1,\eta}) + Rc^2 u_{2,\eta}]$

$\cdot (Rcw_{1,\zeta\eta} - scw_{1,\eta\eta})$ \hfill (3-162)

and the boundary conditions

$$w_3 = w_{3,\eta} = 0 \qquad \text{at} \quad \eta = \pm 1$$

$$w_3 = w_{3,x} = 0 \qquad \text{at} \quad \zeta = \pm 1$$

\hfill (3-163)

These conditions and the second condition in equation (3-152) are identically satisfied by taking

$$w_3 = (1 - \eta^2)^2 (1 - \zeta^2)^2 (1 - \zeta\eta)(D_1 \eta^2 + D_2 \zeta^2 + D_3 \eta^4 + D_4 \zeta^4 + D_5 \zeta^2 \eta^2)$$
\hfill (3-164)

The procedure of the determination of D_i and q_3 is very similar to that in the first-order approximation.

Following much the same procedure as outlined herein, variable coefficients u_4, v_4, and w_5 and constant coefficient q_5 can be found. Such details are omitted here for brevity.

Let us define the nondimensional bending and membrane stresses by

$$[\sigma_\zeta^b, \sigma_\eta^b, \sigma_\zeta^m, \sigma_\eta^m] = \frac{b^2(1 - v^2)}{Eh^2}[\sigma_x^b, \sigma_y^b, \sigma_x^m, \sigma_y^m]$$

\hfill (3-165)

$$[\sigma_{\zeta\eta}^b, \sigma_{\zeta\eta}^m] = \frac{b^2}{Gh^2}[\sigma_{xy}^b, \sigma_{xy}^m]$$

in which σ_x^b, σ_y^b, σ_{xy}^b are the extreme-fiber bending stresses and σ_x^m, σ_y^m, σ_{xy}^m are the membrane stresses in the middle surface. In terms of rectangular coordinates these stresses are related to displacement components by equations (1-121), (1-122), and (1-123). By means of the transformation equations (3-144) these non-dimensional stresses can be expressed in terms of the nondimensional oblique coordinates as follows

$$\sigma_\zeta^b = -\tfrac{1}{2}[R^2 \sec^2 \theta \ W_{,\zeta\zeta} - 2R \sec \theta \tan \theta \ W_{,\zeta\eta}$$
$$+ (v + \tan^2 \theta)W_{,\eta\eta}]$$

$$\sigma_\eta^b = -\tfrac{1}{2}[(1 + v \tan^2 \theta)W_{,\eta\eta} + v(R^2 \sec^2 \theta \ W_{,\zeta\zeta}$$
$$- 2R \sec \theta \tan \theta \ W_{,\zeta\eta})]$$
\hfill (3-166)

$$\sigma_{\zeta\eta}^b = R \sec \theta \ W_{,\zeta\eta} - \tan \theta \ W_{,\eta\eta}$$

and

$$\sigma_\zeta^m = R^2 \sec \theta \ U_{,\zeta} - R \tan \theta \ U_{,\eta} + vRV_{,\eta}$$
$$+ \tfrac{1}{2}[R^2 \sec^2 \theta \ W_{,\zeta}^2 + (v + \tan^2 \theta)$$
$$\cdot W_{,\eta}^2 - 2R \sec \theta \tan \theta \ W_{,\zeta} W_{,\eta}]$$

$$\sigma_\eta^m = RV_{,\eta} + \tfrac{1}{2}(1 + \nu \tan^2 \theta)W_{,\eta}^2$$
$$+ \nu\{R^2 \sec \theta \ U_{,\zeta} - R \tan \theta \ U_{,\eta}$$
$$+ \tfrac{1}{2}[R^2 \sec^2 \theta \ W_{,\zeta}^2 - 2R \sec \theta \tan \theta \ W_{,\zeta} W_{,\eta}]\} \tag{3-167}$$
$$\sigma_{\zeta\eta}^m = RU_{,\eta} + R^2 \sec \theta \ V_{,\zeta} - R \tan \theta \ V_{,\eta} + W_{,\eta}(R \sec \theta \ W_{,\zeta} - \tan \theta \ W_{,\eta})$$

The maximum deflection w_0 at the center of a skewed plate is plotted in Fig. 3.13 against the uniform transverse pressure q_0 for various values of the skew angle θ and the side ratio b/a. This figure indicates that the maximum deflection decreases with increasing the skew angle. This is mainly because the rigidity of the obtuse corners increases as the skew angle increases. Furthermore, the maximum deflection also decreases with increasing the ratio b/a (≤ 1). It is observed that the present result for rectangular plates ($\theta = 0°$) does not agree very well with the perturbation solution discussed in Sec. 2.5. The discrepancy arises from the fact that the present assumed expressions for the three displacement components provide polar symmetry rather than quadrant symmetry which is required for rectangular plates. Due to the restrictive symmetry, numerical results were obtained by taking the terms in equations (3-151) up to the fifth power of W_0. In some cases with the skew angle as high as 60 degrees, the fifth-order approximations, however, were discarded since the results with their inclusion began to diverge. This phenomenon of divergence associated with the perturbation expansion technique has been fully discussed in Sec. 1.9 and Ref. 3.17.

It is pointed out in Ref. 3.16 that experimental results were in close agreement with the present theoretical values for deflections and total principal edge and center stresses, but the experimental results are not reproduced herein.

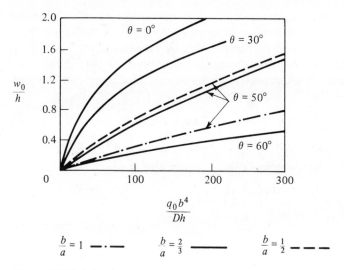

Figure 3.13 Relation between uniform lateral load and maximum deflection of skewed plate with rigidly clamped edges for various values of skew angle and aspect ratio ($\nu = 0.333$).

PROBLEMS

3.1 Verify formulas (3-40).

3.2 A rigidly clamped isotropic circular plate of radius a is subjected to a concentrated load P at its center. As an approximate solution to the moderately large deflection behavior of the plate the transverse deflection w and radial displacement u_r may be taken to be

$$w = w_0\left(1 - \frac{r^2}{a^2}\right)^2 \qquad u_r = Cr(a - r)$$

where w_0 and C are constants to be determined. These expressions satisfy the required boundary conditions.

    Use the given displacement functions to obtain the load-deflection relation by virtue of the Ritz method and evaluate the membrane force N_r at the center as well as at the boundary of the plate. Compare the numerical results with those obtained from formulas (3-62) and (3-63).

3.3 Derive the load-deflection relation for the graphical results shown in Fig. 3.7.

3.4 Solve the boundary-value problem in Sec. 3.8 by use of the perturbation technique. (See the exact solution of the small-deflection equation for a clamped elliptical plate on page 311 of Ref. 1.4).

3.5 Employ the Ritz energy method to solve the boundary-value problem in Sec. 3.9.

3.6 The thickness of an isotropic skew plate of lateral dimensions $a \times b$ with oblique coordinates α, β is assumed to vary only in the α direction, i.e.,

$$h(\alpha) = h_0\left(1 + \xi\frac{\alpha}{a}\right)$$

where $(1 + \xi)$ is the ratio of the plate thickness at $\alpha = a$ to that at $\alpha = 0$. If the plate is subjected to uniform transverse pressure q_0 and simply supported along its edges, the deflection function for small ξ may be approximated by

$$w = w_0 \sin\frac{\pi\alpha}{a} \sin\frac{\pi\beta}{b}$$

    Use the governing equations given in Prob. 1.4 to obtain an approximate load-deflection relation.

REFERENCES

3.1. E. H. Mansfield: "The Bending and Stretching of Plates," Pergamon Press, 1964.

3.2. J. J. Stoker: "Nonlinear Elasticity," Gordon and Breach Science Publishers, 1968.

3.3. W. Z. Chien: Large Deflection of a Circular Clamped Plate Under Uniform Pressure, *Chinese J. Phys.*, vol. 7, pp. 102–113, 1947.

3.4. S. Way: Bending of Circular Plate with Large Deflection, *Trans. ASME*, vol. 56, pp. 627–636, 1934.

3.5. W. Z. Chien and K. Y. Yeh: On the Large Deflection of Circular Plates, *Sci. Sin.*, vol. 3, pp. 405–436, 1954.

3.6. R. Schmidt: Large Deflections of a Clamped Circular Plate, *J. Eng. Mech. Div., Proc. ASCE*, vol. 94, no. EM6, pp. 1603–1606, 1968.

3.7. R. Schmidt: Finite Deflections of a Loosely Clamped Circular Plate Loaded at its Center, *J. Indust. Math. Soc.*, vol. 23, pp. 45–51, part 1, 1973.

3.8. D. Y. Panov and V. I. Feodos'ev: On Equilibrium and Loss of Stability of Shallow Shells with Large Deflections, *Prikl. Mat. Mekh.*, no. 4, pp. 398–406, 1948.

3.9. R. Schmidt and D. A. DaDeppo: Several Perturbation Solutions in the Nonlinear Theory of Circular Plates and Membranes, *J. Indust. Math. Soc.*, vol. 25, part 2, pp. 83–96, 1975.

3.10. A. S. Vol'mir: Flexible Plates and Shells (in Russian), Moscow, p. 193, 1956.

3.11. G. A. Wempner and R. Schmidt: Large Symmetric Deflections of Annular Plates, *ASME J. Appl. Mech.*, vol. 25, pp. 449–452, 1958.

3.12. K. Y. Yeh: Large Deflection of a Circular Plate With a Circular Hole at the Center, *Acta Sci. Sin.*, vol. 2, pp. 127–144, 1953.

3.13. R. Bolton: Stresses in Circular Plates on Elastic Foundations, *J. Eng. Mech. Div., Proc. ASCE*, vol. 98, no. EM3, pp. 629–640, 1972.

3.14. Y. L. Luke: "Integrals of Bessel Functions," McGraw-Hill Book Company, New York, pp. 254–259, 1962.

3.15. N. A. Weil and N. M. Newark: Large Deflections of Elliptical Plates, *ASME J. Appl. Mech.*, vol. 23, pp. 21–26, 1956.

3.16. J. B. Kennedy and S. Ng: Linear and Nonlinear Analyses of Skewed Plates, *ASME J. Appl. Mech.*, vol. 34, pp. 271–277, 1967.

3.17. M. Van Dyke: "Perturbation Methods in Fluid Mechanics," Academic Press Inc., New York, p. 27, 1964.

ADDITIONAL REFERENCES

Abdelmigid, S. B., and N. W. Williamson: A Grid Analogy for the Non-Linear Behaviour of Elastic Flat Plates, *Int. J. Mech. Sci.*, vol. 9, pp. 257–269, 1967.

Alzheimer, W. E., and R. T. Davis: Nonlinear Unsymmetrical Bending of an Annular Plate, *ASME J. Appl. Mech.*, vol. 35, pp. 190–192, 1968.

Ashwell, D. G.: The Equilibrium Equations of the Inextensional Theory for Thin Flat Plates, *Q. J. Mech. Appl. Math.*, vol. 10, part 2, pp. 170–182, 1957.

Banerjee, B.: Large Deflection of a Semi-Circular Plate Under a Uniform Load, *Bul. Acad. Polonaise Sci. Ser. Sci. Tech.*, vol. 15, pp. 183–187, 1967.

———: Note on the Large Deflection of a Circular Plate with Clamped Edge Under Symmetrical Load, *Bul. Calcutta Math. Soc.*, vol. 59, pp. 175–179, 1967.

———: Large Deflection of a Circular Plate of Variable Thickness Under Uniform Load by Strain Energy Method, *Bul. Calcutta Math. Soc.*, vol. 61, pp. 103–107, 1969.

Banerjee, M. M.: Note on the Large Deflections of Irregular Shaped Plates by the Method of Conformal Mapping, *ASME J. Appl. Mech.*, vol. 43, pp. 356–357, 1976.

Basuli, S.: Note on the Large Deflection of a Circular Plate Under a Concentrated Load, *Z. Angew, Math. Phys.*, vol. 12, pp. 357–362, 1961.

———: Note on the Large Deflection of a Circular Plate of Variable Thickness Under Lateral Loads, *Bul. Inst. Polit. Jasy.*, vol. 10, pp. 63–66, 1964.

Berger, H. M.: A New Approach to the Analysis of Large Deflections of Plates, *ASME J. Appl. Mech.*, vol. 22, pp. 465–472, 1955.

Bromberg, E.: Non-Linear Bending of a Circular Plate Under Normal Pressure, *Commun. Pure Appl. Math.* vol. 9, pp. 633–659, 1956.

Chien, W. Z.: Asymptotic Behavior of a Clamped Circular Plate Under Uniform Normal Pressure at Very Large Deflection, *Sci. Rep. Nat. Tsing Hua Univ.*, Ser. A, vol. 5, pp. 71–94, 1948.

Colville, J., E. B. Becker, and R. W. Furlong: Large Displacement Analysis of Thin Plates, *J. Struct. Div. Proc. ASCE*, vol. 99, no. ST3, pp. 349–364, 1973.

Cooley, I. D.: Large Deflections of a Clamped-Edge Thin Elliptical Plate Subject to an Elliptic Paraboloidal Loading, *Dev. Theor. Appl. Mech.*, vol. 4, Pergamon Press, pp. 597–610, 1970.

Cummins, G. W., J. L. Kaul, B. B. Parikh, R. Schmidt, and R. D. Wetjen: Correction of an Error in a Nonlinear Analysis of a Circular Plate, *J. Indust. Math. Soc.*, vol. 20, part 2, pp. 97–99, 1970.

Datta, S.: Large Deflection of a Circular Plate on Elastic Foundation Under a Concentrated Load at the Center. *ASME J. Appl. Mech.*, vol. 42, pp. 503–505, 1975.

Federhofer, K.: Über die Berechnung der dünnen Kreisplatte mit grosser Ausbiegung, *Eisenbau*, vol. 9, pp. 152–166, 1918.

————: Zur Berechnung der dünnen Kreispatte mit grosser Ausbiegung, *Forsch. Geb. Ingenieurwes.*, vol. 7, pp. 148–151, 1936.

————, and H. Egger: *Sitzungsber. Akad. Wiss. Wien.* IIa. vol. 155, p. 15, 1946.

Fung, Y. C., and W. H. Wittrick: A Boundary Layer Phenomenon in the Large Deflexion of Thin Plates, *Q. J. Mech. Appl. Math.*, vol. 8, part 2, pp. 191–210, 1955.

Hencky, H.: Über den Spannungszustand in kreisrunden Platten mit verschwinderden Biegungssteifigkeit, *Z. Math. Phys.*, vol. 63, pp. 311–317, 1915.

Koenig, H. A., R. E. Llorens, and P. C. Chou: Finite Deflections of an Elastic Circular Plate with a Central Hole, *ASME J. Appl. Mech.*, vol. 36, pp. 285–291, 1969.

Mah, G. B. J.: Axisymmetric Finite Deformation of Circular Plates, *J. Eng. Mech. Div. Proc. ASCE*, vol. 95, no. EM5, pp. 1125–1143, 1969.

Mansfield, E. H.: The Inextensional Theory for Thin Flat Plates, *Q. J. Mech. Appl. Math.*, vol. 8, part 3, pp. 338–352, 1955.

Mazumdar, J., and R. Jones: A Simplified Approach to the Analysis of Large Deflections of Plates, *ASME J. Appl. Mech.*, vol. 41, pp. 523–524, 1974.

Murthy, S. D. N., and A. N. Sherbourne: Nonlinear Bending of Elastic Plates of Variable Profile, *J. Eng. Mech. Div., Proc. ASCE*, vol. 100, no. EM2, pp. 251–265, 1974.

Nash, W. A., and I. D. Cooley: Large Deflections of a Clamped Elliptical Plate Subjected to Uniform Pressure, *ASME J. Appl. Mech.*, vol. 26, pp. 291–293, 1959.

Newman, M., and M. Forray: Axisymmetric Large Deflections of Circular Plates Subjected to Thermal and Mechanical Loads, *J. Aerosp. Sci.*, vol. 29, pp. 1060–1066, 1962.

Nowinski, J.: Large Deflections of Circular Plates Supported Along Their Boundary and Along Concentric Circumferences Inside, *MRC Tech. Sum. Rep. No. 67*, U.S. Army, University of Wisconsin, 1959.

Nowinski, J. L., and H. Ohnabe: On Certain Inconsistencies in Berger Equations for Large Deflections of Elastic Plates, *Int. J. Mech. Sci.*, vol. 14, pp. 165–170, 1972.

Pal, M. C.: Large Deflections of Heated Circular Plates, *Acta Mech.*, vol. 8, pp. 82–103, 1969.

Pao, Y. C.: A Generalized Analysis of Conically Bent Plates by Large Deflection Theory. *ASME J. Appl. Mech.*, vol. 35, pp. 778–781, 1968.

Reissner, E.: On Finite Deflections of Circular Plates, *Proc. Symp. Appl. Math.*, vol. 1, pp. 213–219, 1949.

————: A Problem of Finite Bending of Circular Ring Plates, *Q. Appl. Math.*, vol. 10, no. 2, pp. 167–173, 1952.

————: On Finite Twisting and Bending of Circular Ring Sector Plates and Shallow Helicoidal Shells, *Q. Appl. Math.*, vol. 11, no. 4, pp. 473–483, 1954.

Rivlin, R. S.: Large Elastic Deformations of Isotropic Materials, III. Some Simple Problems in Cylindrical Polar Coordinates, *Philos. Trans. R. Soc. London*, ser. A, vol. 240, pp. 509–525, 1948.

Schmidt, R.: A Remark on Berger's Method in the Nonlinear Theory of Plates, *J. Indust. Math. Soc.*, vol. 22, part 2, pp. 83–86, 1972.

————: On Berger's Method in the Nonlinear Theory of Plates, *ASME J. Appl. Mech.*, vol. 41, pp. 512–523, 1974.

————, and D. A. DaDeppo: A New Approach to the Analysis of Shells, Plates and Membranes with Finite Deflections, *Int. J. Non-Linear Mech.*, vol. 9, pp. 409–419, 1974.

————, and D. A. DaDeppo: On Nonlinear Equations Governing Axisymmetric Deflections of Circular Elastic Plates, *J. Indust. Math. Soc.*, vol. 25, part 2, pp. 67–81, 1975.

Srubshchik, L. S., and V. I. Indovich: The Asymptotic Representation of Equations of a Large Deflection of a Circular Symmetrical Loaded Plate, *Sib. Mat. Zh.*, vol. 4, no. 3, 1963.

Stippes, M., and A. H. Hausrath: Large Deflection of Circular Plates, *J. Appl. Mech., Trans. ASME*, vol. 74, pp. 287–292, 1952.

Srinivasan, R. S., and S. V. Ramachandran: Nonlinear Analysis of Skew Plates with Variable Thickness, *AIAA J.*, vol. 13, pp. 843–844, 1975.

Tadjbakhsh, I., and E. Saibel: On the Large Elastic Deflections of Plates, *ZAMM*, vol. 40, pp. 259–268, 1960.

FOUR

POSTBUCKLING BEHAVIOR AND NONLINEAR FLEXURAL VIBRATION OF ISOTROPIC PLATES

The two problems indicated in the title are discussed in this chapter. The first part is concerned with the postbuckling behavior of isotropic plates, and the second with the nonlinear flexural vibration. Brief introductions to these plate problems follow.

a Postbuckling Behavior

When a thin flat plate is under the action of edge compression in its middle plane, the plate is deformed but remains completely flat when the edge forces are sufficiently small. By increasing the load a state is reached when the flat form of equilibrium of the plate becomes unstable and the plate bends slightly. The in-plane compressive load which is just sufficient to keep the plate in a slightly bent form is called the critical load or the buckling load. Once the critical load is exceeded, the load-deflection relationship exhibits a stable character due to membrane forces which come into play. It is well known that, after buckling, a thin plate is still capable of carrying a much increased load without failure provided the buckling stress is in the elastic range. Therefore it is essential to consider the behavior of the plate after buckling, or the postbuckling behavior, in order to benefit from this additional strength and consequent weight savings of the plate material.

A precise analysis of postbuckling behavior is likely to prove quite difficult because of the use of the nonlinear plate theory and of the changes that occur in the buckled form with the load in the postbuckling range. These changes occur when the energy stored in the plate is sufficient to carry the plate from one buckled form to the other. In the usual postbuckling analysis the buckled form of thin plates is assumed to remain unchanged. This is a reasonable assumption in the immediate postbuckling range (for the postbuckling load less than about three times the buckling load). To obtain an accurate analysis of thin plates in a wide postbuckling range the changes in buckling mode must be taken into account. The most general method of dealing with this situation is to use more terms in the postbuckling analysis. This will describe accurately the behavior of plates at loads much higher than the buckling load.

Solutions are formulated for the postbuckling of square, rectangular, and circular plates with various edge conditions. The effects of transverse load and initial curvature of the middle surface are also included in Secs. 4.1 and 4.3. It will be recalled that solutions for the postbuckling of orthotropic, anisotropic, and laminated plates presented in Chaps. 6 and 8 can be specified for isotropic plates.

b Nonlinear Flexural Vibration

The external loads applied to a structural system invariably change with time. If the variations in time are small and occur over an extended interval, the inertial effects may be neglected and the behavior of the system can be approximately determined from considerations of equilibrium and material properties. However, in modern aircraft, spacecraft vehicles, and some civil engineering constructions, rapid time variations of loadings occur that must be considered in formulating structural design. In such cases inertial effects must be taken into account and the dynamic behavior of the system must be treated as a function of time. When the amplitudes of vibration of structures such as plates subjected to the effect of nuclear weapons and other blast loads do not remain small in comparison with the plate thickness, the nonlinear dynamic equations of plates are required to perform the analysis. Therefore, the moderately large-amplitude flexural vibrations of isotropic rectangular, circular, and skew plates with various boundary conditions are discussed in Secs. 4.7 to 4.12, with small-amplitude vibrations treated as a special case. In these investigations only single-mode expressions for the transverse deflection are used because a multimode approach leads to highly coupled nonlinear ordinary differential equations for the time function. The single-mode approach, however, gives good approximations for isotropic plates as shown in Sec. 6.8.

4.1 POSTBUCKLING OF SQUARE AND LONG RECTANGULAR PLATES

The double Fourier series solution formulated in Sec. 2.7 for a rectangular plate under the combined lateral and inplane loads can be used in discussion of the postbuckling behavior of the plate. The edges of the plate have been assumed to be

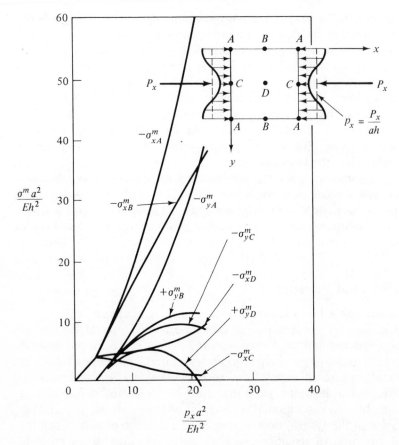

Figure 4.1 Membrane stresses for simply supported square plate under uniaxial edge compression ($v = 0.316$).

clamped in such a manner that they remain straight during loading. All-simply supported edges and the mixed simply supported and clamped edges can be treated as special cases. Let us consider the postbuckling behavior of the following simply supported plates.

a Square plate under uniaxial compression

In this case a solution (Ref. 2.13) is obtained by deleting equations (2-104) and (2-115) and setting $q_{mn} = 0$, $P_y = 0$, $\lambda = 1$, $A_p = B_p = C_q = H_q = 0$ in the equations of Sec. 2.7. In calculation the deflection function w given by equation (2-114) is limited to w_{11}, w_{13}, w_{31}, w_{33}, w_{15}, and w_{51}. For the stress function F, the first twenty-three F_{mn} terms in equation (2-116), with m and n always being even, are taken into account. The procedure for the solution is described in Sec. 2.7. Numerical results for $v = 0.316$ are shown in Fig. 4.1 for membrane stresses at various points in the plate, and in Fig. 4.5 for maximum deflections in comparison with the other solution. In this case the deflection coefficients w_{51} and w_{15} were found much smaller than w_{11}. Thus the solution converges rapidly.

b Long rectangular plate under combined uniform lateral pressure and uniaxial load

The rectangular plate under consideration is subjected to uniaxial compression P_x and uniform lateral pressure q_0 up to axial loads considerably exceeding the corresponding buckling load of the plate. A solution of this problem (Ref. 4.1) can be similarly obtained as in Case (a). In calculation the ratio of width to length of the plate is taken to be $\lambda = 4$ since this is typical of both hull-bottom plating and airplane wings. The deflection w is limited to $w_{11}, w_{31}, w_{51},$ and w_{71}. This will lead to four simultaneous cubic equations for the deflection coefficients. It was found that these equations could have more than one real solution. The numerical results for $q_0 b^4/Eh^4 = 12.02$ are shown graphically in Fig. 4.2 for axial load P_x as a function of average edge strain e. The most striking feature of this figure is that under some given values of q_0 and P_x the plate can be in equilibrium in more than

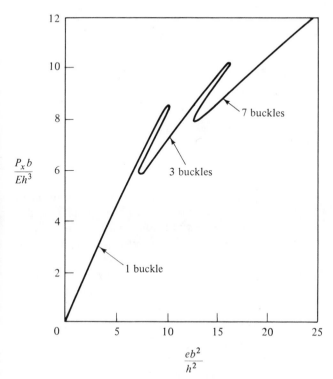

Figure 4.2 Relation between uniaxial compression and average edge strain for simply supported long rectangular plate under combined loads for $a/b = 4$ and $q_0 b^4/Eh^4 = 12.02$.

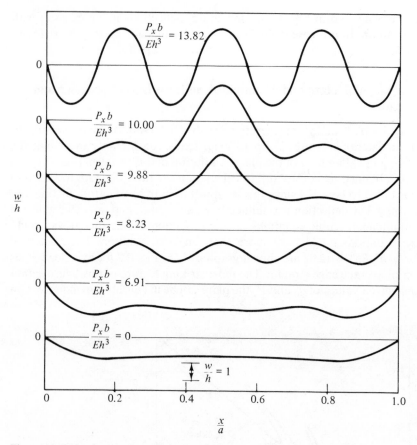

Figure 4.3 Deflection profiles along longitudinal center line of simply supported long rectangular plate $(a/b = 4)$ under combined loads for $q_0 b^4/Eh^4 = 12.02$.

one buckle pattern. For example, the long plate for $P_x b/Eh^3 = 8.0$ can be in stable equilibrium with 1 buckle at $eb^2/h^2 \approx 9.1$, 3 buckles at $eb^2/h^2 \approx 11.7$, and 7 buckles at $eb^2/h^2 \approx 13.2$, and in unstable equilibrium with 3 buckles at $eb^2/h^2 \approx 9.9$ and 7 buckles at $eb^2/h^2 \approx 12.6$. This behavior has also been observed experimentally.

The uniaxial compressive load P_x at which buckling occurs for a given lateral load is presented in Table 4.1. This table indicates that the critical load of the plate increases as the lateral load increases. Figure 4.3 shows the development of the buckled pattern along the longitudinal center line of the plate for a given q_0 and various values of P_x. The deflection profile is a single long bulge for lower values of P_x and gradually builds up to a regular buckled pattern at larger values of P_x. The shifting of the buckle pattern from 3 to 7 buckles is accompanied by a decrease in uniaxial load. The initial deflection produced by lateral load is almost entirely wiped out at large values of P_x.

Table 4.1 Critical load of long rectangular plate under combined loads ($\lambda = 4$)

$\dfrac{q_0 b^4}{Eh^4}$	0	2.40	12.02	24.03
$\dfrac{P_{cr} b}{Eh^3}$	3.84	4.05	8.56	11.8

4.2 POSTBUCKLING OF SIMPLY SUPPORTED RECTANGULAR PLATE UNDER UNIAXIAL COMPRESSION

Consider a rectangular isotropic plate of length $2a_0$ in the x direction, width $2b_0$ in the y direction, and thickness h in the z direction. The plate is assumed to be under the combined action of normal pressure $q(x, y)$ and inplane uniaxial compression P_x in the x direction, and to be simply supported along its four edges. The loaded edges are uniformly displaced and the unloaded edges are free from boundary forces. The boundary conditions for simply supported edges are

$$w = w_{,xx} = 0 \quad\quad \text{at} \quad x = \pm a_0$$
$$w = w_{,yy} = 0 \quad\quad \text{at} \quad y = \pm b_0$$
(4-1)

The additional conditions are, for the uniformly displaced edges,

$$u^{\circ} = \int_0^{a_0} \left[\frac{1}{E}(F_{,yy} - \nu F_{,xx}) - \tfrac{1}{2}w_{,x}^2 \right] dx = \delta$$

$$h \int_{-b_0}^{b_0} F_{,yy}\, dy = P_x$$

at $\quad x = \pm a_0$ (4-2)

and for the unloaded edges,

$$F_{,xx} = 0 \quad\quad \int_{-a_0}^{a_0} F_{,xx}\, dx = 0 \quad\quad \text{at} \quad y = \pm b_0 \quad (4\text{-}3)$$

in which δ is a constant normal displacement at $x = a_0$. It may be noticed that the boundary condition of zero shearing stress requires the resultant load to be constant, which is given by the last of conditions (4-2) and (4-3).

The differential equations governing the large-deflection behavior of the plate under lateral and inplane loads are given by equations (2-1) and (2-2). A solution of these equations is sought in the form of double Fourier series (Ref. 4.2)

$$w = \sum_{m=1,3,\ldots}^{\infty} \sum_{n=1,3,\ldots}^{\infty} W_{mn} \cos \frac{m\pi x}{2a_0} \cos \frac{n\pi y}{2b_0} \quad (4\text{-}4)$$

$$F = -\frac{p_x y^2}{2} + \sum_{r=0,\,2,\,\ldots}^{\infty} \sum_{s=0,\,2,\,\ldots}^{\infty} a_{rs} \cos \frac{r\pi x}{2a_0} \cos \frac{s\pi y}{2b_0} + F_2 \qquad (4\text{-}5)\dagger$$

where

$$F_2 = \sum_{r=2,\,4,\,\ldots}^{\infty} \cos \frac{r\pi x}{2a_0} \left[A_r \cosh \frac{r\pi y}{2a_0} + B_r \left(\frac{r\pi y}{2a_0} \right) \sinh \frac{r\pi y}{2a_0} \right]$$

$$+ \sum_{s=2,\,4,\,\ldots}^{\infty} \cos \frac{s\pi y}{2b_0} \left[C_s \cosh \frac{s\pi x}{2b_0} + D_s \left(\frac{s\pi x}{2b_0} \right) \sinh \frac{s\pi x}{2b_0} \right]$$

in which p_x is the average stress in the x direction at the edges $x = \pm a_0$. The series (4-4) for w satisfies the boundary conditions (4-1). Introduction of the series (4-5) for F in the last of conditions (4-2) and (4-3) yields

$$A_r = -B_r \left(1 + \frac{r\pi}{2\lambda} \coth \frac{r\pi}{2\lambda} \right)$$

$$C_s = -D_s \left(1 + \frac{s\pi\lambda}{2} \coth \frac{s\pi\lambda}{2} \right) \qquad (4\text{-}6)$$

where $\lambda = a_0/b_0$ is the aspect ratio of the plate. The first of conditions (4-2) and (4-3) requires

$$C_s = D_s = 0$$

$$\left(\cosh \frac{r\pi}{2\lambda} + \frac{r\pi/2\lambda}{\sinh \left(r\pi/2\lambda \right)} \right) B_r = \sum_{s=0,\,2,\,\ldots}^{\infty} (-1)^{s/2} a_{rs} \qquad (4\text{-}7)$$

Inserting equations (4-4) and (4-5) into the compatibility equation (2-2), transferring the multiple products of odd sines and cosines on the right-hand side into simple products of even cosines, and equating the coefficients of like cosine products, the following relation between the general coefficients of stress function and deflection is obtained

$$a_{rs} = \frac{E\lambda^2}{4(r^2 + s^2\lambda^2)^2} \sum_{k=1}^{9} d_k \qquad (4\text{-}8)$$

where

$$d_1 = \sum_{m=1}^{r-1} \sum_{n=1}^{s-1} [mn(r-m)(s-n) - m^2(s-n)^2] w_{mn} w_{(r-m)(s-n)}$$

$$\text{if } r \neq 0 \text{ and } s \neq 0$$

$$d_1 = 0 \qquad\qquad\qquad\qquad\qquad\qquad \text{if } r = 0 \text{ or } s = 0$$

$$d_2 = -\sum_{m=1}^{\infty} \sum_{n=1}^{s-1} [mn(m+r)(s-n) + m^2(s-n)^2] w_{mn} w_{(m+r)(s-n)}$$

$$\text{if } s \neq 0$$

$$d_2 = 0 \qquad\qquad\qquad\qquad\qquad\qquad\qquad \text{if } s = 0 \qquad\qquad \blacktriangledown$$

$\dagger$ F_2 satisfies the biharmonic equation $\nabla^4 F_2 = 0$.

$$d_3 = -\sum_{m=1}^{\infty}\sum_{n=1}^{s-1}[(m+r)nm(s-n)+(m+r)^2(s-n)^2]w_{(m+r)n}w_{m(s-n)} \qquad \blacktriangle$$

$$\text{if} \quad r \neq 0 \quad \text{and} \quad s \neq 0$$

$$d_3 = 0 \qquad\qquad\qquad \text{if} \quad r = 0 \quad \text{or} \quad s = 0$$

$$d_4 = -\sum_{m=1}^{r-1}\sum_{n=1}^{\infty}[mn(r-m)(n+s)+m^2(n+s)^2]w_{mn}w_{(r-m)(n+s)}$$

$$\text{if} \quad r \neq 0$$

$$d_4 = 0 \qquad\qquad\qquad \text{if} \quad r = 0$$

$$d_5 = -\sum_{m=1}^{r-1}\sum_{n=1}^{\infty}[m(n+s)(r-m)n+m^2n^2]w_{m(n+s)}w_{(r-m)n}$$

$$\text{if} \quad r \neq 0 \quad \text{and} \quad s \neq 0$$

$$d_5 = 0 \qquad\qquad\qquad \text{if} \quad r = 0 \quad \text{or} \quad s = 0$$

$$d_6 = \sum_{m=1}^{\infty}\sum_{n=1}^{\infty}[mn(m+r)(n+s)-m^2(n+s)^2]w_{mn}w_{(m+r)(n+s)} \qquad \blacktriangle$$

$$\text{if} \quad s \neq 0 \qquad\qquad (4\text{-}9)$$

$$d_6 = 0 \qquad\qquad\qquad \text{if} \quad r = 0 \quad \text{and} \quad s = 0$$

$$d_7 = \sum_{m=1}^{\infty}\sum_{n=1}^{\infty}[m(n+s)(m+r)n-m^2n^2]w_{m(n+s)}w_{(m+r)n}$$

$$\text{if} \quad r \neq 0 \quad \text{and} \quad s \neq 0$$

$$d_7 = 0 \qquad\qquad\qquad \text{if} \quad r = 0 \quad \text{or} \quad s = 0$$

$$d_8 = \sum_{m=1}^{\infty}\sum_{n=1}^{\infty}[(m+r)mn(n+s)-(m+r)^2(n+s)^2]w_{(m+r)n}w_{m(n+s)}$$

$$\text{if} \quad r \neq 0 \quad \text{and} \quad s \neq 0$$

$$d_8 = 0 \qquad\qquad\qquad \text{if} \quad r = 0 \quad \text{or} \quad s = 0$$

$$d_9 = \sum_{m=1}^{\infty}\sum_{n=1}^{\infty}[(m+r)(n+s)mn-(m+r)^2n^2]w_{(m+r)(n+s)}w_{mn}$$

$$\text{if} \quad r \neq 0$$

$$d_9 = 0 \qquad\qquad\qquad \text{if} \quad r = 0 \quad \text{and} \quad s = 0$$

For later use the following function of y is represented by a Fourier cosine series as

$$-B_r\left[\left(1+\frac{r\pi}{2\lambda}\coth\frac{r\pi}{2\lambda}\right)\cosh\frac{r\pi y}{2a_0}-\frac{r\pi y}{2a_0}\sinh\frac{r\pi y}{2a_0}\right] = \sum_{s=0,\,2,\,\ldots}^{\infty} b_{rs}\cos\frac{s\pi y}{2b_0} \qquad (4\text{-}10)$$

In this series the Fourier coefficients are given by

$$b_{rs} = (-1)^{(s+2)/2} \frac{\alpha r^3 \sinh (r\pi/2\lambda)}{\pi a_0^3 b_0 [(r/a_0)^2 + (s/b_0)^2]^2} B_r \tag{4-11}$$

where

$$\alpha = \begin{cases} 4 & \text{if} \quad s = 0 \\ 8 & \text{if} \quad s \neq 0 \end{cases} \tag{4-12}$$

Upon substitution equation (4-5) becomes

$$F = -\frac{p_x y^2}{2} + \sum_{r=0, 2, \ldots}^{\infty} \sum_{s=0, 2, \ldots}^{\infty} c_{rs} \cos \frac{r\pi x}{2a_0} \cos \frac{s\pi y}{2b_0} \tag{4-13}$$

in which

$$c_{rs} = a_{rs} + b_{rs} \tag{4-14}$$

The lateral normal pressure is also expanded into a double Fourier cosine series

$$q = \sum_{r=1, 3, \ldots}^{\infty} \sum_{s=1, 3, \ldots}^{\infty} q_{rs} \cos \frac{r\pi x}{2a_0} \cos \frac{s\pi y}{2b_0} \tag{4-15}$$

Substituting expressions (4-4), (4-13), and (4-15) into the equilibrium equation (2-1), transforming to simple products of odd cosines, and equating the coefficients of like terms, we obtain the following general relationship

$$q_{rs} = D \left[\left(\frac{r\pi}{2a_0} \right)^2 + \left(\frac{s\pi}{2b_0} \right)^2 \right]^2 w_{rs} - p_x h \left(\frac{r\pi}{2a_0} \right)^2 w_{rs} - \frac{h\pi^4}{64 a_0^2 b_0^2} \sum_{n=1}^{9} e_n \tag{4-16}$$

where

$$e_1 = \sum_{m=1, 3, \ldots}^{r} \sum_{n=1, 3, \ldots}^{s} [(s-n)m - (r-m)n]^2 c_{(r-m)(s-n)} w_{mn}$$

$$e_2 = \sum_{m=0, 2, \ldots}^{\infty} \sum_{n=0, 2, \ldots}^{\infty} [n(m+r) - m(n+s)]^2 c_{mn} w_{(m+r)(n+s)}$$

$$e_3 = \sum_{m=0, 2, \ldots}^{\infty} \sum_{n=1, 3, \ldots}^{\infty} [(m+r)(n+s) - mn]^2 c_{m(n+s)} w_{(m+r)n}$$

$$e_4 = \sum_{m=1, 3, \ldots}^{\infty} \sum_{n=0, 2, \ldots}^{\infty} [mn - (m+r)(n+s)]^2 c_{(m+r)n} w_{m(n+s)} \tag{4-17}$$

$$e_5 = \sum_{m=1, 3, \ldots}^{\infty} \sum_{n=1, 3, \ldots}^{\infty} [(n+s)m - (m+r)n]^2 c_{(m+r)(n+s)} w_{mn}$$

$$e_6 = \sum_{m=1, 3, \ldots}^{r} \sum_{n=0, 2, \ldots}^{\infty} [mn + (r-m)(n+s)]^2 c_{(r-m)n} w_{m(n+s)}$$

$$e_7 = \sum_{m=1, 3, \ldots}^{r} \sum_{n=1, 3, \ldots}^{\infty} [(n+s)m + (r-m)n]^2 c_{(r-m)(n+s)} w_{mn}$$

$$e_8 = \sum_{m=0, 2, \ldots}^{\infty} \sum_{n=1, 3, \ldots}^{\infty} [(s-n)(m+r) + mn]^2 c_{m(s-n)} w_{(m+r)n}$$

$$e_9 = \sum_{m=1, 3, \ldots}^{\infty} \sum_{n=1, 3, \ldots}^{\infty} [(s-n)m + n(m+r)]^2 c_{(m+r)(s-n)} w_{mn}$$

Introducing expressions (4-4) and (4-13) into the first of conditions (4-2) and performing the indicated integration, the displacement at $x = \pm a_0$ is found to be

$$\delta = -\frac{p_x a_0}{E} - \frac{\pi^2}{32 a_0} \sum_{m=1, 3, \ldots}^{\infty} \sum_{n=1, 3, \ldots}^{\infty} m^2 w_{mn}^2 \tag{4-18}$$

which is constant. Hence the solution formulated above satisfies the governing equations (2-1) and (2-2) and all the prescribed boundary conditions (4-1) to (4-3). It is observed that the present supported (or unloaded) edges are free from membrane stresses but those in the previous section are uniformly displaced.

Numerical results for a square plate under uniaxial compression ($q = p_y = 0$) with $v = 0.316$ are obtained by taking the first three terms in equation (4-4) and the first ten c_{rs}-terms in equation (4-13). As soon as these coefficients are determined, deflections, stresses, and strains can be found. In comparison with the experimental values (Ref. 4.2) the present results for axial membrane and extreme fiber strains ε_x° and ε_x at the plate center and at the midpoint of the loaded edge are plotted in Fig. 4.4 against the load ratio p_x/p_{cr} in which p_{cr} is the corresponding critical stress (Ref. 1.4) given by

$$p_{cr} = 0.3704 \frac{\pi^2 E h^2}{(2 a_0)^2} \tag{4-19}$$

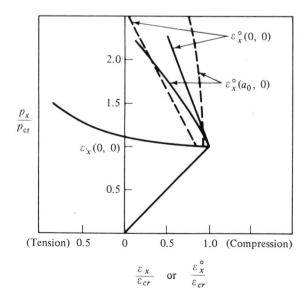

(Tension) 0.5   0   0.5   1.0 (Compression)

$$\frac{\varepsilon_x}{\varepsilon_{cr}} \quad \text{or} \quad \frac{\varepsilon_x^\circ}{\varepsilon_{cr}}$$

Figure 4.4 Strain ratios at center and midpoint of loaded edge for square plate under uniaxial edge compression (Theoretical ———, Experimental — — —).

and ε_{cr} is the critical strain. The specimen used in the study was made of fiberglass $(0.1 < v < 0.2)$ with initial maximum deflection being approximately $0.05h$. It is evident that the differences between the present theoretical and experimental results arise partially from the material and initial imperfection of the specimen. The additional results for the maximum deflection of a square plate will be compared in Fig. 4.6 with those obtained in the next section.

4.3 POSTBUCKLING OF INITIALLY DEFLECTED RECTANGULAR PLATE WITH VARIOUS EDGE CONDITIONS

It is essential to consider the effect of initial imperfections of a thin plate on its elastic behavior. This can be accomplished by use of Marguerre equations (2-175) and (2-176) as in Sec. 2.11 for initially deflected plates under transverse load. Let us consider an initially deflected rectangular plate of length a in the x direction and width b in the y direction under uniaxial compression P_y in the y direction. The plate is assumed to be compressed by frictionless loading heads. By virtue of the second of equations (2-167) the conditions along the loading edges are

$$v^\circ = \int_0^{\pm b/2} \left[\frac{1}{E} (F_{,xx} - vF_{,yy}) - \tfrac{1}{2}w_{,y}^2 - \xi_{,y}\,w_{,y} \right] dy = \delta_y$$

$$y = \pm \frac{b}{2} \quad (4\text{-}20)$$

$$P_y = h \int_{-a/2}^{a/2} F_{,xx}\, dx = -p_y ah \qquad F_{,xy} = 0$$

in which ξ is the initial deflection, δ_y is the edge displacement in the loading direction, and p_y is the average compressive stress in the y direction. It is observed that $P_y = \text{const}$ implies zero boundary shear stress. Concerning the conditions along the unloaded edges we consider the following two cases:

(a) Unloaded edges uniformly displaced by a distribution of normal stresses with zero resultant. These conditions can be written as

$$u^\circ = \int_0^{\pm a/2} \left[\frac{1}{E} (F_{,yy} - vF_{,xx}) - \tfrac{1}{2}w_{,x}^2 - \xi_{,x}\,w_{,x} \right] dx = \delta_x$$

$$x = \pm \frac{a}{2} \quad (4\text{-}21a)$$

$$P_x = h \int_{-b/2}^{b/2} F_{,yy}\, dy = 0 \qquad F_{,xy} = 0$$

(b) Unloaded edges free from stresses. The corresponding conditions are

$$F_{,yy} = F_{,xy} = 0 \qquad x = \pm \frac{a}{2} \qquad (4\text{-}21b)$$

in which δ_x is the elongation of the unloaded edges in the x direction. The out-of-plane or supporting conditions for the transverse deflection considered are as follows:

I. All edges simply supported

$$w = w_{,xx} + \nu w_{,yy} = 0 \qquad \text{at} \quad x = \pm \frac{a}{2}$$

$$w = w_{,yy} + \nu w_{,xx} = 0 \qquad \text{at} \quad y = \pm \frac{b}{2}$$

(4-22)

II. All edges clamped

$$w = w_{,x} = 0 \qquad \text{at} \quad x = \pm \frac{a}{2}$$

$$w = w_{,y} = 0 \qquad \text{at} \quad y = \pm \frac{b}{2}$$

(4-23)

III. Loaded edges clamped and the other edges simply supported

$$w = w_{,xx} + \nu w_{,yy} = 0 \qquad \text{at} \quad x = \pm \frac{a}{2}$$

$$w = w_{,y} = 0 \qquad \text{at} \quad y = \pm \frac{b}{2}$$

(4-24)

IV. Loaded edges simply supported and the other edges clamped

$$w = w_{,x} = 0 \qquad \text{at} \quad x = \pm \frac{a}{2}$$

$$w = w_{,yy} + \nu w_{,xx} = 0 \qquad \text{at} \quad y = \pm \frac{b}{2}$$

(4-25)

The above two kinds of loading conditions and four kinds of supporting conditions can be combined into eight different sets of boundary conditions. Each boundary-value problem consists in determining the deflection and stress functions, w and F, so as to satisfy the governing equations (2-175) and (2-176), and the prescribed boundary conditions. It is assumed that the initial deflection of the plate, ξ, satisfies the same conditions as w in each case. Approximate solutions for these problems will be obtained by Galerkin's method (Ref. 4.3) as in Sec. 2.2.

These supporting conditions (4-22) to (4-25) are satisfied if the initial and additional deflections are taken to be

$$\xi = h \sum_m \sum_n \xi_{mn} X_m(x) Y_n(y)$$

$$w = h \sum_m \sum_n w_{mn} X_m(x) Y_n(y)$$

(4-26)

in which ξ_{mn} and w_{mn} are the prescribed and undetermined coefficients, respectively, and in which

$$X_m(x) = \begin{cases} \cos \dfrac{m\pi x}{a} & (m = 1, 3, 5, \ldots) \\[2mm] \quad \text{for Cases I and III} \\[2mm] (-1)^{m+1} + \cos \dfrac{2m\pi x}{a} & (m = 1, 2, 3, \ldots) \\[2mm] \quad \text{for Cases II and IV} \end{cases}$$

$$Y_n(y) = \begin{cases} \cos \dfrac{n\pi y}{b} & (n = 1, 3, 5, \ldots) \\[2mm] \text{or} \quad \sin \dfrac{n\pi y}{b} & (n = 2, 4, 6, \ldots) \\[2mm] \quad \text{for Cases I and II} \\[2mm] (-1)^{n+1} + \cos \dfrac{2n\pi y}{b} & (n = 1, 2, 3, \ldots) \\[2mm] \quad \text{for Cases III and IV} \end{cases} \tag{4-27}$$

These expressions for ξ and w are substituted into the compatibility equation (2-175). The result can be expressed as

$$\nabla^4 F = \frac{\pi^4 E h^2}{a^2 b^2} \sum_{p=0}^{\infty} \sum_{q=0}^{\infty} a_{pq} \cos \frac{2p\pi x}{a} \cos \frac{2q\pi y}{b} \tag{4-28}$$

where a_{pq} are quadratic functions of ξ_{mn} and w_{mn}, differing in each case.

A particular solution of equation (4-28) is written in the form

$$F_p = E h^2 \sum_{p=0}^{\infty} \sum_{q=0}^{\infty} b_{pq} \cos \frac{2p\pi x}{a} \cos \frac{2q\pi y}{b} \tag{4-29}$$

where

$$b_{pq} = \frac{\lambda^2 a_{pq}}{16(p^2 + q^2 \lambda^2)} \qquad \lambda = \frac{a}{b} \tag{4-30}$$

Equations (2-175), (4-20), and (4-21a) are satisfied by taking

$$F_a = -\tfrac{1}{2} p_y x^2 + F_p \tag{4-31}$$

Thus F_a is the stress function for Case (a). To determine the stress function F_b for Case (b) the following form is assumed

$$F_b = -\tfrac{1}{2} p_y x^2 + F_p + F_c \tag{4-32}$$

Inserting this expression into equations (2-175), (4-20), and (4-21b) we find

$$\nabla^4 F_c = 0 \tag{4-33}$$

Noting that F_c should be an even function in x and y, the general solution of equation (4-33) can be expressed in the form

$$
F_c = A_0 x^2 + C_0 y^2 + Eh^2 \sum_{n=1}^{\infty} \left[\left(A_n \cosh \frac{2n\pi y}{a} + B_n y \sinh \frac{2n\pi y}{a} \right) \right.
$$
$$
\left. \cdot \cos \frac{2n\pi x}{a} + \left(C_n \cosh \frac{2n\pi x}{b} + D_n x \sinh \frac{2n\pi x}{b} \right) \cos \frac{2n\pi y}{b} \right] \quad (4\text{-}34)
$$

The constants A_i, B_i, C_i, and D_i in this expression are to be determined by the loading conditions (4-20) and (4-21b). Upon substitution these conditions become

$$
\int_0^{\pm b/2} (F_{c,\,xx} - \nu F_{c,\,yy})\, dy = 0
$$
$$
\int_{-a/2}^{a/2} F_{c,\,xx}\, dx = 0 \qquad F_{c,\,xy} = 0 \qquad \text{at} \quad y = \pm \frac{b}{2} \qquad (4\text{-}35)
$$

and

$$
F_{c,\,yy} = \frac{4\pi^2 Eh^2}{b^2} \sum_{p=0}^{\infty} \sum_{q=0}^{\infty} (-1)^p q^2 b_{pq} \cos \frac{2q\pi y}{b}
$$
$$
\qquad \text{at} \quad x = \pm \frac{a}{2} \quad (4\text{-}36)
$$
$$
F_{c,\,xy} = 0
$$

Introduction of expression (4-34) into conditions (4-35) and (4-36) leads to

$$
F_c = Eh^2 \sum_{n=1}^{\infty} K_n \left[(\sinh n\pi\lambda + n\pi\lambda \cosh n\pi\lambda) \cosh \frac{2n\pi x}{b} \right.
$$
$$
\left. - \frac{2n\pi x}{b} \sinh n\pi\lambda \sinh \frac{2n\pi x}{b} \right] \cos \frac{2n\pi y}{b} \quad (4\text{-}37)
$$

where

$$
K_n = (\sinh n\pi\lambda \cosh n\pi\lambda + n\pi\lambda)^{-1} \sum_{m=0}^{\infty} (-1)^{m+1} b_{mn} \quad (4\text{-}38)
$$

For convenience the biharmonic function F_c is represented by a double cosine series

$$
F_c = Eh^2 \sum_{p=0}^{\infty} \sum_{q=0}^{\infty} c_{pq} \cos \frac{2p\pi x}{a} \cos \frac{2q\pi y}{b} \quad (4\text{-}39)
$$

in which the Fourier coefficients are given by

$$
c_{pq} = \frac{4\varepsilon_p (-1)^{p+1} q^3 \lambda^3}{\pi (p^2 + q^2\lambda^2)^2} \frac{\sinh^2 q\pi\lambda}{\sinh q\pi\lambda \cosh q\pi\lambda + q\pi\lambda} \sum_{m=0}^{\infty} (-1)^m b_{mq} \quad (4\text{-}40)
$$

with ε_p being

$$
\varepsilon_0 = \tfrac{1}{2} \qquad \varepsilon_1 = \varepsilon_2 = \cdots = 1 \quad (4\text{-}41)
$$

Thus the stress function F can be written in the form

$$F = -\tfrac{1}{2}p_y x^2 + Eh^2 \sum_{p=0}^{\infty} \sum_{q=0}^{\infty} d_{pq} \cos \frac{2p\pi x}{a} \cos \frac{2q\pi y}{b} \qquad (4\text{-}42)$$

where

$$d_{pq} = \begin{cases} b_{pq} & \text{for Case } (a) \\ b_{pq} + c_{pq} & \text{for Case } (b) \end{cases} \qquad (4\text{-}43)$$

In the foregoing formulation, w and F satisfy the compatibility equation (2-175) and all the boundary conditions in each case, but generally not the equilibrium equation (2-176). Now Galerkin's method is applied to this equation in determining the deflection coefficients. This leads to the following conditions to be satisfied by each function $X_r(x)Y_s(y)$ in the series for w

$$\int_0^{a/2} \int_0^{b/2} \left\{ \nabla^4 w - \frac{h}{D} \left[F_{,yy}(w + \xi)_{,xx} + F_{,xx}(w + \xi)_{,yy} - 2F_{,xy}(w + \xi)_{,xy} \right] \right\}$$

$$\cdot X_r(x)Y_s(y)\, dx\, dy = 0 \quad (4\text{-}44)$$

Upon substitution and integration, equation (4-44) yields in each case

I. $4s^2\Omega(\xi_{rs} + w_{rs}) - [3(1 - v^2)\lambda^2]^{-1}(r^2 + s^2\lambda^2)^2 w_{rs}$

$\qquad + \sum_m \sum_n (\xi_{mn} + w_{mn})[(ms - nr)^2(d_{\alpha\beta} + d_{\alpha\gamma} + d_{\theta\beta} + d_{\theta\gamma} \pm d_{\mu\rho})$

$\qquad + (ms + nr)^2(d_{\mu\beta} + d_{\mu\gamma} \pm d_{\alpha\rho} \pm d_{\theta\rho})] = 0$

$$m, r = 1, 3, 5, \ldots \qquad n, s = \begin{cases} 1, 3, 5, \ldots \text{ for upper signs} \\ 2, 4, 6, \ldots \text{ for lower signs} \end{cases} \quad (4\text{-}45)$$

II. $s^2\Omega \sum_m (\xi_{ms} + w_{ms})[2(-1)^{m+r} + \delta_{mr}]$

$\qquad - [12(1 - v^2)\lambda^2]^{-1} \sum_m w_{ms}[2(-1)^{m+r}s^4\lambda^4 + (4r^2 + s^2\lambda^2)^2\, \delta_{mr}]$

$\qquad + \sum_m \sum_n (\xi_{mn} + w_{mn})\{2(-1)^{r+1}m^2s^2(d_{m\beta} + d_{m\gamma} \pm d_{m\rho})$

$\qquad + 2(-1)^{m+1}n^2r^2(d_{r\beta} + d_{r\gamma} \pm d_{r\rho}) + (ms - nr)^2$

$\qquad \cdot [d_{(m-r)\beta} + d_{(m-r)\gamma} + d_{(r-m)\beta} + d_{(r-m)\gamma} + d_{(m+r)\rho}]$

$\qquad + (ms + nr)^2[d_{(m+r)\beta} + d_{(m+r)\gamma} \pm d_{(m-r)\rho} \pm d_{(r-m)\rho}]\} = 0$

$$m, r = 1, 2, 3, \ldots \qquad n, s = \begin{cases} 1, 3, 5, \ldots \text{ for upper signs} \\ 2, 4, 6, \ldots \text{ for lower signs} \end{cases} \quad (4\text{-}46)$$

III. $4s^2\Omega(\xi_{rs} + w_{rs}) - [12(1 - v^2)\lambda^2]^{-1} \sum_n w_{rn}$

$\qquad \cdot [2(-1)^{n+s}r^4 + (r^2 + 4s^2\lambda^2)^2\delta_{ns}] + \sum_m \sum_n (\xi_{mn} + w_{mn})$

$\qquad \cdot \{2(-1)^{n+1}m^2s^2(d_{\alpha s} + d_{\theta s} + d_{\mu s})$

▼

$$+ 2(-1)^{s+1}n^2r^2(d_{\alpha n} + d_{\theta n} + d_{\mu n}) \quad \blacktriangle$$

$$+ (ms - nr)^2[d_{\alpha(n-s)} + d_{\alpha(s-n)} + d_{\theta(n-s)} + d_{\theta(s-n)} + d_{\mu(n+s)}]$$

$$+ (ms + nr)^2[d_{\alpha(n+s)} + d_{\theta(n+s)} + d_{\mu(n-s)} + d_{\mu(s-n)}]\} = 0 \quad \blacktriangle$$

$$m, r = 1, 3, 5, \ldots \qquad n, s = 1, 2, 3, \ldots \quad (4\text{-}47)$$

IV. $s^2\Omega \sum_m (\xi_{ms} + w_{ms})[2(-1)^{m+r} + \delta_{mr}] - [3(1 - v^2)\lambda^2]^{-1} \sum_m \sum_n w_{mn}$

$\cdot [2(-1)^{n+s}r^4\delta_{mr} + 2(-1)^{m+r}s^4\lambda^4\delta_{ns} + (r^2 + s^2\lambda^2)^2\delta_{mr}\delta_{ns}]$

$+ \sum_m \sum_n (\xi_{mn} + w_{mn})\{2(-1)^{n+1}m^2s^2$

$\cdot [2(-1)^{r+1}d_{ms} + d_{(m+r)s} + d_{(m-r)s} + d_{(r-m)s}]$

$+ 2(-1)^{m+1}n^2r^2[2(-1)^{s+1}d_{rn} + d_{r(n+s)} + d_{r(n-s)} + d_{r(s-n)}]$

$+ 2(-1)^{r+1}m^2s^2[d_{m(n-s)} + d_{m(s-n)} + d_{m(n+s)}]$

$+ 2(-1)^{s+1}n^2r^2[d_{(m-r)n} + d_{(r-m)n} + d_{(m+r)n}]$

$+ (ms - nr)^2[d_{(m-r)(n-s)} + d_{(m-r)(s-n)} + d_{(r-m)(n-s)}$

$+ d_{(r-m)(s-n)} + d_{(m+r)(n+s)}] + (ms + nr)^2$

$\cdot [d_{(m+r)(n-s)} + d_{(m+r)(s-n)} + d_{(m-r)(n+s)} + d_{(r-m)(n+s)}]\} = 0$

$$m, n, r, s = 1, 2, 3, \ldots \quad (4\text{-}48)$$

In equations (4-45) to (4-48), δ_{ij} is the Kronecker delta, d_{ij} vanishes for either i or j being negative, and

$$\Omega = \frac{p_y a^2}{\pi^2 E h^2} \qquad \alpha = \frac{m - r}{2} \qquad \beta = \frac{n - s}{2}$$

$$\gamma = -\beta \qquad \theta = -\alpha \qquad \mu = \frac{m + r}{2} \qquad \rho = \frac{n + s}{2}$$

$$(4\text{-}49)$$

The foregoing equations in each case give a set of simultaneous equations involving cubic products of deflection coefficients w_{mn}. These algebraic equations can be solved for a given value of the load parameter Ω, and hence the corresponding deflection and stress function can be determined. The solutions for Cases I(a) to IV(a) are equivalent to those obtained from Sec. 2.7, and the solution for Case I(b) is equivalent to that discussed in Sec. 4.2.

The concept of "effective width" is often used to describe the postbucking behavior of thin plates. The ratio of the effective width to the initial width is defined as that of the actual load carried by the plate to the load which the plate would have carried if the stress had been uniform and equal to the Young's modulus times the average edge strain. This ratio, denoted by R, is given by

$$R = \frac{p_y}{E(\delta_y/b)} \quad (4\text{-}50)$$

Table 4.2 Nonzero deflection coefficients in equations (4-26)

Case	ξ_{mn}	w_{mn}			
I	ξ_{11}	w_{11}	w_{13}	w_{31}	w_{33}
II	ξ_{11}	w_{11}	w_{12}	w_{21}	w_{22}
III	ξ_{11}	w_{11}	w_{12}	w_{31}	w_{32}
IV	ξ_{12}	w_{12}	w_{22}	w_{32}	w_{16}

In calculation only a finite number of terms in the series for ξ and w are taken into account. These nonzero terms are shown in Table 4.2. In each case ξ_{mn} corresponds to the fundamental mode of initial deflection and w_{mn} is chosen so as to minimize the buckling load. Thus the coefficients in Case IV have been chosen to correspond to the deflection surface with two half-waves in the y direction. Numerical results are obtained for initially flat square plates ($\xi = 0$) and initially deflected square plates with amplitude $\xi_{\max} = 0.1h$. Taking $\nu = \frac{1}{3}$ the values of the deflection coefficients shown in Table 4.2 for different cases are given in Appendix B for various values of edge loads and amplitude of the initial deflection. It is noticed that the fourth coefficient in each case is much smaller than the others. The values of critical loads for flat square plates are obtained by setting $\xi_{mn} = 0$ and $w_{mn} \to 0$ in equations (4-45) to (4-48) and then solving the resulting linear equations with the result

$$\Omega_{cr} = 0.3750, \ 0.9559, \ 0.6323, \ 0.72742$$

for Cases I, II, III and IV, respectively.

The relations between postbuckling load and maximum net deflection, w_m, of square plates are shown in Fig. 4.5 for Case (a) and in Fig. 4.6 for Case (b) with various supporting conditions. In these figures the solid lines correspond to the initially flat plates and the dotted lines to the plates with maximum initial deflection being $0.1h$. It is noted that the deflection for Case (b) is always larger than the corresponding one for Case (a). This may arise from the fact that tensile stresses in Case (a) acting along the middle portion of the edges constrain the edges straight. The effect of the edge constraint for Case IV is not quite so severe because the plate buckles in two half-waves in the y direction. For large values of the postbuckling load, the net deflection of the initially deflected plate is less than that of the initially flat plate. However, the total deflection, $w_m + 0.1h$, of the former is always larger than that of the latter. A comparison of the present results for maximum deflections with the two previous solutions is also made in these figures. A good agreement is found between these results. The membrane stresses at various points in an initially flat square plate for Case I(a) by taking $\nu = \frac{1}{3}$ are in good agreement with those shown in Fig. 4.1. The extreme-fiber bending stresses at the center and the corner of an initially flat square plate and a square plate with maximum initial deflection $\xi_{\max} = 0.1h$ are shown in Fig. 4.7 for $\nu = \frac{1}{3}$. The results for an initially flat plate agree well with those obtained in Sec. 4.1 but the latter is

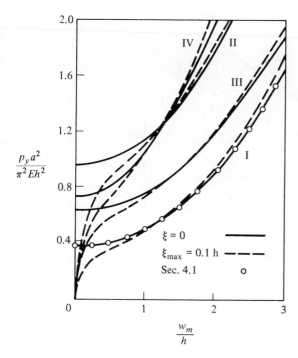

Figure 4.5 Relations between uniaxial compression and maximum deflection of initially flat and deflected square plates for Case (*a*) having $v = \frac{1}{3}$ in comparison with solution obtained in Sec. 4.1 for $v = 0.316$.

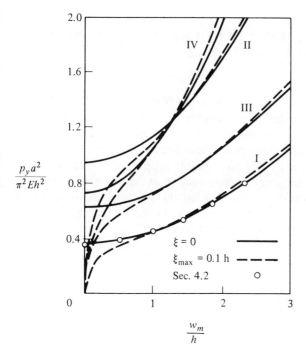

Figure 4.6 Relations between uniaxial compression and maximum deflection of initially flat and deflected square plates for Case (*b*) having $v = \frac{1}{3}$ in comparison with solution obtained in Sec. 4.2 for $v = 0.316$.

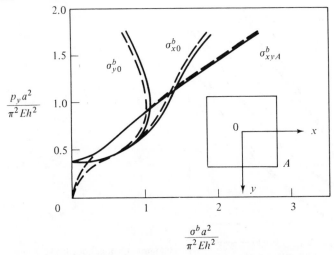

Figure 4.7 Extreme-fiber bending stresses at center and corner of initially flat (———) and deflected ($\xi_{11} = 0.1$ — — —) square plates for Case I (a) having $v = \frac{1}{3}$.

not presented herein. The effective width given by equation (3-50) will be shown later, in Fig. 4.8, against the shortening of the loaded edges for comparison with the solution discussed in the next section.

4.4 POSTBUCKLING OF RECTANGULAR PLATE WITH UNLOADED EDGES ELASTICALLY RESTRAINED AGAINST ROTATION

The postbuckling behavior of rectangular plates has been discussed for all-simply supported edges, all-clamped edges, and a combination of simply supported and clamped edges. These boundary conditions are very important as they are the limiting conditions for the compressed plates. It is known, however, that in practice plate elements of structures do not have simply supported or clamped edges but are generally restrained elastically against rotation at the boundaries. Thus, in this section, the effect of rotational restraints on the postbuckling behavior of plates is examined by use of the principle of minimum potential energy (Ref. 4.4).

The plate under consideration is assumed to be rectangular, perfectly flat, uniformly compressed, simply supported on the loaded edges, and rotationally restrained to an equal degree on both unloaded edges. The boundary conditions along the loaded edges are

$$w = w_{,xx} = F_{,xy} = 0$$

$$x = \pm a_0 \qquad (4\text{-}51)$$

$$u^\circ = \delta$$

and those along the unloaded edges are

$$w = 0 \qquad w_{,yy} = \pm \xi w_{,y}$$
$$F_{,xx} = F_{,xy} = 0 \qquad \qquad y = \pm b_0 \quad (4\text{-}52)$$

The constant δ represents the shortening of the loaded edges and a_0 and b_0 the half-length and half-width of the rectangular plate. The moments applied to the unloaded edges have been assumed to be proportional to the rotations of these edges with ξ being the proportionality constant or the rotational edge restraint coefficient. The values of ξ vary between 0 for a simply supported edge and ∞ for a clamped edge.

The energy stored in the plate after buckling is equal to the sum of the strain energy of the plate and that of the restraining medium, i.e.,

$$\Pi = V_b + V_c + V_r \qquad (4\text{-}53)$$

in which Π is the total potential energy of the elastic system, V_b and V_c are the strain energies due to bending and compression, and V_r is the strain energy in the restraining medium. They can be expressed in terms of transverse deflection and Airy stress function as

$$V_b = \frac{D}{2} \int_{-a_0}^{a_0} \int_{-b_0}^{b_0} \{(w_{,xx} + w_{,yy})^2 - 2(1 - v)$$
$$\cdot [w_{,xx} w_{,yy} - w_{,xy}^2]\} \, dx \, dy \qquad (4\text{-}54)$$

$$V_c = \frac{h}{2E} \int_{-a_0}^{a_0} \int_{-b_0}^{b_0} \{(F_{,xx} + F_{,yy})^2 - 2(1 + v)$$
$$\cdot [F_{,xx} F_{,yy} - F_{,xy}^2]\} \, dx \, dy \qquad (4\text{-}55)$$

$$V_r = \frac{D}{2} \int_{-a_0}^{a_0} \left[(w_{,yy} + v w_{,xx}) w_{,y} \right]_{y=-b_0}^{y=b_0} dx \qquad (4\text{-}56)$$

which will be simplified later by virtue of the boundary conditions.

It is well known that the stress function is related to the transverse deflection by the equation of compatibility (2-2), i.e.,

$$F_{,xxxx} + 2F_{,xxyy} + F_{,yyyy} = E[w_{,xy}^2 - w_{,xx} w_{,yy}] \qquad (4\text{-}57)$$

Once the deflections of the buckled plate are found, the stress function can be determined by solving equation (4-57) and satisfying the relevant stress boundary conditions as in the previous section.

In a case when uniaxial loads are not greater than about three times the buckling load, the deflected form of the plate in the x direction can be approximated by a cosine wave

$$w = \cos \frac{\pi x}{eb_0} \sum_{n=1}^{\infty} A_n Y_n(y) \qquad (4\text{-}58)$$

where e specifies the buckle half-wavelength and where

$$Y_n(y) = \alpha_n + \cos \frac{\beta_n y}{b_0} \tag{4-59}$$

with α_n and β_n being constant coefficients. The first two of conditions (4-52) are fulfilled by taking

$$\alpha_n = -\cos \beta_n \qquad \beta_n \cot \beta_n - b_0 \xi = 0 \tag{4-60}$$

in which there is an infinite number of roots for the last equation so that any required number of functions Y_n can be obtained. It is observed that for the limiting cases of simply supported edges ($\xi = 0$) and clamped edges ($\xi = \infty$) the values of α_n and β_n are

$$\alpha_n = 0 \quad \text{(all } n\text{)} \qquad \beta_n = \frac{n\pi}{2} \quad (n = 1, 3, 5, \ldots)$$

and

$$\alpha_n = (-1)^{n+1} \qquad \beta_n = n\pi \quad (n = 1, 2, 3, \ldots) \tag{4-61}$$

Substituting expression (4-58) into equation (4-57) yields

$$F_{,xxxx} + 2F_{,xxyy} + F_{,yyyy} = \frac{\pi^2 E}{2e^2 b_0^2} \sum_{m=1}^{\infty} \sum_{n=1}^{\infty} A_m A_n$$

$$\cdot \left[(Y_m Y_{n,\,yy} + Y_{m,\,y} Y_{n,\,y}) + (Y_m Y_{n,\,yy} - Y_{m,\,y} Y_{n,\,y}) \cos \frac{2\pi x}{eb_0} \right] \tag{4-62}$$

From this equation F can be expressed as

$$F = F_1(y) + F_2(y) \cos \frac{2\pi x}{eb_0} \tag{4-63}$$

Consequently, we obtain

$$F_{1,\,yyyy} = \frac{E\pi^2}{2e^2 b_0^2} \sum_{m=1}^{\infty} \sum_{n=1}^{\infty} A_m A_n (Y_m Y_{n,\,yy} + Y_{m,\,y} Y_{n,\,y}) \tag{4-64}$$

$$F_{2,\,yyyy} - 2\left(\frac{2\pi}{eb_0}\right)^2 F_{2,\,yy} + \left(\frac{2\pi}{eb_0}\right)^4 F_2$$

$$= \frac{\pi^2 E}{4e^2 b_0^2} \sum_{m=1}^{\infty} \sum_{n=1}^{\infty} A_m A_n (Y_m Y_{n,\,yy} - Y_{m,\,y} Y_{n,\,y}) \tag{4-65}$$

Integrating equation (4-64) twice yields

$$F_{1,\,yy} = \frac{E\pi^2}{4e^2 b_0^2} \sum_{m=1}^{\infty} \sum_{n=1}^{\infty} A_m A_n Y_m Y_n + B_1 y - B_2 \tag{4-66}$$

Noting that the second derivative $F_{1,\,yy}(y)$, which constitutes a stress system in the x direction, is the only significant part of $F_1(y)$ in the analysis, the function $F_1(y)$

itself need not be evaluated. The constants B_1 and B_2 are to be determined by boundary conditions.

Inserting expression (4-59) into equation (4-65) leads to

$$
F_{2, yyyy} - 2\left(\frac{2\pi}{eb_0}\right)^2 F_{2, yy} + \left(\frac{2\pi}{eb_0}\right)^4 F_2
$$

$$
= -\frac{\pi^2 E}{2e^2 b_0^4} \sum_{m=1}^{\infty} \sum_{n=1}^{\infty} A_m A_n \left\{ \alpha_m \beta_n^2 \cos \frac{\beta_n y}{b_0} \right.
$$

$$
\left. + \tfrac{1}{2}\beta_n \left[(\beta_n - \beta_m) \cos \frac{(\beta_m + \beta_n)y}{b_0} + \frac{\beta_n}{2} (\beta_m + \beta_n) \cos \frac{(\beta_n - \beta_m)y}{b_0} \right] \right\} \qquad (4\text{-}67)
$$

whose solution is

$$
F_2 = \frac{\pi^2 E}{2e^2 b_0^4} \sum_{m=1}^{\infty} \sum_{n=1}^{\infty} A_m A_n \phi_{mn}(y) \qquad (4\text{-}68)
$$

In equation (4-68) functions ϕ_{mn} are given by

$$
\phi_{mn} = \mu_{1mn} \cos \frac{\beta_n y}{b_0} + \mu_{2mn} \cos \frac{(\beta_n - \beta_m)y}{b_0}
$$

$$
+ \mu_{3mn} \cos \frac{(\beta_m + \beta_n)y}{b_0} + C_{1mn} \cosh \frac{2\pi y}{eb_0} + C_{2mn} \sinh \frac{2\pi y}{eb_0}
$$

$$
+ \frac{y}{b_0}\left(C_{3mn} \cosh \frac{2\pi y}{eb_0} + C_{4mn} \sinh \frac{2\pi y}{eb_0} \right) \qquad (4\text{-}69)
$$

where $C_{1mn}, C_{2mn}, C_{3mn}$ and C_{4mn} are arbitrary constants and where

$$
\mu_{1mn} = \frac{\alpha_m \beta_n^2}{[\beta_n^2 + (2\pi/e)^2]^2}
$$

$$
\mu_{2mn} = \frac{\beta_n(\beta_m + \beta_n)}{2[(\beta_n - \beta_m)^2 + (2\pi/e)^2]^2} \qquad (4\text{-}70)
$$

$$
\mu_{3mn} = \frac{\beta_n(\beta_n - \beta_m)}{2[(\beta_m + \beta_n)^2 + (2\pi/e)^2]^2}
$$

Now the constants B and C are so chosen that the prescribed boundary conditions are satisfied. Upon substitution the third of conditions (4-51) yields

$$
\frac{a_0}{eb_0} = \frac{k}{2} \qquad (k = 1, 3, 5, \ldots) \qquad (4\text{-}71)
$$

and, after integration, the last of conditions (4-51) becomes

$$
u^\circ = \frac{a_0}{E} (B_1 y - B_2) = \delta \qquad \text{at} \quad x = \pm a_0
$$

which requires that

$$B_1 = 0 \qquad B_2 = -\frac{E\delta}{a_0} \tag{4-72}$$

It is noticed that with expression (4-71) the assumed deflection (4-58) satisfies the first two of conditions (4-51). The last two of conditions (4-52) are satisfied by taking

$$\phi_{mn}(-b_0) = \phi_{mn,y}(-b_0) = 0 \tag{4-73}$$

From symmetry, the constants C_{2mn} and C_{3mn} which are multipliers of odd functions, must be taken to be zero. Introduction of expression (4-69) into conditions (4-73) results in

$$C_{1mn} = \frac{1}{\cosh 2\pi/e} \left[\mu_{1mn} \cos \beta_n + \mu_{2mn} \cos (\beta_n - \beta_m) \right.$$

$$\left. + \mu_{3mn} \cos (\beta_m + \beta_n) + \mu_{4mn} \sinh \frac{2\pi}{e} \right] \tag{4-74}$$

$$C_{4mn} = \frac{\mu_{1mn} L(\beta_n) + \mu_{2mn} L(\beta_n - \beta_m) + \mu_{3mn} L(\beta_m + \beta_n)}{2\pi/e \cosh 2\pi/e + \sinh 2\pi/e - 2\pi/e \sinh 2\pi/e \tanh 2\pi/e}$$

where

$$L(\omega) = \frac{2\pi}{e} \tanh \frac{2\pi}{e} \cos \omega - \omega \sin \omega \tag{4-75}$$

In the foregoing formulation the stress function is completely specified in terms of the deflection coefficients A_n. Thus the total strain energy (4-53) can be expressed in terms of these coefficients. By virtue of zero deflection along the four edges and zero normal and shear stresses and zero plate curvature on the unloaded edges, expressions (4-54) to (4-56) are reduced to

$$V_b = \frac{D}{2} \int_{-a_0}^{a_0} \int_{-b_0}^{b_0} (w_{,xx} + w_{,yy})^2 \, dy \, dx$$

$$V_c = \frac{h}{2E} \int_{-a_0}^{a_0} \int_{-b_0}^{b_0} (F_{,xx} + F_{,yy})^2 \, dy \, dx \tag{4-76}$$

$$V_r = \frac{D}{2} \int_{-a_0}^{a_0} \left[w_{,yy} w_{,y} \right]_{y=-b_0}^{y=b_0} dx$$

Substituting equations (4-58), (4-63), (4-66), and (4-68) into expressions (4-76) and integrating in the x direction, the total energy expression (4-53) becomes

$$\Pi = \frac{a_0 h}{2E} \left\{ \sum_{m=1}^{\infty} \sum_{n=1}^{\infty} \sum_{p=1}^{\infty} \sum_{q=1}^{\infty} A_m A_n A_p A_q \int_{-b_0}^{b_0} \frac{\pi^4 E^2}{8e^4 b_0^4} \right.$$

$$\cdot \left[Y_m Y_n Y_p Y_q + 2 \left(\phi_{mn,yy} - \frac{4\pi^2}{e^2 b_0^2} \phi_{mn} \right) \left(\phi_{pq,yy} - \frac{4\pi^2}{e^2 b_0^2} \phi_{pq} \right) \right] dy$$

$$+ \int_{-bo}^{bo} B_2^2 \, dy - \frac{\pi^2 E}{e^2 b_0^2} \sum_{m=1}^{\infty} \sum_{n=1}^{\infty} A_m A_n \int_{-bo}^{bo} B_2 Y_m Y_n \, dy \Bigg\}$$

$$+ \frac{a_0 D}{2} \sum_{m=1}^{\infty} \sum_{n=1}^{\infty} A_m A_n \Bigg\{ \int_{-bo}^{bo} \left[Y_{m,yy} - \left(\frac{\pi}{eb_0} \right)^2 Y_m \right] \right.$$

$$\cdot \left[Y_{n,yy} - \left(\frac{\pi}{eb_0} \right)^2 Y_n \right] dy + \left[Y_{m,y} Y_{n,yy} \right]_{y=-bo}^{y=bo} \Bigg\} \tag{4-77}$$

By the principle of minimum potential energy, expression (4-77) is minimized with respect to the deflection coefficients A_n. In other words the total potential energy Π is differentiated with respect to each A_n and the resulting expressions are set to zero. In calculation only the coefficients A_1 and A_2 are taken to be nonzero values since this investigation is concerned with postbuckling loads of less than about three times the buckling load. The result is

$$4H_1 A_1^3 + 3H_2 A_1^2 A_2 + 2H_3 A_1 A_2^2 + H_4 A_2^3 = 2A_1(K_1 - K_2) + 2A_2(K_3 - K_4) \tag{4-78}$$

$$H_2 A_1^3 + 2H_3 A_1^2 A_2 + 3H_4 A_1 A_2^2 + 4H_5 A_2^3 = 2A_1(K_3 - K_4) + 2A_2(K_5 - K_6) \tag{4-79}$$

In these equations H and K are given by

$$H_1 = c_1 \int_{-bo}^{bo} [2f_{11}^2 + Y_1^4] \, dy$$

$$H_2 = c_1 \int_{-bo}^{bo} [2f_{11}f_{12} + Y_1^3 Y_2] \, dy$$

$$H_3 = c_1 \int_{-bo}^{bo} [8f_{12}^2 + 4f_{11}f_{22} + 6Y_1^2 Y_2^2] \, dy$$

$$H_4 = c_1 \int_{-bo}^{bo} [2f_{12}f_{22} + Y_1 Y_2^3] \, dy$$

$$H_5 = c_1 \int_{-bo}^{bo} [2f_{22}^2 + Y_2^4] \, dy \tag{4-80}$$

$$K_1 = c_2 \int_{-bo}^{bo} B_2 Y_1^2 \, dy$$

$$K_2 = c_3 \left\{ \int_{-bo}^{bo} g_1^2 \, dy + \left[Y_{1,y} Y_{1,yy} \right]_{y=-bo}^{y=bo} \right\}$$

$$K_3 = c_3 \int_{-bo}^{bo} B_2 Y_2^2 \, dy$$

$$K_4 = c_3 \left\{ \int_{-bo}^{bo} g_2^2 \, dy + \left[Y_{2,y} Y_{2,yy} \right]_{y=-bo}^{y=bo} \right\}$$

$$K_5 = c_2 \int_{-b_0}^{b_0} B_2 Y_1 Y_2 \, dy$$

$$K_6 = c_3 \left\{ \int_{-b_0}^{b_0} g_1 g_2 \, dy + \frac{1}{2} \left[Y_{1,y} Y_{2,yy} + Y_{1,yy} Y_{2,y} \right]_{y=-b_0}^{y=b_0} \right\}$$

where

$$f_{mn} = \phi_{mn,yy} - \left(\frac{2\pi}{eb_0} \right)^2 \phi_{mn}$$

$$g_n = Y_{n,yy} - \left(\frac{\pi}{eb_0} \right)^2 Y_n \qquad (4\text{-}81)$$

$$c_1 = \frac{\pi^4 a_0 Eh}{32 e^4 b_0^4} \qquad c_2 = \frac{\pi^2 a_0 h}{2 e^2 b_0^2} \qquad c_3 = \frac{a_0 D}{2}$$

For any specified value of end compression, given by the constant B_2, equations (4-78) and (4-79) can be solved for the deflection coefficients A_1 and A_2. Then the plate deflection, stresses, and the applied load can be evaluated.

The effective width, denoted by $2b_e$, can be calculated as follows. The inplane load on the plate, denoted by P_x, is given by

$$P_x = -h \int_{-b_0}^{b_0} \left[F_{1,yy} + F_{2,yy} \cos \frac{2\pi x}{eb_0} \right] dy$$

which, by virtue of zero shear on the edges and of equation (4-66), becomes

$$P_x = h \int_{-b_0}^{b_0} \left[B_2 - \frac{\pi^2 E}{4 e^2 b_0^2} \sum_{m=1}^{\infty} \sum_{n=1}^{\infty} A_m A_n Y_m Y_n \right] dy$$

For an unbuckled plate, the load to cause the same compression, $\delta = -a_0 B_2 / E$, would be simply

$$h \int_{-b_0}^{b_0} B_2 \, dy$$

The ratio of the effective width to the initial width can be thus written as

$$\frac{b_e}{b_0} = 1 - \frac{\int_{-b_0}^{b_0} \frac{\pi^2 E}{4 e^2 b_0^2} \sum_{m=1}^{\infty} \sum_{n=1}^{\infty} A_m A_n Y_m Y_n \, dy}{\int_{-b_0}^{b_0} B_2 \, dy} \qquad (4\text{-}82)$$

The results for maximum deflections of square plates with the unloaded edges simply supported and clamped (not shown here) are found to be in good agreement with the graphical results shown in Fig. 4.6 for Cases I(b) and II(b) without initial imperfections. It should be pointed out that the natural buckle half-wavelength for a simply supported plate is equal to the plate width, and that the buckle half-wavelength for the clamped plate is only half of the plate width, since a square plate clamped on the unloaded edges will buckle into two half-wavelengths. The effective widths for square plates with simply supported (SS)

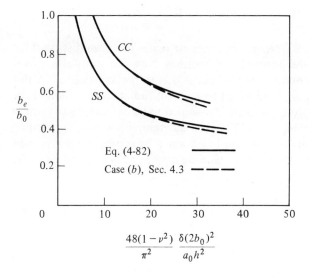

Figure 4.8 axis labels: vertical $\dfrac{b_e}{b_0}$; horizontal $\dfrac{48(1-\nu^2)}{\pi^2}\dfrac{\delta(2b_0)^2}{a_0 h^2}$

Eq. (4-82) ————

Case (*b*), Sec. 4.3 — — — —

Figure 4.8 Comparison of effective widths for initially flat square plates.

and clamped (*CC*) unloaded edges are compared in Fig. 4.8 with Cases I(*b*) and II(*b*) for initial flat square plates discussed in Sec. 4.3. The four-term solutions obtained previously are seen to give lower values of b_e. However, the difference is not great for this range of loading and shows that the present two-term solution is reasonably accurate. Figure 4.9 shows the maximum deflections w_m of the plates with square buckles for different rotational restraint coefficients. For a fixed value of P_x the deflection decreases with increase in restraint in edge rotation.

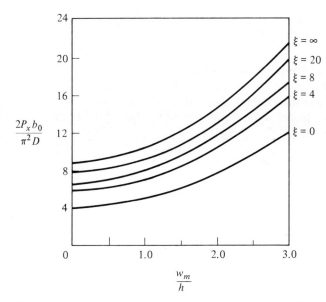

Figure 4.9 vertical axis $\dfrac{2P_x b_0}{\pi^2 D}$; horizontal axis $\dfrac{w_m}{h}$; curves labeled $\xi = \infty$, $\xi = 20$, $\xi = 8$, $\xi = 4$, $\xi = 0$.

Figure 4.9 Maximum deflections of plates with square buckles for various values of rotational edge restraint coefficient.

4.5 POSTBUCKLING OF CLAMPED CIRCULAR PLATE

The postbuckling behavior of isotropic rectangular plates has been discussed for various edge conditions in the previous four sections. Now our study is confined to the problem of isotropic nonrectangular plates. Let us first consider a circular plate of radius a and thickness h subjected to uniform radial compression in the plane of the plate. In the analysis the plate is assumed to be deformed axisymmetrically with respect to the plate axis z. Thus the differential equations governing the postbuckling behavior of the plate can be obtained by setting the lateral load $q = 0$ in equations (3-18) and (3-19). The resulting equations can be written in the form

$$\frac{1}{\rho^3}(\rho^3 \zeta_{,\rho})_{,\rho} = -\zeta \eta \tag{4-83}$$

$$\frac{1}{\rho^3}(\rho^3 \eta_{,\rho})_{,\rho} = \tfrac{1}{2}\zeta^2 \tag{4-84}$$

In these equations

$$\rho = \frac{\alpha r}{a} \qquad (0 \le \rho \le \alpha)$$

$$\zeta = -\frac{a}{\alpha^2 c r} w_{,r} \qquad \eta = -\frac{\sigma_r^m}{\alpha^2 c^2 E} \tag{4-85}$$

where α is an arbitrary parameter and σ_r^m is the radial membrane stress, and where

$$c^2 = \frac{D}{a^2 E h} \tag{4-86}$$

Equations (4-83) and (4-84) are solved for a simply supported circular plate under uniform edge compression by use of the power series method (Refs. 3.2, 4.5, 4.6). In the current study this method is extended to the postbuckling behavior of a clamped circular plate under uniform radial pressure (Ref. 4.7). The boundary conditions can be written as

$$\zeta = 0 \qquad \eta = \bar{\eta} \qquad \text{at} \quad \rho = \alpha$$

$$\zeta_{,\rho} = 0 \qquad \eta_{,\rho} = 0 \qquad \text{at} \quad \rho = 0 \tag{4-87}$$

in which $\bar{\eta}$ is a prescribed constant.

Noting that both the parameters ζ and η in circumferential curvature and radial membrane stress are functions of ρ, these functions are expanded as power series

$$\zeta = \sum_{n=0}^{\infty} b_n \rho^{2n} \qquad \eta = \sum_{n=0}^{\infty} c_n \rho^{2n} \tag{4-88}$$

Substituting expressions (4-88) into equations (4-83) and (4-84) and equating the coefficients of like powers of ρ yields the recurrence relations

$$2n(2n + 2)b_n = -\sum_{m=0}^{n-1} \eta_m \zeta_{n-m-1}$$

$$2n(2n + 2)c_n = \frac{1}{2}\sum_{m=0}^{n-1} \zeta_m \zeta_{n-m-1}$$

(4-89)

These formulas determine all the coefficients b_n and c_n $(n > 0)$ in terms of the leading coefficients b_0 and c_0.

The conditions (4-87) require that

$$\sum_{n=0}^{\infty} b_n \alpha^{2n} = 0 \qquad \sum_{n=0}^{\infty} c_n \alpha^{2n} = \bar{\eta}$$

(4-90)

The computing procedure consists of prescribing b_0 and c_0 and solving equations (4-90) for α and $\bar{\eta}$. The value of α is the lowest root of the first of equations (4-90). It is noted that a solution for large ratios of the edge compression to the critical stress may not be found if b_0 and c_0 are arbitrarily assigned. This power series method can be applied to the values of the ratio up to about 15.

4.6 POSTBUCKLING OF SIMPLY SUPPORTED AND CLAMPED CIRCULAR PLATES

The power series solution discussed in the foregoing section or elsewhere (Refs. 3.2, 4.6), which is essentially the trial-and-error method, was found to be valid only for limited values of the edge load. In this study the finite-difference technique (Ref. 4.8) is applied to the postbuckling problem for simply supported and clamped circular plates. For generality the nonlinear bending of these plates is also considered herein. In the case of axisymmetrical deformation the differential equations (3-18) and (3-19), governing the geometrically nonlinear behavior of a circular plate of radius a under uniform lateral load and uniform radial compression in the plane of the plate, can be written in the nondimensional form

$$L(f) = -fg - Qx^2 \qquad L(g) = \tfrac{1}{2}f^2$$

(4-91)

where

$$x = \frac{r}{a} \qquad f = -\frac{ak}{h}w_{,r} \qquad g = -\frac{ak^2}{Eh^2}F_{,r}$$

$$Q = \frac{k^3}{2E}\left(\frac{a}{h}\right)^4 q_0 \qquad k = [12(1 - v^2)]^{1/2}$$

(4-92)

$$L(\ ) = x\left\{\frac{1}{x}[x(\ )]_{,x}\right\}_{,x}$$

The radial and circumferential bending and membrane stresses σ_r^b, σ_θ^b and σ_r^m, σ_θ^m are also expressed in the nondimensional form

$$\sigma_\zeta^b = f_{,x} + v\frac{f}{x} \qquad \sigma_\eta^b = vf_{,x} + \frac{f}{x}$$

$$\sigma_\zeta^m = -\frac{g}{x} \qquad \sigma_\eta^m = -g_{,x}$$

(4-93)

in which

$$(\sigma_\zeta^b, \sigma_\eta^b) = \frac{a^2 k^3}{6Eh^2}(\sigma_r^b, \sigma_\theta^b)$$

$$(\sigma_\zeta^m, \sigma_\eta^m) = \frac{a^2 k^2}{Eh^2}(\sigma_r^m, \sigma_\theta^m)$$

(4-94)

The boundary conditions at the edge of the plate are assumed to be of the form

$$C_1 f_{,x} + C_2 f = 0 \qquad C_3 g_{,x} + C_4 g = \xi \qquad \text{at} \quad x = 1 \qquad (4\text{-}95)$$

in which C's are constants defining a particular set of edge conditions and ξ is the nondimensional edge stress defined by

$$\xi = -\frac{a^2 k^2}{Eh^2}\sigma_c$$

(4-96)

with σ_c being the radial membrane stress at the edge of the plate. The constants C's are specified for the following cases:

(a) Simply supported edge with radial membrane stress prescribed

$$C_1 = 1 \qquad C_2 = v \qquad C_3 = 0 \qquad C_4 = 1 \qquad \xi > 0 \qquad (4\text{-}97)$$

(b) Clamped edge with radial membrane stress prescribed

$$C_1 = 0 \qquad C_2 = 1 \qquad C_3 = 0 \qquad C_4 = 1 \qquad \xi > 0 \qquad (4\text{-}98)$$

(c) Rigidly clamped edge

$$C_1 = 0 \qquad C_2 = 1 \qquad C_3 = 1 \qquad C_4 = -v \qquad \xi = 0 \qquad (4\text{-}99)$$

(d) Hinged edge

$$C_1 = 1 \qquad C_2 = v \qquad C_3 = 1 \qquad C_4 = -v \qquad \xi = 0 \qquad (4\text{-}100)$$

(e) Simply supported edge

$$C_1 = 1 \qquad C_2 = v \qquad C_3 = 0 \qquad C_4 = 1 \qquad \xi = 0 \qquad (4\text{-}101)$$

in which Cases (a) and (b) are postbuckling problems and the others are nonlinear bending problems for deflections having the order of the thickness of the plate. In addition the regularity at the center of the plate requires for all the cases

$$f = g = 0 \qquad \text{at} \quad x = 0 \qquad (4\text{-}102)$$

Approximate solutions to these boundary-value problems are obtained by the finite-difference method. We proceed by placing a uniform mesh of points

$$x_i = i\Delta x \qquad \Delta x = \frac{1}{m} \qquad (i = 0, 1, \ldots, m) \qquad (4\text{-}103)$$

on the nondimensional radius of the plate, $0 \le x \le 1$. Replacing the derivatives by central finite-difference equivalents, equations (4-91) can be approximated by

$$L_\delta f_i = -f_i g_i - Q x_i^2$$

$$L_\delta g_i = \tfrac{1}{2} f_i^2 \qquad\qquad 0 < i < m \quad (4\text{-}104)$$

in which L_δ is the difference operator defined by

$$L_\delta \phi_i = \frac{x_i}{(\Delta x)^2} \left[\frac{1}{x_i + \frac{1}{2}\Delta x} (x_{i+1}\phi_{i+1} - x_i\phi_i) - \frac{1}{x_i - \frac{1}{2}\Delta x} (x_i\phi_i - x_{i-1}\phi_{i-1}) \right]$$

$$(4\text{-}105)$$

At the end points, $i = 0$ and m, the meshing functions $f(x_i)$ and $g(x_i)$ which are defined only at the meshing points must satisfy the finite-difference equivalents of the conditions (4-95) and (4-102),

$$C_1(f_m - f_{m-1}) + C_2 f_m \Delta x = 0$$

$$C_3(g_m - g_{m-1}) + C_4 g_m \Delta x = \xi \Delta x \qquad (4\text{-}106)$$

$$f_0 = g_0 = 0$$

Equations (4-104) and (4-106) constitute a system of $2m$ nonlinear algebraic equations for $2m$ unknowns, f_i and g_i. These equations are solved by a simple iterative procedure

$$L_\delta f_i^{(n)} = -f_i^{(n-1)} g_i^{(n-1)} - Q x_i^2 \qquad (0 < i < m) \qquad (4\text{-}107)$$

$$L_\delta g_i^{(n)} = \tfrac{1}{2} [f_i^{(n)}]^2 \qquad (0 < i < m) \qquad (4\text{-}108)$$

Each pair of iterates, $f_i^{(n)}$ and $g_i^{(n)}$, is required to satisfy conditions (4-106) at the endpoints, $i = 0, m$. In each iteration equations (4-107) form a system of $(m-2)$ linear equations in the $(m-2)$ unknowns $f_i^{(n)}$, $i \ne 0, m$. These equations may be solved explicitly in a simple manner. Similarly $g_i^{(n)}$ may be obtained from equations (4-108). It is, however, proved (in Ref. 4.9) that the simply iterative procedure for application to Cases (c), (d) and (e) converges only for a limited range of values of Q, and actually diverges for sufficiently large values of Q. Thus a new iterative procedure, which converges for an unlimited range of values of Q, is formulated by examining a physical explanation of the divergence of iterations.

In each iteration $f_i^{(n)}$ may be thought of as the solution for the linear bending of a plate under nonuniformly distributed lateral load consisting of a uniform pressure and a nonuniform pressure. The latter results from membrane stresses and deflections obtained in the previous iteration. For divergence, the stresses and deflections produced by this nonuniform portion of the load are, in absolute magnitude, sufficiently larger than those of the previous iterates. These new deformations in turn produce a nonuniform pressure of considerable magnitude. Hence the sequence should diverge. Essentially the new iterative procedure eliminates divergence by properly correcting equations (4-107) for overestimates in the next iteration. As in Sec. 2.8 such a correction can be made by introducing the provisional iterate $\bar{f}_i^{(n)}$, as in equations (4-107), by

$$L_\delta \bar{f}_i^{(n)} = -f_i^{(n-1)}g_i^{(n-1)} - Qx_i^2 \qquad (0 < i < m) \qquad (4\text{-}109)$$

and then interpolating between this and the previous iterate to obtain

$$f_i^{(n)} = \alpha \bar{f}_i^{(n)} + (1 - \alpha)f_i^{(n-1)} \qquad (4\text{-}110)$$

in which α is an interpolating parameter and must lie between 0 and 1. Equations (4-108) are still solved for $g_i^{(n)}$ and both iterates are required to satisfy conditions (4-106). The process is repeated until a desired accuracy will be reached. It is clear that the interpolated iterative procedure reduces to the simple iteration by taking $\alpha = 1$ in equation (4-110).

It is found that the number of iterations required, starting from an initial guess for $f_i^{(0)}$ and $g_i^{(0)}$, depends strongly upon the value of α used in equation (4-110). For a given Q the number of iterations for convergence, denoted by N, can

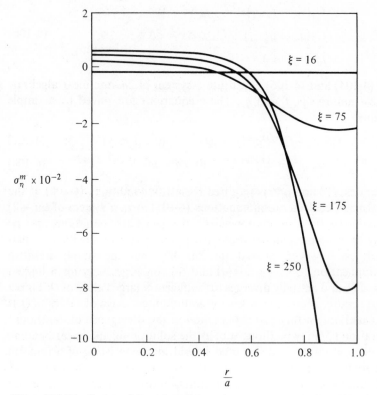

Figure 4.10 Distribution of circumferential membrane stress along radius of simply supported circular plate under uniform edge compression.

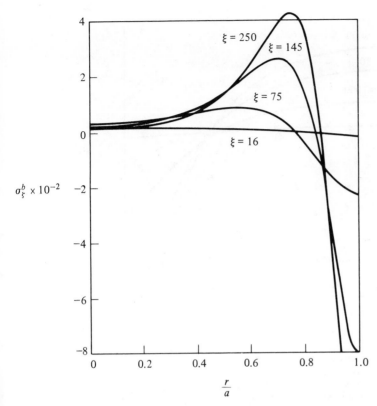

Figure 4.11 Distribution of radial bending stress along radius of simply supported circular plate under uniform edge compression.

be plotted against α. The best α is α^*, that for which $N(\alpha)$ is a minimum. For a sequence of values of Q, a corresponding sequence of values of $\alpha^*(Q)$ can be obtained. From a smooth curve through the points (Q, α^*) good estimates of α^* for an entire range of values of the lateral load parameter Q may be determined. It was found that α^* does not change appreciably for significant changes in the mesh spacing Δx. From a series of test calculations with successively finer meshes, it was found that accurate solutions were obtained for the range of values of loads considered by taking $\Delta x = 0.02$.

It is well known that solutions for buckling problems are not unique. Thus the foregoing procedure must be applied with care. As shown in Refs. 4.5 and 4.6, for the edge load parameter ξ below the critical value ξ_{cr} the only solution to the nonlinear equations is the trivial one, $f(x) = 0$ and $g(x) = \xi x$. For $\xi \geq \xi_{cr}$, in addition to the trivial solution, two others, differing in sign only, are possible. To obtain nontrivial solutions the nonzero initial values $f_i^{(0)} = x_i$ are always used for $\xi > \xi_{cr}$. As soon as a nontrivial solution is obtained, it is used as the initial values for the next value of ξ, and the procedure is followed as in the bending problem.

Numerical results are graphically presented for nonlinear bending and buckling of a simply supported circular plate. Figures 4.10 and 4.11 show the postbuck-

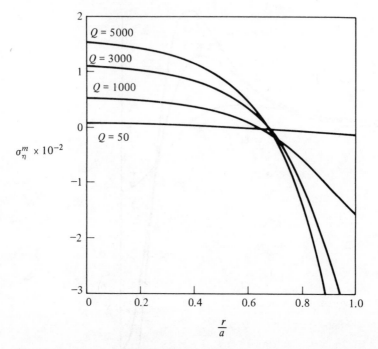

Figure 4.12 Distribution of circumferential membrane stress along radius of simply supported circular plate under transverse load.

ling behavior of the plate. For ξ slightly greater than ξ_{cr} the circumferential membrane stresses σ_θ^m shown in Fig. 4.10 are tensile in the central region, and flatten in this region as ξ increases. These stresses decrease rapidly and become compressive, reaching a compressive maximum near the edge. The maximum occurs at the edge for the radial membrane stresses. In Fig. 4.11 the radial bending stresses σ_r^b are also tensile in the central region but increase for large values of ξ, reaching a tensile maximum near the edge. Then these stresses decrease rapidly to compressive with the maximum at the edge. As ξ increases, these stresses in the central region approach zero, and the locations of tensile maximum and zero stress shift toward the edge. The distribution of the circumferential bending stress σ_θ^b (not shown) is quite similar to that of σ_r^b. For a given ξ the tensile and compressive maxima of σ_θ^b are less than that of σ_ζ^b. The nonlinear bending behavior of the plate is presented in Figs. 4.12 and 4.13. The circumferential membrane stress shown in Fig. 4.12 remains tensile and rather flat in the central region, and changes rapidly to compressive with its maximum at the edge. This sharp transition of the stress near the edge, from tension to compression, is characteristic of the boundary-layer behavior. The radial membrane stress has a maximum at the center but is not shown here. Figure 4.13 shows that the radial bending stress generally has a maximum near the edge rather than at the center, and the location

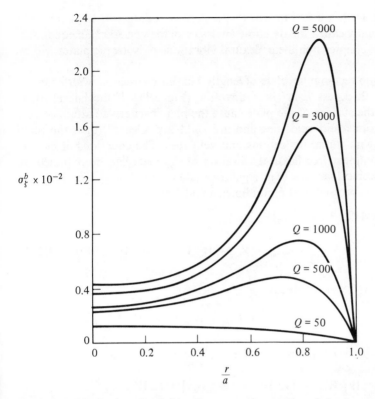

Figure 4.13 Distribution of radial bending stress along radius of simply supported circular plate under uniform transverse load.

of the maximum stress shifts toward the edge as the load Q increases. The circumferential bending stress behaves similarly as σ_r^b with a smaller magnitude for a given value of Q.

4.7 FREE VIBRATION OF HINGED RECTANGULAR PLATE

The von Kármán nonlinear equations of isotropic plates in rectangular cartesian coordinates and cylindrical coordinates have been applied to the study of various plate problems on the moderately large-deflection behavior in Chaps. 2 and 3, and on the postbuckling behavior in this chapter. The most significant features of these problems are independent of time. The other type of plate problem with which this book is concerned is the dynamic behavior of thin plates. The differential equations of motion governing the moderately large-amplitude flexural vibrations of isotropic plates can be obtained from equations (1-117) to (1-119) in terms of three displacement components, and from equations (1-161) and (1-162) in terms of transverse deflection and force function. These equations, which, except for the transverse inertia term are identical with the corresponding von Kármán plate equations, are usually called the dynamic analogue of the von Kármán equations. In the rest of this chapter nonlinear flexural vibrations of isotropic plates will be treated.

Consider a thin rectangular plate of length a in the x direction, width b in the y direction, and thickness h in the z direction (Fig. 2.11). If the lateral loads distributed over the surface of the plate cause the plate particles to attain certain transverse deflections and velocities and are suddenly released, then the plate tends to vibrate with initial deflections and velocities. The equations of motion governing the nonlinear free flexural vibration of the plate can be obtained by setting the transverse load $q = 0$ in equations (1-117) to (1-119). The resulting equations can be expressed in the nondimensional form

$$U_{,\zeta\zeta} + W_{,\zeta} W_{,\zeta\zeta} + v(V_{,\zeta\eta} + W_{,\eta} W_{,\zeta\eta})$$

$$+ \frac{1-v}{2}(U_{,\eta\eta} + V_{,\zeta\eta} + W_{,\zeta} W_{,\eta\eta} + W_{,\eta} W_{,\zeta\eta}) = 0 \quad (4\text{-}111)$$

$$V_{,\eta\eta} + W_{,\eta} W_{,\eta\eta} + v(U_{,\zeta\eta} + W_{,\zeta} W_{,\zeta\eta}) + \frac{1-v}{2}$$

$$\cdot (V_{,\zeta\zeta} + U_{,\zeta\eta} + W_{,\eta} W_{,\zeta\zeta} + W_{,\zeta} W_{,\zeta\eta}) = 0 \quad (4\text{-}112)$$

$$\frac{\delta^2}{12}(W_{,\zeta\zeta\zeta\zeta} + 2W_{,\zeta\zeta\eta\eta} + W_{,\eta\eta\eta\eta}) = U_{,\zeta} W_{,\zeta\zeta}$$

$$+ \tfrac{1}{2}W_{,\zeta}^2 W_{,\zeta\zeta} + v[V_{,\eta} W_{,\zeta\zeta} + \tfrac{1}{2}W_{,\eta}^2 W_{,\zeta\zeta}] + V_{,\eta} W_{,\eta\eta}$$

$$+ \tfrac{1}{2}W_{,\eta}^2 W_{,\eta\eta} + v[U_{,\zeta} W_{,\eta\eta} + \tfrac{1}{2}W_{,\zeta}^2 W_{,\eta\eta}]$$

$$+ (1-v)(U_{,\eta} W_{,\zeta\eta} + V_{,\zeta} W_{,\zeta\eta} + W_{,\zeta} W_{,\eta} W_{,\zeta\eta}) - \frac{\delta^2}{12} W_{,\tau\tau} \quad (4\text{-}113)$$

where

$$\zeta = \frac{x}{a} \qquad \eta = \frac{y}{a} \qquad \tau = \frac{c_p \delta}{\sqrt{12}\,a} t \qquad \delta = \frac{h}{a}$$

$$U = \frac{u^\circ}{a} \qquad V = \frac{v^\circ}{a} \qquad W = \frac{w}{a} \qquad \lambda = \frac{a}{b} \quad (4\text{-}114)$$

In equations (4-114) c_p is the flexural wave velocity in the plate given by

$$c_p^2 = \frac{Eh}{\rho(1-v^2)} \quad (4\text{-}115)$$

If the four edges of the plate are simply supported and immovable, the non-dimensional boundary conditions are

$$U = W = W_{,\zeta\zeta} = 0 \qquad \text{at} \quad \zeta = 0, 1$$

$$V = W = W_{,\eta\eta} = 0 \qquad \text{at} \quad \eta = 0, \frac{1}{\lambda} \quad (4\text{-}116)$$

with the fourth boundary condition being allowed to have what it will be. Furthermore, there is no need to specify the initial conditions since only free vibrations are to be investigated.

The governing equations (4-111) to (4-113), are solved by the perturbation method (Ref. 4.10). The nondimensional variables U, V, and W are expressed as the perturbation series with respect to the small parameter δ. This parameter depends only on the geometry of the plate but not on the type of motion. It is to be noted that the inplane displacements u° and v° neglected in the classical linear theory are of one order higher than the transverse displacement w, and that u° and v° are even functions of δ, and w is an odd function. Thus the perturbation series for these displacements are given by

$$U = u_2(\zeta, \eta, \tau)\delta^2 + u_4(\zeta, \eta, \tau)\delta^4 + \cdots$$

$$V = v_2(\zeta, \eta, \tau)\delta^2 + v_4(\zeta, \eta, \tau)\delta^4 + \cdots \tag{4-117}$$

$$W = w_1(\zeta, \eta, \tau)\delta + w_3(\zeta, \eta, \tau)\delta^3 + \cdots$$

Substituting expressions (4-117) into equations (4-111) to (4-113) and retaining terms of the lowest order in δ only, we obtain the following equations

$$u_{2,\zeta\zeta} + w_{1,\zeta}w_{1,\zeta\zeta} + v(v_{2,\zeta\eta} + w_{1,\eta}w_{1,\zeta\eta})$$
$$+ \frac{1-v}{2}(u_{2,\eta\eta} + v_{2,\zeta\eta} + w_{1,\zeta}w_{1,\eta\eta} + w_{1,\eta}w_{1,\zeta\eta}) = 0 \tag{4-118}$$

$$v_{2,\eta\eta} + w_{1,\eta}w_{1,\eta\eta} + v(u_{2,\zeta\eta} + w_{1,\zeta}w_{1,\zeta\eta})$$
$$+ \frac{1-v}{2}(v_{2,\zeta\zeta} + u_{2,\zeta\eta} + w_{1,\eta}w_{1,\zeta\zeta} + w_{1,\zeta}w_{1,\zeta\eta}) = 0 \tag{4-119}$$

$$\tfrac{1}{12}(w_{1,\zeta\zeta\zeta\zeta} + 2w_{1,\zeta\zeta\eta\eta} + w_{1,\eta\eta\eta\eta}) = u_{2,\zeta}w_{1,\zeta\zeta}$$
$$+ \tfrac{1}{2}(w_{1,\zeta})^2 w_{1,\zeta\zeta} + v[v_{2,\eta}w_{1,\zeta\zeta} + \tfrac{1}{2}(w_{1,\eta})^2 w_{1,\zeta\zeta}]$$
$$+ v_{2,\eta\eta}w_{1,\eta\eta} + \tfrac{1}{2}(w_{1,\eta})^2 w_{1,\eta\eta} + v$$
$$\cdot [u_{2,\zeta}w_{1,\eta\eta} + \tfrac{1}{2}(w_{1,\zeta})^2 w_{1,\eta\eta}] + (1 - v)$$
$$\cdot (u_{2,\eta}w_{1,\zeta\eta} + v_{2,\zeta}w_{1,\zeta\eta} + w_{1,\zeta}w_{1,\eta}w_{1,\zeta\eta}) - \tfrac{1}{12}w_{1,\tau\tau} \tag{4-120}$$

Similarly, the boundary conditions (4-116) yield

$$u_2 = w_1 = w_{1,\zeta\zeta} = 0 \quad \text{at} \quad \zeta = 0, 1$$

$$v_2 = w_1 = w_{1,\eta\eta} = 0 \quad \text{at} \quad \eta = 0, \frac{1}{\lambda} \tag{4-121}$$

A solution of equations (4-118) to (4-120) is sought in the separable form

$$u_2 = \frac{\pi W_m^2 Z^2(\tau)}{16}(\cos 2\pi\lambda\eta - 1 + v\lambda^2)\sin 2\pi\zeta$$

$$v_2 = \frac{\pi W_m^2 Z^2(\tau)}{16}\left(\lambda \cos 2\pi\zeta - \lambda + \frac{v}{\lambda}\right)\sin 2\pi\lambda\eta \tag{4-122}$$

$$w_1 = W_m Z(\tau)\sin \pi\zeta \sin \pi\lambda\eta$$

in which $Z(\tau) \leq 1$ and $W_m = w_m/h$, with w_m being the amplitude of the nonlinear free vibration. It can be verified that expressions (4-122) satisfy equations (4-118) and (4-119) and boundary conditions (4-121). On substitution equation (4-120) reduces to

$$\left\{\frac{W_m}{12}[Z_{,\tau\tau} + \pi^4(1 + \lambda^2)^2 Z] + \frac{\pi^4}{16} W_m^3 Z^3[(3 - v^2)(1 + \lambda^4) + 4v\lambda^2]\right\} \cdot$$

$$\cdot \sin \pi\zeta \sin \pi\lambda\eta + \tfrac{1}{16}\pi^4 W_m^3 Z^3(1 - v^2)$$

$$\cdot (\sin \pi\zeta \sin 3\pi\lambda\eta + \lambda^4 \sin 3\pi\zeta \sin \pi\lambda\eta) = 0 \qquad (4\text{-}123)$$

which indicates that a coupling phenomenon exists between the fundamental mode contained in the first group of terms and the two higher modes contained in the second. For small nonlinearities this effect of higher modes† can be neglected. Thus we obtain the following nolinear ordinary second-order differential equation for the time function

$$Z_{,\tau\tau} + \pi^4(1 + \lambda^2)^2 Z + 3\pi^4 W_m^2 Z^3[\tfrac{1}{4}(3 - v^2)(1 + \lambda^4) + v\lambda^2] = 0 \quad (4\text{-}124)$$

Measuring the nondimensional time τ such that

$$Z = 1 \qquad Z_{,\tau} = 0 \qquad \text{at} \quad \tau = 0$$

the solution of equation (4-124) is obtained in the form of elliptic cosine cn (Ref. 4.11)

$$Z = \text{cn} \, (\mu\tau, \kappa) \qquad (4\text{-}125)$$

where

$$\mu = \pi^2[(1 + \lambda^2)^2 + 3v\lambda^2 W_m^2 + \tfrac{3}{4}W_m^2(3 - v^2)(1 + \lambda^4)]^{1/2}$$

$$\kappa^2 = \left\{2 + \frac{8(1 + \lambda^2)^2}{3W_m^2[(3 - v^2)(1 + \lambda^4) + 4v\lambda^2]}\right\}^{-1} \qquad (4\text{-}126)$$

In equations (4-126) κ is the modulus of the elliptic function and μ may be taken as the "circular frequency." The period T of cn $(\mu\tau, \kappa)$ is

$$T = \frac{4\pi^2 K(\kappa)}{\mu} \qquad (4\text{-}127)$$

in which K is the complete elliptic integral of the first kind. The corresponding linear period T_0 may be obtained by observing that as $W_m \to 0$, $\mu \to \pi^2(1 + \lambda^2)$ and $K \to \pi/2$.

$$T_0 = \frac{2\pi}{1 + \lambda^2} \qquad (4\text{-}128)$$

The ratio of nonlinear period T to linear period T_0 is thus given by

$$\frac{T}{T_0} = \frac{2}{\pi}(1 + \lambda^2)K$$

$$\cdot \{(1 + \lambda^2)^2 + \tfrac{3}{4}W_m^2[(3 - v^2)(1 + \lambda^4) + 4v\lambda^2]\}^{-1/2} \qquad (4\text{-}129)$$

---

† See Sec. 6.8.

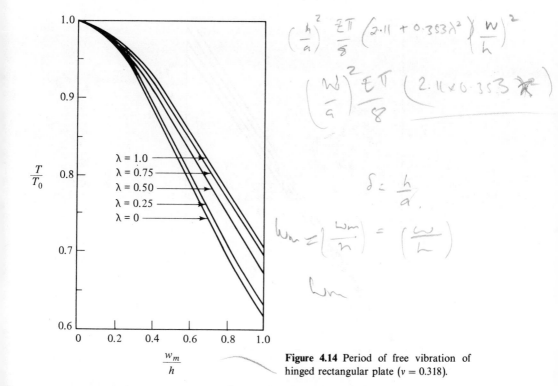

Figure **4.14** Period of free vibration of hinged rectangular plate ($v = 0.318$).

This ratio is plotted in Fig. 4.14 versus the nondimensional amplitude for various values of the aspect ratio λ and for $v = 0.318$, which is typical of aluminum alloys. This figure shows that the period decreases with increasing the amplitude. Hence only a hardening type of nonlinearity is observed.

The perturbation series (4-117) is now approximated by

$$U = u_2 \delta^2 \qquad V = v_2 \delta^2 \qquad W = w_1 \delta \qquad (4\text{-}130)$$

from which the stresses in the plate can be calculated from equations (1-121) to (1-123) and (1-163). The maximum extreme-fiber stress occurs at the center of the plate. The membrane and extreme-fiber bending stresses at the center are, for $Z_{max} = 1$ and $v = 0.318$,

$$(\sigma^m_x)_{max} = \frac{E\pi}{8} (2.11 + 0.353\lambda^2)\left(\frac{h}{a}\right)^2 W^2_m$$

$$(\sigma^b_x)_{max} = \frac{E\pi^2}{2} (1.111 + 0.353\lambda^2)\left(\frac{h}{a}\right)^2 W_m \qquad (4\text{-}131)$$

The nondimensional total maximum stress is at the center

$$\frac{(\sigma_x)_{max}}{(\sigma^b_x)_{max}} = 1 + \frac{1.899 + 0.318\lambda^2}{4\pi(1 + 0.318\lambda^2)} W_m \qquad (4\text{-}132)$$

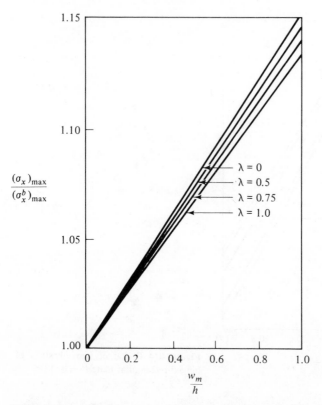

Figure 4.15 Extreme-fiber stress at center of hinged rectangular plate undergoing free vibration ($v = 0.318$).

in which $(\sigma_x)_{\max}$ is the total maximum stress at the center of the plate and $(\sigma_x^b)_{\max}$ is the only stress in the classical linear plate theory. Figure 4.15 indicates that, as a consequence of moderately large amplitudes, the total stress may be considerably larger than that predicted by the linear theory. However, it appears that the large amplitudes affect the period of vibration markedly greater than the stress.

4.8 VIBRATION OF RECTANGULAR PLATE DUE TO HARMONIC FORCE FOR VARIOUS EDGE CONDITIONS

Suppose that a thin rectangular plate of length a in the x direction, width b in the y direction, and thickness h in the z direction (Fig. 2.1) is subjected to a harmonic exciting pressure $q(x, y) \cos \omega t$ in which ω is the frequency of the transverse load. Equations (1-161) and (1-162) governing the transverse motion of the plate are rewritten in the form

$$L(w, F) = D\nabla^4 w + \rho w_{,tt} - h(w_{,xx} F_{,yy} + w_{,yy} F_{,xx} - 2w_{,xy} F_{,xy})$$

$$- q(x, y) \cos \omega t = 0 \quad (4\text{-}133)$$

$$\nabla^4 F = E[w_{,xy}^2 - w_{,xx} w_{,yy}] \tag{4-134}$$

in which $F = \psi/h$ is the Airy stress function.

Now the boundary conditions of the plate are specified. The out-of-plane conditions under consideration are of the following two types:

I. All edges simply supported

$$w = w_{,xx} + vw_{,yy} = 0 \quad \text{at} \quad x = \pm\frac{a}{2}$$

$$\tag{4-135}$$

$$w = w_{,yy} + vw_{,xx} = 0 \quad \text{at} \quad y = \pm\frac{b}{2}$$

II. All edges clamped

$$w = w_{,x} = 0 \quad \text{at} \quad x = \pm\frac{a}{2}$$

$$\tag{4-136}$$

$$w = w_{,y} = 0 \quad \text{at} \quad y = \pm\frac{b}{2}$$

For the inplane conditions the following three cases are considered:

(a) All edges free from stresses

$$F_{,yy} = F_{,xy} = 0 \quad \text{at} \quad x = \pm\frac{a}{2}$$

$$\tag{4-137}$$

$$F_{,xx} = F_{,xy} = 0 \quad \text{at} \quad y = \pm\frac{b}{2}$$

(b) All edges immovably constrained

$$u^\circ = F_{,xy} = 0 \quad \text{at} \quad x = \pm\frac{a}{2}$$

$$\tag{4-138}$$

$$v^\circ = F_{,xy} = 0 \quad \text{at} \quad y = \pm\frac{b}{2}$$

(c) All edges uniformly displaced with zero resultant of normal stresses

$$P_x = F_{,xy} = 0 \qquad u^\circ = \text{const}$$

$$P_y = F_{,xy} = 0 \qquad v^\circ = \text{const} \tag{4-139}$$

in which P_x and P_y are the inplane resultant forces in the x and y directions, respectively, given by

$$P_x = h \int_{-b/2}^{b/2} F_{,yy} \, dy \qquad P_y = h \int_{-a/2}^{a/2} F_{,xx} \, dx \tag{4-140}$$

and in which the inplane displacements $u°$ and $v°$ are related to the stress function by equations (2-91). Conditions (4-135) to (4-139) can be combined into six sets of boundary conditions.

One-term approximate solution of the governing equations (4-133) and (4-134) satisfying the prescribed boundary conditions in each case is formulated by application of the Galerkin method (Ref. 2.4) furnishing the equation for the time function. The conditions (4-135) and (4-136) respectively are satisfied by assuming the deflection function in each case as

I. $w = h\phi(t) \cos \dfrac{\pi x}{a} \cos \dfrac{\pi y}{b}$

II. $w = h\phi(t) \cos^2 \dfrac{\pi x}{a} \cos^2 \dfrac{\pi y}{b}$
$$\tag{4-141}$$

in which ϕ is a function of time t with its maximum value being

$$\phi_{\max} = \frac{w_m}{h} = W_m \tag{4-142}$$

In this expression w_m is the maximum deflection of the plate. Substituting expressions (4-141) into the compatibility equation (4-134) yields

$$\nabla^4 f = \frac{\pi^4 E h^2}{a^2 b^2} \sum_{p=0}^{\infty} \sum_{q=0}^{\infty} a_{pq} R_p(x) S_q(y) \tag{4-143}$$

in which a_{pq} are known Fourier coefficients in each case and in which

$$f = \frac{F}{\phi^2} \qquad R_p = \cos \frac{2p\pi x}{a} \qquad S_q = \cos \frac{2q\pi y}{b} \tag{4-144}$$

The general solution of equation (4-143) is

$$f = f_c + f_p \tag{4-145}$$

where f_c is the complementary function and f_p is a particular integral which may be expressed as

$$f_p = E h^2 \sum_{p=0}^{\infty} \sum_{q=0}^{\infty} b_{pq} R_p(x) S_q(y) \tag{4-146}$$

where

$$b_{pq} = \frac{\lambda^2 a_{pq}}{16(p^2 + q^2 \lambda^2)^2} \qquad \lambda = \frac{a}{b} \tag{4-147}$$

After some manipulation the nonzero coefficients b_{pq} in each case are

I. $b_{01} = -\dfrac{1}{32\lambda^2}$ $\quad b_{10} = -\dfrac{\lambda^2}{32}$

II. $b_{01} = -\dfrac{1}{32\lambda^2}$ $\quad b_{10} = -\dfrac{\lambda^2}{32}$ $\quad b_{11} = -\dfrac{\lambda^2}{16(1 + \lambda^2)^2}$

$b_{02} = -\dfrac{1}{512\lambda^2}$ $\quad b_{20} = -\dfrac{\lambda^2}{512}$ $\quad b_{12} = -\dfrac{\lambda^2}{32(1 + 4\lambda^2)^2}$ $\qquad$ (4-148)

$b_{21} = -\dfrac{\lambda^2}{32(4 + \lambda^2)^2}$

It is observed that f_p is an even function in x and y satisfying the condition for zero shear stress along the edges of the plate. With these properties the complementary function of equation (4-143) is obtained by setting $F_c = f_c$ and $W_m = 1$ in equation (2-26). The constants C_1, C_2, A_n, and B_n are to be determined by the inplane boundary conditions. Inserting the expressions for w and F in conditions (4-138) and (4-139), by use of equations (2-91) and (4-140) we obtain, for Case (b),

$$A_n = B_n = 0 \qquad C_1 = \gamma \frac{\pi^2 Eh^2(\lambda^2 + v)}{a^2(1 - v^2)}$$

$$C_2 = \gamma \frac{\pi^2 Eh^2(1 + v\lambda^2)}{a^2(1 - v^2)}$$
$\qquad$ (4-149)

and for Case (c),

$$A_n = B_n = C_1 = C_2 = 0 \qquad (4\text{-}150)$$

in which $\gamma = \frac{1}{8}$ for Case I and $\gamma = \frac{3}{32}$ for Case II. Following the procedure as in Sec. 2.2, these arbitrary constants for Case (a) are obtained by setting $F_c = f_c$ and $W_m = 1$ in equations (2-27) to (2-32). It is noticed that $C_1 = C_2 = 0$ in this case. Furthermore the representation of the complementary function f_c for Case (a) by a double cosine series is obtained by setting $F_c = f_c$ and $W_m = 1$ in equations (2-33) to (2-35).

Now the function f in each case can be written in the general form

$$\frac{F}{\phi^2} = f = \tfrac{1}{2}(C_1 x^2 + C_2 y^2) + Eh^2 \sum_{p=0}^{\infty} \sum_{q=0}^{\infty} d_{pq} R_p(x) S_q(y) \qquad (4\text{-}151)$$

in which the constants C_1, C_2, and d_{pq} in each case are

(a) $C_1 = C_2 = 0 \quad d_{pq} = b_{pq} + c_{pq}$
(b) $d_{pq} = b_{pq}$ $\qquad\qquad\qquad\qquad\qquad\qquad$ (4-152)
(c) $C_1 = C_2 = 0 \quad d_{pq} = b_{pq}$

In Case (b) C_1 and C_2 are given by equation (4-149).

Instead of satisfaction of equation (4-133), the Galerkin procedure is applied to this equation. This leads to the following condition on F and w

$$\int_0^{a/2} \int_0^{b/2} L(w, F)w \, dx \, dy = 0 \tag{4-153}$$

Upon substitution and integration we obtain a nonlinear ordinary differential equation for the time function ϕ in each case

I. $\rho h \phi_{,tt} + \dfrac{\pi^4 Dh}{a^4}(1 + \lambda^2)^2 \phi + \dfrac{\pi^2 h^2}{a^2}(\lambda^2 C_1 + C_2)\phi^3$

$\qquad - \dfrac{2\pi^4 Eh^4}{a^2 b^2}(d_{01} + d_{10})\phi^3 = \dfrac{16}{\pi^2} q_0 \cos \omega t$

II. $\rho h \phi_{,tt} + \dfrac{16\pi^4 Dh}{9a^4}(3 + 2\lambda^2 + 3\lambda^4)\phi + \dfrac{4\pi^2 h^2}{3a^2}(\lambda^2 C_1 + C_2)\phi^3 \tag{4-154}$

$\qquad - \dfrac{32\pi^4 Eh^4}{9a^2 b^2}(d_{01} + d_{10} + d_{11} + \tfrac{1}{2}d_{12} + \tfrac{1}{2}d_{21} + d_{02} + d_{20})\phi^3$

$\qquad = \dfrac{16}{9} q_0 \cos \omega t$

in which q has been treated as a uniform lateral pressure q_0. For Case I(b) we obtain

$$\rho h \phi_{,tt} + \frac{\pi^4 Dh}{a^4}(1 + \lambda^2)^2 \phi + \frac{3\pi^4 Dh}{4a^4}[(3 - v^2)(1 + \lambda^4) + 4v\lambda^2]\phi^3 = 0 \tag{4-155}$$

which is precisely equivalent to equation (4-124).

Equations (4-154) are specified for a square plate ($\lambda = 1$) with the result

I. $\rho h \phi_{,tt} + \dfrac{\pi^4 Eh^4}{a^4}\left[\dfrac{\phi}{3(1 - v^2)} + k_1 \phi^3\right] = \dfrac{16}{\pi^2} q_0 \cos \omega t$

$\tag{4-156}$

II. $\rho h \phi_{,tt} + \dfrac{16\pi^4 Eh^4}{9a^4}\left[\dfrac{2\phi}{3(1 - v^2)} + k_2 \phi^3\right] = \dfrac{16}{9} q_0 \cos \omega t$

in which k_1 and k_2 are constants given in Table 4.2. In calculation, A_n and B_n for Case (a) were obtained by taking $n = 1, 2, 3, \ldots, 8$ in equations (2-32). Equations (4-156) can be written in the form

$$\phi_{,tt} + \omega_0^2 \phi + \alpha^2 \phi^3 = Q \cos \omega t \tag{4-157}$$

which is the well-known Duffing's equation. The two-term approximate solution (Ref. 4.11) is

$$\phi(t) = A \cos \omega t + \frac{\alpha^2 A^3}{32(\omega_0^2 + \tfrac{3}{4}\alpha^2 A^2 - Q/A)} \cos 3\omega\tau \tag{4-158}$$

Table 4.2 Constants k_1 and k_2 in equations (4-156)

Case	(a)	(b)	(c)
k_1	0.06492	$\dfrac{3-v}{8(1+v)}$	$\frac{1}{8}$
k_2	0.14903	$0.16656 + \dfrac{0.14063}{1-v}$	0.16656

which indicates that A is the nondimensional amplitude $\phi(0)$, or w_m/h, of the component with the circular frequency ω and in which A is related to ω by

$$\frac{\omega^2}{\omega_0^2} = 1 + \frac{3}{4}\left(\frac{\alpha}{\omega_0}A\right)^2 - \frac{Q}{A\omega_0^2} \qquad (4\text{-}159)$$

This expression shows that the frequency, hence the period, depends on amplitude A. In view of equations (4-156) to (4-159) the response of the square plate to the harmonic exciting pressure can be determined. The result for Case I(b) is shown in Fig. 4.16 for $v = 0.3$. The ratio w_m/h is negative to the right of the free vibration curve $q_0 a^4/Eh^4 = 0$, called the backbone curve, and positive to the left of it. This means that the vibrating plate and the driving force are out of phase or in phase according to whether the forcing frequency is greater or less than that of free vibration for a particular amplitude. The solid curves represent the stable motion and the dashed curves correspond to the unstable vibration. (See experimental

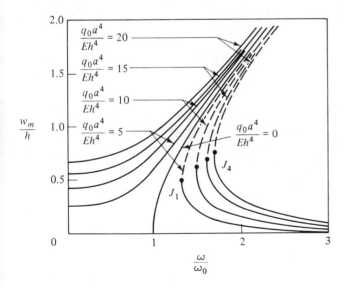

Figure 4.16 Relationship between forcing frequency and amplitude of vibration for simply supported square plate with immovable edges subjected to harmonic exciting pressure ($v = 0.3$).

data in Fig. 4.23.) The points of vertical tangencies $(J_1, \ldots, J_4)$ are points which give a rise to a jump phenomenon commonly found in nonlinear vibratory elastic systems. Similar results are obtained for other boundary conditions.

Now the foregoing result is specified for static large deflection and nonlinear free flexural vibration. In the static case, by putting $\phi(t) = W_m$ and $\cos \omega t = 1$ into equations (1-156) we obtain

$$\text{I.} \quad \frac{q_0 a^4}{Eh^4} = \frac{\pi^6}{16}\left[\frac{W_m}{3(1 - v^2)} + k_1 W_m^3\right]$$

$$\text{II.} \quad \frac{q_0 a^4}{Eh^4} = \pi^4\left[\frac{2W_m}{3(1 - v^2)} + k_2 W_m^3\right]$$

(4-160)

which are the relationships between uniform transverse load q_0 and maximum deflection w_m of a square plate in each case. It is observed that the results for static cases II(a), I(a), II(b), and I(b) are identical with formulas (2-40), (2-50), (2-98) and (2-102), respectively.

In the case of free vibration, by setting $q_0 = 0$ in equation (4-157) we obtain

$$\phi_{,tt} + \omega_0^2 \phi + \alpha^2 \phi^3 = 0 \qquad (4\text{-}161)$$

For vibrations with small amplitudes the last term in equation (4-161) can be neglected in comparison with the second, and hence equation (4-161) becomes linear with the natural circular frequency given by ω_0. The value of ω_0 is given by $(2\pi^2/a^2)\sqrt{D/\rho}$ for the simply supported square plate and by $(37.22/a^2)\sqrt{D/\rho}$ for the clamped square plate. The former value is identical with the result obtained from the linear theory (Ref. 4.12) and the latter is 3.5 percent larger than the accurate value (Ref. 4.13).

A solution of the equation (4-161) satisfying the initial conditions $\phi(0) = A$ and $\phi_{,t}(0) = 0$ is

$$\phi = A \text{ cn } (pt, k) \qquad (4\text{-}162)$$

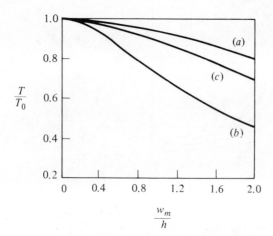

Figure 4.17 Period of vibration of simply supported square plate for various in-plane boundary conditions ($v = 0.3$).

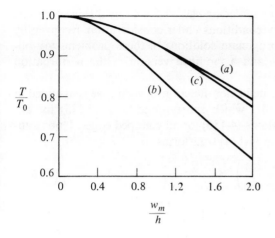

Figure 4.18 Period of vibration of clamped square plate for different inplane boundary conditions ($\nu = 0.3$).

where

$$p = (\omega_0^2 + \alpha^2 A^2)^{1/2} \qquad k = \left[\frac{\alpha^2 A^2}{2(\omega_0^2 + \alpha^2 A^2)}\right]^{1/2} \qquad (4\text{-}163)$$

The period T of the elliptic cosine is

$$T = \frac{4K(k)}{p} \qquad (4\text{-}164)$$

in which K is the complete elliptic integral of the first kind. The corresponding linear period T_0 is

$$T_0 = \frac{2\pi}{\omega_0} \qquad (4\text{-}165)$$

Hence the ratio of nonlinear period T to linear period T_0 is given by

$$\frac{T}{T_0} = \frac{2\omega_0 K}{\pi\sqrt{\omega_0^2 + \alpha^2 A^2}} \qquad (4\text{-}166)$$

This ratio is plotted against the nondimensional amplitude A in Fig. 4.17 for simply supported plates and in Fig. 4.18 for clamped plates. It is seen that the period decreases with increasing amplitude in each case, and this tendency is most pronounced for Case (b).

4.9 RESPONSE OF RECTANGULAR PLATE TO PULSE EXCITATIONS FOR VARIOUS EDGE CONDITIONS

Consider the vibration of a rectangular plate due to pulse excitation $q(t)$, such as the step function, and the exponentially decaying pulse of which the latter can be used for an adequate description of a blast load on the plate. The equations of motion for the plate are obtained by replacing $q(x, y) \cos \omega t$ by $q(t)$ in equations (4-133) and (4-134). The boundary conditions under consideration are given by equations (4-135) to (4-138). Approximate solutions of these problems are obtained by the Galerkin procedure and a modified version of the perturbation method (Ref. 4.14).

As in the previous section, the deflection function in each case is assumed in the form given by equations (4-141) which satisfy conditions (4-135) for all-simply supported edges, and conditions (4-136) for all-clamped edges. Upon substitution the compatibility equation (4-134) transforms to

$$\text{I. } \nabla^4 f = -\frac{\pi^4 E h^2}{2a^2 b^2}\left(\cos\frac{2\pi x}{a} + \cos\frac{2\pi y}{b}\right) \tag{4-167a}$$

$$\text{II. } \nabla^4 f = -\frac{\pi^4 E h^2}{2a^2 b^2}\left(\cos\frac{2\pi x}{a} + \cos\frac{2\pi y}{b}\right.$$

$$+ 2\cos\frac{2\pi x}{a}\cos\frac{2\pi y}{b} + \cos\frac{4\pi x}{a} + \cos\frac{4\pi y}{b}$$

$$\left. + \cos\frac{2\pi x}{a}\cos\frac{4\pi y}{b} + \cos\frac{4\pi x}{a}\cos\frac{2\pi y}{b}\right) \tag{4-167b}$$

which can be expressed in the form of equation (4-143) with solution given by expression (4-151). Employing the Galerkin method for the solution of the dynamic equation (4-133) leads to condition (4-153). On substitution and integration we obtain a nonlinear ordinary differential equation of order two for the time function $\phi(t)$ in each case. These equations are of the form

$$\phi_{,tt} + \omega_0^2 \phi + \varepsilon\omega_0^2 \phi^3 = Q(t) \tag{4-168}$$

in which ω_0 is the natural circular frequency, ε is a constant characterizing the degree of nonlinearity, and $Q(t)$ is the load parameter. They are given below for each case.

I. Simply supported square plate

$$\omega_0^2 = \frac{\pi^4 E h^3}{3a^4 \rho(1 - v^2)} \qquad Q(t) = \frac{16q(t)}{\pi^2 \rho h}$$

(a) stress-free $\qquad \varepsilon = 0.19476(1 - v^2)$ $\qquad$ (4-169)

(b) immovably constrained $\qquad \varepsilon = \frac{3}{8}(1 - v)(3 - v)$

II. Clamped square plate

$$\omega_0^2 = \frac{32\pi^4 E h^3}{27a^4 \rho(1 - v^2)} \qquad Q(t) = \frac{16q(t)}{9\rho h}$$

(a) stress-free $\qquad \varepsilon = 0.22355(1 - v^2)$ $\qquad$ (4-170)

(b) immovably constrained $\qquad \varepsilon = \frac{27}{128}(1 + v) + \frac{8.49}{32}(1 - v^2)$

Suppose that at the time $t = 0$ at which the plate is at rest

$$\phi(0) = 0 \qquad \phi_{,t}(0) = 0 \qquad \text{at} \quad t = 0 \tag{4-171}$$

a pressure pulse $q(t)$ is suddenly applied to the plate. Let

$$\phi(t) = p(t) + g(t) \tag{4-172}$$

in which $p(t)$ and $g(t)$ are as yet unknown functions. Inserting equations (4-172) into (4-168) yields

$$p_{,tt} + \omega_0^2 p + g_{,tt} + \omega_0^2 g + \varepsilon \omega_0^2 (p + g)^3 = Q(t) \tag{4-173}$$

Now $g(t)$ is chosen so as to satisfy the equation

$$g_{,tt} + \omega_0^2 g = Q(t) \tag{4-174}$$

Thus $g(t)$ is the particular response of the linearized system. If a particular solution of equation (4-173) is denoted by g_p, then the initial conditions (4-171) become

$$p(0) = -g_p(0) \qquad p_{,t}(0) = -g_{p,t}(0) \tag{4-175}$$

and equation (4-173) reduces to

$$p_{,tt} + \omega_0^2 p + \varepsilon \omega_0^2 (p + g_p)^3 = 0 \tag{4-176}$$

For small values of ε an approximate solution of equation (4-176) can be obtained by an extension of the perturbation method (Ref. 4.15). The object is to produce in the vicinity of $\varepsilon = 0$ a uniformly convergent series, which converges to the linear solution as $\varepsilon \to 0$. This is achieved by introducing a new variable ξ and expanding the time function $p(t)$ and the time t in the form of power series with respect to ε

$$p = \sum_{n=0}^{\infty} p_n(\xi) \varepsilon^n$$

$$t = \xi + \sum_{n=1}^{\infty} s_n(\xi) \varepsilon^n \tag{4-177}$$

in which p_n and s_n are unknown functions to be determined. Substituting equations (4-177) into (4-175) and (4-176), and expanding g_p and $g_{p,\xi}$ into Taylor series yields a set of linear differential equations

$$p_{0,\xi\xi} + \omega_0^2 p_0 = 0 \tag{4-178}$$

$$p_{1,\xi\xi} + \omega_0^2 p_1 = 2s_{1,\xi} p_{0,\xi\xi} + p_{0,\xi} s_{1,\xi\xi} - \omega_0^2 (p_0 + g_p)^3 \tag{4-179}$$

$$p_{2,\xi\xi} + \omega_0^2 p_2 = 2s_{2,\xi} p_{0,\xi\xi} + 2s_{1,\xi} p_{1,\xi\xi} - 3p_{0,\xi\xi}(s_{1,\xi})^2$$
$$+ p_{1,\xi} s_{1,\xi\xi} - 3p_{0,\xi} s_{1,\xi} s_{1,\xi\xi} - 3\omega_0^2 (p_1 + g_{p,\xi} s_1)$$
$$\cdot (p_0 + g_p)^2 \tag{4-180}$$

. . . .

and a set of initial conditions

$$p_0(0) = -g_p(0) \qquad p_n(0) = 0$$
$$p_{0,\xi}(0) = -g_{p,\xi}(0) \qquad p_{n,\xi}(0) = 0 \qquad\qquad n \neq 1 \qquad (4\text{-}181)$$

Equations (4-178) to (4-180) can be solved successively in conjunction with the corresponding conditions (4-181). For the linear case the solution of equation (4-178) is

$$p_0(\xi) = -\left[g_p(0) \cos \omega_0 \xi + \frac{1}{\omega_0} g_{p,\xi}(0) \sin \omega_0 \xi \right] \qquad (4\text{-}182)$$

Inserting this expression into equation (4-179) leads to

$$p_{1,\xi\xi} + \omega_0^2 p_1 = 2\omega_0^2 s_{1,\xi}\left[g_p(0) \cos \omega_0 \xi + \frac{1}{\omega_0} g_{p,\xi}(0) \sin \omega_0 \xi \right]$$

$$+ \omega_0 s_{1,\xi\xi}\left[g_p(0) \sin \omega_0 \xi - \frac{1}{\omega_0} g_{p,\xi}(0) \cos \omega_0 \xi \right]$$

$$- \omega_0^2 \left[g_p(\xi) - g_p(0) \cos \omega_0 \xi - \frac{1}{\omega_0} g_{p,\xi}(0) \sin \omega_0 \xi \right]^3 \qquad (4\text{-}183)$$

whose solution exhibits secular terms of the form $\xi \cos \omega_0 \xi$ and $\xi \sin \omega_0 \xi$ for the terms $\sin \omega_0 \xi$ and $\cos \omega_0 \xi$ on the right-hand side. The removal of the secular terms, which grow up indefinitely when $t \to 0$, can be accomplished by setting their coefficients equal to zero. The results are, for $g_p(\xi) \neq \text{const}$,

$$s_{1,\xi\xi} - \frac{2\omega_0^2 g_p(0)}{g_{p,\xi}(0)} s_{1,\xi} = \frac{3\omega_0^2 g_p(0)}{4g_{p,\xi}(0)}\left\{ g_p^2(0) + \frac{1}{\omega_0^2} [g_{p,\xi}(0)]^2 \right\}$$

$$s_{1,\xi\xi} - \frac{2g_{p,\xi}(0)}{g_p(0)} s_{1,\xi} = -\frac{3g_{p,\xi}(0)}{4g_p(0)}\left\{ g_p^2(0) + \frac{1}{\omega_0^2} [g_{p,\xi}(0)]^2 \right\} \qquad (4\text{-}184)$$

Noting that $s_n(0) = 0$, these conditions are satisfied simultaneously by taking

$$s_1(\xi) = -\frac{3\xi}{8}\left\{ g_p^2(0) + \frac{1}{\omega_0^2} [g_{p,\xi}(0)]^2 \right\} \qquad (4\text{-}185)$$

Thus the second approximation for the time expression is

$$t = \frac{\xi}{8}\left\{ 8 - 3\varepsilon g_p^2(0) + \frac{3\varepsilon}{\omega_0^2} [g_{p,\xi}(0)]^2 \right\} \qquad (4\text{-}186)$$

and the first approximation for the time function is

$$p_1(\xi) = \frac{X(0)}{\omega_0} \cos \omega_0 \xi - \frac{Y(0)}{\omega_0} \sin \omega_0 \xi + \frac{Y(\xi)}{\omega_0} \sin \omega_0 \xi - \frac{X(\xi)}{\omega_0} \cos \omega_0 \xi$$

$$(4\text{-}187)$$

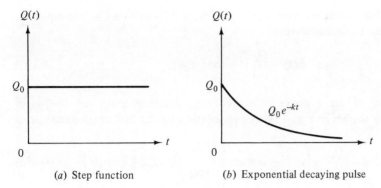

(a) Step function (b) Exponential decaying pulse

Figure 4.19 Loadings on plates.

where

$$X(\xi) = \int F(\xi) \sin \omega_0 \xi \, d\xi$$

$$Y(\xi) = \int F(\xi) \cos \omega_0 \xi \, d\xi$$

(4-188)

with $F(\xi)$ being the leftover right-hand side of the differential equation (4-183). On substitution we obtain

$$p(\xi) = -\left[g_p(0) \cos \omega_0 \xi + \frac{1}{\omega_0} g_{p,\xi}(0) \sin \omega_0 \xi \right]$$

$$+ \frac{\varepsilon}{\omega_0} \{ [X(0) - X(\xi)] \cos \omega_0 \xi + [Y(\xi) - Y(0)] \sin \omega_0 \xi \} + \cdots \quad (4\text{-}189)$$

in which the higher-order terms denoted by dots can be similarly obtained.

Now the solution formulated above is specified for two types of loadings. For the load in the form of step function shown in Fig. 4.19(a), the solution of the problem to the second approximation is

$$\phi(t) = \frac{Q_0}{\omega_0^2} \{ 1 - \cos \omega_0 \xi + \varepsilon^* [-\tfrac{5}{2} + \tfrac{65}{32} \cos \omega_0 \xi$$

$$+ \tfrac{1}{2} \cos 2\omega_0 \xi - \tfrac{1}{32} \cos 3\omega_0 \xi] + (\varepsilon^*)^2 [\tfrac{18257}{1024} \cos \omega_0 \xi$$

$$+ \tfrac{75}{512} \cos 3\omega_0 \xi - \tfrac{1}{32} \cos 4\omega_0 \xi + \tfrac{1}{1024} \cos 5\omega_0 \xi - \tfrac{543}{32}] \} \quad (4\text{-}190)$$

where

$$\varepsilon^* = \varepsilon \left(\frac{Q_0}{\omega_0^2} \right)^2$$

(4-191)

$$\omega_0 \xi = \tau [1 - \tfrac{15}{8} \varepsilon^* - \tfrac{2715}{256} (\varepsilon^*)^2] \qquad (\omega_0 t = \tau)$$

The corresponding linear solution which is obtained by setting $\varepsilon = 0$ in equation (4-189) yields the well-known result

$$\phi(t) = \frac{Q_0}{\omega_0^2}(1 - \cos \omega_0 t) \tag{4-192}$$

In the case of an exponentially decaying pressure pulse of the form $Q(t) = Q_0 e^{-kt}$ as shown in Fig. 4.19(b), the solution to the first approximation is

$$\phi(t) = \frac{Q_0}{k^2 + \omega_0^2}\left(e^{-kt} - \cos \omega_0 \xi + \frac{k}{\omega_0} \sin \omega_0 \xi\right) + \varepsilon p_1(\xi) \tag{4-193}$$

where

$$
\begin{aligned}
p_1(\xi) = {} & \frac{Q_0^3 \omega_0^2}{(k^2 + \omega_0^2)^3}\left\{\left[\frac{\omega_0^2 - 3k^2}{32\omega_0^4} + \frac{3}{2\omega_0^2} + \frac{1}{\omega_0^2 + 9k^2}\right.\right. \\
& \left.\left. + \frac{3(\omega_0^2 - k^2)(k^2 - 3\omega_0^2) - 24k^2\omega_0^2}{2\omega_0^2(k^2 - 3\omega_0^2)^2 + 32k^2\omega_0^4}\right]\right\}\cos \omega_0 \xi \\
& + \frac{Q_0^3 \omega_0}{(k^2 + \omega_0^2)^3}\left\{\frac{9k}{4\omega_0^2} + \frac{3k(k^2 - 3\omega_0^2)}{32\omega_0^4} + \frac{3k}{9k^2 + \omega_0^2}\right. \\
& \left. + \frac{6k(3k^2 + \omega_0^2)}{(k^2 - 3\omega_0^2)^2 + 16k^2\omega_0^2} - \frac{3k(k^2 - 3\omega_0^2)(\omega_0^2 - k^2)}{2\omega_0^2[(k^2 - \omega_0^2)^2 + 16k^2\omega_0^2]}\right\} \\
& \cdot \sin \omega_0 \xi - \frac{Q_0^3}{32\omega_0^2(k^2 + \omega_0^2)^3}\left[(\omega_0^2 - 3k^2)\cos 3\omega_0 \xi\right. \\
& \left. + \frac{k}{\omega_0}(k^2 - 3\omega_0^2)\sin 3\omega_0 \xi\right] - \frac{3Q_0^3}{2(k^2 + \omega_0^2)^3}e^{-k\xi} \\
& - \frac{Q_0^3 \omega_0^2 e^{-3k\xi}}{(k^2 + \omega_0^2)^3(9k^2 + \omega_0^2)} - \frac{3Q_0^3 e^{-k\xi}}{2(k^2 + \omega_0^2)^3[(k^3 - 3\omega_0^2)^2 + 16k^2\omega_0^2]} \\
& \cdot \{[2k\omega_0(k^2 - 3\omega_0^2) + 4k\omega_0(\omega_0^2 - k^2)]\sin 2\omega_0 \xi \\
& + [8k^2\omega_0^2 - (\omega_0^2 - k^2)(k^2 - 3\omega_0^2)]\cos 2\omega_0 \xi\} \\
& - \frac{3Q_0^3 \omega_0}{4(k^2 + \omega_0^2)^3}e^{-2k\xi}\sin \omega_0 \xi
\end{aligned}
\tag{4-194}
$$

$$\xi = t\left[1 - \frac{3\varepsilon Q_0^2}{8\omega_0^2(k^2 + \omega_0^2)}\right]^{-1} \tag{4-195}$$

In calculation the response of a simply supported square plate due to a step-function load is evaluated by taking

$$\frac{h}{a} = 0.04 \qquad \nu = \tfrac{1}{3} \qquad E = 10^7 \text{ psi} \qquad Q_0 = 100 \text{ and } 200 \text{ psi}$$

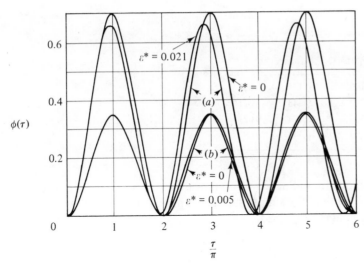

Figure 4.20 Time-response function of simply supported plate with stress-free edges for different step-function loads: (a) $Q_0/\omega^2 = 0.348$; (b) $Q_0/\omega^2 = 0.174$.

The values of Q_0/ω_0^2 and ε^* are given in Table 4.3 for different inplane boundary conditions. The stress function is, for immovably constrained edges,

$$F(x, y, t) = \frac{Eh^2}{32}\left[\frac{2\pi^2}{a^2(1-v)}(x^2 + y^2) - \cos\frac{2\pi x}{a} - \cos\frac{2\pi y}{a}\right]\phi^2(t) \quad (4\text{-}196)$$

in which $\phi(t)$ for the step-function load is shown in Fig. 4.21. It is seen that the linear case ($\varepsilon^* = 0$) always exhibits a larger deflection than the nonlinear response

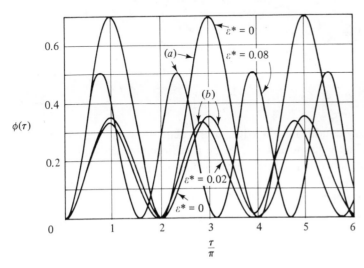

Figure 4.21 Time-response function of simply supported plate with immovably constrained edges for different values of step-function loads: (a) $Q_0/\omega^2 = 0.348$; (b) $Q_0/\omega^2 = 0.174$.

Table 4.3

Inplane conditions	Q_0 (psi)	Q_0/ω_0^2	ε^*
Stress-free	$\begin{cases}100 \\ 200\end{cases}$	0.174 0.348	0.005 0.021
Immovably Constrained	$\begin{cases}100 \\ 200\end{cases}$	0.174 0.348	0.021 0.08

($\varepsilon^* \neq 0$). Furthermore the influence of nonlinearities of immovably constrained edges upon the response of the simply supported plate is much more pronounced than the stress-free edges (Fig. 4.20).

4.10 OSCILLATION OF CIRCULAR PLATE WITH VARIOUS EDGE CONDITIONS

In the analysis of circular plates the cylindrical coordinates r, θ, z are naturally adopted. Let us consider the vibration of a circular plate excited by a harmonic force $q_0 \cos \omega t$. In the case of axisymmetrical modes of vibration, stresses and displacements are independent of the polar angle θ. The equations of motion of the plate are obtained from equations (3-7) and (3-8). The result is

$$L(w, F) = D\nabla^2\nabla^2 w + \rho w_{,tt} - \frac{h}{r}(F_{,r} w_{,r})_{,r} - q_0 \cos \omega t = 0 \qquad (4\text{-}197)$$

$$\nabla^2\nabla^2 F = -\frac{E}{r} w_{,r} w_{,rr} \qquad (4\text{-}198)$$

where

$$\nabla^2(\ ) = \frac{1}{r}[r(\ )_{,r}]_{,r} \qquad (4\text{-}199)$$

As for the boundary conditions, the edges of the plate of radius a are assumed to be clamped and simply supported and to be free from stresses and immovably constrained. These out-of-plane boundary conditions are

I. for a simply supported plate

$$w = w_{,rr} + \frac{v}{r} w_{,r} = 0 \qquad \text{at} \quad r = a \qquad (4\text{-}200)$$

II. for a clamped plate

$$w = w_{,r} = 0 \qquad \text{at} \quad r = a \qquad (4\text{-}201)$$

and these inplane boundary conditions are

(a) for a stress-free edge

$$F_{,r} = 0 \qquad \text{at} \quad r = a \qquad (4\text{-}202a)$$

(b) for an immovably constrained edge

$$F_{,rr} - \frac{v}{a} F_{,r} = 0 \qquad \text{at} \quad r = a \qquad (4\text{-}202b)$$

in which equation (3-21) has been used for the last expression.

For approximate solutions of these problems the Galerkin procedure (Ref. 2.4) is used furnishing the equation for the time function. Boundary conditions (4-200) and (4-201) respectively are satisfied by expressing the deflection in the separable form

$$w = h\phi(t)(1 + b\xi^2 + c\xi^4) \qquad \xi = \frac{r}{a} \qquad (4\text{-}203)$$

in which ϕ is an unknown function of t with its maximum being the nondimensional maximum deflection defined by w_m/h and in which b and c in each case are constants given by

I. $b = -\dfrac{6 + 2v}{5 + v} \qquad c = \dfrac{1 + v}{5 + v}$

II. $b = -2 \qquad c = 1$

$$\qquad (4\text{-}204)$$

Clearly, assumption (4-203) leads to the fundamental (first) mode of vibration. Inserting expression (4-203) into the compatibility equation (4-198) and letting $F = f(r)\phi^2(t)$, the solution of the resulting equation can be expressed as

$$f = -Eh^2(k\xi^2 + \tfrac{1}{16}b^2\xi^4 + \tfrac{1}{18}bc\xi^6 + \tfrac{1}{48}c^2\xi^8) \qquad (4\text{-}205)$$

where k is an arbitrary constant. Introduction of this expression in conditions (4-202) yields, in each case,

(a) $k = -\tfrac{1}{24}(3b^2 + 4bc + 2c^2)$

(b) $k = -\dfrac{1}{24(1 - v)}[3(3 - v)b^2 + 4(5 - v)bc + 2(7 - v)c^2]$

$$\qquad (4\text{-}206)$$

Applying the Galerkin procedure to equation (4-197) the following condition is obtained

$$\int_0^a L(w, F)wr \, dr = 0 \qquad (4\text{-}207)$$

Taking $v = 0.3$ and performing integration leads to an ordinary differential equation for the time function in each case

$$\text{I. } \rho h \phi_{,tt} + \frac{Eh^4}{a^4}(2.242\phi + C_1\phi^3) = 1.560q_0 \cos \omega t$$

$$\text{(4-208)}$$

$$\text{II. } \rho h \phi_{,tt} + \frac{Eh^4}{a^4}(9.768\phi + C_2\phi^3) = \frac{5}{3}q_0 \cos \omega t$$

in which $C_1 = 0.591$ and $C_2 = 1.429$ for Case (a) and $C_1 = 4.148$ and $C_2 = 4.602$ for Case (b).

Now equations (4-208) are specified for the static deflection. In this case we obtain by setting $\phi(t) = w_m/h$ and $\cos \omega t = 1$ in equations (4-208)

$$\text{I}(a). \quad \frac{q_0 a^4}{Eh^4} = 1.438\frac{w_m}{h} + 0.3789\left(\frac{w_m}{h}\right)^3$$

$$\text{I}(b). \quad \frac{q_0 a^4}{Eh^4} = 1.438\frac{w_m}{h} + 2.659\left(\frac{w_m}{h}\right)^3$$

$$\text{(4-209)}$$

$$\text{II}(a). \quad \frac{q_0 a^4}{Eh^4} = 5.861\frac{w_m}{h} + 0.8571\left(\frac{w_m}{h}\right)^3$$

$$\text{II}(b). \quad \frac{q_0 a^4}{Eh^4} = 5.861\frac{w_m}{h} + 2.761\left(\frac{w_m}{h}\right)^3$$

These results are in excellent agreement with equation (n) on page 412 of Ref. 1.4 in which the coefficients are given in Table 82.

The nonlinear free flexural vibrations of the circular plate can be obtained by setting $q_0 = 0$ in equations (4-208). The resulting equations are identical with equation (4-161) in form. The solution of the latter is applicable to the present equations. The linear natural frequency ω_0 in each case is

$$\text{I. } \omega_0 = 1.497\frac{h}{a^2}\sqrt{\frac{Eh}{\rho}}$$

$$\text{(4-210)}$$

$$\text{II. } \omega_0 = 3.125\frac{h}{a^2}\sqrt{\frac{Eh}{\rho}}$$

which respectively are found to be 0.2 and 1 percent larger than the corresponding exact solution (Ref. 4.16). The ratio of nonlinear period T to linear period T_0 can be obtained by following a similar calculation for equation (4-166), and is plotted in Fig. 4.22 versus the amplitude of the plate vibration. It is observed that the effect of large amplitudes on the period of free vibration of the circular plate is greatest for Case I(b) as in Sec. 4.8 for square plates.

Equations (4-208) for forced vibration are of the same form as equation (4-157) and hence the nonlinear response to the harmonic forcing can be obtained in the same manner as in Sec. 4.8.

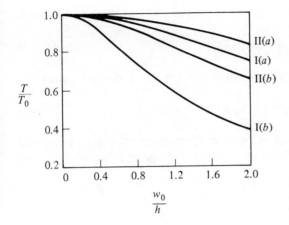

Figure 4.22 Period of vibration versus amplitude of circular plate for various edge conditions ($v = 0.3$).

4.11 VIBRATION OF CLAMPED CIRCULAR PLATE DUE TO SINUSOIDALLY VARYING AXISYMMETRIC LOAD

The equations of motion expressed in terms of transverse displacement and stress function have been used in the previous section in the discussion of nonlinear vibration of a circular plate with various edge conditions. Now the nonlinear response of a rigidly clamped circular plate due to a sinusoidally varying axisymmetric load $q(r, t)$ is considered by making use of the set of differential equations in terms of transverse and radial displacements w and u_r. These equations can be obtained from the change of stress function F in equations (3-7) and (3-8) to u_r by virtue of expression (3-21) and the relations given in Sec. 3.1. However, these equations for the axisymmetric modes of vibration will be derived in the following.

In the absence of the inplane inertia, the equilibrium of the forces in the radial direction requires that

$$N_{r,r} + \frac{1}{r}(N_r - N_\theta) = 0 \tag{4-211}$$

From equations (3-6) and (3-10) the membrane forces are related to displacements by

$$N_r = \frac{Eh}{1 - v^2}\left[u_{r,r} + \tfrac{1}{2}w_{,r}^2 + v\frac{u_r}{r}\right]$$
$$N_\theta = \frac{Eh}{1 - v^2}\left[\frac{u_r}{r} + vu_{r,r} + \frac{v}{2}w_{,r}^2\right] \tag{4-212}$$

Substitution of these expressions into equation (4-211) yields the equation of equilibrium in the terms of w and u_r

$$u_{r,rr} + \frac{1}{r}u_{r,r} - \frac{u_r}{r^2} + w_{,r}w_{,rr} + \frac{1 - v}{2r}w_{,r}^2 = 0 \tag{4-213}$$

The equilibrium equation of bending moments about a circumferential tangent is

$$M_{r,r} + \frac{1}{r}(M_r - M_\theta) = Q_r \tag{4-214}$$

The dynamic equilibrium of a central circular portion with radius r requires that

$$rQ_r = -rN_r w_{,r} - \int_0^r [q(r, t) - \rho w_{,tt}]r \, dr \tag{4-215}$$

in which ρ is the mass per unit area of the plate. Combining equations (4-214) and (4-215) and using equations (3-3) and (4-212) results in the equation of transverse motion

$$D\nabla^2\nabla^2 w + \rho w_{,tt} = q(r, t) + \frac{Eh}{1 - v^2} w_{,rr}\left[u_{r,r} + \tfrac{1}{2}w_{,r}^2 + v\,\frac{u_r}{r}\right]$$

$$+ \frac{Eh}{1 - v^2}\frac{1}{r} w_{,r}\left\{\frac{u_r}{r} + v[u_{r,r} + \tfrac{1}{2}w_{,r}^2]\right\} \tag{4-216}$$

Equations (4-213) and (4-216) governing the axisymmetric large-amplitude forced vibration of the circular plate of radius a constitute a system of two equations for two variables u_r and w. Introducing the nondimensional parameters

$$\xi = \frac{r}{a} \qquad U = \frac{au_r}{h^2} \qquad W = \frac{w}{h} \tag{4-217}$$

these equations transform to

$$U_{,\xi\xi} + \frac{1}{\xi}U_{,\xi} - \frac{U}{\xi^2} + W_{,\xi}W_{,\xi\xi} + \frac{1 - v}{2\xi}W_{,\xi}^2 = 0 \tag{4-218}$$

$$\frac{D}{\rho a^4}\nabla_\xi^2\nabla_\xi^2 W + W_{,tt} = \frac{q(\xi, t)}{\rho h} + \frac{c_p^2 h^2}{a^4} W_{,\xi\xi}$$

$$\cdot \left[U_{,\xi} + \tfrac{1}{2}W_{,\xi}^2 + v\,\frac{U}{\xi}\right] + \frac{c_p^2 h^2}{a^4}\frac{1}{\xi} W_{,\xi}\left\{\frac{U}{\xi} + v[U_{,\xi} + \tfrac{1}{2}W_{,\xi}^2]\right\} \tag{4-219}$$

in which c_p is the flexural wave velocity defined by equation (4-115) and in which

$$\nabla_\xi^2(\ ) = (\ )_{,\xi\xi} + \frac{1}{\xi}(\ )_{,\xi} \tag{4-220}$$

The boundary conditions for a rigidly clamped edge are

$$U = W = W_{,\xi} = 0 \qquad \text{at} \quad \xi = 1 \tag{4-221}$$

For an approximate solution of equations (4-218) and (4-219) satisfying these boundary conditions, the Galerkin procedure (Ref. 4.17) is used furnishing the equation for the time function. The transverse and radial displacements are assumed in the separable form

$$W(\xi, t) = z(t)(1 - \xi^2)^2$$

$$U(\xi, t) = z^2(t)H(\xi) \tag{4-222}$$

in which $(1 - \xi^2)^2$ is the assumed mode function satisfying the transverse boundary conditions in equations (4-221) and H is an unknown function of ξ. Substituting expressions (4-222) into equation (4-218), solving for $H(\xi)$, and imposing the inplane boundary condition, we find

$$H(\xi) = \frac{5 - 3v}{6}\xi - (3 - v)\xi^3 + \frac{10 - 2v}{3}\xi^5 - \frac{7 - v}{6}\xi^7 \qquad (4\text{-}223)$$

Inserting equations (4-222) and (4-223) into (4-219) and applying the Galerkin procedure yields a nonlinear ordinary differential equation for $z(t)$

$$z_{,tt} + \omega_0^2 z + \beta^2 z^3 = \frac{10}{\rho h}\int_0^1 q(\xi, t)\xi(1 - \xi^2)^2 \, d\xi \qquad (4\text{-}224)$$

where

$$\omega_0^2 = \frac{320}{3}\frac{D}{\rho a^4} \qquad \beta^2 = \frac{40}{21}(1 + v)(23 - 9v)\frac{D}{\rho a^4} \qquad (4\text{-}225)$$

The transverse load $q(\xi, t)$ is assumed to vary harmonically in time and to be uniformly distributed over a central circular area with radius b. It then follows that

$$q(\xi, t) = \begin{cases} \dfrac{P}{\pi a^2 \xi_0^2}\cos \omega t & \xi \le \xi_0 = \dfrac{b}{a} \\ 0 & \xi > \xi_0 \end{cases} \qquad (4\text{-}226)$$

in which P is the resultant force and ω is the forcing frequency. Thus equation (4-224) can be written as

$$z_{,tt} + \omega_0^2 z + \beta^2 z^3 = P_0 \cos \omega t \qquad (4\text{-}227)$$

where

$$P_0 = \frac{5P}{\pi a^2 \rho h}(1 - \xi_0^2 + \tfrac{1}{3}\xi_0^4) \qquad (4\text{-}228)$$

Equation (4-227) is specified for static deflection and free vibration. In the static case, by setting $z = w_0/h$ and $\cos \omega t = 1$, and by using equations (4-225) and (4-228), this equation becomes

$$\frac{320}{3}\frac{w_0}{h} + \frac{40}{21}(1 + v)(23 - 9v)\left(\frac{w_0}{h}\right)^3 = \frac{5Pa^2}{\pi Dh}(1 - \xi_0^2 + \tfrac{1}{3}\xi_0^4) \qquad (4\text{-}229)$$

in which w_0 is the maximum deflection. In the case of nonlinear free vibration equation (4-227) reduces to

$$z_{,tt} + \omega_0^2 z + \beta^2 z^3 = 0 \qquad (4\text{-}230)$$

which is identical in form with equation (4-161). The linear period T_0 is given by

$$T_0 = \frac{2\pi a^2}{10.33}\sqrt{\frac{\rho}{D}} \qquad (4\text{-}231)$$

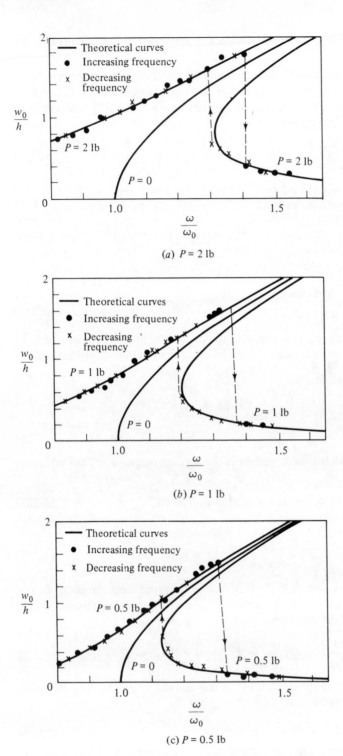

Figure 4.23 Response curves for axisymmetric vibration of rigidly clamped circular steel plate excited by sinusoidally varying load distributed over a central circular area ($a = 9$ in, $b = 1.5$ in, $h = 0.0385$ in, $\rho = 28.13 \times 10^{-6}$ lb/in$^3 \cdot$sec^2, $E = 30 \times 10^6$ lb/in^2, $\nu = 0.3$).

The result for the relationship between the period ratio T/T_0 and the relative amplitude w_0/h is in close agreement with Case II(b) shown in Fig. 4.22.

Equation (4-227) is the one for forced vibration of the plate. This equation is identical in form with equation (4-157) whose solution is given by expression (4-158) and (4-159). The theoretical and experimental response curves are shown in Fig. 4.23 for three different input forces. A description of experiments is referred to Ref. 4.17. For the theoretical curves the calculated linear frequency ($\omega_0 = 47.4$ cps) was used. For the experimental data the measured frequency ($\omega_0 = 53.3$ cps) was used. The driving frequency was first increased from a low value and then decreased from a high value. In the figure the former is denoted by small solid circles and the latter by small crosses. All tests showed clearly the jump phenomenon, but the other experimental results for the amplitude jumped from a higher value to a lower value and vice versa are not shown herein. It is seen that the experimental determined response curves are in good agreement with the theoretical predictions. Both theory and experiment indicate a nonlinearity of the hardening type for large-amplitude vibrations of the plate. In addition, an excellent agreement was found between theory and experiment for deflection shapes of the plate under various loads and frequencies.

4.12 OSCILLATION OF CLAMPED OBLIQUE PANEL WITH INITIAL CURVATURE

Oblique panels are mainly used as standard structural elements of swept-back wings of airplanes and are of the shape of slightly curved skew parallelograms. Oscillations of these wings with large amplitudes may occur at supersonic flight. The analysis is thus concerned with this problem by use of a single-mode approach (Ref. 4.18).† Let us consider an oblique initially doubly curved elastic plate of length a, width b, and thickness h, the angle of the sweepback being θ. The origin of two cartesian coordinate frames, oblique ζ, η and rectangular x, y, is located at the center of the plate (Fig. 4.24). The oblique coordinates are related to the rectangular coordinates by means of the mapping

$$\zeta = \frac{x}{\cos \theta} \qquad \eta = y - x \tan \theta \qquad (4\text{-}232)$$

The Laplace operator in the oblique coordinate system, denoted by ∇^2 is of the form

$$\nabla^2(\ ) = \frac{1}{\cos^2 \theta}[(\ )_{,\zeta\zeta} - 2(\ )_{,\zeta\eta} \sin \theta + (\ )_{,\eta\eta}] \qquad (4\text{-}233)$$

† Reprinted with permission from the American Institute of Aeronautics and Astronautics, *AIAA Journal*, vol. 2, 1964.

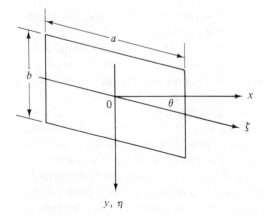

Figure 4.24 Geometry of an oblique panel.

The Marguerre equations (2-175) and (2-176) which govern the moderately large deflection of thin plates with small initial curvature are extended to the dynamic case. The resulting equations can be expressed in terms of ζ and η as

$$J(w, F) = \frac{D}{h} \nabla^2 \nabla^2 w - L(w, F) - L(\xi, F) - \frac{q}{h} + \frac{\rho}{h} w_{,tt} = 0 \qquad (4\text{-}234)$$

$$\frac{1}{E} \nabla^2 \nabla^2 F = -\tfrac{1}{2} L(w, w) - L(\xi, w) \qquad (4\text{-}235)$$

in which ρ is the mass per unit area of the plate, $\xi(\zeta, \eta)$ is the initial deflection of the plate, $w = w(\zeta, \eta, t)$ is an additional deflection produced by the load of intensity $q(\zeta, \eta)$, and

$$L(w, F) = \frac{1}{\cos^2 \theta} \left(w_{,\zeta\zeta} F_{,\eta\eta} + w_{,\eta\eta} F_{,\zeta\zeta} - 2 w_{,\zeta\eta} F_{,\zeta\eta} \right) \qquad (4\text{-}236)$$

It is observed that the membrane stresses σ_ζ^m, σ_η^m and $\sigma_{\zeta\eta}^m$ in the oblique coordinate system can be expressed by means of the stress function $F(\zeta, \eta)$ as

$$\sigma_\zeta^m = \frac{1}{\cos \theta} F_{,\eta\eta} \qquad \sigma_\eta^m = \frac{1}{\cos \theta} F_{,\zeta\zeta}$$

$$\sigma_{\zeta\eta}^m = -\frac{1}{\cos \theta} F_{,\zeta\eta} \qquad (4\text{-}237)$$

which satisfy the equations of equilibrium of forces in the directions tangent to the middle surface of the panel, provided the longitudinal inertia terms are disregarded. This is one of the assumptions made in the formulation of the plate theory in Chap. 1. Such an assumption is commonly accepted in problems in which vibrations occur principally in the direction perpendicular to the middle surface of the plate.

The plate is assumed to be clamped along its edges and hence the boundary conditions are

$$w = w_{,\zeta} = 0 \qquad \text{at} \quad \zeta = \pm \frac{a}{2}$$

$$w = w_{,\eta} = 0 \qquad \text{at} \quad \eta = \pm \frac{b}{2}$$

(4-238)

at the time $t \geq 0$. The inplane boundary conditions will be specified later. The deflection of the plate is expressed in the separable form as

$$w(\zeta, \eta, t) = \sum_m \sum_n A_{mn} \phi_{mn}(t) f_{mn}(\zeta, \eta)$$

(4-239)

in which ϕ_{mn} are unknown functions of time only and f_{mn} are suitably chosen spatial functions satisfying the boundary conditions (4-238). Without loss of generality we take

$$f_{mn}(\zeta, \eta) = \left[1 + (-1)^{m+1} \cos \frac{2m\pi\zeta}{a} \right] \left[1 + (-1)^{n+1} \cos \frac{2n\pi\eta}{b} \right]$$

(4-240)

The initial deflection of the plate is expanded into the Fourier series

$$\xi(\zeta, \eta) = \sum_m \sum_n B_{mn} f^{\circ}_{mn}(\zeta, \eta)$$

(4-241)

in which B_{mn} are known coefficients and the functions $f^{\circ}_{mn}(\zeta, \eta)$ are chosen in the form analogous to equation (2-240). In what follows, we take one term in each series as an approximate solution

$$w(\zeta, \eta, t) = A_{11}\phi(t)(1 + \cos \alpha\zeta)(1 + \cos \beta\eta)$$

$$\xi(\zeta, \eta) = B_{11}(1 + \cos \alpha\zeta)(1 + \cos \beta\eta)$$

(4-242)

where

$$\alpha = \frac{2\pi}{a} \qquad \beta = \frac{2\pi}{b}$$

(4-243)

At considerable expense of computational work, of course, it is possible to employ more than one term in each of these series and to increase the generality as well as the accuracy of the solution. However, we confine ourselves to the single-mode analysis in this chapter.

On the determination of the stress function $F(\zeta, \eta, t)$, expressions (4-242) are substituted into the compatibility equation (4-235). After some manipulation the following particular integral of the resulting equation suitable for the problem is obtained.

$$F(\zeta, \eta, t) = -g(t) \cos^2 \theta \left[\frac{\cos \alpha\zeta}{\alpha^4} + \frac{\cos \beta\eta}{\beta^4} + \frac{\cos 2\alpha\zeta}{16\alpha^4} \right.$$

$$+ \frac{\cos 2\beta\eta}{16\beta^4} + C_1(\cos \alpha\zeta \cos \beta\eta - k_1 \sin \alpha\zeta \sin \beta\eta)$$

$$+ C_2(\cos 2\alpha\zeta \cos \beta\eta - k_2 \sin 2\alpha\zeta \sin \beta\eta)$$

$$\left. + C_3(\cos \alpha\zeta \cos 2\beta\eta - k_3 \sin \alpha\zeta \sin 2\beta\eta) \right]$$

$$+ \tfrac{1}{2} \cos \theta(p_\zeta \eta^2 + p_\eta \zeta^2 - 2p_{\zeta\eta} \zeta\eta) \tag{4-244}$$

in which p_ζ, p_η, and $p_{\zeta\eta}$ are oblique normal and shear stresses, constant throughout the plate, eventually functions of t, and

$$g(t) = EA_{11}\alpha^2\beta^2[\tfrac{1}{2}A_{11}\phi^2(t) + B_{11}\phi(t)]$$

$$C_1 = 2[(\alpha^2 + \beta^2)^2 + 4\alpha^2\beta^2 \sin^2 \theta - 4\alpha\beta(\alpha^2 + \beta^2)k_1 \sin \theta]^{-1}$$

$$C_2 = [(4\alpha^2 + \beta^2)^2 + 16\alpha^2\beta^2 \sin^2 \theta - 8\alpha\beta(4\alpha^2 + \beta^2)k_2 \sin \theta]^{-1}$$

$$C_3 = [(\alpha^2 + 4\beta^2)^2 + 16\alpha\beta^2 \sin^2 \theta - 8\alpha\beta(\alpha^2 + 4\beta^2)k_3 \sin \theta]^{-1}$$

$$k_1 = \frac{4\alpha\beta(\alpha^2 + \beta^2) \sin \theta}{(\alpha^2 + \beta^2)^2 + 4\alpha\beta^2 \sin^2 \theta} \tag{4-245}$$

$$k_2 = \frac{8\alpha\beta(4\alpha^2 + \beta^2) \sin \theta}{(4\alpha^2 + \beta^2)^2 + 16\alpha^2\beta^2 \sin^2 \theta}$$

$$k_3 = \frac{8\alpha\beta(\alpha^2 + 4\beta^2) \sin \theta}{(\alpha^2 + 4\beta^2)^2 + 16\alpha^2\beta^2 \sin^2 \theta}$$

Substitution of expressions (4-244) into (4-237) yields the membrane stresses in terms of ζ and η

$$\sigma_\zeta^m = g(t) \cos \theta \left[\frac{\cos \beta\eta}{\beta^2} + \frac{\cos 2\beta\eta}{4\beta^2} + C_1\beta^2 \cos \alpha\zeta \cos \beta\eta \right.$$

$$- C_1 k_1 \beta^2 \sin \alpha\zeta \sin \beta\eta + C_2\beta^2 \cos 2\alpha\zeta \cos 2\beta\eta$$

$$- C_2 k_2 \beta^2 \sin 2\alpha\zeta \sin \beta\eta + 4C_3\beta^2 \cos \alpha\zeta \cos 2\beta\eta$$

$$\left. - 4C_3 k_3 \beta^2 \sin \alpha\zeta \sin 2\beta\eta \right] + p_\zeta \tag{4-246}$$

$$\sigma_\eta^m = g(t) \cos \theta \left[\frac{\cos \alpha\zeta}{\alpha^2} + \frac{\cos 2\alpha\zeta}{4\alpha^2} + C_1\alpha^2 \cos \alpha\zeta \cos \beta\eta \right.$$

$$- C_1 k_1 \alpha^2 \sin \alpha\zeta \sin \beta\eta + 4C_2\alpha^2 \cos 2\alpha\zeta \cos \beta\eta$$

$$- 4C_2 k_2 \alpha^2 \sin 2\alpha\zeta \sin \beta\eta + C_3 \alpha^2 \cos \alpha\zeta \cos 2\beta\eta \qquad \blacktriangle$$

$$\left. - C_3 k_3 \alpha^2 \sin \alpha\zeta \sin 2\beta\eta \right] + p_\eta$$

$$\sigma_{\zeta\eta}^m = g(t)\alpha\beta \cos \theta [C_1 \sin \alpha\zeta \sin \beta\eta + C_1 k_1 \cos \alpha\zeta \cos \beta\eta$$

$$+ 2C_2 \sin 2\alpha\zeta \sin \beta\eta - 2C_2 k_2 \cos 2\alpha\zeta \cos \beta\eta$$

$$+ 2C_3 \sin \alpha\zeta \sin 2\beta\eta - 2C_3 k_3 \cos \alpha\zeta \cos 2\beta\eta] + p_{\zeta\eta}$$

Upon integration of equations (4-246) along the edges of the plate it can be shown that at the corresponding edge of the plate the contribution of average stresses by the terms enclosed in brackets is nil. Thus the constant stresses p_ζ, p_η, and $p_{\zeta\eta}$ may be regarded as the average edge membrane stresses.

If the edges of the plate are free to move in the plane of the plate, then these conditions require that, along the corresponding edges,

$$p_\zeta = p_\eta = p_{\zeta\eta} = 0 \tag{4-247}$$

In the case of buckling not all of these quantities will be zero.

Instead of satisfaction of equation (4-234), we apply the Galerkin procedure leading to the following condition

$$\int_{-a/2}^{a/2} \int_{-b/2}^{b/2} J(w, F)(1 + \cos \alpha\zeta)(1 + \cos \beta\eta) \, d\zeta \, d\eta = 0 \tag{4-248}$$

Upon substitution and integration this condition transforms to a nonlinear ordinary differential equation for the time function $\phi(t)$

$$9\rho A \phi_{,tt} + \left\{ \frac{A_{11} D}{\cos^4 \theta} [3\alpha^4 + 3\beta^4 + 2\alpha^2\beta^2(1 + 2 \sin^2 \theta)] \right.$$

$$+ \frac{3A_{11} h}{\cos \theta} (\alpha^2 p_\zeta + \beta^2 p_\eta) + EhB_{11}^2 \alpha^2\beta^2\gamma \Bigg\} \phi$$

$$+ \tfrac{3}{2} EhA_{11}^2 B_{11} \alpha^2\beta^2\gamma\phi^2 + \tfrac{1}{2} EhA_{11}^3 \alpha^2\beta^2\gamma\phi^3$$

$$- 4q_0 + \frac{3h}{\cos \theta}(\alpha^2 p_\zeta + \beta^2 p_\eta)B_{11} = 0 \tag{4-249}$$

in which the loading function q has been assumed to be q_0 independent of the space coordinates and in which

$$\gamma = \alpha^2 \left[\frac{17}{8\beta^2} + (2C_1 + C_2 + 2C_3)\beta^2 \right]$$

$$+ \beta^2 \left[\frac{17}{8\alpha^2} + (2C_1 + 2C_2 + C_3)\alpha^2 \right] + 2(C_1 + C_2 + C_3)\alpha^2\beta^2 \tag{4-250}$$

Now the nondimensional parameters are introduced

$$\tau = h\alpha^2 \left(\frac{Eh}{\rho}\right)^{1/2} t \qquad A_0 = \frac{4A_{11}}{h} \qquad B_0 = \frac{4B_{11}}{h}$$

$$\Omega(\tau) = A_0 \phi(t) \qquad Q = \frac{q_0 a^4}{Eh^4} \qquad \lambda = \frac{\beta}{\alpha} = \frac{a}{b} \qquad (4\text{-}251)$$

$$s_\zeta = \frac{p_\zeta}{Eh^2\alpha^2} \qquad s_\eta = \frac{p_\eta}{Eh^2\alpha^2}$$

in which, in view of expressions (4-242), B_0 and A_0 respectively are the nondimensional initial and additional deflections at the center of the plate. Inserting equations (4-251) into (4-249) we obtain

$$\Omega_{\tau\tau} + \mu_1\Omega + \mu_2\Omega^2 + \mu_3\Omega^3 + \frac{B_0}{3\cos\theta}(s_\zeta + \lambda^2 s_\eta) - \frac{Q}{9\pi^2} = 0 \qquad (4\text{-}252)$$

where

$$\mu_1 = \frac{1}{36}\left\{\frac{1}{3(1-v^2)\cos^4\theta}[3 + 3\lambda^4 + 2\lambda^2(1 + 2\sin^2\theta)]\right.$$

$$\left. + \tfrac{1}{4}\lambda^2\gamma B_0^2 + \frac{12}{\cos\theta}(s_\zeta + \lambda^2 s_\eta)\right\}$$

$$\mu_2 = \tfrac{1}{96}\lambda^2\gamma B_0 \qquad \mu_3 = \tfrac{1}{288}\lambda^2\gamma$$

$$\gamma = \lambda^2\left(\frac{17}{8\lambda^4} + 2C_4 + C_5 + C_6 + \frac{17}{8}\right) \qquad (4\text{-}253)$$

$$C_4 = 2[(1 + \lambda^2)^2 + 4\lambda^2\sin^2\theta - 4\lambda k_1(1 + \lambda^2)\sin\theta]^{-1}$$

$$C_5 = [(4 + \lambda^2)^2 + 16\lambda^2\sin^2\theta - 8\lambda k_2(4 + \lambda^2)\sin\theta]^{-1}$$

$$C_6 = [(1 + 4\lambda^2)^2 + 16\lambda^2\sin^2\theta - 8\lambda k_3(1 + 4\lambda^2)\sin\theta]^{-1}$$

Equation (4-252) is now specified for the following cases.

(a) **Buckling of a flat rectangular plate under inplane compressive load** In this case we have to set $B_{11} = \theta = q = 0$, $\phi(t) = 1$ and, say, $p_\eta = 0$. Now that the determination of the critical value of the compressive force $N_\zeta = \sigma_\zeta^m h$, denoted by $(N_\zeta)_{cr}$, is a linear problem, the powers of the amplitude A_0 higher than the first can be disregarded. Equation (4-252) or (4-249) simplifies to yield

$$(N_\zeta)_{cr} = -\tfrac{4}{3}\pi^2 Da^2\left(\frac{3}{a^4} + \frac{3}{b^4} + \frac{2}{a^2b^2}\right) \qquad (4\text{-}254)$$

which is the well-established result as given in Ref. 4.19.

In the case of a skew plate the result for the critical load does not give a good approximation. This arises mainly from the fact that the deflection function given by the first of equations (4-242) does not suitably represent the complex shape of the deformed middle surface of the plate under inplane compressive load.

(*b*) **Linear free vibration of a flat square plate** In this particular case we set $B_{11} = \theta = q = 0$ and $\alpha = \beta = 2\pi/a$. Furthermore, the terms containing ϕ^2, ϕ^3, p_ζ and p_η are disregarded. Equation (4-252) thus yields

$$\phi_{,tt} + \frac{128\pi^4 D}{9\rho a^4} \phi = 0 \tag{4-255}$$

Consequently, the linear (circular) frequency is

$$\omega_0 = \frac{37.2}{a^2} \sqrt{\frac{D}{\rho}} \tag{4-256}$$

which is the result given in Ref. 4.20.

(*c*) **Static large deflection of a flat rectangular plate under uniform transverse load** In this case we set $B_{11} = \theta = 0$ and $\phi(t) = 1$ and hence equation (4-252) becomes

$$\frac{\Omega}{36} \left\{ \frac{1}{3(1 - \eta^2)} [3(1 + \lambda^2) + 2\lambda^2] + 12(s_\zeta + \lambda^2 s_\eta) \right\} + \frac{1}{288} \lambda^2 \gamma \Omega^3 - \frac{Q}{9\pi^4} = 0 \tag{4-257}$$

in accordance with the result on page 112 of Ref. 3.10.

(*d*) **Snap-through phenomenon of a skew panel under uniform transverse load** Suppose that the plate is under the action of a uniformly distributed load in the direction opposite to that of the initial deflection and that the edges of the plate are free to move in the plane of the plate. Thus we set $\phi(t) = 1$ and $p_\zeta = p_\eta = 0$ in addition to reversing the sign in q_0 in equation (4-252). The result is

$$\frac{Q}{9\pi^4} = \mu_1 \Omega - \mu_2 \Omega^2 + \mu_3 \Omega^3 \tag{4-258}$$

This relation between the nondimensional intensity of load and center deflection of a rhombic panel ($\theta = 45°$) is shown in Fig. 4.25 for various values of the initial maximum deflection. The dotted line is obtained from the linear theory. It is seen that, in a certain range of the load and beyond a certain value of the initial maximum deflection, three different states of equilibrium of the plate generally correspond to each value of Q. The load corresponding to the limit point such as point P is called the Euler load of the initial deflected plate or the shallow shell. Furthermore, Fig. 4.25 clearly indicates that for the skew angle $\theta = 45°$ the initial maximum deflection $B_0 = 3$ corresponds to a value of B_0 less than the critical value, while $B_0 = 5$ is greater than the critical value of B_0. In other words, the snap-through in the present example will occur for values of the initial maximum-deflection B_0 equal to or greater than 5 but not for those equal to or less than 3. Thus the panel behaves as a shallow shell for the former values of B_0 and as a plate for the latter values of B_0.

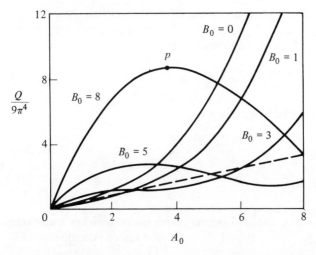

Figure 4.25 Load-deflection curves for clamped rhombic panel ($\theta = 45°$) having different values of initial deflection.

(e) Nonlinear free vibration In this case equation (4-252) reduces to

$$\Omega_{,\tau\tau} + \mu_1\Omega - \mu_2\Omega^2 + \mu_3\Omega^3 = 0 \tag{4-259}$$

with the restoring force in the form of a cubic polynomial. A qualitative discussion of this equation can be carried out by means of the phase plane (Refs. 4.11, 4.21). It may be possible to find an explicit integration of this equation through the use of elliptic integrals and functions or of the method of harmonic balance (Ref. 4.22). However, we confine ourselves to the particular case of a rhombic flat plate in which $B_0 = 0$ and $\lambda = 1$. Thus equation (4-259) simplifies to

$$\Omega_{,\tau\tau} + \mu_1\Omega + \mu_3\Omega^3 = 0 \tag{4-260}$$

which is identical in form with equation (4-161) and in which

$$\mu_1 = \frac{2 + \sin^2\theta}{27(1 - v^2)\cos^4\theta} \qquad \mu_3 = \frac{C_4 + C_5 + \frac{17}{8}}{144}$$

$$C_4 = \frac{1 + \sin^2\theta}{2(1 - \sin^2\theta)^2} \qquad C_5 = \frac{25 + 16\sin^2\theta}{(24 - 16\sin^2\theta)^2} \tag{4-261}$$

Taking as initial conditions, at $t = 0$, $A_0 = A$ (so that $\phi(0) = 1$) $\Omega_{,t} = 0$, A represents the nondimensional amplitude of oscillations. Thus the period of nonlinear oscillations is

$$T = \frac{4K(k)}{p} \tag{4-262}$$

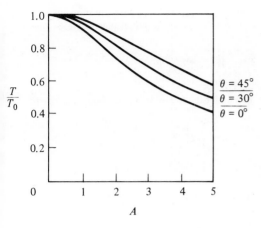

Figure 4.26 Relative period of nonlinear free oscillations versus amplitude for clamped rhombic flat plate with different values of skew angle.

where

$$k^2 = \frac{1}{2}\frac{\mu_3 A}{\mu_1 + \mu_3 A^2} \qquad p = (\mu_1 + \mu_3 A^2)^{1/2} \qquad (4\text{-}263)$$

Since the period of linear oscillations is

$$T_0 = \frac{2\pi}{\sqrt{\mu_1}}$$

the relative period of nonlinear oscillations appears as

$$\frac{T}{T_0} = \frac{2K}{\pi[1 + (\mu_3/\mu_1)A^2]^{1/2}} \qquad (4\text{-}264)$$

which indicates that in view of the multiplier $[1 + (\mu_3/\mu_1)A^2]^{-1/2}$, the periodic time of nonlinear oscillations decreases with an increase of amplitude A. The dependence of the relative period on the amplitude of nonlinear oscillations is shown in Fig. 4.26 for various values of the skew angle θ. The corresponding curves become flatter for large values of θ so that a sweepback of the plate makes the phenomenon of decreasing period less pronounced. Clearly, a decrease of θ and an increase of A affect the period ratio T/T_0 in the opposite directions. Thus, by a suitable combination of the values of θ and A, it is possible to set up the period of nonlinear oscillations on some desired level.

PROBLEMS

4.1 Determine the critical buckling pressure of a simply supported isotropic rectangular plate (Fig. 2-1) subjected to uniform biaxial inplane compression p per unit length by assuming that

$$w = w_0 \cos\frac{\pi x}{2a_0} \cos\frac{\pi y}{2b_0}$$

Also derive an approximate load-deflection relation in the postbuckling region.

4.2 Consider a loosely clamped isotropic rectangular plate (Fig. 2.1) under uniform inplane edge compression n_x and $n_y = n_x/2$ per unit length. As a solution in the initial postbuckling range the deflection function is taken to be

$$w = \frac{w_0}{4}\left(1 + \cos\frac{\pi x}{a_0}\right)\left(1 + \cos\frac{\pi y}{b_0}\right)$$

where w_0 is the deflection at the center of the plate.

Find an approximate relation between n_x and w_0 for the following inplane boundary conditions

$$\frac{h}{2b_0}\int_{-b_0}^{b_0} [\sigma_x^m]_{x=\pm a_0}\, dy = n_x \qquad \frac{h}{2b_0}\int_{-b_0}^{b_0} [\sigma_{xy}^m]_{x=\pm a_0}\, dy = 0$$

$$\frac{h}{2a_0}\int_{-a_0}^{a_0} [\sigma_y^m]_{y=\pm b_0}\, dx = n_y \qquad \frac{h}{2a_0}\int_{-a_0}^{a_0} [\sigma_{xy}^m]_{y=\pm b_0}\, dx = 0$$

4.3 A simply supported isotropic rectangular plate shown in Fig. 2.11 is subjected to nonuniform inplane compression $n_x = n_0[1 - \alpha(y/b)]$ at the edges $x = 0$, a where α is a constant. If the unloaded edges are free from stresses, the transverse deflection for small α may be approximated by

$$w = w_0 \sin\frac{\pi x}{a} \sin\frac{\pi y}{b}$$

Obtain an approximate relationship between postbuckling load and maximum deflection.

4.4 If the plate considered in Prob. 3.6 is subjected to uniform inplane compression n_z per unit length in the α direction, investigate the postbuckling behavior of the plate of constant thickness with the unloaded edges free from stresses.

4.5 An isotropic rectangular plate of lateral dimensions $a \times b$ is vibrating with moderately large amplitudes. The edges of the plate are simply supported at $x = \pm a/2$ and elastically restrained against rotation at $y = \pm b/2$. As an approximate solution the deflection is taken to be

$$w = f(t)\left|\frac{4C_1}{b^2}\left(y^2 - \frac{b^2}{4}\right) - \left(\frac{4C_1}{b^2}\pi - C_2\right)\cos\frac{\pi y}{b}\right|\cos\frac{\pi x}{a}$$

which indicates that the edges, $y = \pm b/2$, are simply supported for $C_1 = 0$ and clamped for $C_2 = 0$.

Find the corresponding equation for the time function $f(t)$.

4.6 A simply supported isotropic rectangular plate shown in Fig. 2.1 is undergoing the nonlinear free flexural vibration.

Taking

$$w = f(t) \cos\frac{\pi x}{2a_0} \cos\frac{\pi y}{2b_0}$$

solve the two inplane equilibrium equations (1-117) and (1-118) for u° and v° with the following boundary conditions

$$w = w_{,xx} = u^\circ = \sigma_{xy}^m = 0 \qquad \text{at} \quad x = \pm a_0$$

$$w = w_{,yy} = v^\circ = \sigma_{xy}^m = 0 \qquad \text{at} \quad y = \pm b_0$$

Also determine the equation for the time function $f(t)$.

4.7 Consider the moderately large-amplitude free flexural vibration of an isotropic annular plate rigidly clamped along the inner edge, $r = b$, and the outer edge, $r = a$. The transverse deflection and radial displacement may be approximated by

$$w = f(t)\left\{C_1\left[1 - \left(\frac{r}{b}\right)^2\right]\left[1 - \left(\frac{r}{a}\right)^2\right]\log\left(\frac{r}{a}\right)\right.$$

$$\left. + C_2\left[1 - \left(\frac{r}{b}\right)^2\right]\left[1 - \left(\frac{r}{a}\right)^2\right]^2\right\}$$

$$u_r = g(t)(r - a)(r - b)$$

Determine the amplitude-frequency response of the plate.

4.8 An isotropic rectangular plate shown in Fig. 2.11 has a concentrated mass M situated at $x = x_1$, $y = y_1$ $(0 \leq x_1 \leq a; 0 \leq y_1 \leq b)$ and is vibrating at moderately large amplitudes. The equations of transverse motion are given by

$$D\nabla^4 w + [\rho + M\delta(x - x_1)\delta(y - y_1)]w_{,tt} = w_{,xx}\psi_{,yy} + w_{,yy}\psi_{,xx} - 2w_{,xy}\psi_{,xy}$$

$$\nabla^4\psi = Eh[(w_{,xy})^2 - w_{,xx}w_{,yy}]$$

where $\delta(\zeta - \zeta_1)$ is a singularity function called the Dirac delta function or unit impulse function. By definition

$$\delta(\zeta - \zeta_1) = 0 \qquad \text{for} \quad \zeta \neq \zeta_1$$

$$\int_{-\infty}^{\infty} \delta(\zeta - \zeta_1)\, d\zeta = 1$$

Taking

$$w = \tfrac{1}{4}f(t)\left(1 + \cos\frac{\pi x}{a}\right)\left(1 + \cos\frac{\pi y}{b}\right)$$

investigate the effect of the presence of this mass on the amplitude-frequency response of the plate for loosely clamped edges.

REFERENCES

4.1. S. Levy, D. Goldenberg, and G. Zibritosky: Simply Supported Long Rectangular Plate Under Combined Axial Load and Normal Pressure, *Nat. Advis. Comm. Aeronaut., Tech. Note No. 949*, Washington D.C., 1944.

4.2. J. M. Coan: Large-Deflection Theory for Plates with Small Initial Curvature Loaded in Edge Compression, *ASME J. Appl. Mech.*, vol. 18, pp. 143–151, 1951.

4.3. N. Yamaki: Postbuckling Behavior of Rectangular Plates with Small Initial Curvature Loaded in Edge Compression, *ASME J. Appl. Mech.*, (a) vol. 26, pp. 407–414, 1959, (b) vol. 27, pp. 335–342, 1960.

4.4. J. Rhodes and J. M. Harvey: The Post-buckling Behaviour of Thin Flat Plates in Compression with the Unloaded Edges Elastically Restrained Against Rotation, *J. Mech. Eng. Sci.*, vol. 13, Institution of Mechanical Engineers (London), pp. 82–91, 1971.

4.5. K. O. Friedrichs and J. J. Stoker: The Nonlinear Boundary Value Problem of the Buckled Plate, *Am. J. Math.*, vol. 63, pp. 839–880, 1941.

4.6. K. O. Friedrichs and J. J. Stoker: Buckling of the Circular Plate Beyond the Critical Thrust, *ASME J. Appl. Mech.*, vol. 9, pp. A7–A14, 1942.

4.7. S. R. Bodner: The Post Buckling Behavior of a Clamped Circular Plate, *Q. Appl. Math.*, vol. 12, no. 4, pp. 397–401, 1954.

4.8. H. B. Keller and E. L. Reiss: Non-linear Bending and Buckling of Circular Plates, *Proc. 3d U.S. Nat. Cong. Appl. Mech., Am. Soc. Mech. Eng.*, pp. 375–385, 1958.

4.9. H. B. Keller and E. L. Reiss: Iterative Solutions for the Non-linear Bending of Circular Plates, *Commun. Pure Appl. Math.*, vol. 11, pp. 273–292, 1958.

4.10. H. N. Chu and G. Herrmann: Influence of Large Amplitudes on Free Flexural Vibrations of Rectangular Elastic Plates, *ASME J. Appl. Mech.*, vol. 23, pp. 532–540, 1956.

4.11. J. J. Stoker: "Nonlinear Vibrations in Mechanical and Electrical Systems," Interscience Publishers, p. 83, 1950.

4.12. S. Timoshenko and D. H. Young: "Vibration Problems in Engineering," 3d ed., D. Van Nostrand Co., p. 443, 1955.

4.13. D. Young: Vibration of Rectangular Plates by the Ritz Method, *ASME J. Appl. Mech.*, vol. 17, pp. 448–453, 1950.

4.14. H. F. Bauer: Nonlinear Response of Elastic Plates to Pulse Excitations, *ASME J. Appl. Mech.*, vol. 35, pp. 47–52, 1968.

4.15. M. J. Lighthill: A Technique for Rendering Approximate Solutions to Physical Problems Uniformly Valid, *Philos. Mag.*, vol. 40, series 7, pp. 1179–1201, 1949.

4.16. J. Prescott: Applied Elasticity, 1st ed., Longmans, Green and Company (London), pp. 597–598, 1924.

4.17. G. C. Kung and Y. H. Pao: Nonlinear Flexural Vibrations of a Clamped Circular Plate, *ASME J. Appl. Mech.*, vol. 39, pp. 1050–1054, 1972.

4.18. J. L. Nowinski: Large-amplitude Oscillations of Oblique Panels with an Initial Curvature, *AIAA J.*, vol. 2, pp. 1025–1031, 1964.

4.19. S. Timoshenko: "Theory of Elastic Stability," McGraw-Hill Book Company, p. 364, 1936.

4.20. S. G. Lekhnitskii: "Anisotropic Plates," Translated from Russian (2d ed.) by S. W. Tsai and T. Cheron, Gordon and Breach Science Publishers, p. 431, 1968.

4.21. N. W. McLachlan: "Ordinary Non-linear Differential Equations," Clarendon Press, Oxford, 1958, Chap. 9.

4.22. C. Hayashi: "Nonlinear Oscillations in Physical Systems," McGraw-Hill Book Company, 1964.

ADDITIONAL REFERENCES

Postbuckling Behavior of Isotropic Plates

Ahmad, J.: Dynamic Post-buckling Characteristics of Circular Plates, *J. Franklin Inst.*, vol. 289, pp. 57–66, 1970.

——, and S. Shore: Post-buckling Response of a Circular Plate, *Dev. Mech.*, vol. 4, pp. 273–288, 1968, (*Proc. 10th Midwest. Mech. Conf., Fort Collins, Colorado, 1967*).

Alwar, R. S., and Y. Nath: Application of Chebyshev Polynomials to the Nonlinear Analysis of Circular Plates, *Int. J. Mech. Sci.*, vol. 18, pp. 589–595, 1976.

Bera, R.: A Note on the Buckling of Plates Due to Large Deflections, *J. Sci. Eng. Res.*, vol. 9, pp. 343–350, 1965.

Bleich, H.: "Buckling Strength of Metal Structures," McGraw-Hill Book Company, 1952.

Boley, S. R.: A Procedure for the Approximate Analysis of Buckled Plates, *J. Aeronaut. Sci.*, vol. 22, pp. 337–339, 1955.

Bulson, P. S.: "The Stability of Flat Plates," American Elsevier Publishing Co., pp. 376–399, 1969.

Chilver, A. H.: Coupled Modes of Elastic Buckling, *J. Mech. Phys. Solids*, vol. 15, p. 15, 1967.

Cox, H. L.: The Buckling of Thin Plates in Compression, *British Aeronaut. Res. Comm., Rep. Memo. 1554*, 1933.

——: The Buckling of a Flat Rectangular Plate under Axial Compression and its Behaviour After Buckling, *Aeronaut. Res. Counc., Rep. Memo, 2041, 2175*, 1945.

——: "The Buckling of Plates and Shells," The Macmillan Co., pp. 47–70, 1963.

Dombourian, E. M., C. V. Smith, and R. L. Carlson: A Perturbation Solution to a Plate Postbuckling Problem, *Int. J. Non-Linear Mech.*, vol. 11, pp. 49–58, 1976.

Federhofer, K.: Tragfähigkeit der über die Beulgrenze belasteten Kreisplatte, *Forsch. Geb. Ingenieurwes.*, vol. 11, pp. 97–107, 1940.

Friedrichs, K. O. and J. J. Stoker: The Non-linear Boundary Value Problem of the Buckled Plate, *Proc. Nat. Acad. Sci.*, vol. 25, pp. 535–540, 1939.

Hu, P. C., E. E. Lundquist, and S. B. Batdorf: Effect of Small Deviations from Flatness on Effective Width and Buckling of Plates in Compression, *NACA Tech. Note 1124*, 1946.

Kisliakov, S. D.: On the Non-linear Dynamic Stability Problem for Thin Elastic Plates, *Int. J. Non-Linear Mech.*, vol. 11, pp. 219–228, 1976.

Leggett, D. M. A.: The Stresses in a Flat Panel under Shear when the Buckling Load has been Exceeded, *Aeronaut. Res. Counc., Rep. & Memo. 2430*, 1940.

Levy, S.: Bending of Rectangular Plates with Large Deflection, *NACA Tech. Rep. 737*, 1942.

———, K. L. Fienup, and R. M. Wooley: Analysis of Square Shear Web above Buckling Load, *NACA Tech. Note 962*, 1945.

——— and P. Krupen: Large-deflection Theory for End Compression of Long Rectangular Plates Rigidly Clamped Along Two Edges, *NACA Tech. Note 884*, 1943.

Malko, P., C. Leech, and W. Johnson: Damage in Plates Due to Surface Rings of Explosive, *Int. J. Mech. Sci.*, vol. 18, pp. 33–36, 1976.

Mansfield, E. M.: "The Bending and Stretching of Plates," Pergamon Press, pp. 117–127, 1964.

Marguerre, K.: Die über die Ausbeulgrenze belastete Platte, *Z. Angew. Math. Mech.* vol. 16, pp. 353–355, 1936.

——— and E. Trefftz: Über die Tragfähigkeit eines längsbelateten Plattenstreifens nach Überschreiten der Beullast, *ZAMM*, vol. 17, p. 85, 1937.

Matkowsky, B. J., and L. J. Putnick: Multiple Buckled States of Rectangular Plates, *Int. J. Non-Linear Mech.*, vol. 9, pp. 89–103, 1974.

Masur, E. F.: On the Analysis of Buckled Plates, *Proc. 3d U.S. Nat. Cong. Appl. Mech.*, pp. 411–417, 1958.

Needleman, A.: Axisymmetric Buckling of Elastic-plastic Annular Plates, *AIAA J.*, vol. 12, pp. 1594–1596, 1974.

———: Postbifurcation Behavior and Imperfection Sensitivity of Elastic-plastic Circular Plates, *Int. J. Mech. Sci.*, vol. 17, pp. 1–13, 1975.

Polubarinova-Kotschina, P.: Zum Problem der Plattenstabilität, *Appl. Math. Mech.*, vol. 3, pp. 16–22, 1936.

Rellich, F.: Die Randbedingungen der Airyschen Spannungsfunktion bei vorgegebenen Randverscheibungen, *ZAMM*, vol. 25/27, pp. 13–17, 1947.

Rhodes, J., and J. M. Harvey: Plates in Uniaxial Compression with Various Support Conditions at the Unloaded Boundaries, *Int. J. Mech. Sci.*, vol. 13, pp. 787–802, 1971.

——— and ———: Effects of Eccentricity of Load or Compression on the Buckling and Postbuckling Behaviour of Flat Plates, *Int. J. Mech. Sci.*, vol. 13, pp. 867–879, 1971.

——— and ———: Examination of Plate Post-buckling Behavior, *J. Eng. Mech. Div., Proc. ASCE*, vol. 103, no. EM3, pp. 461–478, 1977.

———, ———, and W. C. Fok: The Load-carrying Capacity of Initially Imperfect Eccentrically Loaded Plates, *Int. J. Mech. Sci.*, vol. 17, pp. 161–175, 1975.

Ritchie, D., and J. Rhodes: Buckling and Post-buckling Behaviour of Plates with Holes, *Aeronaut. Q.*, vol. 26, pp. 281–296, 1975.

Roberts, T. M., and D. G. Ashwell: The Use of Finite Element Mid-increment Stiffness Matrices in the Post-buckling Analysis of Imperfect Structures, *Int. J. Solids Struct.*, vol. 7, pp. 805–823, 1971.

Rockey, K. C.: Shear Buckling of Thin-walled Sections, "Thin-Walled Structures," ed. A. H. Chilver, Chatto and Windus, London, pp. 248–270, 1967.

Rushton, K. R.: Postbuckling of Tapered Plates, *Int. J. Mech. Sci.*, vol. 11, pp. 461–480, 1969.

———: Post-buckling of Rectangular Plates with Various Boundary Conditions, *Aeronaut. Q.*, vol. 21, pp. 163–181, 1970.

Schnadel, G.: Die Überschreitung Der Knickgrenge Bei Dünner Platten, *Proc. 3d Int. Congr. Appl. Mech.*, Stockholm, vol. 3, pp. 73–81, 1930.

Sherbourne, A. N.: Elastic, Post-buckling Behaviour of a Simply Supported Circular Plate, *J. Mech. Eng. Sci.*, vol. 3, pp. 133–141, 1961.

Stein, M.: Loads and Deformations of Buckled Rectangular Plates, *NASA Tech. Rep. 40*, 1959.

Supple, W. J.: Coupled Branching Configurations in the Elastic Buckling of Symmetric Structural Systems, *Int. J. Mech. Sci.*, vol. 9, pp. 97–112, 1967.

———: On the Change in Buckle Pattern in Elastic Structures, *Int. J. Mech. Sci.*, vol. 10, pp. 737–745, 1968.

———: Changes of Wave-form of Plates in the Post-buckling Range, *Int. J. Solids Struct.*, vol. 6, pp. 1243–1258, 1970.

——— and A. H. Chilver: Elastic Post-buckling of Compressed Rectangular Flat Plates, "Thin-Walled Structures," ed. A. H. Chilver, Chatto and Windus, London, pp. 136–152, 1967.

von Kármán, T.: The Engineer Grapples with Nonlinear Problems, *Bul. Amer. Math. Soc.*, vol. 46, pp. 615–683 (pp. 629–632), 1940.

———, E. E. Sechler, and L. H. Donnell: The Strength of Thin Plates in Compression, *Trans. ASME*, vol. 54, pp. APM-54–55, 1932.

Walker, A. C.: Flat Rectangular Plates Subjected to a Linearly-varying Edge Compressive Loading, "Thin-Walled Structures," ed. A. H. Chilver, Chatto and Windus, London, pp. 208–247, 1967.

———: The Post-buckling Behaviour of Simply-supported Square Plates, *Aeronaut. Q.*, vol. 20, pp. 203–222, 1969.

Wolkowisky, J. H.: Existence of Buckled States of Circular Elastic Plates, *Commun. Pure Appl. Math.*, vol. 20, pp. 549–560, 1967.

Yamaki, N.: Postbuckling Behavior of a Simply Supported Infinite Strip under the Action of Shearing Forces, *ZAMM*, vol. 44, pp. 107–117, 1964.

———: Postbuckling Behavior of a Clamped Infinite Strip under the Action of Shearing Forces, *ZAMM*, vol. 46, pp. 249–252, 1966.

Yamamoto, M., and K. Kondo: Buckling and Failure of Thin Rectangular Plates in Compression, *Rep. Aeronaut. Res. Inst. Univ. Tokyo 119*, 1937.

Yanowitch, M.: Nonlinear Buckling of Circular Elastic Plates, *Commun. Pure Appl. Math.*, vol. 9, pp. 661–672, 1956.

Nonlinear Flexural Vibration of Isotropic Plates

Aggarwala, B. D.: Vibrations of Rectilinear Plates, *ZAMM*, vol. 49, pp. 711–716, 1969.

Banerjee, B.: Large Amplitude Free Vibration of Elliptic Plates, *J. Phys. Soc. Japan*, vol. 23, pp. 1169–1172, 1967.

———: Large Amplitude Free Vibration of an Isosceles Right Angled Triangular Plate with Simply Supported Edges, *J. Sci. Eng. Res.*, vol. 12, pp. 45–49, 1968.

Bulkeley, P. Z.: An Axisymmetric Nonlinear Vibration of Circular Plates, *ASME J. Appl. Mech.*, vol. 4, pp. 630–631, 1963.

Chiang, D. C., and S. S. H. Chen: Large Amplitude Vibration of a Circular Plate with Concentric Rigid Mass, *ASME J. Appl. Mech.*, vol. 39, pp. 577–583, 1972.

Crawford, J.: Non-linear Vibrations of a Flat Plate with Initial Stresses, *J. Sound Vib.*, vol. 43, pp. 117–129, 1975.

Datta, S.: Large Amplitude Free Vibrations of Irregular Plates Placed on Elastic Foundation, *Int. J. Non-Linear Mech.*, vol. 11, pp. 337–345, 1976.

Dowell, E. H.: Nonlinear Oscillations of a Fluttering Plate, *AIAA J.*, vol. 4, pp. 1267–1275, 1966.

Eisley, J. G.: Large Amplitude Vibration of Buckled Beams and Rectangular Plates, *AIAA J.*, vol. 2, pp. 2207–2209, 1964.

———: Nonlinear Vibrations of Beams and Rectangular Plates, *ZAMP*, vol. 15, pp. 167–175, 1964.

Eringen, A. E.: On the Nonlinear Vibration of Circular Membrane, *Proc. 1st U.S. Nat. Cong. Appl. Mech.*, Chicago, pp. 139–149, 1951.

Evensen, D. A.: Influence of Nonlinearities on Degenerate Vibration Modes of Square Plate, *J. Acoust. Soc. Am.*, vol. 44, pp. 84–89, 1968.

Freynik, H. S.: The Nonlinear Response of Windows to Random Noise, *NASA Tech. Note* D-2025, 1963.

Gajendar, N.: Large Amplitude Vibrations of Plates on Elastic Foundations, *Int. J. Non-Linear Mech.*, vol. 2, pp. 163–172, 1967.

Greenspan, J. E.: A Simplified Expression for the Period of Nonlinear Oscillations of Curved and Flat Panels, *J. Aerosp. Sci.*, vol. 27, pp. 138–139, 1960.

Harris, G. Z. and E. H. Mansfield: On the Large-deflection Vibrations of Elastic Plates, *Phil. Trans. Roy. Soc. London, Series A, Math. Phys. Sci.*, vol. 261, pp. 289–343, 1967.

Herbert, R. E.: Random Vibrations of Plates with Large Amplitudes, *ASME J. Appl. Mech.*, vol. 32, pp. 547–552, 1965.

Huang, C. L., and Y. J. Meng: Nonlinear Oscillations of a Nonuniform Fixed Circular Plate, *Int. J. Non-Linear Mech.*, vol. 7, pp. 557–569, 1972.

————, and B. E. Sandman: Large Amplitude Vibrations of a Rigidly Clamped Circular Plate, *Int. J. Non-Linear Mech.*, vol. 6, pp. 451–468, 1971.

————, H. K. Woo, and H. S. Walker: Nonlinear Flexural Oscillations of a Partially Tapered Annular Plate, *Int. J. Non-Linear Mech.*, vol. 11, pp. 89–97, 1976.

Kaul, R. K.: Finite Thermal Oscillations of Thin Plates, *Int. J. Solids Struct.*, vol. 2, pp. 337–350, 1966.

Kellner, T.: Der Einfluss Grosser Amplituden auf die Eigen frequenzen der Biegenschwingungen etc. *ZAMM*, vol. 45, Special Issue, pp. 123–125, 1965.

Kelly, R. E.: A Simplified Expression on the Period of Nonlinear Oscillations of Curved and Flat Panels, *J. Aerosp. Sci.*, vol. 27, pp. 621–622, 1960.

Kirchman, E. J. and J. E. Greenspan: Nonlinear Response of Aircraft Panels to Acoustic Noise, *J. Acoust. Soc. Am.*, vol. 29, pp. 854–857, 1959.

Kishor, B.: Nonlinear Transverse Vibration Analysis of a Rectangular Plate with Lumped M-S-D Systems, *ASME J. Appl. Mech.*, vol. 40, pp. 825–826, 1973.

Kisliakov, S.: Determination of the Amplitudes of the Parametric Resonance of Thin Elastic Plates and Shells (in Bulgarian), *Bulg. Akad. Nauk.*, vol. 10, pp. 223–229, 1969.

Lassiter, L. W., R. W. Hess, and H. W. Hubbard: An Experimental Study of the Response of Simple Panels to Intense Acoustic Loading, *J. Aeronaut. Sci.*, vol. 24, pp. 19–24, 1957.

Lin, Y. K.: Response of a Nonlinear Flat Panel to Periodic and Randomly Varying Loadings, *J. Aerosp. Sci.*, vol. 29, pp. 1029–1034, 1962.

Lyon, R. H.: Observations on the Role of Nonlinearity in Random Vibration of Structures, *NASA Tech. Note* D-1872, 1963.

Massa, E.: Free Vibration of Thin Circular Plates with Internal Plane Stresses in the Case of Large Deflections (in Italian), *Rend. 1st Lombardo Sci. Lett.*, vol. 97, pp. 346–368, 1963.

Massa, N. E.: Sulle Vibrazioni libere con Inflessione non Piccola di Piastre circolari Sottoposte a Stati Piani di Coazione (in Polish), *Inst. Lombardo (Rend. Sci.)* vol. A-97, pp. 346–358, 1963.

Metsaveer, Y. A.: Nonlinear Vibrations of Rigidly Clamped Rectangular Plates (in Russian), *Tr. Tbilis, Politenkhn, In-ta A*, 257, pp. 127–139, 1967.

Morozov, N. F.: The Existence of Smooth Solution to the Problem of the Nonlinear Vibrations of a Thin Plate, *USSR Computat. Math. and Math. Phys.*, vol. 6, pp. 228–232, 1966.

Murthy, D. N. S., and A. N. Sherbourne: Free Flexural Vibrations of Clamped Plates, *ASME J. Appl. Mech.*, vol. 39, pp. 298–300, 1972.

Nash, W. A. and J. R. Modeer: Certain Approximate Analysis of Non-linear Behaviour of Plates and Shells, Proc. I.U.T.A.M. on the Theory of Thin Elastic Shells, ed. W. T. Koiter, North-Holland Publishing Co. Amsterdam, pp. 331–354, 1960.

Nowinski, J.: Nonlinear Transverse Vibrations of Circular Elastic Plates Built-in at the Boundary, *Proc. 4th U.S. Nat. Congr. App. Mech.*, vol. 1, pp. 325–334, 1962.

Pal, M. C.: Large Amplitude Free Vibrations of Rectilinear Plates, *J. Sci. Eng. Res.*, vol. 11, pp. 317–326, 1967.

————: Large Amplitude Free Vibration of Circular Plates Subjected to Aerodynamic Heating, *Int. J. Solids Struct.*, vol. 6, pp. 301–313, 1970.

————: Large Amplitude Free Vibrations of Rectangular Plates Subjected to Aerodynamic Heating, *J. Eng. Math.*, vol. 4, pp. 39–49, 1970.

Pandalai, K. A. V.: General Conclusions Regarding the Large Amplitude Flexural Vibrations of Beams and Plates, *Israel J. Technol.*, vol. 11, pp. 321–324, 1973.

Pandalai, K. A. V., M. Sathyamoorthy, and T. K. Varadan: On the Phenomena of Large Amplitude Flexural Vibration and Postbuckling of Structures, *J. Aeronaut. Soc. India*, vol. 26, pp. 73–79, 1974.

Prathap, G., and T. K. Varadan: Large Amplitude Flexural Vibration of Stiffened Plates, *J. Sound Vib.*, vol. 57, pp. 583–593, 1978.

Ramachandran, J.: Nonlinear Vibrations of a Rectangular Plate Carrying a Concentrated Mass, *ASME J. Appl. Mech.*, vol. 40, pp. 630–632, 1973.

————: Large Amplitude Vibrations of Elastically Restrained Rectangular Plates, *ASME J. Appl. Mech.*, vol. 40, pp. 811–813, 1973.

Sathyamoorthy, M.: Shear and Rotatory Inertia Effects on Large Amplitude Vibration of Skew Plates, *J. Sound Vib.*, vol. 25, pp. 155–163, 1977.

Silver, R. L., and J. H. Somerset: Experiments on the Large Amplitude Parametric Response of Rectangular Plates Under In-plane Random Loads, *Shock Vibr. Bul. 39, part 3, (39th Symp. Shock Vibr., Pacific Grove, Calif., 1968).*

Smith, P. W., C. I. Malme, and C. M. Goods: Nonlinear Response of Simple Clamped Panel, *J. Acoust. Soc. Am.*, vol. 33, pp. 1476–1482, 1961.

Srinivasan, A. V.: Large Amplitude Free Oscillations of Beams and Plates, *AIAA J.*, vol. 3, pp. 1951–1953, 1965.

Somerset, J. H.: Transition Mechanisms Attendant to Large Amplitude Parametric Vibrations of Rectangular Plates, *ASME J. Eng. for Industry*, vol. 89, pp. 619–625, 1967.

———, and R. M. Evan-Iwanowski: Experiments on Large Amplitude Parametric Vibrations of Rectangular Plates, *Dev. Theo. Appl. Mech.*, vol. 3, pp. 331–355, 1966.

———, and ———: Influence of Nonlinear Inertia on the Parametric Response of Rectangular Plates, *Int. J. Non-Linear Mech.*, vol. 2, pp. 217–232, 1967.

Sunakawa, M.: Influence of Temperature Changes and Large Amplitudes on Free Flexural Vibration of Rectangular Elastic Plates, *Trans. JSME*, vol. 30, p. 558, 1964.

Tadera, K., M. Koseki, and H. Izumi: Influence of Large Amplitude on Flexural Vibrations of Rectangular Elastic Plates under Initial Tension or Compression, *Nat. Aerosp. Lab., Japan, Tech. Rep. 79*, 1965.

Ventres, C. S. and E. H. Dowell: Comparison of Theory and Experiment for Nonlinear Flutter of Loaded Plates, *AIAA J.*, vol. 8, pp. 2022–2030, 1977.

Verizhenko, E. P., P. M. Varvak, and B. Z. Itenberg: Large Amplitude Oscillations of Rectangular Plates (in Russian), *Sopr. Mater. Teor. Sooruzh., Mozhved. Resp. Nauchn. Sb. 7*, pp. 45–51, 1968.

Wah, T.: Large Amplitude Flexural Vibrations of Rectangular Plates, *Int. J. Mech. Sci.*, vol. 5, pp. 425–438, 1963.

———: Vibrations of Circular Plates at Large Amplitudes, *J. Eng. Mech. Div., Proc. ASCE*, vol. 89, no. EM5, pp. 1–15, 1963.

———: The Normal Modes of Vibration of Certain Nonlinear Continuous Systems, *ASME J. Appl. Mech.*, vol. 31, pp. 139–140, 1964.

MODERATELY LARGE DEFLECTIONS OF
ANISOTROPIC PLATES

This chapter is mainly concerned with the moderately large deflections of ortho-tropic plates with material axes of symmetry parallel to the plate axes. The non-linear bending of anisotropic plates and symmetric laminates are discussed in the last three sections. Approximate solutions are obtained by the perturbation method for rectilinearly orthotropic rectangular and elliptical plates, cylindrically orthotropic circular plates and anisotropic rectangular plates, all uniformly loaded and rigidly clamped, and by the Galerkin procedure for uniformly loaded, rectilinearly orthotropic, simply supported rectangular and loosely clamped tri-angular plates. The multiple Fourier method is applied to a nonuniformly loaded orthotropic rectangular plate with stiffened edges elastically supported against rotation. Accurate solutions are also obtained by use of the generalized double Fourier series for orthotropic rectangular plates with movable edges elastically supported against rotation and for all-clamped and all-simply supported, sym-metrically laminated and homogeneous anisotropic plates under nonuniformly distributed transverse loads. In the case of a simply supported orthotropic rectan-gular plate under the combined action of lateral and inplane loads, a solution is presented by using a double cosine series for the transverse deflection and a generalized double Fourier series for the stress function. In addition static solutions will be obtained as special cases of nonlinear vibrations by the Galerkin procedure in Section 6.7 for all-clamped and all-simply supported orthotropic rec-tangular plates, in Sec. 6.9 for clamped rectilinearly orthotropic circular plates, in Sec. 6.10 for loosely clamped orthotropic skew plates, and in Sec. 6.11 for loosely and rigidly clamped orthotropic right and isosceles triangular plates. Furthermore, the solutions for laminated plates presented in Chap. 7 can be specified for ortho-tropic plates.

5.1 CLAMPED ORTHOTROPIC RECTANGULAR PLATE UNDER UNIFORM TRANSVERSE LOAD

Consider a thin rectangular plate of rectilinear orthotropy with its material axes of symmetry parallel to the rectangular cartesian coordinate axes of the plate as shown in Fig. 5.1. The plate may rest on an elastic foundation such as a concrete road, and is subjected to a uniformly distributed load q_0. The intensity of the reaction of the foundation is assumed to be proportional to the deflections of the plate. Thus the lateral load q is equal to the difference, $q_0 - kw$, in which k is the foundation modulus. The differential equations governing the moderately large-deflection behavior of the plate may be obtained from equations (1-109) to (1-111). These equations in the static case are given by

$$u^\circ_{,xx} + w_{,x}w_{,xx} + c_1(u^\circ_{,yy} + w_{,x}w_{,yy}) + c_2(v^\circ_{,xy} + w_{,y}w_{,xy}) = 0 \qquad (5\text{-}1)$$

$$c_1(v^\circ_{,xx} + w_{,y}w_{,xx}) + c_3(v^\circ_{,yy} + w_{,y}w_{,yy}) + c_2(u^\circ_{,xy} + w_{,x}w_{,xy}) = 0 \qquad (5\text{-}2)$$

$$w_{,xxxx} + 2c_4 w_{,xxyy} + c_3 w_{,yyyy} - \frac{q_0 - kw}{D_1}$$

$$- \frac{12}{h^2}\{w_{,xx}[u^\circ_{,x} + v_{21}v^\circ_{,y} + \tfrac{1}{2}w^2_{,x} + \tfrac{1}{2}v_{21}w^2_{,y}]$$

$$+ c_3 w_{,yy}[v_{12}u^\circ_{,x} + v^\circ_{,y} + \tfrac{1}{2}v_{12}w^2_{,x} + \tfrac{1}{2}w^2_{,y}]$$

$$+ 2c_1[u^\circ_{,y} + v^\circ_{,x} + w_{,x}w_{,y}]\} = 0 \qquad (5\text{-}3)$$

where

$$c_1 = \frac{\mu G_{12}}{E_1} \qquad c_2 = v_{21} + c_1 \qquad c_3 = \frac{E_2}{E_1} \qquad c_4 = v_{21} + 2c_1 \qquad (5\text{-}4)$$

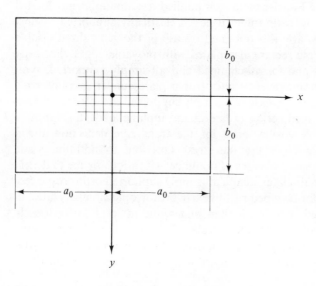

Figure 5.1 Geometry and elastic directions of orthotropic rectangular plate.

Making the resulting solution more general these equations are written in the nondimensional form

$$U_{,\zeta\zeta} + \lambda^2 c_1 U_{,\eta\eta} + \lambda c_2 V_{,\zeta\eta} = -W_{,\zeta}(W_{,\zeta\zeta} + \lambda^2 c_1 W_{,\eta\eta}) - \lambda^2 c_2 W_{,\eta} W_{,\zeta\eta} \quad (5\text{-}5)$$

$$\lambda c_2 U_{,\zeta\eta} + c_1 V_{,\zeta\zeta} + \lambda^2 c_3 V_{,\eta\eta} = -\lambda W_{,\eta}(c_1 W_{,\zeta\zeta} + \lambda^2 c_3 W_{,\eta\eta}) - \lambda c_2 W_{,\zeta} W_{,\zeta\eta} \quad (5\text{-}6)$$

$$W_{,\zeta\zeta\zeta\zeta} + 2\lambda^2 c_4 W_{,\zeta\zeta\eta\eta} + \lambda^4 c_3 W_{,\eta\eta\eta\eta} = Q + W_{,\zeta\zeta}(U_{,\zeta} + \lambda v_{21} V_{,\eta})$$
$$+ \lambda^2 W_{,\eta\eta}(v_{21} U_{,\zeta} + \lambda c_3 V_{,\eta}) + 2\lambda c_1 W_{,\zeta\eta}(\lambda U_{,\eta} + V_{,\zeta} + \lambda W_{,\zeta} W_{,\eta})$$
$$+ \tfrac{1}{2} W_{,\zeta\zeta}[W_{,\zeta}^2 + \lambda^2 v_{21} W_{,\eta}^2]$$
$$+ \tfrac{1}{2}\lambda^2 W_{,\eta\eta}[v_{21} W_{,\zeta}^2 + \lambda^2 c_3 W_{,\eta}^2] \qquad (5\text{-}7)$$

in which λ, ζ, η, U, V, and W are defined by equations (2-67) and the value of k has been taken to be zero, and in which

$$Q = \frac{24\sqrt{3}\,\mu q_0 a_0^4}{E_1 h^4} \qquad (5\text{-}8)$$

If the plate is rigidly clamped along its edges, the nondimensional boundary conditions can be written as

$$U = V = W = W_{,\zeta} = 0 \quad \text{at} \quad \zeta = \pm 1$$
$$U = V = W = W_{,\eta} = 0 \quad \text{at} \quad \eta = \pm 1 \qquad (5\text{-}9)$$

An approximate solution of equations (5-5) to (5-7) satisfying boundary conditions (5-9) is formulated by the method of perturbation (Ref. 5.1) as in Sec. 2.5. Thus equations (2-72), (2-73), (2-75), (2-77), and (2-79) to (2-83) are also used herein. The linear differential equations corresponding to equations (2-74), (2-76), and (2-78) are given by

$$w_{1,\zeta\zeta\zeta\zeta} + 2\lambda^2 c_4 w_{1,\zeta\zeta\eta\eta} + \lambda^4 c_3 w_{1,\eta\eta\eta\eta} = q_1 \qquad (5\text{-}10)$$

$$u_{2,\zeta\zeta} + \lambda^2 c_1 u_{2,\eta\eta} + \lambda c_2 v_{2,\zeta\eta} = -w_{1,\zeta}(w_{1,\zeta\zeta} + \lambda^2 c_1 w_{1,\eta\eta}) - \lambda^2 c_2 w_{1,\eta} w_{1,\zeta\eta} \quad (5\text{-}11)$$

$$\lambda c_2 u_{2,\zeta\eta} + c_1 v_{2,\zeta\zeta} + \lambda^2 c_3 v_{2,\eta\eta} = -\lambda w_{1,\eta}(c_1 w_{1,\zeta\zeta} + \lambda^2 c_3 w_{1,\eta\eta}) - \lambda c_2 w_{1,\zeta} w_{1,\zeta\eta}$$
$$(5\text{-}12)$$

$$w_{3,\zeta\zeta\zeta\zeta} + 2\lambda^2 c_4 w_{3,\zeta\zeta\eta\eta} + \lambda^4 c_3 w_{3,\eta\eta\eta\eta}$$
$$= q_3 + w_{1,\zeta\zeta}(u_{2,\zeta} + \lambda v_{21} v_{2,\eta}) + \lambda^2 w_{1,\eta\eta}(v_{21} u_{2,\zeta} + \lambda c_3 v_{2,\eta})$$
$$+ 2\lambda c_1 w_{1,\zeta\eta}(\lambda u_{2,\eta} + v_{2,\zeta} + \lambda w_{1,\zeta} w_{1,\eta})$$
$$+ \tfrac{1}{2} w_{1,\zeta\zeta}[(w_{1,\zeta})^2 + \lambda^2 v_{21}(w_{1,\eta})^2]$$
$$+ \tfrac{1}{2}\lambda^2 w_{1,\eta\eta}[v_{21}(w_{1,\zeta})^2 + \lambda^2 c_3(w_{1,\eta})^2] \qquad (5\text{-}13)$$

It is observed that the perturbation series (2-72) in the orthotropic case is also approximated by expression (2-83). The nondimensional form of average membrane stresses σ_x^m, σ_y^m, σ_{xy}^m can be expressed as

$$\sigma_\zeta^m = U_{,\zeta} + \lambda v_{21} V_{,\eta} + \tfrac{1}{2}[W_{,\zeta}^2 + \lambda^2 v_{21} W_{,\eta}^2]$$

$$\sigma_\eta^m = \lambda c_3 V_{,\eta} + v_{21} U_{,\zeta} + \tfrac{1}{2}[\lambda^2 c_3 W_{,\eta}^2 + v_{21} W_{,\zeta}^2] \tag{5-14}$$

$$\sigma_{\zeta\eta}^m = c_1(\lambda U_{,\eta} + V_{,\zeta} + \lambda W_{,\zeta} W_{,\eta})$$

and that of extreme-fiber bending stresses σ_x^b, σ_y^b, and σ_{xy}^b as

$$\sigma_\zeta^b = \pm\sqrt{3}(W_{,\zeta\zeta} + \lambda^2 v_{21} W_{,\eta\eta})$$

$$\sigma_\eta^b = \pm\sqrt{3}(\lambda^2 c_3 W_{,\eta\eta} + v_{21} W_{,\zeta\zeta}) \tag{5-15}$$

$$\sigma_{\zeta\eta}^b = \pm 2\sqrt{3}\,\lambda c_1 W_{,\zeta\eta}$$

where

$$(\sigma_\zeta^m, \sigma_\eta^m, \sigma_{\zeta\eta}^m) = \frac{12\mu a_0^2}{E_1 h^2}(\sigma_x^m, \sigma_y^m, \sigma_{xy}^m)$$

$$ \tag{5-16}$$

$$(\sigma_\zeta^b, \sigma_\eta^b, \sigma_{\zeta\eta}^b) = \frac{12\mu a_0^2}{E_1 h^2}(\sigma_x^b, \sigma_y^b, \sigma_{xy}^b)$$

From equations (2-83), (5-14), and (5-15) the nondimensional parameters Q, U, V, W, σ^m and σ^b can be determined for given values of λ, v_{21}, E_2/E_1, G_{12}/E_1, and W_0. To avoid confusion, it is best to regard E_1 as fixed in magnitude and to think of large values of E_2/E_1 and G_{12}/E_1 as representing high moduli. In the case of an isotropic plate the present solution reduces to that given in Sec. 2.5.

In calculation the values of elastic constants typical of glass-epoxy composites are taken to be

$$E_2/E_1 = 3.00 \qquad G_{12}/E_1 = 0.50 \qquad v_{21} = 0.25$$

which imply that the reinforced fibers are parallel to the y axis.

The relation between load and central deflection w_0 of a glass-epoxy plate is shown in Fig. 5.2 for various values of the aspect ratio λ. For a given pressure the maximum deflection increases with decreasing the aspect ratio as in the case of isotropic plates. The dotted line is the load-deflection curve for a square isotropic plate $(v = \tfrac{1}{3})$ which approaches the $\lambda = \tfrac{3}{4}$ curve. Evidently, this arises from the fact that the tensile modulus of the isotropic plate is equal to that of the orthotropic plate in the transverse direction and one-third of that in the filament direction. Figures 5.3 to 5.5 show the bending and membrane stresses at the midpoints of the sides and at the center of the plate. Due to different tensile moduli, the stresses of a square plate at the midpoints are not equal to each other and the stress in the y direction associated with the higher tensile modulus is greater than that in the x direction. At large values of w_0/h, the $\lambda = 0$ curve for the bending stress at the midpoint of the long side (not shown here) exceeds that when $\lambda = \tfrac{2}{3}$. Thus the limitation of the two terms of the perturbation series solution for orthotropic plates is quite similar to that for isotropic plates in Sec. 2.5. The $\lambda = 0, \tfrac{1}{2}$ curves for the membrane stresses in the x direction at the plate center nearly coincide with

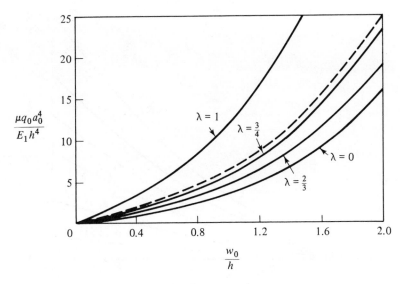

Figure 5.2 Load-deflection curves for glass-epoxy plate.

each other, but not with those in the y direction. The dotted lines shown in Fig. 5.3 and 5.4 are, respectively, the bending and membrane stresses of a square isotropic plate at the midpoints, and that shown in Fig. 5.5 is the bending stress in the transverse direction at the center of an isotropic plate having $\lambda = 0.75$. The membrane-stress curve at the center of a square isotropic plate (not shown here)

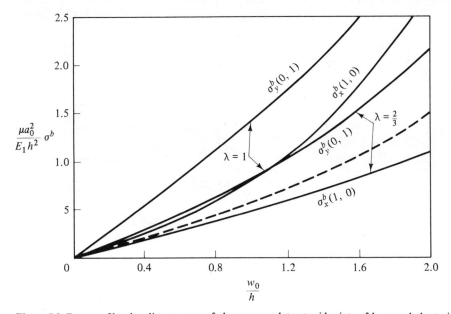

Figure 5.3 Extreme-fiber bending stresses of glass-epoxy plate at midpoints of long and short sides.

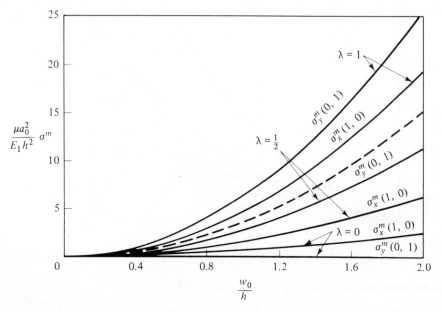

Figure 5.4 Membrane stresses of glass-epoxy plate at midpoints of long and short sides.

approaches and is just above the $\lambda = 1$ curve for σ_x^m in Fig. 5.5. It may be noted that, under the same central deflection, the bending or membrane stress of an isotropic plate at the midpoint of the long side is less than that of the corresponding orthotropic plate, and vice versa at the plate center. This arises from the fact that the pressure required to produce the same central deflection is higher for the

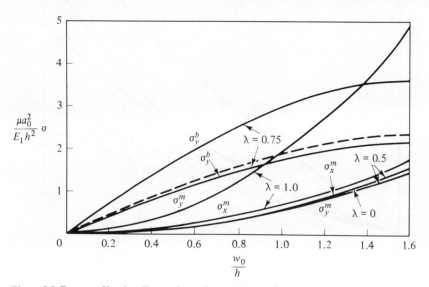

Figure 5.5 Extreme-fiber bending and membrane stresses at center of glass-epoxy plate.

orthotropic plate than for the isotropic plate. Consequently, the orthotropic plate of high-tensile modulus is flatter in the central region and bent or more curved than the isotropic plate in the boundary region. The result shows that the maximum values of bending and membrane stresses both occur at the clamped edges.

In the case of an infinite strip ($b_0 = \infty$ or $\lambda = 0$) the variables w_1 and w_3 are functions of ζ only and coefficients q_1, q_3, w_1, w_3 are independent of the elastic constants. Therefore, the $\lambda = 0$ curves shown in Figs. 5.2 to 5.5 are also applicable to an isotropic plate. The elastic constants of the plate material in this case simply appear in the load parameter Q.

5.2 SIMPLY SUPPORTED UNIFORMLY LOADED ORTHOTROPIC RECTANGULAR PLATE ON ELASTIC FOUNDATION

Equations (5-1) to (5-3) have been used to study the large deflection behavior of a clamped orthotropic rectangular plate. These equations will also be used and solved in conjunction with the boundary conditions for simply supported edges. If the membrane shear stress and the inplane displacement normal to these edges vanish at the edges, the boundary conditions are given by

$$u^\circ = w = w_{,xx} = \sigma^m_{xy} = 0 \qquad \text{at} \quad x = 0, a$$
$$v^\circ = w = w_{,yy} = \sigma^m_{xy} = 0 \qquad \text{at} \quad y = 0, b$$

$$(5\text{-}17)$$

in which a and b are the lateral dimensions of the plate.

The Galerkin procedure (Ref. 5.2) is used to obtain an approximate solution. In the analysis the transverse deflection and two inplane displacements are taken to be

$$w = w_0 \sin \frac{\pi x}{a} \sin \frac{\pi y}{b}$$

$$(5\text{-}18)$$

and

$$u^\circ = \frac{\pi w_0^2}{16a}\left(\cos \frac{2\pi y}{b} + \lambda^2 v_{21} - 1\right)\sin \frac{2\pi x}{a}$$
$$v^\circ = \frac{\pi w_0^2}{16b}\left(\cos \frac{2\pi x}{a} + \frac{v_{21}}{\lambda^2 c_3} - 1\right)\sin \frac{2\pi y}{b}$$

$$(5\text{-}19)$$

where w_0 is the deflection at the center of the plate.

It can easily be verified that these displacement functions satisfy all the boundary conditions (5-17), and the two inplane displacement functions (5-19) also satisfy equations (5-1) and (5-2). Instead of satisfaction of equation (5-3), we apply the Galerkin method and compute the integral

$$\int_0^a \int_0^b L \sin \frac{\pi x}{a} \sin \frac{\pi y}{b} \, dx \, dy = 0$$

$$(5\text{-}20)$$

in which L is the left-hand side of equation (5-3). Performing the integration we obtain

$$\alpha \frac{w_0}{h} + \beta \left(\frac{w_0}{h}\right)^3 = \frac{q_0 a^4}{D_1 h} \tag{5-21}$$

where

$$\alpha = \frac{\pi^6}{16}\left(1 + 2c_4\lambda^2 + c_3\lambda^4 + \frac{ka^4}{\pi^4 D_1}\right)$$

$$\beta = \frac{3\pi^6}{64}\left[3 - \frac{v_{21}^2}{c_3} + \lambda^2(v_{21} + 3v_{12}c_3) + c_3\lambda^4(3 - v_{12}v_{21})\right] \tag{5-22}$$

Equation (5-21) provides us with a simple relation between load and maximum deflection of a simply supported orthotropic plate resting on an elastic foundation. In the case of an isotropic plate, equation (5-21) is simplified to yield

$$4\left[(1 + \lambda^2)^2 + \frac{ka^4}{\pi^4 D}\right]\frac{w_0}{h} + 3[4v\lambda^2 + (3 - v^2)(1 + \lambda^4)]\left(\frac{w_0}{h}\right)^3 = \frac{64q_0 a^4}{\pi^6 Dh} \tag{5-23}$$

in which v and D are Poisson's ratio and flexural rigidity of the isotropic plate, respectively. In the case of $k = 0$, equation (5-23) matches exactly with the result given in Ref. 5.3.

5.3 LATERALLY LOADED ORTHOTROPIC RECTANGULAR PLATE WITH EDGES ELASTICALLY SUPPORTED AGAINST ROTATION

In the foregoing two problems the boundary conditions are associated both with transverse deflection and with two inplane displacements. Consequently, the governing equations for three displacements of an orthotropic plate have been used. In the case of the inplane boundary conditions related to membrane forces, it will be more convenient to adopt the system of equations expressed in terms of transverse deflection and force function. The static version of equations (1-158) and (1-159) for specially orthotropic plates is thus given in the following

$$D_1 w_{,xxxx} + 2D_3 w_{,xxyy} + D_2 w_{,yyyy}$$
$$= q + w_{,xx}\psi_{,yy} + w_{,yy}\psi_{,xx} - 2w_{,xy}\psi_{,xy} \tag{5-24}$$

$$\delta_1 \psi_{,xxxx} + 2\delta_3 \psi_{,xxyy} + \delta_2 \psi_{,yyyy}$$
$$= h[w_{,xy}^2 - w_{,xx}w_{,yy}] \tag{5-25}$$

in which ψ is the force function.

Let us introduce the nondimensional parameters

$$\zeta = \frac{x}{a} \qquad \eta = \frac{y}{b} \qquad \lambda = \frac{a}{b} \qquad F = \frac{\psi}{E_2 h^3} \qquad W = \frac{w}{h}$$

$$Q = \frac{qb^4}{E_2 h^4} \qquad c_5 = \frac{E_1}{E_2} \qquad c_6 = v_{12} + \frac{c_7 G_{12}}{6 E_2} \tag{5-26}$$

$$c_7 = 12(1 - v_{12} v_{21}) \qquad c_8 = \frac{1}{2}\left(\frac{E_1}{G_{12}} - 2 v_{12}\right)$$

Upon substitution equations (5-24) and (5-25) transform to

$$c_5 W_{,\zeta\zeta\zeta\zeta} + 2\lambda^2 c_6 W_{,\zeta\zeta\eta\eta} + \lambda^4 W_{,\eta\eta\eta\eta}$$
$$= \lambda^4 c_7 Q + \lambda^2 c_7 (W_{,\zeta\zeta} F_{,\eta\eta} + W_{,\eta\eta} F_{,\zeta\zeta} - 2 W_{,\zeta\eta} F_{,\zeta\eta}) \tag{5-27}$$

$$c_5 F_{,\zeta\zeta\zeta\zeta} + 2\lambda^2 c_8 F_{,\zeta\zeta\eta\eta} + \lambda^4 F_{,\eta\eta\eta\eta} = c_5 \lambda^2 [W_{,\zeta\eta}^2 - W_{,\zeta\zeta} W_{,\eta\eta}] \tag{5-28}$$

The nondimensional membrane forces N_ζ, N_η, $N_{\zeta\eta}$ are related to the non-dimensional force function F by

$$N_\zeta = F_{,\eta\eta} \qquad N_\eta = \frac{F_{,\zeta\zeta}}{\lambda^2} \qquad N_{\zeta\eta} = -\frac{F_{,\zeta\eta}}{\lambda} \tag{5-29}$$

where

$$(N_\zeta, N_\zeta, N_{\zeta\eta}) = \frac{b^2}{E_2 h^3}(N_x, N_y, N_{xy}) \tag{5-30}$$

The bending moments are also written in the nondimensional form

$$M_\zeta = -\frac{1}{c_7 \lambda^2}(c_5 W_{,\zeta\zeta} + \lambda^2 v_{12} W_{,\eta\eta})$$

$$M_\eta = -\frac{1}{c_7 \lambda^2}(v_{12} W_{,\zeta\zeta} + \lambda^2 W_{,\eta\eta}) \tag{5-31}$$

$$M_{\zeta\eta} = -\frac{G_{12} W_{,\zeta\eta}}{6\lambda E_2}$$

where

$$(M_\zeta, M_\eta, M_{\zeta\eta}) = \frac{b^2}{E_2 h^4}(M_x, M_y, M_{xy}) \tag{5-32}$$

In the analysis the plate is assumed to be rigidly supported against the transverse deflection along the edges. To the same degree opposite edges are taken to be elastically restrained against the rotation. The boundary conditions for the transverse deflection may be written as

$$\begin{aligned} W = 0 \qquad W_{,\zeta\zeta} = \pm \xi_a W_{,\zeta} \qquad \text{at} \quad \zeta = 0, 1 \\ W = 0 \qquad W_{,\eta\eta} = \pm \xi_b W_{,\eta} \qquad \text{at} \quad \eta = 0, 1 \end{aligned} \tag{5-33}$$

Table 5.1 Values of α_m and γ_m in equation (5-36)

m	1	2	3	4	> 4
α_m	4.73004	7.85320	10.9956	14.1372	$(2m+1)\pi/2$
γ_m	0.982502	1.00078	0.999967	1.00000	1.00000

wherein ξ_a and ξ_b are the rotational edge restraint coefficients at the plate edges, $\zeta = 0, 1$ and $\eta = 0, 1$, respectively. If the edges of the plate are free from boundary forces, the nondimensional inplane boundary conditions are

$$F_{,\eta\eta} = 0 \qquad F_{,\zeta\eta} = 0 \qquad \text{at} \quad \zeta = 0, 1$$
$$F_{,\zeta\zeta} = 0 \qquad F_{,\zeta\eta} = 0 \qquad \text{at} \quad \eta = 0, 1 \tag{5-34}$$

A solution of equations (5-27) and (5-28) is expressed in the form of generalized Fourier series (Refs. 5.4 and 5.5)

$$F = \sum_{m=1}^{\infty} \sum_{n=1}^{\infty} F_{mn} X_m(\zeta) Y_n(\eta)$$
$$W = \sum_{p=1}^{\infty} \sum_{q=1}^{\infty} W_{pq} \phi_p(\zeta) \psi_q(\eta) \tag{5-35}$$

in which X_m, Y_n, ϕ_p, and ψ_q are the beam eigenfunctions given by

$$X_m(\zeta) = \cosh \alpha_m \zeta - \cos \alpha_m \zeta - \gamma_m(\sinh \alpha_m \zeta - \sin \alpha_m \zeta)$$
$$Y_n(\eta) = \cosh \alpha_n \eta - \cos \alpha_n \eta - \gamma_n(\sinh \alpha_n \eta - \sin \alpha_n \eta) \tag{5-36}$$

and

$$\phi_p(\zeta) = A_p(\cosh \beta_p \zeta - \cos \beta_p \zeta) + B_p \sinh \beta_p \zeta + \sin \beta_p \zeta$$
$$\psi_q(\eta) = A_q(\cosh \beta_q \eta - \cos \beta_q \eta) + B_q \sinh \beta_q \eta + \sin \beta_q \eta \tag{5-37}$$

Using the values of α_i and γ_i given in Table 5.1, the series for F satisfies the inplane boundary conditions (5-34). Function X_m and Y_n possess the following properties

$$\int_0^1 X_i X_j \, d\zeta = \begin{cases} 0 & \text{if} \quad i \neq j \\ 1 & \text{if} \quad i = j \end{cases} \qquad \int_0^1 Y_i Y_j \, d\eta = \begin{cases} 0 & \text{if} \quad i \neq j \\ 1 & \text{if} \quad i = j \end{cases}$$
$$X_i(0) = X_i(1) = X_{i,\zeta}(0) = X_{i,\zeta}(1) = 0, \qquad X_{i,\zeta\zeta\zeta\zeta} = \alpha_i^4 X_i$$
$$Y_i(0) = Y_i(1) = Y_{i,\eta}(0) = Y_{i,\eta}(1) = 0, \qquad Y_{i,\eta\eta\eta\eta} = \alpha_i^4 Y_i \tag{5-38}$$

Introduction of the second of expressions (5-35) into boundary conditions (5.33) leads to

$$A_i = -\cot \tfrac{1}{2}\beta_i \qquad B_i = \cot \tfrac{1}{2}\beta_i \tanh \tfrac{1}{2}\beta_i$$
$$\beta_i = -\tfrac{1}{2}\xi(\tan \tfrac{1}{2}\beta_i + \tanh \tfrac{1}{2}\beta_i)$$

$$\text{for } i = 1, 3, 5, \ldots \tag{5-39}$$

and

$$A_i = \tan \tfrac{1}{2}\beta_i \qquad B_i = -\tan \tfrac{1}{2}\beta_i \coth \tfrac{1}{2}\beta_i$$

$$\beta_i = \tfrac{1}{2}\xi(\cot \tfrac{1}{2}\beta_i - \coth \tfrac{1}{2}\beta_i)$$

$$\text{for } i = 2, 4, 6, \dots \quad (5\text{-}40)$$

in which ξ is the values of ξ_a and ξ_b in calculation of coefficients A_i, B_i, β_i for functions $\phi_i(\zeta)$ and $\psi_i(\eta)$ respectively. In the case of a clamped plate $(\xi_a = \xi_b = \infty)$, equations (5-39) and (5-40) reduce to (Ref. 5.5)

$$A_i = \frac{\sinh \beta_i - \sin \beta_i}{\cosh \beta_i - \cos \beta_i} \qquad B_i = -1$$

$$\qquad (5\text{-}41)$$

$$1 - \cos \beta_i \cosh \beta_i = 0$$

In the case of a simply supported plate $(\xi_a = \xi_b = 0)$ equations (5-39) and (5-40) become

$$\dot{A}_i = B_i = 0 \qquad \beta_n = n\pi \qquad (5\text{-}42)$$

Utilizing the values of coefficients, A_i, B_i, β_i, obtained from equations (5-39) to (5-40), the series for W given in expressions (5-35) satisfies boundary conditions (5-33). Functions ϕ_i and ψ_j possess the following properties

$$\int_0^1 \phi_i\phi_j \, d\zeta = \begin{cases} 0 & \text{if } i \neq j \\ H_i & \text{if } i = j \end{cases}$$

$$\int_0^1 \psi_i\psi_j \, d\eta = \begin{cases} 0 & \text{if } i \neq j \\ H_i & \text{if } i = j \end{cases}$$

$$\qquad (5\text{-}43)$$

where

$$H_i = \tfrac{1}{2}(2A_i^2 - B_i^2 + 1) + \frac{A_i}{\beta_i}(B_i + 1) \qquad (5\text{-}44)$$

Substituting equations (5-35) into (5-27) and (5-28), multiplying the first of the resulting equations by $\phi_i(\zeta)\psi_j(\eta)$ and the second by $X_i(\zeta)Y_j(\eta)$, integrating with respect to ζ and η from 0 to 1, and using the orthogonality properties (5-38) and (5-43), we obtain

$$W_{ij}(c_5\beta_i^4 + \lambda^4\beta_j^4) + 2\lambda^2 c_6 \sum_p \sum_q W_{pq} \beta_p^2 \beta_q^2 K_1^{ip} L_1^{jq}$$

$$- \lambda^4 c_7 Q_{ij} - \lambda^2 c_7 \sum_m \sum_n \sum_r \sum_s F_{mn} W_{rs}$$

$$\cdot (\alpha_n^2 \beta_r^2 K_2^{imr} L_3^{jns} + \alpha_m^2 \beta_s^2 K_3^{imr} L_2^{jns} - 2\alpha_m \alpha_n \beta_r \beta_s K_4^{imr} L_4^{jns}) = 0$$

$$i, j = 1, 2, 3, \dots \quad (5\text{-}45)$$

$$F_{ij}(c_5\alpha_i^4 + \lambda^4\alpha_j^4) + 2\lambda^2 c_8 \sum_m \sum_n F_{mn}\alpha_m^2 \alpha_n^2 K_5^{im} L_5^{jn}$$

$$= \lambda^2 c_5 \sum_p \sum_q \sum_r \sum_s W_{pq} W_{rs}(\beta_p \beta_q \beta_r \beta_s K_6^{ipr} L_6^{jqs} - \beta_p^2 \beta_s^2 K_7^{ipr} L_7^{jsq})$$

$$i, j = 1, 2, 3, \dots \quad (5\text{-}46)$$

where Q_{ij} are the coefficients in the Fourier series expansion for the transverse load parameter

$$Q = \sum_{i=1}^{\infty} \sum_{j=1}^{\infty} Q_{ij} \phi_i(\zeta) \psi_j(\eta) \tag{5-47}$$

and where constants K_1 to K_7 are defined by

$$K_1^{ip} = \frac{1}{\beta_p^2 H_i} \int_0^1 \phi_i \phi_p'' \, d\zeta$$

$$K_2^{imr} = \frac{1}{\beta_r^2 H_i} \int_0^1 \phi_i \phi_r'' X_m \, d\zeta$$

$$K_3^{imr} = \frac{1}{\alpha_m^2 H_i} \int_0^1 \phi_i \phi_r X_m'' \, d\zeta$$

$$K_4^{imr} = \frac{1}{\alpha_m \beta_r H_i} \int_0^1 \phi_i \phi_r' X_m' \, d\zeta \tag{5-48}$$

$$K_5^{im} = \frac{1}{\alpha_m^2} \int_0^1 X_i X_m'' \, d\zeta$$

$$K_6^{ipr} = \frac{1}{\beta_p \beta_r} \int_0^1 X_i \phi_p' \phi_r' \, d\zeta$$

$$K_7^{ipr} = \frac{1}{\beta_p^2} \int_0^1 X_i \phi_p'' \phi_r \, d\zeta$$

In expressions (5-48) the primes denote the differentiation with respect to the corresponding coordinate. The constants L_1 to L_7 in equations (5-45) and (5-46) are obtained by replacing i, K, m, p, r, X, ζ, and ϕ by j, L, n, q, s, Y, η, and ψ respectively in expressions (5-48).

Equations (5-45) and (5-46) constitute an infinite set of simultaneous algebraic nonlinear equations. In practice only a finite number of these equations are taken into account. The elimination of coefficients F_{ij} from these equations leads to a system of simultaneous cubic equations in W_{ij} which can be solved by the Newton-Raphson method.

Numerical examples are presented for glass-epoxy, boron-epoxy and graphite-epoxy plates. The elastic constants typical of these materials are given in

Table 5.2 Numerical values of elastic constants

Material	E_1/E_2	G_{12}/E_2	ν_{12}
Glass-epoxy	3	0.6	0.25
Boron-epoxy	10	1/3	0.22
Graphite-epoxy	40	0.5	0.25

Table 5.3 Comparison of nine-term and four-term solutions for square plates
$$(Q_u = q_0 b^4/E_2 h^4 \text{ and } Q_t = q_m b^4/E_2 h^4)$$

SS Glass-epoxy plate			CC/Boron-epoxy plate		
Uniform load Q_u	w_0/h		Triangular load Q_t	w_0/h	
	4 terms	9 terms		4 terms	9 terms
50	1.1315	1.1326	200	0.7539	0.7465
100	1.7794	1.7922	400	1.2899	1.2523
150	2.2504	2.2676	600	1.7019	1.6523
200	2.6197	2.6488	800	2.0759	1.9961
300	3.2386	3.2540	1000	2.4188	2.3036

Table 5.2. The value of the tensile-modulus ratio E_1/E_2 in the table implies that the filaments are parallel to the x axis. To check the convergence of the present series solution, calculations were carried out by taking the first four terms and nine terms in each of the truncated series for F and W. Table 5.3 presents the central deflection w_0 of a square simply supported (SS) glass-epoxy plate under uniform transverse load of intensity q_0 and a square clamped (CC) boron-epoxy plate under triangular load with maximum intensity q_m at $\zeta = 0.5$. It can be seen from the table that these series converge quite rapidly.

Numerical results are obtained by taking the first nine terms of the truncated series for F and W. Figure 5.6 shows the relation between triangular load and central deflection for a boron-epoxy plate. The triangular load with the maximum intensity q_m is in the form of a triangular prism in the x direction and uniform in

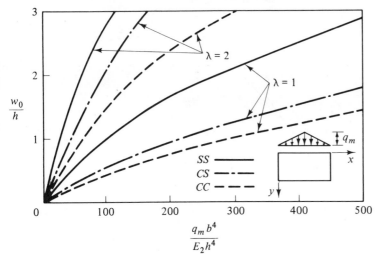

Figure 5.6 Load-deflection relations for boron-epoxy plates under triangular load.

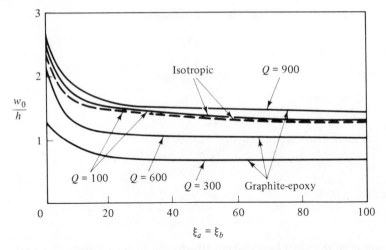

Figure 5.7 Effect of rotational edge restraint on central deflection of square isotropic and graphite-epoxy plate for various uniform transverse loads ($Q = q_0 b^4/E_2 h^4$).

the y direction. The edges of the plate are assumed to be all simply supported and all clamped. The mixed boundary conditions with the pair of opposite edges clamped along $y = 0, b$ and the other pair simply supported along $x = 0, a$ are denoted by CS. It is seen that the central deflection increases with the aspect ratio λ for any set of boundary conditions considered. In Fig. 5.7 the central deflection is plotted against the rotational edge restraint coefficient for square isotropic and graphite-epoxy plates under various values of uniform transverse load. The

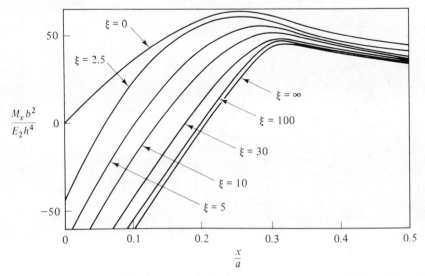

Figure 5.8 Distribution of bending moment M_x along the line $y = b/2$ in square uniformly loaded graphite-epoxy plate for different rotational edge restraints ($q_0 b^4/E_2 h^4 = 600$, $\xi_a = \xi_b = \xi$).

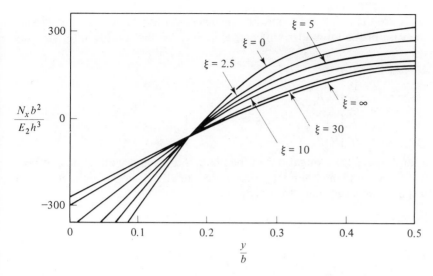

Figure 5.9 Distribution of membrane force N_x along the line $x = a/2$ in square uniformly loaded graphite-epoxy plate for different rotational edge restraints $(q_0 b^4/E_2 h^4 = 600, \xi_a = \xi_b = \xi)$.

dashed curve is obtained from the finite-difference method for an isotropic plate (Ref. 5.6). Figures 5.8 and 5.9 show the distribution of the bending moment M_x along the x axis and that of the membrane force N_x along the y axis for a square graphite-epoxy plate under uniform load with different rotational edge restraints. It may be observed from Figs. 5.7 to 5.9 that the results for $\xi = 100$ are close to those obtained for a clamped plate.

Numerical examples for a graphite-epoxy plate under central and eccentric patch loads and hydrostatic pressure can be found in Ref. 5.5.

5.4 ORTHOTROPIC RECTANGULAR PLATE WITH STIFFENED EDGES ELASTICALLY SUPPORTED AGAINST ROTATION

Suppose that an orthotropic rectangular plate of length a and width b under transverse load $q(x, y)$ is rigidly supported against the transverse deflection and elastically restrained against rotations along its four edges. These boundary conditions may be written as

$$w = 0 \quad \text{at} \quad x = 0, a \quad \text{and} \quad y = 0, b \tag{5-49}$$

and

$$D_1 w_{,xx}\Big|_{x=0} = \xi_1 w_{,x}\Big|_{x=0} \qquad D_1 w_{,xx}\Big|_{x=a} = -\xi_2 w_{,x}\Big|_{x=a}$$

$$D_2 w_{,yy}\Big|_{y=0} = \xi_3 w_{,y}\Big|_{y=0} \qquad D_2 w_{,yy}\Big|_{y=b} = -\xi_4 w_{,y}\Big|_{y=b} \tag{5-50}$$

in which ζ's are the rotational restraint coefficients at the corresponding edges.

In the case of the four sides stiffened as in Sec. 2.7, the condition for straight edges is

$$\int_0^a \left[\frac{1}{E_1 h} \psi_{,yy} - \frac{v_{12}}{E_1 h} \psi_{,xx} - \tfrac{1}{2} w_{,x}^2 \right] dx = \delta_x$$

$$\int_0^b \left[\frac{1}{E_2 h} \psi_{,xx} - \frac{v_{12}}{E_1 h} \psi_{,yy} - \tfrac{1}{2} w_{,y}^2 \right] dy = \delta_y$$

(5-51)

where δ_x and δ_y are the elongations of the plate in the x and y directions, respectively. If the total inplane boundary force is denoted by P_x in the x direction and by P_y in the y direction, then this condition is

$$\psi_{,y} \Big|_{y=b} - \psi_{,y} \Big|_{y=0} = P_x$$

$$\psi_{,x} \Big|_{x=a} - \psi_{,x} \Big|_{x=0} = P_y$$

(5-52)

In practice only two of the quantities δ_x, δ_y, P_x, and P_y will be prescribed, and the other two must be determined.

A solution of equations (5-24) and (5-25) satisfying the foregoing boundary conditions is formulated on the basis of the double Fourier series approach (Ref. 5.7) used in Sec. 2.7. The condition (5-49) is satisfied if w is given by equation (2-114). In allowing for elastic rotational constraints in the problem, bending moments will be developed along the sides of the plate. If these edge moments are replaced by an equivalent lateral pressure distribution $q_e(x, y)$ as shown in Fig. 2.12, and q_e is given by equations (2-107) to (2-110), the total lateral load is a combination of $q(x, y)$ and $q_e(x, y)$

$$p(x, y) = q(x, y) + q_e(x, y)$$

(5-53)

where q is the applied load given by equation (2-111).

The condition (5-50) is fulfilled by setting

$$m_{x0} = -\zeta_1 w_{,x} \Big|_{x=0} \qquad m_{xa} = \zeta_2 w_{,x} \Big|_{x=a}$$

$$m_{y0} = -\zeta_3 w_{,y} \Big|_{y=0} \qquad m_{yb} = \zeta_4 w_{,y} \Big|_{y=b}$$

(5-54)

Substituting expressions (2-108) and (2-114) into these relations and equating coefficients of similar trigonometric terms lead to

$$A_n = -\frac{2\pi^2 \zeta_1}{a^3} \sum_{m=1}^{\infty} m w_{mn}$$

$$B_n = \frac{2\pi^2 \zeta_2}{a^3} \sum_{m=1}^{\infty} (-1)^m m w_{mn}$$

(5-55)

▼
▼

$$C_n = -\frac{2\pi^2 \xi_3}{b^3} \sum_{m=1}^{\infty} m w_{mn}$$

$$H_n = \frac{2\pi^2 \xi_4}{b^3} \sum_{m=1}^{\infty} (-1)^m m w_{mn}$$

▼

which give the edge moment coefficients A_i, B_i, C_i, and H_i in terms of deflection coefficients w_{mn}.

The condition (5-52) is satisfied if the force function ψ is taken to be

$$\psi = \frac{P_x y^2}{2b} + \frac{P_y x^2}{2a} + \sum_{m=0}^{\infty} \sum_{n=0}^{\infty} \psi_{mn} \cos \frac{m\pi x}{a} \cos \frac{n\pi y}{b} \qquad (5\text{-}56)$$

Inserting expressions (2-114) and (5-56) into the compatibility relation (5-25) and equating coefficients of like terms, we obtain

$$\psi_{mn} = \frac{a_{mn}}{4} \sum_{k=1}^{\infty} \sum_{l=1}^{\infty} \sum_{r=1}^{\infty} \sum_{s=1}^{\infty} b_{klrs}^{mn} w_{kl} w_{rs} \qquad (5\text{-}57)$$

where

$$a_{mn} = \frac{h}{(n^4/E_1)(a/b)^2 + (m^4/E_2)(b/a)^2 + m^2 n^2 (1/G_{12} - 2\nu_{12}/E_1)}$$

$$b_{klrs}^{mn} = klrs[\delta_{m,(k+r)} + \delta_{m,|k-r|}][\delta_{n,(l+s)} + \delta_{n,|l-s|}] \qquad (5\text{-}58)$$
$$- \tfrac{1}{2}(k^2 s^2 + l^2 r^2)[\delta_{m,(k+r)} - \delta_{m,|k-r|}][\delta_{n,(l+s)} - \delta_{n,|l-s|}]$$

with δ_{ij} being the Kronecker delta symbol. Equation (5-57) relates the coefficients of the force function to those of the deflection.

Introducing equations (2-114), (5-53), and (5-56) into the equilibrium equation (5-24) and equating coefficients of like trigonometric terms yields

$$q_{mn} + k_{mn} = \left(\frac{\pi^4}{a^2 b^2} c_{mn} + \frac{m^2 \pi^2}{a^2 b} P_x + \frac{n^2 \pi^2}{ab^2} P_y\right) w_{mn}$$

$$+ \frac{\pi^4}{4a^2 b^2} \sum_{k=1}^{\infty} \sum_{l=1}^{\infty} \sum_{r=1}^{\infty} \sum_{s=1}^{\infty} d_{klrs}^{mn} \psi_{kl} w_{rs} \qquad (5\text{-}59)$$

where k_{mn} is given by expression (2-110) and where

$$c_{mn} = D_1 m^4 \left(\frac{b}{a}\right)^2 + 2(\nu_{12} D_2 + 2D_3)m^2 n^2 + D_2 n^4 \left(\frac{a}{b}\right)^2$$

$$d_{klrs}^{mn} = 2klrs[\delta_{m,(k+r)} + \delta_{m,(k-r)} - \delta_{m,(r-k)}]$$
$$\cdot [\delta_{n,(l+s)} + \delta_{n,(l-s)} - \delta_{n,(s-l)}] - (l^2 r^2 + k^2 s^2) \qquad (5\text{-}60)$$
$$\cdot [\delta_{m,(r+k)} + \delta_{m,(r-k)} - \delta_{m,(k-r)}]$$
$$\cdot [\delta_{n,(s+l)} + \delta_{n,(s-l)} - \delta_{n,(l-s)}]$$

Substituting equation (5-56) into condition (5-52) and taking into account expressions (2-111) and (5-57) lead to

$$P_x = \frac{E_1^2 h}{E_1 - E_2 v_{12}^2}\left(\frac{b}{a}\delta_x + v_{21}\delta_y\right) + \frac{\pi^2}{a}\sum_{m=1}^{\infty}\sum_{n=1}^{\infty} R_{mn} w_{mn}^2$$

$$P_y = \frac{E_1 E_2 h}{E_1 - E_2 v_{12}^2}\left(\frac{a}{b}\delta_y + v_{12}\delta_x\right) + \frac{\pi^2}{b}\sum_{m=1}^{\infty}\sum_{n=1}^{\infty} S_{mn} w_{mn}^2$$

(5-61)

where

$$R_{mn} = \frac{E_1^2 h}{8(E_1 - E_2 v_{12}^2)}\left(\frac{b}{a}m^2 + \frac{a}{b}v_{21}n^2\right)$$

$$S_{mn} = \frac{E_1 E_2 h}{8(E_1 - E_2 v_{12}^2)}\left(\frac{a}{b}n^2 + \frac{b}{a}v_{12}m^2\right)$$

(5-62)

For the reduction of the foregoing algebraic equations to a system of equations in the final form, we consider the following cases:

Case (a) No clamped edges When all the ζ's are zero or finite, equations (2-110), (5-55), (5-57), and (5-61) may be combined with equation (5-59) to yield a system of cubic equations in deflection coefficients w_{mn}.

$$q_{mn} = \frac{\pi^4}{a^2 b^2} c_{mn} w_{mn} + \frac{2\pi^2 n}{b^3}\left[\zeta_3 \sum_{r=1}^{\infty} r w_{mr} + (-1)^n \zeta_4 \sum_{r=1}^{\infty}(-1)^r r w_{mr}\right]$$

$$+ \frac{2\pi^2 m}{a^3}\left[\zeta_1 \sum_{r=1}^{\infty} r w_{rn} + (-1)^m \zeta_2 \sum_{r=1}^{\infty}(-1)^r r w_{rn}\right]$$

$$+ \frac{m^2 \pi^4}{a^3 b} w_{mn} \sum_{r=1}^{\infty}\sum_{s=1}^{\infty} R_{rs} w_{rs}^2$$

$$+ \frac{n^2 \pi^4}{a b^3} w_{mn} \sum_{r=1}^{\infty}\sum_{s=1}^{\infty} S_{rs} w_{rs}^2 + \frac{\pi^2}{16 a^2 b^2}\sum_{k=0}^{\infty}\sum_{l=0}^{\infty}\sum_{r=1}^{\infty}\sum_{s=1}^{\infty}$$

$$\cdot d_{klrs}^{mn} w_{rs}\left[a_{kl} \sum_{i=1}^{\infty}\sum_{j=1}^{\infty}\sum_{p=1}^{\infty}\sum_{q=1}^{\infty} b_{ijpq}^{kl} w_{ij} w_{pq}\right]$$

(5-63)

Case (b) One or more clamped edges In a case in which one or more ζ's are infinite, the reduction of the problem to one set of equations such as (5-63) cannot be achieved. Let us assume that only the edge at $x = 0$ is clamped. Since ζ_1 approaches infinity, the first of equations (5-55) is to be replaced by

$$\sum_{m=1}^{\infty} m w_{mn} = 0$$

(5-64)

Now it is no longer possible to eliminate A_n from equations (2-110). A combination of equations (2-110), (5-57), (5-59), (5-61), (5-64) and the last three of (5-55) will result in a set of equations for coefficients A_n and w_{mn}. For every additional clamped edge another set of edge-moment coefficients becomes unknowns in the final equations, and an additional set of equations such as (5-64) is available.

Case (c) All clamped edges All the ζ's are infinite in this case. The set of equations which must be solved is of the form

$$\frac{\pi^4}{a^2b^2}C_{mn}W_{mn} - q_{mn} - n[C_m - (-1)^nH_m] - m[A_n - (-1)^mB_n]$$

$$+ \frac{\pi^4}{ab}W_{mn}\sum_{r=1}^{\infty}\sum_{s=1}^{\infty}\left[\frac{m^2}{a^2}R_{rs} + \frac{n^2}{b^2}S_{rs}\right]w_{rs}^2$$

$$+ \frac{\pi^4}{16a^2b^2}\sum_{i=0}^{\infty}\sum_{j=0}^{\infty}\sum_{k=1}^{\infty}\sum_{l=1}^{\infty}d_{ijkl}^{mn}w_{kl}$$

$$\cdot\left[a_{ij}\sum_{p=1}^{\infty}\sum_{q=1}^{\infty}\sum_{r=1}^{\infty}\sum_{s=1}^{\infty}b_{pqrs}^{ij}w_{pq}w_{rs}\right] = 0 \tag{5-65}$$

and

$$\sum_{m=1}^{\infty}mw_{mn} = 0 \qquad \sum_{m=1}^{\infty}(-1)^mmw_{mn} = 0$$

$$\sum_{m=1}^{\infty}nw_{mn} = 0 \qquad \sum_{m=1}^{\infty}(-1)nw_{mn} = 0 \tag{5-66}$$

These equations can be further simplified by solving equations (5-65) for the linear terms in w_{mn} and then substituting these values into equations (5-66). The resulting equations are cubic in w_{mn} and linear in A_i, B_i, C_i, and H_i. The application of the result to an orthogonally stiffened plate which is treated as an equivalent orthotropic plate can be found in the reference cited above.

5.5 ORTHOTROPIC RECTANGULAR PLATE UNDER COMBINED LATERAL AND INPLANE LOADS

Consider an orthotropic plate of length $2a_0$ in the x direction and width $2b_0$ in the y direction with its material axes of symmetry parallel to the edges of the plate and with its fibers parallel to the x axis. The plate is assumed to be simply supported on its edges and subjected to the combined action of uniform transverse pressure q_0 and inplane compressive forces per unit length, n_x in the x direction and n_y in the y direction. The appropriate boundary conditions are

$$w = w_{,xx} = \psi_{,xy} = 0 \qquad \psi_{,yy} = -n_x \qquad \text{at} \quad x = \pm a_0$$

$$w = w_{,yy} = \psi_{,xy} = 0 \qquad \psi_{,xx} = -n_y \qquad \text{at} \quad y = \pm b_0 \tag{5-67}$$

To make the solution more general in its application, the dimensionless parameters are introduced as follows

$$\zeta = \frac{x}{a_0} \qquad \eta = \frac{y}{b_0} \qquad \lambda = \frac{a_0}{b_0} \qquad F = \frac{\psi}{E_1 h^3}$$

$$R = \frac{n_x b_0^2}{E_1 h^3} \qquad k = \frac{n_y}{n_x} \qquad Q = \frac{q_0(2b_0)^4}{E_1 h^4}$$

$$W = \frac{w}{h} \qquad k_1 = \frac{D_3}{D_1} \qquad k_2 = \frac{E_2}{E_1}$$

$$k_3 = 12(1 - \nu_{12}\nu_{21}) \qquad k_4 = \frac{1}{2}\left(\frac{E_2}{G_{12}} - 2\nu_{21}\right)$$

(5-68)

in which ζ, η, F, and Q are defined differently from those in equations (5-26). With these notations equations (5-24) and (5-25) can be written in the dimensionless form

$$W_{,\zeta\zeta\zeta\zeta} + 2\lambda^2 k_1 W_{,\zeta\zeta\eta\eta} + \lambda^4 k_2 W_{,\eta\eta\eta\eta}$$
$$= \tfrac{1}{16}\lambda^4 k_3 Q + \lambda^2 k_3 (W_{,\zeta\zeta} F_{,\eta\eta} + W_{,\eta\eta} F_{,\zeta\zeta} - 2W_{,\zeta\eta} F_{,\zeta\eta}) \quad (5\text{-}69)$$

$$F_{,\zeta\zeta\zeta\zeta} + 2\lambda^2 k_4 F_{,\zeta\zeta\eta\eta} + \lambda^4 k_2 F_{,\eta\eta\eta\eta} = \lambda^2 k_2 [W_{,\zeta\eta}^2 - W_{,\zeta\zeta} W_{,\eta\eta}] \quad (5\text{-}70)$$

Similarly, the boundary conditions (5-67) transform to

$$W = W_{,\zeta\zeta} = F_{,\zeta\eta} = 0 \qquad F_{,\eta\eta} = -R \qquad \text{at} \quad \zeta = \pm 1$$
$$W = W_{,\eta\eta} = F_{,\zeta\eta} = 0 \qquad F_{,\zeta\zeta} = -\lambda^2 kR \qquad \text{at} \quad \eta = \pm 1$$

(5-71)

Now the problem consists in determining W and F so as to satisfy the governing equations (5-69) and (5-70) and the boundary conditions (5-71).

The deflection W and the force function F are assumed to be of the form†
(Refs. 5.8, 5.9)

$$F = -\frac{R}{2}(\eta^2 + k\lambda^2\zeta^2) + \sum_{m=1}^{\infty}\sum_{n=1}^{\infty} F_{mn} X_m(\zeta) Y_n(\eta)$$

$$W = \sum_{p=1, 3, \ldots}^{\infty} \sum_{q=1, 3, \ldots}^{\infty} W_{pq} \cos\frac{p\pi\zeta}{2} \cos\frac{q\pi\eta}{2}$$

(5-72)

where

$$X_m(\zeta) = \frac{\cosh\alpha_m\zeta}{\cosh\alpha_m} - \frac{\cos\alpha_m\zeta}{\cos\alpha_m}$$

$$Y_n(\eta) = \frac{\cosh\alpha_n\eta}{\cosh\alpha_n} - \frac{\cos\alpha_n\eta}{\cos\alpha_n}$$

(5-73)

These functions possess the orthogonality relations

$$\int_{-1}^{+1} X_i X_j \, d\zeta = \int_{-1}^{+1} Y_i Y_j \, d\eta = \begin{cases} 0 & \text{if } i \neq j \\ 2 & \text{if } i = j \end{cases}$$

(5-74)

† The application of this solution should be with care because F and W are even functions in ζ and η.

It is observed that expressions (5-72) satisfy boundary conditions (5-71) except for $F_{,\zeta\eta} = 0$ at $\zeta = \pm 1$, $\eta = \pm 1$. Introduction of the second of expressions (5-72) in this condition yields

$$\tanh \alpha_i + \tan \alpha_i = 0 \qquad (5\text{-}75)$$

whose roots are given in Table 2.1.

Substituting equations (5-72) into (5-69) and (5-70), multiplying the first of the resulting equations by $X_i(\zeta)Y_j(\eta)$ and the second by $\cos(m\pi\zeta/2)\cos(n\pi\eta/2)$, integrating from -1 to $+1$, and using relations (5-74) result in

$$F_{ij}(\alpha_i^4 + \lambda^4 k_2 \alpha_j^4) + \sum_{m=1}^{\infty}\sum_{n=1}^{\infty} 2\lambda^2 k_4 \alpha_m^2 \alpha_n^2 K_1^{im} L_1^{jn} F_{mn}$$

$$- \lambda^4 k_2 \pi^4 \sum_{p=1,3,\ldots}^{\infty} \sum_{q=1,3,\ldots}^{\infty} \sum_{r=1,3,\ldots}^{\infty} \sum_{s=1,3,\ldots}^{\infty} W_{pq} W_{rs}$$

$$\cdot \left[pqrs K_2^{ipr} L_2^{jqs} - p^2 s^2 K_3^{ipr} L_3^{jqs} \right] = 0 \qquad i,j = 1,2,3,\ldots \quad (5\text{-}76)$$

$$W_{mn}\left[m^4 + 2\lambda^2 k_1 m^2 n^2 + \lambda^4 k_2 n^4 - k_3 \tau(\lambda^2 m^2 + \lambda^4 k n^2) \right]$$

$$+ \frac{4}{\pi^2}\lambda^2 k_3 \sum_{p=1,3,\ldots}^{\infty} \sum_{q=1,3,\ldots}^{\infty} \sum_{r=1}^{\infty} \sum_{s=1}^{\infty} W_{pq} F_{rs}$$

$$\cdot \left[p^2 \alpha_s^2 K_4^{mrp} L_5^{nsq} + q^2 \alpha_r^2 K_5^{mrp} L_4^{nsq} + 2pq\alpha_r \alpha_s K_6^{rmp} L_6^{snq} \right]$$

$$= \frac{1}{\pi^4}\lambda^4 k_3 Q_{mn} \qquad\qquad m,n = 1,3,5,\ldots \quad (5\text{-}77)$$

where

$$\tau = \frac{n_x (2b_0)^2}{\pi^2 E_1 h^3}$$

$$Q = \sum_{m=1,3,\ldots}^{\infty} \sum_{n=1,3,\ldots}^{\infty} Q_{mn} \cos\frac{m\pi\zeta}{2} \cos\frac{n\pi\eta}{2}$$

$$K_1^{im} = \frac{1}{2\alpha_m^2} \int_{-1}^{+1} X_i X_m'' \, d\zeta$$

$$K_2^{ipr} = \frac{1}{2} \int_{-1}^{+1} X_i \sin\frac{p\pi\zeta}{2} \sin\frac{r\pi\zeta}{2} \, d\zeta$$

$$K_5^{mrp} = \frac{1}{\alpha_r^2} \int_{-1}^{+1} X_r'' \cos\frac{m\pi\zeta}{2} \cos\frac{p\pi\zeta}{2} \, d\zeta \qquad (5\text{-}78)$$

$$K_3^{ipr} = \frac{1}{2} \int_{-1}^{+1} X_i \cos\frac{p\pi\zeta}{2} \cos\frac{r\pi\zeta}{2} \, d\zeta$$

$$K_4^{mrp} = \int_{-1}^{+1} X_r \cos\frac{m\pi\zeta}{2} \cos\frac{p\pi\zeta}{2} \, d\zeta$$

$$K_6^{mrp} = \frac{1}{\alpha_r} \int_{-1}^{+1} X_r' \cos\frac{m\pi\zeta}{2} \cos\frac{p\pi\zeta}{2} \, d\zeta$$

Taking a finite number of terms in each of the truncated series (5-72) for W and F, equations (5-76) and (5-77) can be solved for the unknown coefficients F_{mn} and W_{pq} in terms of the applied loads q_0, n_x, and n_y, material properties k_1, k_2, k_3, and k_4, and aspect ratio λ. As soon as these coefficients are determined, the deflection and the force function can be found from expressions (5-72). The dimensionless membrane stresses, denoted by σ_ζ^m, σ_η^m, and $\sigma_{\zeta\eta}^m$, may be expressed as

$$\sigma_\zeta^m = 4F_{,\eta\eta} \qquad \sigma_\eta^m = \frac{4}{\lambda^2} F_{,\zeta\zeta} \qquad \sigma_{\zeta\eta}^m = -\frac{4}{\lambda} F_{,\zeta\eta} \qquad (5\text{-}79)$$

and the dimensionless extreme-fiber bending stresses, denoted by σ_ζ^b, σ_η^b, and $\sigma_{\zeta\eta}^b$, as

$$\sigma_\zeta^b = \pm \frac{24}{k_3}\left(\frac{1}{\lambda^2} W_{,\zeta\zeta} + v_{21} W_{,\eta\eta}\right)$$

$$\sigma_\eta^b = \pm \frac{24}{k_3}\left(k_2 W_{,\eta\eta} + \frac{v_{21}}{\lambda^2} W_{,\zeta\zeta}\right) \qquad (5\text{-}80)$$

$$\sigma_{\zeta\eta}^b = \pm \frac{4G_{12}}{\lambda E_1} W_{,\zeta\eta}$$

where

$$\{\sigma_\zeta^m, \sigma_\eta^m, \sigma_{\zeta\eta}^m\} = \frac{(2b_0)^2}{E_1 h^2}\{\sigma_x^m, \sigma_y^m, \sigma_{xy}^m\}$$

$$\{\sigma_\zeta^b, \sigma_\eta^b, \sigma_{\zeta\eta}^b\} = \frac{(2b_0)^2}{E_1 h^2}\{\sigma_x^b, \sigma_y^b, \sigma_{xy}^b\} \qquad (5\text{-}81)$$

Numerical results are presented for glass-epoxy, boron-epoxy and graphite-epoxy plates with elastic constants given in Table 5.4. The uniaxial edge compression ($n_y = 0$) is expressed as the ratio $\beta = n_x/n_{cr}$ with n_{cr} being the critical load in the x direction and the uniform biaxial compression as $\beta = n_x/n_{cr} = n_y/n_{cr}$. The values of n_{cr} are given in Sec. 6.1 but the value of n_x is taken to be not greater than its critical value.

In order to check the convergence of the present series solution, calculations are carried out by taking, respectively, four terms for F and one for W, four for F and four for W, and sixteen for F and nine for W in the series. The number of

Table 5.4 Numerical values of elastic constants

Material	E_2/E_1	G_{12}/E_1	v_{12}
Glass-epoxy	0.3333	0.1667	0.25
Boron-epoxy	0.1000	0.0333	0.22
Graphite-epoxy	0.0250	0.0150	0.25

Table 5.5 Convergence of series solution for the central deflection of a glass-epoxy plate $(\lambda = 1, p_y = 0)$

Number of terms in W		1	4	9
Number of terms in F		4	4	16
Q	β			
50	0.0	2.3122	2.3791	2.4022
50	1.0	3.0433	3.2285	3.2865
150	0.0	3.8701	4.1031	4.2252
150	1.0	4.4726	4.8915	5.0126
250	0.0	4.8688	5.2408	5.3772
250	1.0	5.4294	5.9247	6.1084

terms taken in the series for Q is the same as that for W. It is in practice difficult to obtain a solution with more than nine terms in the series for W. For example, with nine terms in the series for W, nine simultaneous cubic equations, each of which consists of 165 terms after eliminating F, have to be solved for the deflection coefficients W_{pq}. The convergence of the present series solution for the central deflection in the case of a square glass-epoxy plate under the transverse load and the combined action of transverse load and uniaxial inplane compression is illustrated in Table 5.5. A comparison of the last two columns shows that the solution with the first sixteen terms for F and nine terms for W should be adequate for engineering purposes and hence are used in the following numerical results.

The variation of the central deflection w_0 with the transverse load Q is shown in Fig. 5.10 for the uniaxial edge compression $\beta = 1.0$, and for different values of the aspect ratio λ and material properties. For fixed values of Q and λ, the central deflection increases as the ratio E_2/E_1 decreases. This deflection is found to

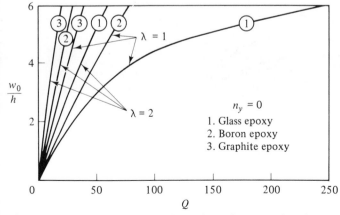

Figure 5.10 Load deflection curves for orthotropic rectangular plate under transverse and inplane loads $(\beta = 1.0)$.

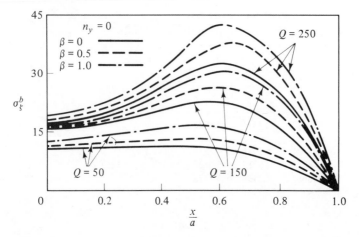

Figure 5.11 Distribution of bending stress along the x axis of a square glass epoxy plate.

increase with λ. Figure 5.11 shows the distribution of the bending stress σ_ζ^b along the x axis for a square glass-epoxy plate with different transverse and inplane loads. The effect of the membrane action on the bending stress is very significant for large values of Q. Unlike in the case of linear bending, the maximum bending stress for large values of Q does not occur at the center of the plate but in some region between the center and the edges. Such behavior, called the development of boundary layers, has also been observed in the case of isotropic plates. The distribution of the membrane stress σ_ζ^m in the filament direction along the transverse center line $(x = 0)$ is shown in Fig. 5.12 for a square glass-epoxy plate. It is found that, for given values of the transverse and inplane loads, the largest value of

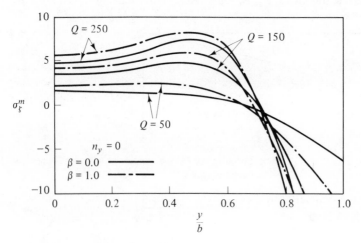

Figure 5.12 Distribution of membrane stress along the y axis for different transverse and inplane loads in a square glass epoxy plate.

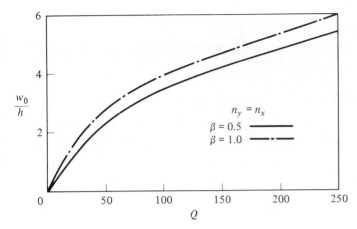

Figure 5.13 Load-deflection curves for a square glass epoxy plate under transverse load and uniform biaxial compression.

this stress occurs at the middle of the longitudinal side. In the central and boundary regions, the stress increases in magnitude with the transverse load for a given n_x and increases with the inplane load for a given Q. The deflection at the center of a glass-epoxy plate is shown in Fig. 5.13 for different values of transverse loads and uniform biaxial compressions. It may be observed that the deflections at the center of a square glass-epoxy plate shown in Figs. 5.10 and 5.13 for $\beta = 1.0$ are identical with each other. This arises from the fact that the buckling load in the case of biaxial compression is one-half of that in the case of uniaxial compression.

5.6 CLAMPED ORTHOTROPIC ELLIPTICAL PLATE UNDER UNIFORM TRANSVERSE LOAD

Consider an elliptical plate of rectilinear orthotropy with its filaments parallel to the x axis as shown in Fig. 3.10. The axes of the plate are $2a$ in the x direction and $2b$ in the y direction. Either $2a$ or $2b$ may be the major axis. If the plate is rigidly clamped along its boundary, the appropriate boundary conditions as in Sec. 3.8 may be written as

$$u^\circ = v^\circ = w = w_{,x} = w_{,y} = 0 \quad \text{along} \quad 1 - \frac{x^2}{a^2} - \frac{y^2}{b^2} = 0 \quad (5\text{-}82)$$

Letting w_0 be the deflection at the plate center and introducing the following nondimensional parameters

$$U = \frac{12au^\circ}{h^2} \qquad V = \frac{12av^\circ}{h^2}$$

▼

$$W = 2\sqrt{3}\,\frac{w}{h} \qquad Q = 24\sqrt{3}\,\mu\,\frac{q_0\,a^4}{E_2\,h^4}$$

$$K_1 = \frac{E_1}{E_2} \qquad K_2 = \frac{\mu G_{12}}{E_2} \qquad K_3 = v_{12} + K_2 \tag{5-83}$$

$$K_4 = v_{12} + 2K_2 \qquad \mu = 1 - v_{12}v_{21}$$

the governing equations (1-109) to (1-111) for the moderately large deflection of the plate under uniformly distributed load of intensity q_0 can be written in the nondimensional form

$$K_1 U_{,\zeta\zeta} + \lambda^2 K_2 U_{,\eta\eta} + \lambda K_3 V_{,\zeta\eta} + W_{,\zeta}(K_1 W_{,\zeta\zeta} + \lambda^2 K_2 W_{,\eta\eta})$$
$$+ \lambda^2 K_3 W_{,\eta} W_{,\zeta\eta} = 0 \tag{5-84}$$

$$\lambda^2 V_{,\eta\eta} + K_2 V_{,\zeta\zeta} + \lambda K_3 U_{,\zeta\eta} + \lambda W_{,\eta}(\lambda^2 W_{,\eta\eta} + K_2 W_{,\zeta\zeta})$$
$$+ \lambda K_3 W_{,\zeta} W_{,\zeta\eta} = 0 \tag{5-85}$$

$$K_1 W_{,\zeta\zeta\zeta\zeta} + 2\lambda^2 K_4 W_{,\zeta\zeta\eta\eta} + \lambda^4 W_{,\eta\eta\eta\eta} = Q$$
$$+ K_1 W_{,\zeta\zeta}[U_{,\zeta} + \tfrac{1}{2}W_{,\zeta}^2 + \lambda v_{21} V_{,\eta} + \tfrac{1}{2}\lambda^2 v_{21} W_{,\eta}^2]$$
$$+ \lambda^2 W_{,\eta\eta}[\lambda V_{,\eta} + \tfrac{1}{2}\lambda^2 W_{,\eta}^2 + v_{12} U_{,\zeta} + \tfrac{1}{2}v_{12} W_{,\zeta}^2]$$
$$+ 2\lambda K_2 W_{,\zeta\eta}(\lambda U_{,\eta} + V_{,\zeta} + \lambda W_{,\zeta} W_{,\eta}) \tag{5-86}$$

in which ζ, η, and λ are given in equations (5-26). Similarly, the boundary conditions (5-82) transform to

$$U = V = W = W_{,\zeta} = W_{,\eta} = 0 \qquad \text{along} \qquad 1 - \zeta^2 - \eta^2 = 0 \tag{5-87}$$

It seems difficult to obtain an exact solution of equations (5-84) to (5-86) satisfying boundary conditions (5-87). An approximate solution is thus formulated by the perturbation method (Ref. 5.10) as in Sec. 5.1. The parameters Q, U, V, and W are expressed as perturbation series in the nondimensional central deflection W_0 ($= w_0/h$). For the plate having a twofold symmetry, these parameters are assumed to be of the form

$$Q = \sum_{n=1,\,3,\,\ldots}^{\infty} q_n W_0^n \qquad W = \sum_{n=1,\,3,\,\ldots}^{\infty} w_n(\zeta, \eta)W_0^n$$

$$U = \sum_{n=2,\,4,\,\ldots}^{\infty} u_n(\zeta, \eta)W_0^n \qquad V = \sum_{n=2,\,4,\,\ldots}^{\infty} v_n(\zeta, \eta)W_0^n \tag{5-88}$$

It follows that at the center of the plate

$$w_1(0, 0) = 1 \qquad w_3(0, 0) = w_5(0, 0) = \cdots = 0 \tag{5-89}$$

Substituting equations (5-88) into (5-84) to (5-87) and equating the like powers of W_0 leads to an infinite set of linear differential equations and boundary conditions from which q_i, w_i, u_i, and v_i can be successively determined.

Equating the coefficients of W_0 results in the linear equation

$$K_1 w_{1,\zeta\zeta\zeta\zeta} + 2\lambda^2 K_4 w_{1,\zeta\zeta\eta\eta} + \lambda^4 w_{1,\eta\eta\eta\eta} = q_1 \tag{5-90}$$

and the boundary conditions

$$w_1 = w_{1,\zeta} = w_{1,\eta} = 0 \quad \text{along} \quad 1 - \zeta^2 - \eta^2 = 0 \tag{5-91}$$

These are nothing but the governing differential equation and boundary conditions for the small deflection of a clamped elliptical plate, and the solution is sought in the form

$$w_1 = (1 - \zeta^2 - \eta^2)^2 \tag{5-92}$$

which satisfies the boundary conditions (5-91), the requirement of symmetry, and the first of conditions (5-89). Inserting this solution in equation (5-90), we obtain

$$q_1 = 24K_1 + 16\lambda^2 K_4 + 24\lambda^4 \tag{5-93}$$

By equating the coefficients of W_0^2, the following set of simultaneous equations for u_2 and v_2 is obtained

$$K_1 u_{2,\zeta\zeta} + \lambda^2 K_2 u_{2,\eta\eta} + \lambda K_3 v_{2,\zeta\eta}$$
$$= -w_{1,\zeta}(K_1 w_{1,\zeta\zeta} + \lambda^2 K_2 w_{1,\eta\eta}) - \lambda^2 K_3 w_{1,\eta} w_{1,\zeta\eta} \tag{5-94}$$

$$\lambda^2 v_{2,\eta\eta} + K_2 v_{2,\zeta\zeta} + \lambda K_3 u_{2,\zeta\eta}$$
$$= -\lambda w_{1,\eta}(\lambda^2 w_{1,\eta\eta} + K_2 w_{1,\zeta\zeta}) - \lambda K_3 w_{1,\zeta} w_{1,\zeta\eta} \tag{5-95}$$

The appropriate boundary conditions for u_2 and v_2 are

$$u_2 = v_2 = 0 \quad \text{along} \quad 1 - \zeta^2 - \eta^2 = 0 \tag{5-96}$$

These conditions are satisfied by taking

$$u_2 = \zeta(1 - \zeta^2 - \eta^2)(A_1 + A_2\zeta^2 + A_3\eta^2 + A_4\zeta^4 + A_5\eta^4 + A_6\zeta^2\eta^2)$$
$$v_2 = \eta(1 - \zeta^2 - \eta^2)(B_1 + B_2\zeta^2 + B_3\eta^2 + B_4\zeta^4 + B_5\eta^4 + B_6\zeta^2\eta^2) \tag{5-97}$$

which satisfy the requirement that, $u_2 = 0$ along $\zeta = 0$ and $v_2 = 0$ along $\eta = 0$. Substituting u_2 and v_2 from expressions (5-97) and w_1 from expression (5-92) into equations (5-94) and (5-95) and equating the coefficients of $\zeta, \eta, \zeta^3, \eta^3, \zeta^2\eta, \zeta\eta^2, \zeta^5, \eta^5, \zeta^4\eta, \zeta\eta^4, \zeta^3\eta^2$, and $\zeta^2\eta^3$ to zero yields twelve linear algebraic equations which can be solved for twelve coefficients A_i and B_i. It may be observed that coefficients of $\zeta^2, \eta^2, \zeta\eta, \zeta^4$, etc., are identically zero.

By equating the coefficients of W_0^3, the following differential equation for w_3 is obtained

$$K_1 w_{3,\zeta\zeta\zeta\zeta} + 2\lambda^2 K_4 w_{3,\zeta\zeta\eta\eta} + \lambda^2 w_{3,\eta\eta\eta\eta} = q_3$$
$$+ K_1 w_{1,\zeta\zeta}[u_{2,\zeta} + \tfrac{1}{2}(w_{1,\zeta})^2 + \lambda v_{21} v_{2,\eta} + \tfrac{1}{2}\lambda^2 v_{21}(w_{1,\eta})^2]$$
$$+ \lambda^2 w_{1,\eta\eta}[\lambda v_{2,\eta} + \tfrac{1}{2}\lambda^2 (w_{1,\eta})^2 + v_{12} u_{2,\zeta} + \tfrac{1}{2} v_{12}(w_{1,\zeta})^2]$$
$$+ 2\lambda K_2 w_{1,\zeta\eta}(\lambda u_{2,\eta} + v_{2,\zeta} + \lambda w_{1,\zeta} w_{1,\eta}) \tag{5-98}$$

and the associated boundary conditions are

$$w_3 = w_{3,\zeta} = w_{3,\eta} = 0 \qquad \text{along} \quad 1 - \zeta^2 - \eta^2 = 0 \qquad (5\text{-}99)$$

An approximate solution of equation (5-98) satisfying the boundary conditions (5-99), the symmetry conditions, and the second of conditions (5-89), may be chosen as

$$w_3 = (1 - \zeta^2 - \eta^2)^2 (C_1 \zeta^2 + C_2 \eta^2 + C_3 \zeta^4 + C_4 \eta^4 + C_5 \zeta^2 \eta^2$$
$$+ C_6 \zeta^6 + C_7 \eta^6 + C_8 \zeta^4 \eta^2 + C_9 \zeta^2 \eta^4) \quad (5\text{-}100)$$

Since the function w_1, u_2, and v_2 are given by expressions (5-92) and (5-97), substituting these functions and expression (5-100) for w_3 into equation (5-98) and equating like powers of ζ and η, we may generate a set of ten linear algebraic equations which can be solved for the unknown coefficients C_i and q_3.

Higher-order approximations can be obtained similarly, but the first three successive approximations are taken to be the solution of the present boundary-value problem. Therefore, expressions (5-88) are approximated by

$$Q = q_1 W_0 + q_3 W_0^3 \qquad U = u_2 W_0^2$$
$$V = v_2 W_0^2 \qquad W = w_1 W_0 + w_3 W_0^3 \qquad (5\text{-}101)$$

The nondimensional form of membrane and extreme-fiber bending stresses can be written as

$$\sigma_\zeta^m = \frac{K_1}{12\mu\lambda^2} [U_{,\zeta} + \lambda v_{21} V_{,\eta} + \tfrac{1}{2} W_{,\zeta}^2 + \tfrac{1}{2}\lambda^2 v_{21} W_{,\eta}^2]$$

$$\sigma_\eta^m = \frac{1}{12\mu\lambda^2} [\lambda V_{,\eta} + v_{12} U_{,\zeta} + \tfrac{1}{2}\lambda^2 W_{,\eta}^2 + \tfrac{1}{2} v_{12} W_{,\zeta}^2] \qquad (5\text{-}102)$$

$$\sigma_{\zeta\eta}^m = \frac{K_2}{12\mu\lambda^2} (\lambda U_{,\eta} + V_{,\zeta} + \lambda W_{,\zeta} W_{,\eta})$$

and

$$\sigma_\zeta^b = \frac{\sqrt{3} K_1}{12\mu\lambda^2} (W_{,\zeta\zeta} + \lambda^2 v_{21} W_{,\eta\eta})$$

$$\sigma_\eta^b = \frac{\sqrt{3}}{12\mu\lambda^2} (\lambda^2 W_{,\eta\eta} + v_{12} W_{,\zeta\zeta}) \qquad (5\text{-}103)$$

$$\sigma_{\zeta\eta}^b = \frac{\sqrt{3} K_2}{6\mu\lambda} W_{,\zeta\eta}$$

where

$$(\sigma_\zeta^m, \sigma_\eta^m, \sigma_{\zeta\eta}^m) = \frac{b^2}{E_2 h^2} (\sigma_x^m, \sigma_y^m, \sigma_{xy}^m)$$

$$(\sigma_\zeta^b, \sigma_\eta^b, \sigma_{\zeta\eta}^b) = \frac{b^2}{E_2 h^2} (\sigma_x^b, \sigma_y^b, \sigma_{xy}^b) \qquad (5\text{-}104)$$

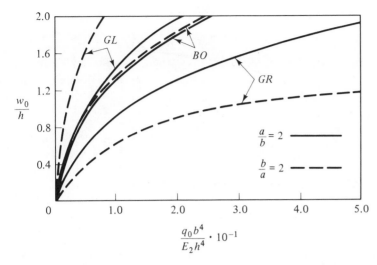

Figure 5.14 Relationship between load and central deflection for an elliptical plate with filaments parallel to the major and minor axis respectively.

The numerical calculations are carried for an elliptical plate having the ratio of major to minor axis of $2 : 1$. The major axis may be either in the x direction or in the y direction. The elastic constants of the glass-epoxy, boron-epoxy, and graphite-epoxy composite materials used in calculation are given in Table 5.2 except for taking $G_{12}/E_2 = 0.6$ for a graphite-epoxy plate. The variation of central deflection with uniform lateral pressure for an elliptical plate with filaments parallel to the x axis is shown in Fig. 5.14 for different material properties. In this figure the glass-epoxy, boron-epoxy, and graphite-epoxy plates are represented by GL, BO, and GR respectively. The value of the load parameter $q_0 b^4/E_2 h^4$ for the plate with filaments parallel to the minor axis ($b/a = 2$) is that obtained from the dashed curves and then multiplied by the factor 10^{-2}. It may be observed that the bending rigidity of a plate with filaments parallel to the minor axis ($b/a = 2$) is much higher than that parallel to the major axis ($a/b = 2$). In the case of an isotropic plate the present solution is in good agreement with that given by the Ritz method in Sec. 3.8 but the results are not presented herein. In Fig. 5.15 the central bending and membrane stresses in the direction of the major axis (x axis) increase rapidly with the deflection, whereas these stresses in the direction of the minor axis simply change slightly. Figure 5.16 indicates that, at the ends of the major axis of the elliptical plate, the bending and membrane stresses in the direction of the major axis (x axis) increase rapidly with the deflection and that, at the ends of the minor axis, these stresses in the direction of the minor axis are slightly affected. The stresses at the center and at the ends of major and minor axes of glass-epoxy and boron-epoxy plates are graphically presented in Ref. 5.10. Based on these results it may be concluded that the central bending and membrane stresses in the direction of the major axis (x axis) increase with the tensile modulus in the filament direction whereas these stresses in the direction of the minor axis change slightly.

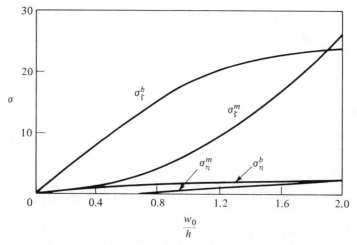

Figure 5.15 Membrane and extreme-fiber bending stresses at the center of an elliptical graphite-epoxy plate with filaments parallel to the major axis.

Similarly, at the ends of the minor axis (y axis) the stresses in the direction of the minor axis decrease with increasing the tensile modulus in the filament direction, but the stresses in the direction parallel to the major axis are slightly affected. Again, at the ends of the major axis, the increase in the tensile modulus in the filament direction results in an increase in the bending and membrane stresses in the direction of the major axis (x axis) and a decrease in the stresses parallel to the

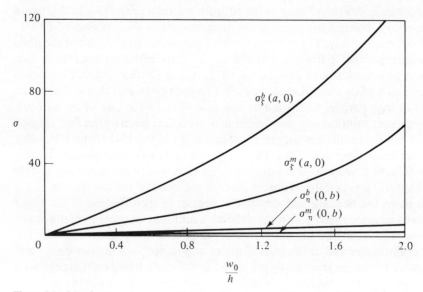

Figure 5.16 Membrane and extreme-fiber bending stresses at the ends of the major and minor axes in an elliptical graphite-epoxy plate with filaments parallel to the major axis.

minor axis. This is to be expected in view of the fact that the pressure required to produce a given central deflection is larger for a plate with high-tensile modulus in the direction of the major axis than for that of a low-modulus plate.

5.7 ORTHOTROPIC TRIANGULAR PLATE UNDER UNIFORM LATERAL LOAD

Consider a thin elastic plate of thickness h in the form of a right triangle with legs of length a and b as shown in Fig. 5.17. The plate is subjected to a uniformly distributed load q_0 and made of rectilinearly orthotropic material with elastic axes of symmetry parallel to the axes of coordinates. If the edges of the plate are clamped and free from the inplane boundary forces, these boundary conditions are

$$w = w_{,x} = N_x = N_{xy} = 0 \qquad \text{at} \quad x = 0$$

$$w = w_{,y} = N_y = N_{xy} = 0 \qquad \text{at} \quad y = 0 \qquad \qquad (5\text{-}105)$$

$$w = w_{,n} = N_n = N_{ns} = 0 \qquad \text{at} \quad 1 - \frac{x}{a} - \frac{y}{b} = 0$$

in which n and s denote the outward normal and tangential directions at the inclined face and in which N_n and N_{ns} can be expressed in terms of N_x, N_y, and N_{xy} by the use of conditions of statics.

The appropriate differential equations governing the large deflections of the boundary-value problem are given by equations (5-24) and (5-25), and written in the form

$$L_1(w, \psi) = w_{,xxxx} + 2k_1 w_{,xxyy} + k_2 w_{,yyyy}$$

$$- \frac{1}{D_1}(q_0 + w_{,xx}\psi_{,yy} + w_{,yy}\psi_{,xx} - 2w_{,xy}\psi_{,xy}) = 0 \qquad (5\text{-}106)$$

$$L_2(w, \psi) = \psi_{,xxxx} + 2k_4 \psi_{,xxyy} + k_2 \psi_{,yyyy}$$

$$- E_2 h[(w_{,xy})^2 - w_{,xx}w_{,yy}] = 0 \qquad (5\text{-}107)$$

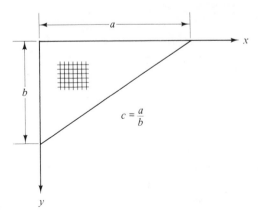

Figure 5.17 Geometry and elastic directions of right triangular plate.

in which ψ is the force function and k_1, k_2, and k_4 are elastic constants defined in equations (5-68).

An approximate solution of equations (5-106) and (5-107) associated with boundary conditions (5-105) is formulated by the Galerkin method (Ref. 5.11). The boundary conditions (5-105) are satisfied by taking

$$w = w_c f(x, y) \qquad \psi = \psi_c f(x, y) \tag{5-108}$$

where w_c is the deflection at the centroid of the plate and ψ_c is the undetermined constant and where

$$f(x, y) = x^2 y^2 \left(1 - \frac{x}{a} - \frac{y}{b}\right)^2 \tag{5-109}$$

This function appears to represent the fundamental-mode shape of the deflected middle surface of the plate because the deflection vanishes on the boundary, retains its sign throughout, and possesses a maximum at the central portion of the plate.

The Galerkin technique requires

$$\int_0^b \int_0^{a(b-y)/b} L_2(w, \psi) f(x, y) \, dx \, dy = 0 \tag{5-110}$$

$$\int_0^b \int_0^{a(b-y)/b} L_1(w, \psi) f(x, y) \, dx \, dy = 0 \tag{5-111}$$

Inserting equations (5-107) to (5-109) into (5-110) and performing the indicated integration, we obtain

$$\psi_c = -\frac{1}{4 \cdot 7 \cdot 11 \cdot 13} \frac{E_2 b^4 c^2}{2(1 + k_4 c^2 + k_2 c^4)} w_c^2 \tag{5-112}$$

where $c = a/b$. With this relation in mind we evaluate the integral (5-111). An equally laborious calculation leads to

$$\alpha_1 D_1 w_c + \alpha_2 E_2 h w_c^3 = \alpha_3 q_0 \tag{5-113}$$

where

$$\alpha_1 = 4d(1 + k_1 c^2 + k_2 c^4)$$
$$\alpha_2 = [8d(1 + k_4 c^2 + k_2 c^4)]^{-1} \tag{5-114}$$
$$\alpha_3 = \frac{5}{4} c^2 d \qquad d = \frac{7 \cdot 11 \cdot 13}{b^4 c^4}$$

The formula (5-113) is in full agreement with the result obtained on page 388 of Ref. 4.19 for the linear case.

The relationship between uniform transverse load and deflection w_c at the plate center of gravity is shown in Fig. 5.18 for a right triangular plate. The elastic constants of two orthotropic materials and an isotropic material are presented in Table 5.6. The solid curves are given by equation (5-113) for a loosely clamped plate. In the range of $w_c/h < 2$, the difference between the values of the deflection

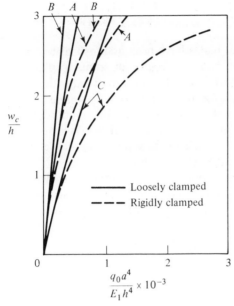

Figure 5.18 Load-deflection curves for clamped right triangular plates with $c = 1$.

w_c for a given q_0 obtained from linear and nonlinear theories does not exceed 7 percent for the isotropic case with $c = 1$, and the percentage becomes notably smaller for other values of c and some orthotropic materials. This unusual behavior arises partly from a strong influence of the edge conditions on the generation of membrane stresses in the triangular plate. That is, the membrane stresses increase considerably more slowly with the distance from the free movable contour of the plate than from the corresponding immovable edges. The dashed curves are obtained from equation (6-154) for a rigidly clamped orthotropic right triangular plate which will be discussed in Sec. 6.11. Therefore, the deflections of the plate are greatly influenced by the membrane boundary conditions. The present result in the large-deflection regime, however, will be improved by taking more terms for the force function as discussed on page 43.

Table 5.6 Elastic properties of plate materials

Case	Material	E_1	E_2	G_{12}	v_{12}	v_{21}
A	Plywood	1×10^5	0.5×10^5	0.1×10^5	0.05	0.025
B	Epoxy resin	28×10^5	2.24×10^5	2.24×10^5	0.2	0.016
C	Isotropic	1×10^5	1×10^5	G	0.3	0.3

Case	E_2/E_1	D_3/D_1	$(E_2/G_{12}) - 2v_{21}$
A	0.5	0.223	5
B	0.08	0.176	0.968
C	1	1	2

5.8 CYLINDRICALLY ORTHOTROPIC CIRCULAR PLATE SUBJECTED TO UNIFORMLY DISTRIBUTED LOAD

In the foregoing sections the materials of plates have been assumed to be rectilinearly orthotropic. In the orthotropic case a circular or annular plate of thickness h is generally composed of cylindrically orthotropic material with radial planes of elastic symmetry passing through the anisotropic axis. Customarily, the axis of anisotropy is taken to be the z axis of the system of cylindrical coordinates r, θ, z passing through the center of the plate and the x or polar axis is arbitrarily directed in the middle plane. Consequently, all infinitesimally small elements $hr\, dr\, d\theta$ as shown in Fig. 3.1 have identical elastic properties.

Let us consider a cylindrically orthotropic plate of radius a under the combined action of distributed load of intensity $q(r)$ and a single concentrated load P applied at the center. In the case of rotationally axisymmetric deformations,† stresses and displacements are independent of the polar angle θ. In the absence of body forces, the inplane force equilibrium requires

$$(rN_r)_{,r} - N_\theta = 0 \tag{5-115}$$

the moment equilibrium gives

$$(rM_r)_{,r} - M_\theta - rQ_r = 0 \tag{5-116}$$

and the transverse equilibrium of a central circular portion with radius r yields

$$rQ_r + rN_r w_{,r} + \frac{P}{2\pi} + \int_0^r rq(r)\, dr = 0 \tag{5-117}$$

From equations (3-10), the strains in the radial and tangential directions are

$$\varepsilon_r^\circ = u_{r,r} + \tfrac{1}{2}w_{,r}^2 \qquad \varepsilon_\theta^\circ = \frac{u_r}{r} \tag{5-118}$$

It is observed that equations (5-115) and (5-116) are the same as equations (4-211) and (4-214). By the generalized Hooke's law the inplane strains are related to the inplane forces by

$$\varepsilon_r^\circ = \frac{1}{E_r h} N_r - \frac{v_{\theta r}}{E_\theta h} N_\theta$$

$$\varepsilon_\theta^\circ = \frac{1}{E_\theta h} N_\theta - \frac{v_{r\theta}}{E_r h} N_r \tag{5-119}$$

The bending moments are

$$M_r = -D_r\left(w_{,rr} + \frac{v_{\theta r}}{r} w_{,r} \right)$$

$$M_\theta = -D_\theta\left(v_{r\theta} w_{,rr} + \frac{1}{r} w_{,r} \right) \tag{5-120}$$

---

† Governing differential equations and basic relations for general deformation of cylindrically orthotropic plates will be presented in Sec. 6.4.

where D_r and D_θ are bending rigidities given by

$$D_r = \frac{E_r h^3}{12(1 - v_{r\theta} v_{\theta r})} \qquad D_\theta = \frac{E_\theta h^3}{12(1 - v_{r\theta} v_{\theta r})} \tag{5-121}$$

A combination of equations (5-116) and (5-117) leads to

$$M_\theta - (rM_r)_{,r} = rN_r w_{,r} + \frac{P}{2\pi} + \int_0^r rq(r)\, dr \tag{5-122}$$

Eliminating ε_r°, ε_θ°, and u_r from equations (5-118) and (5-119), and taking into account equation (5-115), we obtain the equation of compatibility

$$[r(rN_r)_{,r}]_{,r} - k^2 N_r = -\tfrac{1}{2} E_\theta h w_{,r}^2 \tag{5-123}$$

where

$$k^2 = \frac{E_\theta}{E_r} = \frac{v_{\theta r}}{v_{r\theta}} \tag{5-124}$$

In view of equations (5-118) and (5-119) the radial displacement u_r can be expressed as

$$u_r = \frac{r}{E_\theta h}(N_\theta - v_{\theta r} N_r) \tag{5-125}$$

Equations (5-115), (5-122), and (5-123) constitute a system of equations governing the axisymmetrical large deflection of a cylindrically orthotropic plate. These equations will be solved by the perturbation method (Ref. 5.12) in conjunction with appropriate boundary conditions for the case of a uniform lateral pressure q_0.

In the general case of elastically built-in edge and radial-displacement elastic resistance of the support, the boundary conditions are

$$w = 0 \qquad N_r = -\xi_\alpha u_r \qquad M_r = -\xi_\beta w_{,r} \qquad \text{at} \quad r = a \tag{5-126}$$

In these expressions ξ_α and ξ_β are elastic coefficients of radial-displacement and rotational edge restraints, respectively. If the plate is rigidly clamped along its edge, then

$$u_r = w = w_{,r} = 0 \qquad \text{at} \quad r = a \tag{5-127}$$

Defining the nondimensional parameters as

$$\rho = \frac{r}{a} \qquad \delta = \frac{w}{h} \qquad \delta_0 = \frac{w(0)}{h} \qquad \omega = \frac{q_0 a^4}{2D_r h}$$

$$n_r = \frac{a^2}{D_r} N_r \qquad n_\theta = \frac{a^2}{D_r} N_\theta \qquad \tau = \frac{E_\theta h a u_r}{D_r} \tag{5-128}$$

equations (5-115), (5-122), and (5-123) transform to

$$n_\theta = n_r + \rho n_{r,\,\rho} \tag{5-129}$$

$$\rho(\rho\delta_{,\rho\rho})_{,\rho} - k^2\delta_{,\rho} = \rho^3\omega + \rho^2 n_r\delta_{,\rho} \tag{5-130}$$

$$[\rho(\rho n_r)_{,\rho}]_{,\rho} - k^2 n_r + c^2\delta_{,\rho}^2 = 0 \tag{5-131}$$

where

$$c^2 = 6(k^2 - v_{\theta r}^2) \tag{5-132}$$

Similarly equation (5-125) can be written as

$$\tau = \rho n_{r,\,\rho} + (1 - v_{\theta r})n_r \tag{5-133}$$

and boundary conditions as

$$\delta = \delta_{,\rho} = \tau = 0 \qquad \text{at} \quad \rho = 1 \tag{5-134}$$

In the application of the perturbation method to obtaining an approximate solution of the boundary value problem, we write

$$\omega = \sum_{m=1,\,3,\,\ldots}^{\infty} \omega_m \delta_0^m \qquad \delta = \sum_{m=1,\,3,\,\ldots}^{\infty} \delta_m(\rho)\delta_0^m$$

$$n_r = \sum_{m=2,\,4,\,\ldots}^{\infty} \alpha_m(\rho)\delta_0^m \qquad n_\theta = \sum_{m=2,\,4,\,\ldots}^{\infty} \beta_m(\rho)\delta_0^m \tag{5-135}$$

It requires that

$$\delta_1(0) = 1 \qquad \delta_3(0) = \delta_5(0) = \cdots = 0 \tag{5-136}$$

Substituting expressions (5-135) into equations (5-129) to (5-131) and boundary conditions (5-134), and equating the coefficients of δ_0 lead to

$$\rho(\rho\delta_{1,\,\rho\rho})_{,\,\rho} - k^2\delta_{1,\,\rho} = \rho^3\omega_1 \tag{5-137}$$

$$\delta_1(1) = \delta_{1,\,\rho}(1) = \delta_{1,\,\rho}(0) = 0 \tag{5-138}$$

The solution of this system is

$$\delta_1 = \frac{1}{3-k}[3 - k - 4\rho^{k+1} + (k+1)\rho^4]$$

$$\omega_1 = 4(k+1)(k+3) \tag{5-139}$$

which also satisfies the first condition in expressions (5-136). It may be noticed that expression (5-139) is the solution for the small deflection of a clamped cylindrically orthotropic circular plate given on page 371 of Ref. 4.19.

By equating the coefficients of δ_0^2 we find

$$[\rho(\rho\alpha_2)_{,\rho}]_{,\rho} - k^2\alpha_2 + c^2(\delta_{1,\,\rho})^2 = 0 \tag{5-140}$$

$$\alpha_{2,\,\rho}(1) + (1 - v_{\theta r})\alpha_2(1) = 0 \tag{5-141}$$

and

$$\beta_2(\rho) = \alpha_2(\rho) + \rho\alpha_{2,\rho}(\rho) \tag{5-142}$$

in which the boundary condition (5-141) follows from equations (5-128) and (5-133), and the last expression from equation (5-129). A solution of equation (5-140) satisfying the condition (5-141) may be expressed as

$$\alpha_2 = A_1 \left[-A_2\rho^{k-1} + \frac{\rho^6}{49 - k^2} - \frac{\rho^{k+2}}{4(k+2)} + \frac{\rho^{2k}}{(k+1)(3k+1)} \right] \tag{5-143}$$

where

$$A_1 = - \left[\frac{4c(1+k)}{3-k} \right]^2$$

$$\tag{5-144}$$

$$A_2 = \frac{1}{k - v_{\theta r}} \left[\frac{7 - v_{\theta r}}{49 - k^2} - \frac{k + 4 - v_{\theta r}}{4(k+2)} + \frac{2k + 1 - v_{\theta r}}{(k+1)(3k+1)} \right]$$

By equating the coefficients of δ_0^3 the following equation and boundary conditions are obtained

$$\rho(\rho\delta_{3,\rho\rho})_{,\rho} - k^2\delta_{3,\rho} = \rho^2(\rho\omega_3 + \alpha_2\delta_{1,\rho}) \tag{5-145}$$

$$\delta_3(1) = \delta_{3,\rho}(1) = \delta_{3,\rho}(0) = 0 \tag{5-146}$$

whose solution is

$$\delta_3 = \frac{384(k+1)^3(k^2 - v_{\theta r}^2)}{(k-3)^4}$$

$$\cdot \left\{ B_1\rho^{k+1} - (k-3)\rho^4 \left[C_1\left(\rho^{k+1} + \frac{4}{k-3} \right) \right. \right.$$

$$+ C_2\left(\rho^{2k-2} + \frac{k+1}{k+3} \right) + C_3\left(\rho^8 - \frac{k-1}{k-3} \right) + C_4\left(\rho^{k+5} + \frac{8}{k-3} \right)$$

$$\left. \left. + C_5\left(\rho^{2k+2} + \frac{k+5}{k-3} \right) + C_6\left(\rho^{3k-1} + \frac{2k+2}{k-3} \right) \right] \right\} \tag{5-147}$$

$$\omega_3 = 4B_2(9 - k^2)$$

in which B_i and C_j are constants given by

$$C_1 = \frac{A_2}{8(k+2)(k+5)} \qquad C_2 = -\frac{A_2}{2(k+1)(3k^2 + 4k + 1)}$$

$$C_3 = -\frac{1}{12(k^2 - 49)(k^2 - 121)}$$

$$C_4 = \frac{k^2 - 4k - 57}{64(k+2)(k+4)(k+9)(k^2 - 49)}$$

$$C_5 = -\frac{3k^2 + 8k + 9}{8(k + 1)(k + 2)(k + 3)(3k + 1)(3k^2 + 20k + 25)} \quad \blacktriangle$$

$$C_6 = \frac{1}{12(k + 1)^2(3k + 1)(2k^2 + 3k + 1)}$$

$$B_1 = C_1(k + 1) + 2C_2(k - 1) + 8C_3 + C_4(k + 5) \qquad \text{(5-148)}$$
$$+ 2C_5(k + 1) + C_6(3k - 1) \quad \blacktriangle$$

$$B_2 = \frac{384(k + 1)^3(v_{\theta r}^2 - k^2)}{(k - 3)^4}$$

$$\cdot [4C_1 + C_2(k + 1) - C_3(k - 11) + 8C_4 + C_5(k + 5) + 2C_6(k + 1)]$$

As in the foregoing section the present solution is approximated by

$$\omega = \omega_1 \delta_0 + \omega_3 \delta_0^3 \qquad \delta = \delta_1 \delta_0 + \delta_3 \delta_0^3$$
$$n_r = \alpha_2 \delta_0^2 \qquad n_\theta = \beta_2 \delta_0^2 \qquad \text{(5-149)}$$

In view of expression (5-128) the load is related to the central deflection by

$$\frac{q_0 a^4}{D_r h} = 2(\omega_1 \delta_0 + \omega_3 \delta_0^3) \qquad \text{(5-150)}$$

in which ω_1 and ω_3 are given in equations (5-139) and (5-147).

In the case of $k < 1$ or $E_\theta < E_r$, the center is a singular point brought about by the anisotropy of the material. Due to the terms containing ρ^{k+1} in expressions (5-139) and (5-147), the bending moments for $k < 1$ increase infinitely at the center of the plate. Moreover, on account of the terms $A_1 A_2 \rho^{k-1}$ in expressions (5-143) and (5-144), the membrane forces for $k < 1$ also increase infinitely at the plate center. On the other hand the bending moments and membrane forces for $k > 1$ vanish at the center of the plate. When $k = 1$, the solution reduces to that for an isotropic plate.

Alternately, an approximate solution of the above boundary-value problem will be formulated by the multiparameter perturbation technique (Ref. 1.80).

The first perturbation parameter is chosen to be a quantity ε_1 which describes the deviation of the cylindrically orthotropic properties from those of the isotropy. Let us take

$$p^2 = 1 + \varepsilon_1 \qquad \text{(5-151)}$$

It is observed that $p^2 = 1$ in the isotropic case. If the deviation $p^2 - 1$ is greater than n but less than $n + 1$ ($n = $ integer), the parameter ε_1 may be defined as $p^2 = n + \varepsilon_1$. Clearly in such a relation ε_1 may be either negative or positive provided $\varepsilon_1 < 1$. As the second perturbation parameter ε_2 the following dynamical quantity is chosen

$$\varepsilon_2 = \frac{q_0 a^4}{2 D_0 h} \qquad \text{(5-152)}$$

where D_0 is the flexural rigidity in the isotropic case defined by

$$D_0 = \frac{E_r h^3}{12(1 - v_{r\theta}^2)} \tag{5-153}$$

The parameter ε_2 describes, in an indirect way, the deformation of the plate. Since

$$D_r = \frac{E_r h^3}{12(1 - p^2 v_{r\theta}^2)} \tag{5-154}$$

the following relation holds

$$\frac{1}{D_r} = \frac{1}{D_0}(1 - \varepsilon_1 \alpha) \tag{5-155}$$

where

$$\alpha = \frac{v_{r\theta}^2}{1 - v_{r\theta}^2} \tag{5-156}$$

This admits the representation

$$n_r = \eta(1 - \alpha \varepsilon_1) \qquad \omega = \varepsilon_2(1 - \alpha \varepsilon_1) \tag{5-157}$$

where

$$\eta = \frac{a^2}{D_0} N_r \tag{5-158}$$

Now the two-parameter expansion of δ and η appears as

$$
\begin{aligned}
\delta &= \varepsilon_1 f_1(\rho) + \varepsilon_2 g_1(\rho) + \varepsilon_1^2 f_2(\rho) + \varepsilon_2^2 g_2(\rho) + \varepsilon_1 \varepsilon_2 f_{12}(\rho) \\
&\quad + \varepsilon_1^3 f_3(\rho) + \varepsilon_2^3 g_3(\rho) + \varepsilon_1^2 \varepsilon_2 g_{12}(\rho) + \varepsilon_1 \varepsilon_2^2 h_{12}(\rho) + \cdots \\
\eta &= \varepsilon_1^2 r_2(\rho) + \varepsilon_2^2 s_2(\rho) + \varepsilon_1 \varepsilon_1 r_{12}(\rho) + \varepsilon_1^3 r_3(\rho) + \cdots
\end{aligned}
\tag{5-159}
$$

The standard procedure (substituting these expressions into the governing equations and equating like powers of ε_1 and ε_2) furnishes a sequence of linear boundary-value problems associated with the terms of the successive order in ε_i, $i = 1, 2$. The derivatives of functions f, g, h, r, and s are assumed to remain bounded at $\rho = 0$.

The first approximation is obtained by the solution of the following set of two boundary value problems

$$\rho(\rho f_{1,\rho\rho})_{,\rho} - f_{1,\rho} = 0 \qquad f_1(1) = f_{1,\rho}(1) = 0 \tag{5-160}$$

$$\rho(\rho g_{1,\rho\rho})_{,\rho} - g_{1,\rho} = \rho^3 \qquad g_1(1) = g_{1,\rho}(1) = 0 \tag{5-161}$$

whose solution is

$$f_1(\rho) = 0 \qquad g_1(\rho) = \tfrac{1}{32}(\rho^2 - 1)^2 \tag{5-162}$$

in which $g_1(\rho)$ represents the classical solution to the small deflection problem of a clamped, uniformly loaded plate.

A similar argument leads to the set of three boundary-value problems related to the second approximation

$$\rho(\rho f_{2,\rho\rho})_{,\rho} - f_{2,\rho} = f_{1,\rho}$$
$$[\rho(\rho r_2)_{,\rho}]_{,\rho} - r_2 = -6(1 - v_{r\theta}^2)(f_{1,\rho})^2 \tag{5-163}$$
$$f_2(1) = f_{2,\rho}(1) = 0 \qquad (1 - v_{r\theta})r_2(1) + r_{2,\rho}(1) = 0$$

$$\rho(\rho g_{2,\rho\rho})_{,\rho} - g_{2,\rho} = 0$$
$$[\rho(\rho s_2)_{,\rho}]_{,\rho} - s_2 = -6(1 - v_{r\theta}^2)(g_{1,\rho})^2 \tag{5-164}$$
$$g_2(1) = g_{2,\rho}(1) = 0 \qquad (1 - v_{r\theta})s_2(1) + s_{2,\rho}(1) = 0$$

$$\rho(\rho f_{12,\rho\rho})_{,\rho} - f_{12,\rho} = g_{1,\rho} - \alpha\rho^3$$
$$[\rho(\rho r_{12})_{,\rho}]_{,\rho} - r_{12} = -12(1 - v_{r\theta}^2)f_{1,\rho}g_{1,\rho} \tag{5-165}$$
$$f_{12}(1) = f_{12,\rho}(1) = 0 \qquad (1 - v_{r\theta})r_{12}(1) + r_{12,\rho}(1) = 0$$

A trivial calculation yields

$$f_2(\rho) = g_2(\rho) = r_2(\rho) = r_{12}(\rho) = 0$$
$$f_{12}(\rho) = \tfrac{1}{32}[(\tfrac{1}{8} - \alpha)\rho^4 - \rho^2 \log \rho + 2(4\alpha - 1)\rho^2 - \alpha - \tfrac{3}{8}] \tag{5-166}$$
$$s_2(\rho) = A - \frac{1 - v_{r\theta}^2}{512}(\rho^6 - 4\rho^4 + 6\rho^2)$$

where

$$A = \frac{1 - v_{r\theta}^2}{256}\left(\frac{3}{2} + \frac{1}{1 - v_{r\theta}^2}\right) \tag{5-167}$$

For simplicity the third approximation is restricted to the determination of the associated deflection only. The respective boundary-value problems are

$$\rho(\rho f_{3,\rho\rho})_{,\rho} - f_{3,\rho} = \rho^2 f_1 r_2 + f_{2,\rho}$$
$$f_3(1) = f_{3,\rho}(1) = 0 \tag{5-168}$$

$$\rho(\rho g_{3,\rho\rho})_{,\rho} - g_{3,\rho} = \rho^2 g_{1,\rho}s_2$$
$$g_3(1) = g_{3,\rho}(1) = 0 \tag{5-169}$$

$$\rho(\rho g_{12,\rho\rho})_{,\rho} - g_{12,\rho} = f_{12,\rho} + \rho^2 g_{1,\rho}r_2$$
$$g_{12}(1) = g_{12,\rho}(1) = 0 \tag{5-170}$$

$$\rho(\rho h_{12,\rho\rho})_{,\rho} - h_{12,\rho} = g_{2,\rho} + \rho^2 f_{1,\rho}s_2$$
$$h_{12}(1) = h_{12,\rho}(1) = 0 \tag{5-171}$$

The solution of the above system is

$$f_3(\rho) = h_{12}(\rho) = 0$$

$$g_3(\rho) = \frac{1 - v_{r\theta}^2}{4096} \left[\frac{32}{1 - v_{r\theta}^2} \left(\frac{\rho^2}{9} - \frac{1}{2} \right) \rho^4 - \frac{1}{8} \left(\frac{\rho^2}{8} - \frac{1}{3} \right) \rho^6 \right.$$

$$\left. + \frac{1}{8} \left(\frac{\rho^2}{25} - \frac{1}{12} \right) \rho^8 - \frac{1}{160} \left(\frac{\rho^2}{9} - \frac{1}{5} \right) \rho^{10} \right]$$

$$+ \frac{1 - v_{r\theta}^2}{24,576} \left(\frac{128A}{1 - v_{r\theta}^2} - \frac{23}{80} \right) \rho^2 + A_0 \tag{5-172}$$

$$g_{12}(\rho) = \frac{1}{256} \left(\frac{1}{8} - \alpha \right) \rho^4 + \frac{1}{8} \left(\frac{7}{32} - \alpha \right) \rho^2 - \frac{1}{128} \rho^2 \log^2 \rho$$

$$+ \frac{1}{8} \left(\alpha - \frac{3}{16} \right) \rho^2 \log \rho + \frac{1}{4} B \rho^2 + B_0$$

where

$$A_0 = \frac{1 - v_{r\theta}^2}{36,864} \left(\frac{77}{320} - \frac{80A}{1 - v_{r\theta}^2} \right)$$

$$B = \frac{1}{32} \left(9\alpha - \frac{17}{8} \right) \qquad B_0 = \frac{3}{256} \left(11\alpha - \frac{19}{8} \right) - \frac{B}{4} \tag{5-173}$$

Upon substitution of the foregoing results, the first of the perturbation series (5-159) at the plate center, $\delta = \delta_\theta$, corresponding to the third approximation may be written as

$$\delta_0 = [\tfrac{1}{32} - \tfrac{1}{32}(\alpha + \tfrac{3}{8})\varepsilon_1 + B_0\varepsilon_1^2]\varepsilon_2 + A_0\varepsilon_2^3 \tag{5-174}$$

In the case when the deflections of the plate are small or the load acting on the plate is small, the term involving ε_2^3 may be disregarded. To the second-degree approximation in ε_1 and with $v_{r\theta} = 0.3$ and $p^2 = 1.21$, say, equation (5-174) reduces to

$$\delta_0 = 0.0141 \frac{q_0 a^4}{D_0 h} \tag{5-175}$$

which is in good agreement with the result derived directly from equation (81.8) on page 371 of Ref. 4.20. In the case of moderately large deflections and with the same numerical values of $v_{r\theta}$ and p, expression (5-174) becomes

$$\delta_0 = 0.0139Q - 2.06 \times 10^{-6} Q^3 \tag{5-176}$$

where $Q = q_0 a^4/D_0 h$ is the nondimensional load. Inverting equation (5-176) leads to

$$Q = 71.76\delta_0 + 54.63\delta_0^3 \tag{5-177}$$

It can be shown that equation (5-177) agrees satisfactorily with the result given by equation (5-150).

5.9 RIGIDLY CLAMPED ANISOTROPIC RECTANGULAR PLATE UNDER UNIFORM TRANSVERSE LOAD

In the previous discussion the plates have been assumed to be made of isotropic and orthotropic materials. The latter includes rectilinear and cylindrical orthotropy whose principal directions of elasticity are those of plate coordinates. In the case of general orthotropy, the material axes of symmetry are not parallel to the axes of the plate and hence the corresponding problem is more complicated than that of an orthotropic plate. The governing differential equations and basic relations for the moderately large deflection of a generally orthotropic plate are the same as those of an anisotropic plate except for the number of independent elastic constants. The material constants C_{11}, C_{12}, C_{16}, C_{22}, C_{26}, and C_{66} in the constitutive equation (1-34) are all independent in the anisotropic case but not in the generally orthotropic case. These six elastic constants for the latter can be obtained from the four independent ones C_L, C_{TL}, C_T, and C_S by the transformation equation (1-38). Thus the elastic problem of generally orthotropic plates will be treated together with that of the anisotropic plates. Of course, isotropic, orthotropic, and generally orthotropic plates are special cases of an anisotropic plate.

Let us consider a rectangular anisotropic plate of length $2a_0$ in the x direction, width $2b_0$ in the y direction, and thickness h in the z direction under a uniformly distributed load of intensity q_0. The origin of the coordinate system is chosen to coincide with the center of the midplane of the undeformed plate. The governing differential equations expressed in terms of three displacements are obtained by deleting the inertial term from equations (1-98) to (1-100) and using relations (1-104). The resulting equations can be expressed in the nondimensional form as

$$L_1^* U + L_2^* V = -W_{,\zeta} L_1^* W - \lambda W_{,\eta} L_2^* W$$

$$L_2^* U + L_3^* V = -W_{,\zeta} L_2^* W - \lambda W_{,\eta} L_3^* W$$

$$L_4^* W = Q + U_{,\zeta} L_5^* W + (\lambda U_{,\eta} + V_{,\zeta}) L_6^* W + \lambda V_{,\eta} L_7^* W$$

$$\qquad + \tfrac{1}{2} W_{,\zeta}^2 L_5^* W + \lambda W_{,\zeta} W_{,\eta} L_6^* W + \tfrac{1}{2} \lambda^2 W_{,\eta}^2 L_7^* W$$

$$(5\text{-}178)$$

where

$$\lambda = \frac{a_0}{b_0} \qquad \zeta = \frac{x}{a_0} \qquad \eta = \frac{y}{b_0} \qquad U = \frac{12 a_0 u^\circ}{h^2}$$

$$V = \frac{12 a_0 v^\circ}{h^2} \qquad W = 2\sqrt{3}\, \frac{w}{h} \qquad Q = 24\sqrt{3}\, \frac{q_0 a_0^4}{C_{11} h^4}$$

$$L_1^*(\ ) = (\ )_{,\zeta\zeta} + 2\lambda \frac{C_{16}}{C_{11}} (\ )_{,\zeta\eta} + \lambda^2 \frac{C_{66}}{C_{11}} (\ )_{,\eta\eta} \qquad (5\text{-}179)$$

$$L_2^*(\ ) = \frac{C_{16}}{C_{11}} (\ )_{,\zeta\zeta} + \lambda \frac{C_{12} + C_{66}}{C_{11}} (\ )_{,\zeta\eta} + \lambda^2 \frac{C_{26}}{C_{11}} (\ )_{,\eta\eta}$$

$$L_3^*(\ ) = \frac{C_{66}}{C_{11}} (\ )_{,\zeta\zeta} + 2\lambda \frac{C_{26}}{C_{11}} (\ )_{,\zeta\eta} + \lambda^2 \frac{C_{22}}{C_{11}} (\ )_{,\eta\eta}$$

▼

▼

$$L_4^*(\ ) = (\ )_{,\zeta\zeta\zeta\zeta} + 4\lambda \frac{C_{16}}{C_{11}}(\ )_{,\zeta\zeta\zeta\eta} + 2\lambda^2 \frac{C_{12} + 2C_{66}}{C_{11}}(\ )_{,\zeta\zeta\eta\eta}$$

$$+ 4\lambda^3 \frac{C_{26}}{C_{11}}(\ )_{,\zeta\eta\eta\eta} + \lambda^4 \frac{C_{22}}{C_{11}}(\ )_{,\eta\eta\eta\eta}$$

$$L_5^*(\ ) = (\ )_{,\zeta\zeta} + 2\lambda \frac{C_{16}}{C_{11}}(\ )_{,\zeta\eta} + \lambda^2 \frac{C_{12}}{C_{11}}(\ )_{,\eta\eta}$$

$$L_6^*(\ ) = \frac{C_{16}}{C_{11}}(\ )_{,\zeta\zeta} + 2\lambda \frac{C_{66}}{C_{11}}(\ )_{,\zeta\eta} + \lambda^2 \frac{C_{26}}{C_{11}}(\ )_{,\eta\eta}$$

$$L_7^*(\ ) = \frac{C_{12}}{C_{11}}(\ )_{,\zeta\zeta} + 2\lambda \frac{C_{26}}{C_{11}}(\ )_{,\zeta\eta} + \lambda^2 \frac{C_{22}}{C_{11}}(\ )_{,\eta\eta}$$

If the plate is rigidly clamped along its edges, the nondimensional boundary conditions are

$$U = V = W = W_{,\zeta} = 0 \qquad \text{at} \quad \zeta = \pm 1$$
$$U = V = W = W_{,\eta} = 0 \qquad \text{at} \quad \eta = \pm 1$$

(5-180)

Equations (5-178) are to be solved in conjunction with boundary conditions (5-180).

An approximate solution of the foregoing boundary-value problem is formulated by the perturbation method (Ref. 5.13). Let the nondimensional central deflection of the plate, $W(0, 0)$, be denoted by W_0. The parameters Q, W, U, and V may be expressed as the perturbation series with respect to W_0

$$Q = q_1 W_0 + q_3 W_0^3 + \cdots$$
$$W = w_1(\zeta, \eta)W_0 + w_3(\zeta, \eta)W_0^3$$
$$U = u_2(\zeta, \eta)W_0^2 + u_4(\zeta, \eta)W_0^4 + \cdots$$
$$V = v_2(\zeta, \eta)W_0^2 + v_4(\zeta, \eta)W_0^4 + \cdots$$

(5-181)

By definition, the following is required

$$w_1(0, 0) = 1 \qquad w_3(0, 0) = w_5(0, 0) = \cdots = 0$$

(5-182)

Introducing equations (5-181) into (5-178) and (5-180) and equating like powers of W_0, we obtain a series of differential equations and boundary conditions. The first approximation is given by the solution of the following boundary-value problem

$$L_4^* w_1 = q_1$$

(5-183)

and

$$w_1 = w_{1,\zeta} = 0 \qquad \text{at} \quad \zeta = \pm 1$$
$$w_1 = w_{1,\eta} = 0 \qquad \text{at} \quad \eta = \pm 1$$

(5-184)

which are the differential equation and boundary conditions in the nondimensional form for small deflections of a clamped anisotropic plate. The second approximation requires a solution of the differential equations

$$L_1^* u_2 + L_2^* v_2 = -w_{1,\zeta} L_1^* w_1 - \lambda w_{1,\eta} L_2^* w_1$$

$$L_2^* u_2 + L_3^* v_2 = -w_{1,\zeta} L_2^* w_1 - \lambda w_{1,\eta} L_3^* w_1$$

(5-185)

and the associated boundary conditions

$$u_2 = v_2 = 0 \quad \text{at} \quad \zeta = \pm 1$$

$$u_2 = v_2 = 0 \quad \text{at} \quad \eta = \pm 1$$

(5-186)

For the third approximation the differential equations are given by

$$L_4^* w_3 = q_3 + u_{2,\zeta} L_5^* w_1 + (\lambda u_{2,\eta} + v_{2,\zeta}) L_6^* w_1$$

$$+ \lambda v_{2,\eta} L_7^* w_1 + \tfrac{1}{2} w_{1,\zeta}^2 L_5^* w_1 + \lambda w_{1,\zeta} w_{1,\eta} L_6^* w_1$$

$$+ \tfrac{1}{2} \lambda^2 w_{1,\eta}^2 L_7^* w_1$$

(5-187)

and the boundary conditions by

$$w_3 = w_{3,\zeta} = 0 \quad \text{at} \quad \zeta = \pm 1$$

$$w_3 = w_{3,\eta} = 0 \quad \text{at} \quad \eta = \pm 1$$

(5-188)

The high-order approximations can be obtained similarly but the perturbation series (5-181) are approximated by

$$Q = q_1 W_0 + q_3 W_0^3 \qquad W = w_1 W_0 + w_3 W_0^3$$

$$U = u_2 W_0^2 \qquad V = v_2 W_0^2$$

(5-189)

Solutions of equations (5-183), (5-185), and (5-187) for a generally orthotropic plate are sought in the form of polynomial

$$w_1 = (1 - \zeta^2)^2 (1 - \eta^2)^2 (1 + H_{20}\zeta^2 + H_{11}\zeta\eta + H_{02}\eta^2$$

$$+ H_{40}\zeta^4 + H_{31}\zeta^3\eta + H_{22}\zeta^2\eta^2 + H_{13}\zeta\eta^3 + H_{04}\eta^4$$

$$+ H_{60}\zeta^6 + H_{51}\zeta^5\eta + H_{42}\zeta^4\eta^2 + H_{33}\zeta^3\eta^3$$

$$+ H_{24}\zeta^2\eta^4 + H_{15}\zeta\eta^5 + H_{06}\eta^6)$$

(5-190)

$$u_2 = (1 - \zeta^2)(1 - \eta^2)(E_{10}\zeta + E_{01}\eta + E_{30}\zeta^3 + E_{21}\zeta^2\eta$$

$$+ E_{12}\zeta\eta^2 + E_{03}\eta^3 + E_{50}\zeta^5 + E_{41}\zeta^4\eta$$

$$+ E_{32}\zeta^3\eta^2 + E_{23}\zeta^2\eta^3 + E_{14}\zeta\eta^4 + E_{05}\eta^5)$$

(5-191)

$$v_2 = (1 - \zeta^2)(1 - \eta^2)(R_{10}\zeta + R_{01}\eta + R_{30}\zeta^3 + R_{21}\zeta^2\eta$$

$$+ R_{12}\zeta\eta^2 + R_{03}\eta^3 + R_{50}\zeta^5 + R_{41}\zeta^4\eta$$

$$+ R_{32}\zeta^3\eta^2 + R_{23}\zeta^2\eta^3 + R_{14}\zeta\eta^4 + R_{05}\eta^5)$$

(5-192)

$$w_3 = (1 - \zeta^2)^2(1 - \eta^2)^2(S_{20}\zeta^2 + S_{11}\zeta\eta + S_{02}\eta^2 + S_{40}\zeta^4$$

$$+ S_{31}\zeta^3\eta + S_{22}\zeta^2\eta^2 + S_{13}\zeta\eta^3 + S_{04}\eta^4 + S_{60}\zeta^6$$

$$+ S_{51}\zeta^5\eta + S_{42}\zeta^4\eta^2 + S_{33}\zeta^3\eta^3 + S_{24}\zeta^2\eta^4$$

$$+ S_{15}\zeta\eta^5 + S_{06}\eta^6) \tag{5-193}$$

which satisfy boundary conditions (5-184), (5-186), and (5-188) respectively, and in which expressions for w_1 and w_3 fulfill the conditions (5-182). It is also observed that expressions (5-190) to (5-193) meet the following physical requirements

$$w_1(-\zeta, -\eta) = w_1(\zeta, \eta) \qquad w_1(\zeta, -\eta) = w_1(-\zeta, \eta)$$

$$u_2(0, 0) = 0 \qquad v_2(0, 0) = 0$$

$$u_2(-\zeta, -\eta) = -u_2(\zeta, \eta) \qquad u_2(\zeta, -\eta) = -u_2(-\zeta, \eta) \tag{5-194}$$

$$v_2(-\zeta, -\eta) = -v_2(\zeta, \eta) \qquad v_2(\zeta, -\eta) = -v_2(-\zeta, \eta)$$

$$w_3(-\zeta, -\eta) = w_3(\zeta, \eta) \qquad w_3(\zeta, -\eta) = w_3(-\zeta, \eta)$$

Upon substitution of expression (5-190) into equation (5-183), sixteen algebraic equations are generated by equating the constant term to q_1 and the terms in ζ^2, $\zeta\eta$, η^2, ζ^4, $\zeta^3\eta$, $\zeta^2\eta^2$, $\zeta\eta^3$, η^4, ζ^6, $\zeta^5\eta$, $\zeta^4\eta^2$, $\zeta^3\eta^3$, $\zeta^2\eta^4$, $\zeta\eta^5$, and η^6 to zero. The fifteen unknowns H_{ij} in expression (5-190) can be determined by solving the last fifteen equations simultaneously. Introduction of these constants in the first leads to the solution for q_1. The procedure for the determination of coefficients E_{ij}, R_{ij}, and S_{ij}, and the unknown q_3, are similar to the above.

It may be observed that functions (5-190) to (5-193) can reduce to the solution for orthotropic plates given in Sec. 5.1 by setting

$$H_{11} = H_{31} = H_{13} = H_{51} = H_{33} = H_{15} = 0$$

$$E_{01} = E_{21} = E_{03} = E_{41} = E_{23} = E_{05} = 0$$

$$R_{10} = R_{30} = R_{12} = R_{50} = R_{32} = R_{14} = 0 \tag{5-195}$$

$$S_{11} = S_{31} = S_{13} = S_{51} = S_{33} = S_{15} = 0$$

In view of equations (1-101) and (1-104), the membrane forces can be written in the nondimensional form

$$\sigma_\zeta^m = f_1 + \frac{C_{12}}{C_{11}}f_2 + \frac{C_{16}}{C_{11}}f_3$$

$$\sigma_\eta^m = \frac{C_{12}}{C_{11}}f_1 + \frac{C_{22}}{C_{11}}f_2 + \frac{C_{26}}{C_{11}}f_3 \tag{5-196}$$

$$\sigma_{\zeta\eta}^m = \frac{C_{16}}{C_{11}}f_1 + \frac{C_{26}}{C_{11}}f_2 + \frac{C_{66}}{C_{11}}f_3$$

where

$$(\sigma_\zeta^m, \sigma_\eta^m, \sigma_{\zeta\eta}^m) = \frac{12a_0^2}{C_{11}h^3}(N_x, N_y, N_{xy})$$

$$f_1 = U_{,\zeta} + \tfrac{1}{2}W_{,\zeta}^2 \qquad f_2 = \lambda V_{,\eta} + \frac{\lambda^2}{2}W_{,\eta}^2 \qquad (5\text{-}197)$$

$$f_3 = V_{,\zeta} + \lambda U_{,\eta} + \lambda W_{,\zeta}W_{,\eta}$$

Similarly, from equations (1-102) and (1-104), the nondimensional bending moments are

$$\sigma_\zeta^b = W_{,\zeta\zeta} + \lambda^2 \frac{C_{12}}{C_{11}}W_{,\eta\eta} + 2\lambda \frac{C_{16}}{C_{11}}W_{,\zeta\eta}$$

$$\sigma_\eta^b = \frac{C_{12}}{C_{11}}W_{,\zeta\zeta} + \lambda^2 \frac{C_{22}}{C_{11}}W_{,\eta\eta} + 2\lambda \frac{C_{26}}{C_{11}}W_{,\zeta\eta} \qquad (5\text{-}198)$$

$$\sigma_{\zeta\eta}^b = \frac{C_{16}}{C_{11}}W_{,\zeta\zeta} + \lambda^2 \frac{C_{26}}{C_{11}}W_{,\eta\eta} + 2\lambda \frac{C_{66}}{C_{11}}W_{,\zeta\eta}$$

where

$$(\sigma_\zeta^b, \sigma_\eta^b, \sigma_{\zeta\eta}^b) = -\frac{24\sqrt{3}\,a_0^2}{C_{11}h^4}(M_x, M_y, M_{xy}) \qquad (5\text{-}199)$$

In the case of small deflections, equations (5-189) reduce to $Q = q_1 W_0$ and $W = w_1 W_0$ in which w_1 is given by equation (5-190). The deflection and bending moment M_x at the center of a clamped anisotropic square plate ($E_L/E_T = 40$, $G_{LT}/E_T = 0.5$, $\nu_{LT} = 0.25$) are in good agreement with those obtained in Refs. 5.14, 5.15 for various values of θ. For small deflections of a square isotropic plate, the present results for center deflection, center moment, and bending moment at the midpoints of plate sides are different from those given on page 102 of Ref. 1.4 by the amounts of 0.02, 1.08, and 0.58 percent respectively.

Numerical results are presented for a glass-epoxy rectangular plate with the filaments oriented at an angle θ with respect to the x axis of the plate. The typical values of orthotropic properties of this composite with respect to the material principal axes L, T are given by

$$\frac{E_L}{E_T} = 3.0 \qquad \frac{G_{LT}}{E_T} = 0.60 \qquad \nu_{LT} = 0.25 \qquad (5\text{-}200)$$

The stiffnesses with respect to these axes can be calculated from equations (1-36), and the elastic constants C_{ij} in the system of the plate coordinates from equation (1-38). The distribution of bending moment M_x along the x axis of a square glass-epoxy plate is presented in Fig. 5.19 for $w_0/h = 1.5$ where w_0 is the center deflection. The bending moment varies slowly in the central region but rapidly decreases with its maximum magnitude at the edge. This bending moment decreases with increasing θ in the central region and so is its absolute value at the edge. For large values of θ, M_x has a relative maximum in some region between

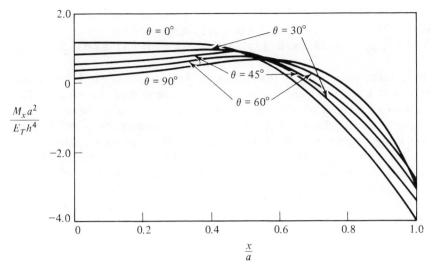

Figure 5.19 Bending-moment distribution along x axis of rigidly clamped glass-epoxy square plate under uniform lateral load for $w_0/h = 1.5$ and for various values of the degree of anistropy.

the center and the edge rather than at the center. The development of boundary layers has been observed also in Fig. 5.11. The location of this maximum bending moment shifts toward the edge as the value of θ increases. The membrane force N_x shown in Fig. 5.20 is tensile at the center of the plate but slowly decreases, reaching a tensile minimum at some point between the center and the edge. Then this force rapidly increases with its maximum at the edge. The force N_x decreases with increasing θ at any point on the x axis.

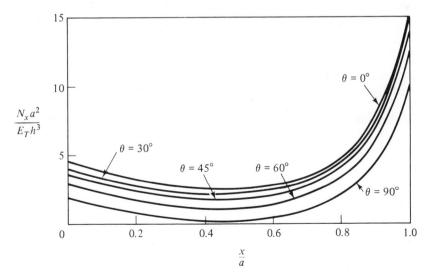

Figure 5.20 Membrane-force distribution along x axis of rigidly clamped glass-epoxy square plate under uniform lateral load for $w_0/h = 1.5$ and for various values of the degree of anisotropy.

5.10 SYMMETRICALLY LAMINATED AND HOMOGENEOUS ANISOTROPIC RECTANGULAR PLATES UNDER TRANSVERSE LOAD FOR LOOSELY CLAMPED EDGES

Consider a rectangular plate of thickness h in the z direction which lies in the region $0 \leq x \leq a, 0 \leq y \leq b$ and is subjected to transverse load of intensity q. The plate consists of n layers of orthotropic sheets perfectly bonded together. Each layer has arbitrary thickness, elastic properties, and orientation of orthotropic axes with respect to the plate axes. However, the layers are so arranged that a midplane symmetry exists. That is, for each layer above the midplane, there is a corresponding layer identical in thickness, elastic properties, and orientation located at the same distance below the midplane. The differential equations governing the moderately large deflection of the plate can be obtained by setting $w_{,tt} = 0$ in equations (1-153) and (1-154). The resulting equations can be expressed in the nondimensional form

$$
\begin{aligned}
\bar{A}_{22} F_{,\zeta\zeta\zeta\zeta} &- 2\lambda \bar{A}_{26} F_{,\zeta\zeta\zeta\eta} + \lambda^2 (2\bar{A}_{12} + \bar{A}_{66}) F_{,\zeta\zeta\eta\eta} \\
&- 2\lambda^3 \bar{A}_{16} F_{,\zeta\eta\eta\eta} + \lambda^4 \bar{A}_{11} F_{,\eta\eta\eta\eta} \\
&= \lambda^2 [(W_{,\zeta\eta})^2 - W_{,\zeta\zeta} W_{,\eta\eta}]
\end{aligned}
\tag{5-201}
$$

$$
\begin{aligned}
\bar{D}_{11} W_{,\zeta\zeta\zeta\zeta} &+ 4\lambda^3 \bar{D}_{16} W_{,\zeta\zeta\zeta\eta} + 2\lambda^2 (\bar{D}_{12} + 2\bar{D}_{66}) W_{,\zeta\zeta\eta\eta} \\
&+ 4\lambda^3 \bar{D}_{26} W_{,\zeta\eta\eta\eta} + \lambda^4 \bar{D}_{22} W_{,\eta\eta\eta\eta} = \lambda^4 Q \\
&+ \lambda^2 [W_{,\zeta\zeta} F_{,\eta\eta} + W_{,\eta\eta} F_{,\zeta\zeta} - 2W_{,\zeta\eta} F_{,\zeta\eta}]
\end{aligned}
\tag{5-202}
$$

where ζ, η, λ and W are defined in equations (5-26) and where

$$
F = \frac{\psi}{A_{22} h^2} \qquad Q = \frac{qb^4}{A_{22} h^3}
$$

$$
\bar{A}_{ij} = A_{22} A_{ij}^* \qquad \bar{D}_{ij} = \frac{D_{ij}}{A_{22} h^2} \qquad (i, j = 12, 6)
\tag{5-203}
$$

The nondimensional membrane forces N_ζ, N_η, $N_{\zeta\eta}$ are related to the nondimensional force function F by

$$
N_\zeta = F_{,\eta\eta} \qquad N_\eta = \frac{1}{\lambda^2} F_{,\zeta\zeta} \qquad N_{\zeta\eta} = -\frac{1}{\lambda} F_{,\zeta\eta}
\tag{5-204}
$$

in which

$$
(N_\zeta, N_\eta, N_{\zeta\eta}) = \frac{b^2}{A_{22} h^2} (N_x, N_y, N_{xy})
\tag{5-205}
$$

The bending moments given by equations (1-102) are written also in the nondimensional form

$$
\begin{Bmatrix} M_\zeta \\ M_v \\ M_{\zeta\eta} \end{Bmatrix} = - \begin{bmatrix} \bar{D}_{11}/\lambda^2 & \bar{D}_{12} & \bar{D}_{16}/\lambda \\ \bar{D}_{12}/\lambda^2 & \bar{D}_{22} & \bar{D}_{26}/\lambda \\ \bar{D}_{16}/\lambda^2 & \bar{D}_{26} & \bar{D}_{66}/\lambda \end{bmatrix} \begin{Bmatrix} W_{,\zeta\zeta} \\ W_{,\eta\eta} \\ 2W_{,\zeta\eta} \end{Bmatrix}
\tag{5-206}
$$

where

$$(M_\zeta, M_\eta, M_{\zeta\eta}) = \frac{b^2}{A_{22}h^3}(M_x, M_y, M_{xy}) \tag{5-207}$$

Equations (5-201) and (5-202) governing the nonlinear bending of the symmetrically laminated anisotropic rectangular plate under transverse load can be reduced to those of a homogeneous anisotropic rectangular plate when the thickness, elastic properties, and orientation of all the layers are taken to be identical with one another.

If the edges of the plate are clamped and free from inplane forces, the nondimensional boundary conditions are

$$\begin{aligned} W = W_{,\zeta} = F_{,\eta\eta} = F_{,\zeta\eta} = 0 \qquad &\text{at} \quad \zeta = 0, 1 \\ W = W_{,\eta} = F_{,\zeta\zeta} = F_{,\zeta\eta} = 0 \qquad &\text{at} \quad \eta = 0, 1 \end{aligned} \tag{5-208}$$

Equations (5-201) and (5-202) are to be solved in conjunction with the boundary conditions (5-208). A solution is formulated by use of the generalized double Fourier series (Ref. 5.16). The two variables F and W are thus assumed to be of the form

$$F = \sum_{m=1}^{\infty} \sum_{n=1}^{\infty} F_{mn} X_m(\zeta) Y_n(\eta)$$

$$W = \sum_{p=1}^{\infty} \sum_{q=1}^{\infty} W_{pq} X_p(\zeta) Y_q(\eta) \tag{5-209}$$

In these expressions X_i and Y_j are the beam eigenfunctions defined by equations (5-36). Using Table 5.1 the series for F and W satisfy all the boundary conditions (5-208). Substituting equations (5-209) into equations (5-201) and (5-202), multiplying the resulting equations by $X_i(\zeta)Y_j(\eta)$, integrating from 0 to 1 with respect to ζ and η, and using the orthogonality relations (5-38), a system of coupled nonlinear algebraic equations is obtained as follows

$$F_{ij}[\alpha_i^4 \bar{A}_{22} + \lambda^4 \alpha_j^4 \bar{A}_{11}] - \sum_m \sum_n F_{mn}$$

$$\cdot [2\lambda \alpha_m^3 \alpha_n \bar{A}_{26} K_1^{im} L_3^{jn} - \lambda^2 \alpha_m^2 \alpha_n^2 K_2^{im} L_2^{jn} (2\bar{A}_{12} + \bar{A}_{66}) + 2\lambda^3 \alpha_m \alpha_n^3 \bar{A}_{16} K_3^{im} L_1^{jn}]$$

$$= \lambda^2 \sum_r \sum_s \sum_k \sum_l W_{rs} W_{kl} [\alpha_r \alpha_k \alpha_s \alpha_l K_4^{irk} L_4^{jsl} - \alpha_r^2 \alpha_l^2 K_5^{irk} L_5^{jls}] \tag{5-210}$$

$$W_{ij}[\alpha_i^4 \bar{D}_{11} + \lambda^4 \alpha_j^4 \bar{D}_{22}] + \sum_p \sum_q W_{pq}$$

$$\cdot [4\lambda \alpha_p^3 \alpha_q \bar{D}_{16} K_1^{ip} L_3^{jq} + 2\lambda^2 \alpha_p^2 \alpha_q^2 K_2^{ip} L_2^{jq}$$

$$\cdot (\bar{D}_{12} + 2\bar{D}_{66}) + 4\lambda^3 \alpha_p \alpha_q^3 \bar{D}_{26} K_3^{ip} L_1^{jq}] - \lambda^2 \sum_r \sum_s \sum_k \sum_l W_{rs} F_{kl}$$

$$\cdot [\alpha_r^2 \alpha_l^2 K_5^{irk} L_5^{jls} + \alpha_k^2 \alpha_s^2 K_5^{ikr} L_5^{jsl} - 2\alpha_r \alpha_k \alpha_l \alpha_s K_4^{irk} L_4^{jsl}] = \lambda^4 Q_{ij} \tag{5-211}$$

In these equations α's are given in Table 5.1 and Q_{ij} and K's, respectively, are the generalized Fourier coefficients in the expansion of the load parameter Q and the definite integrals given by

$$Q = \sum_{i=1}^{\infty} \sum_{j=1}^{\infty} Q_{ij} X_i(\zeta) Y_j(\eta)$$

$$K_1^{im} = \frac{1}{\alpha_m^3} \int_0^1 X_i X_m''' \, d\zeta$$

$$K_2^{im} = \frac{1}{\alpha_m^2} \int_0^1 X_i X_m'' \, d\zeta$$

$$K_3^{im} = \frac{1}{\alpha_m} \int_0^1 X_i X_m' \, d\zeta \tag{5-212}$$

$$K_4^{irk} = \frac{1}{\alpha_r \alpha_k} \int_0^1 X_i X_r' X_k' \, d\zeta$$

$$K_5^{irk} = \frac{1}{\alpha_r^2} \int_0^1 X_i X_r'' X_k \, d\zeta$$

where the primes denote differentiation with respect to the corresponding coordinate. The constants L_1 to L_5 in equations (5-210) and (5-211) are obtained by replacing X, ζ, i, k, m and r in equations (5-212) by Y, η, j, l, n, and s, respectively. Equations (5-210) and (5-211) which constitute a system of simultaneous nonlinear algebraic equations can be solved by taking a finite number of terms in each of the truncated series for F and W.

Numerical results are presented for square symmetrically laminated angle-ply† and homogeneous graphite-epoxy plates. The elastic constants typical of the composite material with respect to its orthotropic axes L and T are

$$\frac{E_L}{E_T} = 40 \qquad \frac{G_{LT}}{E_T} = 0.5 \qquad \nu_{LT} = 0.25 \tag{5-213}$$

Hence elastic constants C_{ij} can be calculated from equations (1-36) and (1-38). In the case of a symmetric angle-ply plate the orthotropic axes of the layers are alternately oriented at $+45°$ and $-45°$ with respect to the plate axes, and all the layers are of equal thickness. For homogeneous anisotropic plates the degree of anisotropy or the angle of orientation, θ, between the material axes of symmetry and the plate axes is taken as $0°$, $15°$, $30°$, and $45°$. In these cases the nondimensional constants $\bar{A}_{ij}$ and $\bar{D}_{ij}$ ($i, j = 1, 2, 6$) in equations (5-203) and expressions (5-205) and (5-207) can be simplified by replacing A_{22} in these equations by $E_T h$. The nondimensional load parameter also simplifies to $Q = qb^4/E_T h^4$. This change will not affect the form of other equations.

The system of nonlinear algebraic equations (5-210) and (5-211) is solved by an iterative procedure. The value of the deflection coefficient W_{11} is prescribed and the values of transverse load parameter Q, other deflection coefficients W_{ij},

---

† See Ref. 1.72 for plate rigidities.

Table 5.7 Comparison of solutions for clamped homogeneous graphite-epoxy square plate ($\theta = 30°$) under uniform pressure

W_A	Q	
	25 terms	49 terms
0.60	469.0	466.0
1.20	968.0	961.0
1.75	1520.0	1503.0
2.30	2133.0	2106.0
2.83	2815.0	2779.0

and force function coefficients F_{ij} are then determined from the system of equations. Once the value of W_{11} is prescribed and an initial guess for W_{ij} $(i \neq 1, j \neq 1)$ is made, equations (5-210) become linear and are solved for the F_{ij} coefficients. These F_{ij} coefficients are then substituted into equations (5-211) and the resulting set of linear equations is solved for Q and W_{ij} $(i \neq 1, j \neq 1)$. These values of W_{ij} and the prescribed value of W_{11} are now used in equations (5-210) to determine the new values of the F_{ij} coefficients, and the process is repeated until the desired accuracy is achieved. The criterion for the convergence of the iterative process is that the difference between the final value of the central deflection and the average of the values in the previous five iterations is less than one percent.

   In order to investigate the convergence of the present series solution, calculations for an anisotropic plate were made by the use of 25 terms $(i, j = 1, 2, ..., 5)$

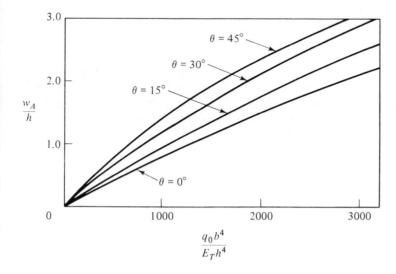

Figure 5.21 Load-deflection curves for loosely clamped graphite-epoxy square plate under uniform lateral pressure having different fiber orientations.

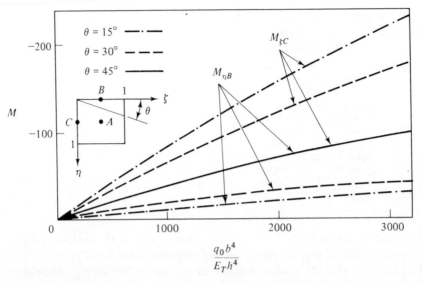

Figure 5.22 Bending moments at midpoints of sides for loosely clamped graphite-epoxy square plate under uniform lateral load having different fiber orientations.

and 49 terms $(i, j = 1, 2, \ldots, 7)$ in the series for F and W. The results are presented in Table 5.7 in which W_A is the nondimensional deflection W at the center of the plate. These results indicate that the series solution converges rapidly and that the 49-term solution should be reasonably accurate for engineering purposes. In the case of small deflections, the numerical results obtained from the present solution for the central deflection of an anisotropic plate with various values of θ agree very well with those obtained in Refs. 5.14 and 5.15.

The relation between load and central deflection w_A is shown in Fig. 5.21 for a clamped anisotropic plate $(\lambda = 1)$. For a fixed load the central deflection increases with increasing θ and reaches the maximum value at $\theta = 45°$. In the orthotropic case $(\theta = 0°$ or $90°)$ this deflection is the smallest. In Fig. 5.22 the bending moments at the midpoints of the sides are presented for various values of θ. The largest bending moment M_ζ in magnitude occurs at the midpoints of sides, $\zeta = 0, 1$. In calculation the first 49 terms in series (5-209) were taken into account.

5.11 SYMMETRICALLY LAMINATED AND HOMOGENEOUS ANISOTROPIC RECTANGULAR PLATES UNDER LATERALLY DISTRIBUTED LOAD FOR SIMPLY SUPPORTED EDGES

The nonlinear bending of a symmetrically laminated anisotropic rectangular plate discussed in the previous section is considered for simply supported edges. Hence equations (5-201) to (5-207) can be used in this study. The boundary conditions for the simply supported plate with stress-free edges are

$$W = M_\zeta = F_{,\eta\eta} = F_{,\zeta\eta} = 0 \qquad \text{at} \quad \zeta = 0, 1$$

$$W = M_\eta = F_{,\zeta\zeta} = F_{,\zeta\eta} = 0 \qquad \text{at} \quad \eta = 0, 1$$

(5-214)

It may be observed that the bending moment M_ζ (or M_η) at the edges of the laminated plate is not equal to $W_{,\zeta\zeta}$ (or $W_{,\eta\eta}$) as in orthotropic plates.

A solution of equations (5-201) and (5-202) is sought in the form of double series (Ref. 5.16)

$$F = \sum_{m=1}^{\infty} \sum_{n=1}^{\infty} F_{mn} X_m(\zeta) Y_n(\eta)$$

(5-215)

$$W = \sum_{p=1}^{\infty} \sum_{q=1}^{\infty} W_{pq} \sin p\pi\zeta \sin q\pi\eta$$

(5-216)

in which $X_m(\zeta)$ and $Y_n(\eta)$ are the beam eigenfunctions as those in equations (5-209) satisfying all the prescribed inplane boundary conditions (5-214). Expression (5-216) for W satisfies the edge condition for the zero deflection but not the edge condition for the vanishing of the normal bending moment. Thus the series for W cannot be differentiated term by term beyond $W_{,\zeta\zeta}$ with respect to ζ and beyond $W_{,\eta\eta}$ with respect to η. The procedure suggested in Ref. 5.17 is used for the fulfillment of the latter condition. Assume that $W_{,\zeta\zeta\zeta}$ can be represented by a cosine-sine series. The Fourier coefficients in the series are determined by integrating by parts and using expression (5-216). Thus the series can be written as

$$W_{,\zeta\zeta\zeta} = \frac{1}{2} \sum_{q=1}^{\infty} a_q \sin q\pi\eta + \sum_{p=2,4}^{\infty} \sum_{q=1}^{\infty} a_q \cos p\pi\zeta \sin q\pi\eta$$

$$+ \sum_{p=1,3}^{\infty} \sum_{q=1}^{\infty} b_q \cos p\pi\zeta \sin q\pi\eta$$

$$- \sum_{p=1}^{\infty} \sum_{q=1}^{\infty} p^3 \pi^3 W_{pq} \cos p\pi\zeta \sin q\pi\eta$$

(5-217)

where

$$a_q = 4 \int_0^1 [W_{,\zeta\zeta}(1, \eta) - W_{,\zeta\zeta}(0, \eta)] \sin q\pi\eta \, d\eta$$

$$b_q = -4 \int_0^1 [W_{,\zeta\zeta}(1, \eta) + W_{,\zeta\zeta}(0, \eta)] \sin q\pi\eta \, d\eta$$

(5-218)

A similar procedure applied to the Fourier sine-cosine representation of $W_{,\eta\eta\eta}$ leads to two sets of constants, say, c_p and d_p. Substituting $W_{,\zeta\eta}$ from equation (5-216) into the condition that $M_\zeta = -\bar{D}_{11} W_{,\zeta\zeta}/\lambda^2 - 2\bar{D}_{16} W_{,\zeta\eta}/\lambda = 0$ at $\zeta = 0, 1$, adding these equations, multiplying the resulting equation by $\sin i\pi\eta$, integrating from 0 to 1 and using the equation (5-218), coefficients b_i can be expressed in terms of W_{pq}. If subtraction instead of addition is carried out in the calculation, a_i can be determined. Similarly, c_i and d_i can be obtained. The result is

$$a_i = \frac{8\lambda\bar{D}_{16}}{\bar{D}_{11}} \sum_{p=1}^{\infty}\sum_{q=1}^{\infty} pq\pi^2 W_{pq} H_1^{iq} \qquad p = \text{odd}$$

$$b_i = \frac{8\lambda\bar{D}_{16}}{\bar{D}_{11}} \sum_{p=1}^{\infty}\sum_{q=1}^{\infty} pq\pi^2 W_{pq} H_1^{iq} \qquad p = \text{even}$$

$$\hspace{10cm}(5\text{-}219)$$

$$c_i = \frac{8\bar{D}_{26}}{\lambda\bar{D}_{22}} \sum_{p=1}^{\infty}\sum_{q=1}^{\infty} pq\pi^2 W_{pq} H_1^{ip} \qquad q = \text{odd}$$

$$d_i = \frac{8\bar{D}_{26}}{\lambda\bar{D}_{22}} \sum_{p=1}^{\infty}\sum_{q=1}^{\infty} pq\pi^2 W_{pq} H_1^{ip} \qquad q = \text{even}$$

in which

$$H_1^{mn} = 0 \qquad \text{if} \quad m + n = \text{even}$$

$$\hspace{10cm}(5\text{-}220)$$

$$H_1^{mn} = \frac{4m}{\pi(m^2 - n^2)} \qquad \text{if} \quad m + n = \text{odd}$$

From equations (5-219) it follows that

$$\bar{D}_{11}[(ia_j)_{i\,\text{even}} + (ib_j)_{i\,\text{odd}}] + \bar{D}_{22}\lambda^4[(jc_i)_{j\,\text{even}} + (jd_i)_{j\,\text{odd}}]$$

$$+ 4\pi^3\lambda \sum_{p=1}^{\infty}\sum_{q=1}^{\infty} W_{pq} pq H_1^{ip} H_1^{jq} (\bar{D}_{16} p^2 + \bar{D}_{26}\lambda^2 q^2)$$

$$= 2\pi^3\lambda \sum_{p=1}^{\infty}\sum_{q=1}^{\infty} W_{pq} pq H_1^{ip} H_1^{jq} [\bar{D}_{16}(i^2 + p^2) + \bar{D}_{26}\lambda^2(j^2 + q^2)] \quad (5\text{-}221)$$

Now the fourth derivatives of the deflection function W in equation (5-202) except for $W_{,\zeta\zeta\eta\eta}$ can be obtained through term-by-term differentiation of $W_{,\zeta\zeta\zeta\zeta}$ and $W_{,\eta\eta\eta\eta}$ as given by equation (5-217). Substituting these derivatives and equations (5-215) and (5-216) into equations (5-201) and (5-202), multiplying the first of the resulting equations by $X_m(\zeta)Y_n(\eta)$ and the second by $\sin i\pi\zeta \sin j\pi\eta$, integrating from 0 to 1 with respect to ζ and η, and using the orthogonality conditions (5-38) as well as equations (5-219) and (5-221), the following system of equations is obtained after some manipulation

$$F_{ij}[\alpha_i^4 \bar{A}_{22} + \lambda^4\alpha_j^4 \bar{A}_{11}] - \sum_m\sum_n F_{mn}$$

$$\cdot [2\alpha_m^3\alpha_n \bar{A}_{26} K_1^{im} L_3^{jn} - \lambda^2\alpha_m^2\alpha_n^2 K_2^{im} L_2^{jn}(2\bar{A}_{12} + \bar{A}_{66}) + 2\lambda^3\alpha_m\alpha_n^3 \bar{A}_{16} K_3^{im} L_1^{jn}]$$

$$= \lambda^2\pi^4 \sum_r\sum_s\sum_k\sum_l W_{rs} W_{kl}[rskl R_1^{ikr} S_1^{jls} - k^2 s^2 R_2^{ikr} S_2^{jsl}] \quad (5\text{-}222)$$

$$W_{ij}[i^4\bar{D}_{11} + 2\lambda^2 i^2 j^2(\bar{D}_{12} + 2\bar{D}_{66}) + \lambda^4 j^4 \bar{D}_{22}]$$

$$- 2\lambda \sum_p \sum_q W_{pq}[pq H_1^{ip} H_1^{jq}\{\bar{D}_{16}(i^2 + p^2) + \lambda^2 \bar{D}_{26}(j^2 + q^2)\}]$$

$$+ \left(\frac{16\lambda^2 \bar{D}_{16}^2}{\pi \bar{D}_{11}}\right) \sum_r \sum_s W_{rs} rs$$

$$\cdot \left[\sum_q q H_2^i H_3^r H_1^{jq} H_1^{qs} + \sum_p \sum_q 2q H_1^{ip} H_1^{jq} H_1^{qs} H_4^{pr}\right] + \frac{16\lambda^2 \bar{D}_{26}^2}{\pi \bar{D}_{22}} \sum_r \sum_s W_{rs} rs$$

$$\cdot \left[\sum_p p H_2^j H_3^s H_1^{ip} H_1^{pr} + \sum_p \sum_q 2p H_1^{ip} H_1^{jq} H_1^{pr} H_4^{qs}\right]$$

$$+ \frac{4\lambda^2}{\pi^2} \sum_m \sum_n \sum_r \sum_s W_{rs} F_{mn}$$

$$\cdot \left[\alpha_m^2 s^2 R_3^{mir} S_2^{njs} + \alpha_n^2 r^2 R_2^{mir} S_3^{njs} + 2\alpha_m \alpha_n rs R_4^{mir} S_4^{njs}\right] = \frac{\lambda^4 Q_{ij}}{\pi^4} \qquad (5\text{-}223)$$

in which α's are given in Table 5.1 and K's and L's are given by equations (5-212), and in which

$$H_2^n = \begin{cases} 0, & n \text{ even} \\ 4/n\pi, & n \text{ odd} \end{cases} \qquad H_3^n = \begin{cases} 0, & n \text{ even} \\ 1, & n \text{ odd} \end{cases} \qquad H_4^{mn} = \begin{cases} 0, & m+n \text{ even} \\ 1, & m+n \text{ odd} \end{cases}$$

$$\qquad (5\text{-}224)$$

$$Q = \sum_{p=1}^{\infty} \sum_{q=1}^{\infty} Q_{pq} \sin p\pi\zeta \sin q\pi\eta$$

and

$$R_1^{ikr} = \int_0^1 X_i \cos k\pi\zeta \cos r\pi\zeta \, d\zeta$$

$$R_2^{ikr} = \int_0^1 X_i \sin k\pi\zeta \sin r\pi\zeta \, d\zeta$$

$$\qquad (5\text{-}225)$$

$$R_3^{ikr} = \frac{1}{\alpha_i^2} \int_0^1 X_i'' \sin k\pi\zeta \sin r\pi\zeta \, d\zeta$$

$$R_4^{ikr} = \frac{1}{\alpha_i} \int_0^1 X_i' \sin k\pi\zeta \cos r\pi\zeta \, d\zeta$$

with primes denoting differentiation with respect to the corresponding coordinate. The constants S_1 to S_4 are obtained by replacing R, X, ζ, i, k, m, and r in expressions (5-225) by S, Y, η, j, l, n, and s, respectively. Equations (5-222) and (5-223) constitute an infinite set of coupled nonlinear algebraic equations which can be solved for coefficients F_{mn} and W_{pq} for given values of material constants, degree of anisotropy, number of layers, and aspect ratio of the plate.

In calculation we consider the graphite-epoxy composite plates with its elastic properties given by equation (5-213). The first 49 terms in each of the truncated

Table 5.8 Comparison of solutions for simply supported five-layer symmetric $\pm 45°$ angle-ply graphite-epoxy square plate under uniform lateral load, $W_A = W(\frac{1}{2}, \frac{1}{2})$

	Q	
W_A	25 terms	49 terms
0.49	173.0	174.0
0.97	354.0	357.0
1.45	553.0	557.0
2.38	1026.0	1030.0
2.82	1303.0	1310.0

series for F and W are taken into account. Table 5.8 indicates that these terms give good approximations. In the case of small deflections, the numerical results for the maximum deflection of a simply supported anisotropic plate with various values of θ are in excellent agreement with those obtained in Ref. 5.18 but are different, by the maximum amount of 5 percent, from those given in Ref. 5.19.

The relationship between uniform lateral load q_0 and central deflection w_A for an anisotropic square plate is shown in Fig. 5.23 for various values of θ. For a given load the central deflection of a simply supported plate increases with increasing θ as in the case of clamped edges, but is larger than that of a corresponding clamped plate. Figure 5.24 shows the load-deflection relations for a simply

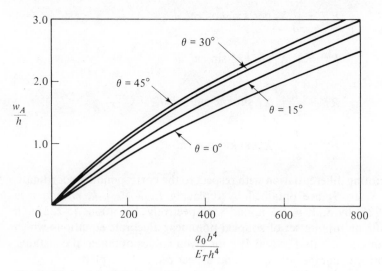

Figure 5.23 Load-deflection curves for simply supported graphite-epoxy square plate under uniform lateral pressure having different fiber orientations.

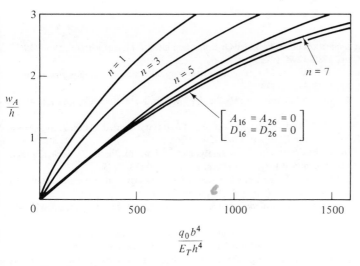

Figure 5.24 Effect of number of layers on maximum deflection for simply supported $\pm 45°$ symmetric angle-ply graphite-epoxy square plate under uniform lateral load.

supported symmetrically laminated anisotropic plate having different numbers of layers. It is found that the central deflection for a fixed value of the transverse load decreases with an increase in the number of layers. For $n = 7$ the central deflection of the plate is very close to that of a specially orthotropic plate ($\theta = \pm 45°$, $A_{16} = A_{26} = D_{16} = D_{26} = 0$).

PROBLEMS

5.1 Verify the orthogonality relations (5-38) and (5-43).

5.2 An orthotropic rectangular plate under uniform lateral load of intensity q_0 rests on an elastic foundation. The nonlinear equations (5-24) and (5-25) including the effect of the elastic foundation are adopted in the analysis.

Derive an approximate load-deflection relation for the plate with loosely clamped edges.

5.3 A simply supported orthotropic rectangular plate is subjected to a concentrated load P at its center. If the boundary conditions are given by equations (5-17), the displacement functions given by equations (5-18) and (5-19) are assumed to be valid in the present loading case. Obtain the load-deflection relation for the moderately large deflections.

5.4 A cylindrically orthotropic clamped circular plate under uniform lateral load of intensity q_0 and concentrated load P at its center is undergoing moderately large deflections. Formulate a power series solution for axisymmetric deformation of the plate.

5.5 Consider the boundary-value problem discussed in Sec. 5.10. Obtain an approximate solution by taking the first term for deflection W in equations (5-209) and applying the Galerkin method to the problem. Also compare the result thus obtained with the graphical results shown in Fig. 5.21 for a square anisotropic plate.

REFERENCES

5.1. C. Y. Chia: Large Deflection of Rectangular Orthotropic Plates, *J. Eng. Mech. Div., Proc. ASCE*, vol. 98, no. EM5, pp. 1285–1298, 1972.

5.2. A. K. Niyogi: Nonlinear Bending of Rectangular Orthotropic Plates, *Int. J. Solids Struct.*, vol. 9, Pergamon Press, pp. 1133–1139, 1973.

5.3. W. Flügge (ed.): "Handbook of Engineering Mechanics," McGraw-Hill Book Company, p. 45–16, 1962.

5.4. M. K. Prabhakara and C. Y. Chia: Large Deflections of Arbitrary Loaded Plates, *J. Eng. Mech. Div.*, Proc. ASCE, vol. 100, no. EM6, pp. 1282–1286, 1974.

5.5. C. Y. Chia and M. K. Prabhakara: Nonlinear Analysis of Orthotropic Plates, *J. Mech. Eng. Sci.*, vol. 17, Institution of Mechanical Engineers (London), pp. 133–138, 1975.

5.6. A. K. Basu and J. C. Chapman: Large-Deflexion Behaviour of Transversely Loaded Rectangular Orthotropic Plates, *Proc. Inst. Civ. Eng.*, vol. 39, pp. 79–110, 1966.

5.7. W. G. Soper: Large Deflection of Stiffened Plates, *ASME J. Appl. Mech.*, vol. 25, pp. 444–448, 1958.

5.8. M. K. Prabhakara and C. Y. Chia: Post-buckling Behaviour of Rectangular Orthotropic Plates, *J. Mech. Eng. Sci.*, vol. 15, Institution of Mechanical Engineers (London), pp. 25–33, 1973.

5.9. M. K. Prabhakara and C. Y. Chia: Large Deflections of Rectangular Orthotropic Plates under Combined Transverse and In-plane Loads, *J. Mech. Eng. Sci.*, vol. 15, Institution of Mechanical Engineers (London), pp. 346–350, 1973.

5.10. M. K. Prabhakara and C. Y. Chia: Bending of Elliptical Orthotropic Plates with Large Deflection, *Acta Mech.*, vol. 21, Springer-Verlag (Austria), pp. 29–40, 1975.

5.11. J. L. Nowinski and I. A. Ismail: Large Oscillations of an Anisotropic Triangular Plate, *J. Franklin Inst.*, vol. 280, no. 5, The Franklin Institute, pp. 417–424, 1965.

5.12. J. Nowinski: Cylindrically Orthotropic Circular Plates, *Z. Angew. Math. Phys.*, vol. 11, Redaction ZAMP (Germany), pp. 218–228, 1960.

5.13. C. Y. Chia: Finite Deflections of Uniformly Loaded, Clamped, Rectangular, Anisotropic Plates, *AIAA J.*, vol. 10, pp. 1399–1400, 1972.

5.14. J. M. Whitney: Fourier Analysis of Clamped Anisotropic Plates, *ASME J. Appl. Mech.*, vol. 38, pp. 530–532, 1971.

5.15. J. E. Ashton and M. E. Waddoups: Analysis of Anisotropic Plates, *J. Comp. Mater.*, vol. 3, pp. 148–165, 1969.

5.16. M. K. Prabhakara and C. Y. Chia: Nonlinear Bending of Symmetrically Laminated and Homogeneous Anisotropic Plates, *Rozpr. Inz.*, vol. 24, Pánstwowe Wydanictwo Naukowe (Poland), pp. 559–570, 1977.

5.17. A. E. Green: Double Fourier Series and Boundary Value Problems, *Proc. Cambridge Philos. Soc.*, vol. 40, pp. 222–228, 1944.

5.18. C. T. Sun: Double Fourier Series Solution to General Anisotropic Plates, *J. Math. Phys. Sci.*, vol. 6, pp. 205–223, 1972.

5.19. J. M. Whitney: Analysis of Anisotropic Rectangular Plates, *AIAA J.*, vol. 10, pp. 1344–1345, 1972.

ADDITIONAL REFERENCES

Aalami, B., and J. C. Chapman: Large Deflexion Behaviour of Rectangular Orthotropic Plates Under Transverse and In-plane Loads, *Proc. Inst. Civ. Eng.*, vol. 42, pp. 347–382, 1969.

Adotte, G. A.: Second-order Theory in Orthotropic Plates, *J. Struct. Div., Proc. ASCE*, vol. 93, No. ST5, pp. 343–362, 1967.

Banerjee, B.: Large Deflection of an Orthotropic Circular Plate Under a Concentrated Load, *Bul. Acad. Polonaise Sci. Ser. Sci. Tech.*, vol. 15, pp. 699–704, 1967.

————: Note on the Large Deflection of an Orthotropic Circular Plate with Clamped Edge Under Symmetrical Load, *J. Indian Inst. Sci.*, vol. 58, pp. 175–180, 1976.

Chandra, R.: On Twisting of Orthotropic Plates in a Large Deflection Regime, *AIAA J.*, vol. 14, pp. 1130–1131, 1976.

Chen, C. H. S.: Finite Twisting and Bending of Thin Rectangular Orthotropic Elastic Plates, *ASME J. Appl. Mech.*, vol. 41, pp. 315–316, 1974.

Datta, S.: Large Deflection of a Triangular Orthotropic Plate on Elastic Foundation, *Def. Sci. J.*, vol. 25, pp. 115–120, 1975.

Iwinski, T., and J. Nowinski: The Problems of Large Deflections of Orthotropic Plates (I), *Arch. Mech. Stos.*, vol. 9, pp. 593–603, 1957.

Marshall, I. H., J. Rhodes, and W. M. Banks: The Nonlinear Behaviour of Thin, Orthotropic, Curved Panels Under Lateral Loading, *J. Mech. Eng. Sci.*, vol. 19, pp. 30–37, 1977.

Zaghloul, S. A., and J. B. Kennedy: Nonlinear Behavior of Symmetrically Laminated Plates, *ASME J. Appl. Mech.*, vol. 42, pp. 234–236, 1975.

POSTBUCKLING BEHAVIOR AND NONLINEAR FLEXURAL VIBRATION OF ANISOTROPIC PLATES

The moderately large static deflections of orthotropic, anisotropic, and symmetrically laminated plates have been discussed in the previous chapter for different plate shapes and boundary conditions. In this chapter nonlinear buckling and vibration of these plates are considered. The first part deals with postbuckling behavior and the second with moderately large amplitude vibration.† Solutions for postbuckling problems are presented by expressing transverse deflection as a double Fourier series, and force function as a generalized double Fourier series for simply supported orthotropic rectangular plates with all movable and all stiffened edges, and for symmetrically laminated and homogeneous anisotropic plates with all-clamped and all-simply supported movable edges. The generalized double Fourier series method is applied to the postbuckling problem of all-clamped and all-simply supported orthotropic rectangular plates. Before presentation of a numerical solution for axisymmetric postbuckling of a cylindrically orthotropic annular plate with free inner edge and loosely clamped and uniformly compressed outer edge, nonlinear equations of motion governing moderately large nonaxisymmetric deformations of cylindrically orthotropic circular plates are derived by the classical method of integration. For problems of moderately large-amplitude flexural vibrations, Galerkin's method is applied to the single-mode analysis for all-clamped and all-simply supported orthotropic rectangular plates with zero

---

† Based on the dynamic von Kármán-type nonlinear equations for moderately large-amplitude flexural vibrations of anisotropic skew plates, a single-mode analysis can be found in Ref. 6.1 for various boundary conditions.

resultant of normal boundary forces, and for loosely clamped rectilinearly orthotropic circular and skew plates. The resulting ordinary differential equations for time functions are solved by standard methods for nonlinear free and forced vibrations. These methods are also used in the fundamental-mode analysis for loosely and rigidly clamped orthotropic right triangular plates and for loosely clamped orthotropic isosceles triangular plates. The multimode approach to the nonlinear free flexural vibration of all-clamped and all-simply supported orthotropic rectangular plates with stress-free edges is discussed by use of the generalized double Fourier series for equations of motion and the method of harmonic balance for the time equation. For large values of amplitude the effect of coupling of vibrating modes on nonlinear frequency is significant for orthotropic plates, especially for high-modulus composite plates, but negligible for isotropic plates.

6.1 POSTBUCKLING OF ORTHOTROPIC RECTANGULAR PLATE WITH SIMPLY SUPPORTED EDGES

Based on the methods of solution for the static large deflection of orthotropic rectangular plates, some of the postbuckling problems of these plates can be discussed. Let us consider a plate with material properties, coordinate system, and edge conditions as described in Sec. 5.5. In the present problem the lateral load q is taken to be zero and the inplane compressive stresses, p_x and p_y, are allowed to have such magnitudes that the maximum deflection of the plate is of the order of the plate thickness. Thus the solution of the differential equations with the associated boundary conditions in the above-mentioned section can be applied to the present postbuckling problem by setting $Q_{ij} = 0$ in equation (5-77).

The symbol τ defined in expressions (5-78) is the nondimensional buckling load of an orthotropic rectangular plate subjected to biaxial compression. The value of τ can be determined by dropping all the nonlinear terms in equation (5-77) and solving the resulting homogeneous equations for the eigenvalue τ. The result is

$$\tau = \frac{D_1(m/\lambda)^2 + 2D_3 n^2 + D_2(\lambda/m)^2 n^2}{E_1 h^3[1 + (p_y/p_x)(\lambda/m)^2 n^2]} \tag{6-1}$$

in which m and n are the number of buckling half-waves in the x and y directions, and which is the result given on page 457 of Ref. 4.19. The least value of τ denoted by τ_{cr} is obtained by considering the first mode of deformation ($m = n = 1$). The values of τ_{cr} for plates of different material properties and aspect ratios under uniaxial compression are given in Table 6.1. Numerical results are presented for glass-epoxy, boron-epoxy, graphite-epoxy, and isotropic plates with the elastic constants given in Table 5.4. The first four terms in each of the truncated series for W and F given by equations (5-72) are taken into account. Table 6.2 shows the values of coefficients W_{ij} and F_{ij} for a square orthotropic plate subjected to uniform biaxial compression. These values decrease rapidly with increasing their

Table 6.1 Values of non-dimensional critical compressive force τ_{cr} for $p_y = 0$

Plate material	τ_{cr}		
	$\lambda = 1.0$	$\lambda = 1.5$	$\lambda = 2.0$
Isotropic	0.3704	0.4074	0.3704
Glass-epoxy	0.1943	0.1825	0.2156
Boron-epoxy	0.1069	0.0788	0.0688
Graphite-epoxy	0.0916	0.0478	0.0358

indices and the value of W_{33} (or F_{22}) is much smaller than the value of W_{11} (or F_{11}) for each of the values of the ratio p_x/p_{cr} in which p_{cr} is the critical compressive stress in the x direction. Thus the first four terms in each series give a good approximation to the corresponding series.

Figure 6.1 shows the relationships between central deflection w_0 and uniaxial compression p_x for square glass-epoxy, boron-epoxy and graphite-epoxy composite plates denoted by GL, BO, and GR, respectively, and also for an isotropic plate. For a fixed value of p_x/p_{cr}, the central deflection increases with the ratio E_2/E_1 and the central deflection of an orthotropic plate is larger than that of the isotropic plate. This may be explained by regarding E_1 as fixed in magnitude and thinking of small values of E_2/E_1 and G_{12}/E_1 as representing a lower-tensile modulus in transverse direction and lower-shear modulus, respectively. Thus all the orthotropic plates considered herein have the same tensile modulus in the filament direction as that of the isotropic plate. Both the tensile modulus in the transverse direction and the shear modulus for the boron-epoxy plate shown in Table 5.4 are higher than those for a graphite-epoxy plate but lower than those for a glass-epoxy plate. The elastic moduli ratio of an isotropic plate, however, are the largest among these elastic constants. Consequently the central deflections of isotropic, glass-epoxy, boron-epoxy and graphite-epoxy plates gradually increase for a given load ratio p_x/p_{cr}. The extreme-fiber bending and membrane stresses in a square glass-epoxy plate subjected to uniaxial compression p_x are plotted in Fig. 6.2 against the load ratio. The maximum magnitude of the membrane stresses

Table 6.2 Values of W_{pq} and F_{mn} for a square glass-epoxy plate, $p_x = p_y$

$\dfrac{p_x}{p_{cr}}$	W_{11}	W_{13}	W_{31}	W_{33}	F_{11}	F_{12}	F_{21}	F_{22}
1.00	0.0000	0.0000	0.0000	0.0000				
1.25	1.3517	−0.0407	−0.0132	0.0024	−0.0196	−0.0003	0.0000	0.0000
1.50	2.0513	−0.1136	−0.0393	0.0110	−0.0412	−0.0020	−0.0001	0.0000
2.00	3.2343	−0.2933	−0.1195	0.0508	−0.0889	−0.0090	−0.0012	0.0001
2.50	4.2691	−0.4708	−0.2221	0.1115	−0.1395	−0.0192	−0.0036	0.0018
3.00	5.1845	−0.6234	−0.3318	0.1771	−0.1909	−0.0308	−0.0069	0.0051

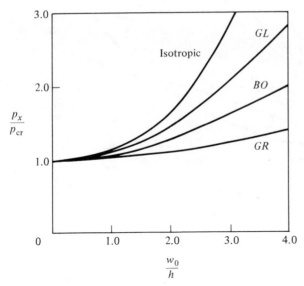

Figure 6.1 Relation between postbuckling load and central deflection for square fiber-reinforced and isotropic plates $(p_y = 0)$.

occurs at the middle point of the unloaded sides. The magnitude of the membrane stress σ_ζ^m at the plate center decreases as the load ratio increases. This is because, at buckling when the plate is still flat, σ_ζ^m is compressive, but the stretching of the middle surface will cause a decrease in this compressive stress as the plate bends. The membrane stress σ_η^m is always tensile and increases with the load ratio. In

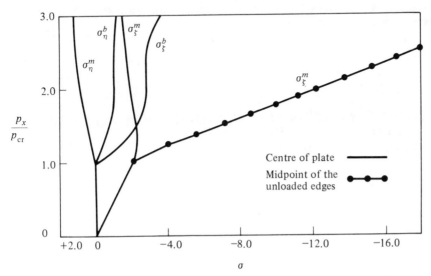

Figure 6.2 Extreme-fibre bending and membrane stresses in a square glass-epoxy plate $(p_y = 0)$.

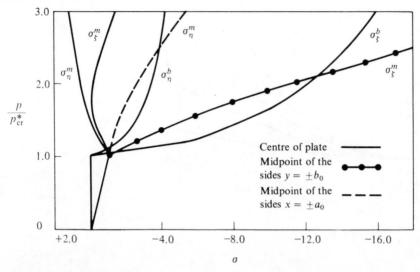

Figure 6.3 Extreme-fibre bending and membrane stresses in a square glass-epoxy plate under uniform biaxial compression ($p_x = p_y = p$).

Fig. 6.3 the extreme-fiber bending and membrane stresses in a square glass-epoxy plate under uniform biaxial compression are plotted against the load ratio. The critical buckling stress p^*_{cr} in this case is smaller than that of the same plate under uniaxial compression. The least value of τ is obtained by considering the first mode of deformation and is equal to 0.0972. The behavior of these stresses is roughly similar to that for uniaxial compression. However, the membrane stress σ^m_η at the midpoint of the sides $x = \pm a_0$, which is negligible in the case of uniaxial compression, becomes large in the case of biaxial compression. Further numerical results can be found in Ref. 5.8. It may be observed that, for the same load ratio, the central deflection of a square glass-epoxy plate under uniform biaxial compression is very nearly the same as that of the plate subjected to uniaxial compression.

6.2 POSTBUCKLING OF ORTHOTROPIC RECTANGULAR PLATE WITH ALL-CLAMPED AND ALL-SIMPLY SUPPORTED EDGES

Suppose that the material axes of symmetry of an orthotropic rectangular plate are parallel to the edges of the plate and that the plate is subjected to inplane compressive forces, n_x and n_y, per unit length along the edges $x = 0$, a and $y = 0$, b, respectively. If the edges of the plate are either all clamped or all simply supported, the nondimensional boundary conditions are, for a clamped plate,

$$W = W_{,\zeta} = F_{,\zeta\eta} = 0 \qquad F_{,\eta\eta} = -R \qquad \text{at} \quad \zeta = 0, 1$$
$$W = W_{,\eta} = F_{,\zeta\eta} = 0 \qquad F_{,\zeta\zeta} = -\lambda^2 kR \qquad \text{at} \quad \eta = 0, 1 \tag{6-2}$$

and, for a simply supported plate,

$$W = W_{,\zeta\zeta} = F_{,\zeta\eta} = 0 \qquad F_{,\eta\eta} = -R \qquad \text{at} \quad \zeta = 0, 1$$
$$W = W_{,\eta\eta} = F_{,\zeta\eta} = 0 \qquad F_{,\eta\eta} = -\lambda^2 kR \qquad \text{at} \quad \eta = 0, 1 \tag{6-3}$$

in which ζ, η, λ, W, and F are defined in equations (5-26) and in which

$$k = \frac{n_y}{n_x} \qquad R = \frac{n_x b^2}{E_2 h^3} \tag{6-4}$$

The nondimensional differential equations governing the postbuckling behavior of the plate are obtained by setting $Q = 0$ in equations (5-27) and (5-28). A solution of these equations is sought in the form of the generalized double Fourier series (Ref. 5.5)

$$F = -\frac{R}{2}(\eta^2 + k\lambda^2\zeta^2) + \sum_{m=1}^{\infty}\sum_{n=1}^{\infty} F_{mn} X_m(\zeta) Y_n(\eta)$$
$$W = \sum_{p=1}^{\infty}\sum_{q=1}^{\infty} W_{pq} \phi_p(\zeta)\psi_q(\eta) \tag{6-5}$$

in which X_n, Y_m, ϕ_p, and ψ_q are beam eigenfunctions given by equations (5-36) and (5-37). Introduction of expression (6-5) into boundary conditions (6-2) and (6-3), in addition to relations (5-41), for a clamped plate, yields

$$\alpha_i = \beta_i \qquad \gamma_i = \frac{1}{A_i} \tag{6-6}$$

and, in addition to relations (5-42), for a simply supported plate, yields

$$\gamma_i = \frac{\cosh \alpha_i - \cos \alpha_i}{\sinh \alpha_i - \sin \alpha_i} \qquad 1 - \cos \alpha_i \cosh \alpha_i = 0 \tag{6-7}$$

The orthogonality relations of functions, X_i, Y_i, ϕ_i, and ψ_j, are given by equations (5-38) and (5-43) in which, for a clamped plate,

$$H_i = A_i^2 \tag{6-8}$$

and, for a simply supported plate,

$$H_i = \tfrac{1}{2} \tag{6-9}$$

Following a similar calculation as in equations (5-45) and (5-46), the differential equations (5-27) and (5-28), in which $Q = 0$, reduce to a set of algebraic equations. The result can be obtained by setting $Q_{ij} = 0$ in equations (5-45) and (5-47), and adding the following terms

$$\lambda^2 c_7 R\left(\sum_{p=1}^{\infty} W_{pj} \beta_p^2 K_1^{ip} + k\lambda^2 \sum_{q=1}^{\infty} W_{iq} \beta_q^2 L_1^{jq}\right) \tag{6-10}$$

to the left-hand side of equation (5-45).

Numerical examples are presented for glass-epoxy (*GL*), boron-epoxy (*BO*) and graphite-epoxy (*GR*) plates with elastic constants given in Table 5.2. The

Table 6.3 Critical buckling load R_{cr}

Material	λ	Clamped	Simply supported
Isotropic ($\nu = 0.316$)	1.0	9.4813	3.7042
Glass-epoxy	1.0	16.2001	4.7478
Boron-epoxy	1.0	38.0690	11.3242
Graphite-epoxy	1.0	137.6497	35.8307
Graphite-epoxy	1.5	68.3005	18.5548
Graphite-epoxy	2.0	48.0099	13.5894

uniaxial edge compression considered is in the filament direction. As in Sec. 5.3 the first nine terms in each of the truncated series (6-5) are taken into account. The procedure for calculating the critical buckling load is briefly outlined. The non-dimensional buckling load is defined by $R_{cr} = n_{cr} b^2 / E_2 h^3$ in which n_{cr} is the critical buckling load per unit length under uniaxial compression in the x direction. The value of R_{cr} can be calculated by omitting all the nonlinear terms in equation (5-45) as modified in the foregoing. The lowest eigenvalue of the system of homogeneous equations corresponds to the critical load with the result shown in Table 6.3.

The relation between central deflection w_A and postbuckling load n_x is shown in Fig. 6.4 for clamped plates of different materials and aspect ratios. The edge compression corresponding to $w_A = 0$ is the critical load. It is seen from the figure that for a given w_A, a high-modulus plate carries a postbuckling load larger than a low-modulus plate and the postbuckling load decreases with increasing the aspect ratio. The dashed curve is the one for a square isotropic plate. The postbuckling

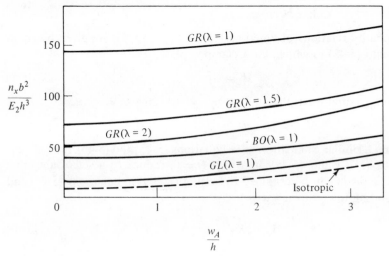

Figure 6.4 Relation between load and central deflection of clamped orthotropic rectangular plate under uniform uniaxial compression in ζ direction for different material properties and aspect ratios.

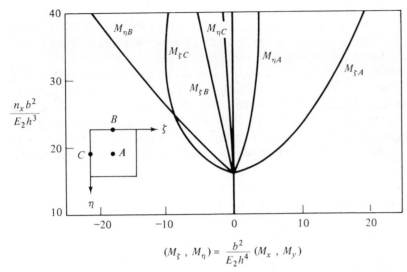

$$(M_\xi , M_\eta) = \frac{b^2}{E_2 h^4} (M_x , M_y)$$

Figure 6.5 Bending moments in clamped glass-epoxy square plate under uniform uniaxial compression in ζ direction.

load of the isotropic plate is the smallest because the ratio $E_1/E_2 > 1$ and E_2 may be regarded as fixed in magnitude. Figure 6.5 shows the variation of bending moments with the uniaxial inplane load at various points on a square glass-epoxy plate. At the center of the plate, the bending moment M_ζ is larger than M_η. For high values of the inplane load, M_η is the largest bending moment in magnitude and occurs at the middle points of longitudinal edges, $\eta = 0$ and 1. In Fig. 6.6 the

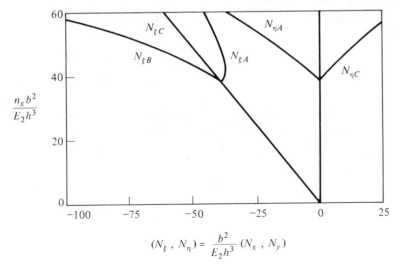

$$(N_\xi , N_\eta) = \frac{b^2}{E_2 h^3} (N_x , N_y)$$

Figure 6.6 Membrane forces in clamped boron-epoxy square plate under uniform uniaxial compression in ζ direction.

membrane forces at different points in a square boron-epoxy plate are plotted against the uniaxial edge compression. Except for the membrane force N_η at the center of the plate, the membrane forces indicated in the figure are in compression. It is observed that the membrane force N_ζ at the plate center increases linearly with the applied edge compression up to the buckling load. Beyond the buckling load this membrane force decreases slightly but again increases for large values of the inplane load. The largest membrane force is N_ζ in compression and occurs at the middle points of the longitudinal sides, $\eta = 0$ and 1. For simply supported orthotropic plates under inplane edge compression the present results agree well with those obtained in the previous section and hence are not presented herein.

6.3 POSTBUCKLING OF ORTHOTROPIC RECTANGULAR PLATE WITH STIFFENED EDGES

The postbuckling behavior of orthotropic rectangular plates has been discussed in the two previous sections for all-clamped and all-simply supported edges. The loaded edges are subjected to uniform edge compressive forces but free from the boundary shear forces. The unloaded edges are stress-free. In this section the elastic behavior of an orthotropic plate with stiffened edges after buckling is considered. It is assumed that the edges of the plate are parallel to the principal directions of its elasticity, which are denoted by x and y. The origin of the coordinates is taken at the plate center and the edges correspond to $x = \pm a_0$ and $y = \pm b_0$. The plate is subjected to the combined lateral pressure q and uniaxial compression P_x in the x direction, and is simply supported along its edges. The loaded edges are uniformly displaced and the unloaded edges are free to displace in the plane of the plate. Thus the boundary conditions are given by equations (4-1) to (4-3), and the governing equations by equations (5-24) and (5-25). A solution to this boundary-value problem (Ref. 6.2) is obtained by modification of the solution discussed in Sec. 4.2. Thus the equations and notation in the section are used in this study but only those to be modified are mentioned in the following.

Prior to formulation of the solution, the force function ψ in equations (5-24) and (5-25) is replaced by the product of Airy stress function F and plate thickness h. The variables w and F are then expressed as two series given by equations (4-4) and (4-5). Substituting these series for w and F in the compatibility equation (5-25) leads to the expression for stress function coefficients a_{rs} in terms of deflection coefficients w_m

$$a_{rs} = \frac{1}{4}\left(\frac{\delta_1 r^4}{\lambda^2} + 2\delta_3 r^2 s^2 + \lambda^2 \delta_2 s^4\right)^{-1} \sum_{k=1}^{9} d_k \qquad (6\text{-}11)$$

in which λ is the plate aspect ratio, a_0/b_0, and δ's and d_k are defined by equations (1-160) and (4-9) respectively. The lateral load is expanded into a double cosine series given by equation (4-15). Upon substitution equilibrium equation (5-24) yields

$$q_{rs} = \frac{\pi^4}{16}\left[D_1\left(\frac{r}{a_0}\right)^4 + 2D_3\left(\frac{rs}{a_0 b_0}\right)^2 + D_2\left(\frac{s}{b_0}\right)^4\right]w_{rs} - hp_x\left(\frac{r\pi}{2a_0}\right)^2 w_{rs}$$

$$- h\left(\frac{\pi^2}{8a_0 b_0}\right)^2 \sum_{n=1}^{9} e_n \qquad (6\text{-}12)$$

which relates the lateral load coefficients to those in the series for w and F and in which p_x is the average edge stress in the loading direction and e's are given by equations (4-17). The other equations required in the analysis are identical in form with those given in Sec. 4.2.

In the postbuckling analysis the lateral load q is set to zero and a finite number of terms in the truncated series for w and F are specified. This will lead to a set of simultaneous cubic equations for the deflection coefficients which can be solved for given values of elastic properties and aspect ratio of the plate. Hence deflections, stresses, and strains can be calculated. For postbuckling loads less than three times the buckling load, a four-term solution generally gives a good approximation.

6.4 GOVERNING EQUATIONS FOR NON-AXISYMMETRICAL FINITE DEFLECTION OF CYLINDRICALLY ORTHOTROPIC PLATE

Cylindrically orthotropic materials are defined in Sec. 5.8. The differential equations governing the moderately large, axisymmetrical deflections of a cylindrically orthotropic circular plate are also given in that section.

Now the nonlinear equations of motion for such plates undergoing general deformation are derived from the joint requirement of compatible strains in the middle surface of the plate and the equations of dynamic equilibrium as in the derivation of the dynamic von Kármán nonlinear plate equations, plus the constitutive equations for orthotropic material properties (Ref. 6.3). The strain displacement relations in the cylindrical system of coordinates r, θ, and z are

$$\varepsilon_r = \varepsilon_r^\circ + z\kappa_r \qquad \varepsilon_\theta = \varepsilon_\theta^\circ + z\kappa_\theta$$

$$\varepsilon_{r\theta} = \varepsilon_{r\theta}^\circ + z\kappa_{r\theta} \qquad (6\text{-}13)$$

in which ε_r°, ε_θ°, and $\varepsilon_{r\theta}^\circ$ are the middle surface strains nonlinearly related to displacements u_r, u_θ, and w by equations (3-10) and κ_r, and $\kappa_{r\theta}$ are the plate curvatures approximated by

$$\kappa_r = -w_{,rr} \qquad \kappa_\theta = -\left(\frac{1}{r}w_{,r} + \frac{1}{r^2}w_{,\theta\theta}\right)$$

$$\kappa_{r\theta} = -2\left(\frac{1}{r}w_{,r\theta} - \frac{1}{r^2}w_{,\theta}\right) \qquad (6\text{-}14)$$

Equations (6-13), (3-10), and (6-14) are the counterpart of equations (1-41) to (1-43) in cartesian coordinates.

In the lagrangian description for finite deformations of an elastic plate, the equations of equilibrium expressed in term of cylindrical coordinates can be found in Ref. 6.4 or elsewhere. Under the ad hoc assumption that the nonlinear terms involving products of stresses and plate slopes are retained, these equations in the dynamic case may be simplified to yield

$$\sigma_{r,r} + \frac{1}{r}\sigma_{r\theta,\theta} + \sigma_{rz,z} + \frac{1}{r}(\sigma_r - \sigma_\theta) = 0 \tag{6-15}$$

$$\sigma_{r\theta,r} + \frac{1}{r}\sigma_{\theta,\theta} + \sigma_{\theta z,z} + \frac{2}{r}\sigma_{r\theta} = 0 \tag{6-16}$$

$$\sigma_r\left(\frac{1}{r}w_{,r} + w_{,rr}\right) + \sigma_\theta\left(\frac{1}{r^2}w_{,\theta\theta}\right) + \sigma_{r\theta}\left(\frac{2}{r}w_{,r\theta}\right)$$

$$+ \frac{1}{r}\sigma_{rz} + \sigma_{r,r}w_{,r} + \sigma_{\theta,\theta}\left(\frac{1}{r^2}w_{,\theta}\right) + \sigma_{z,z}$$

$$+ \sigma_{r\theta,r}\left(\frac{1}{r}w_{,\theta}\right) + \sigma_{r\theta,\theta}\left(\frac{1}{r}w_{,r}\right) + \sigma_{rz,r} + \sigma_{rz,z}w_{,r}$$

$$+ \frac{1}{r}\sigma_{\theta z,\theta} + \sigma_{\theta z,z}\left(\frac{1}{r}w_{,\theta}\right) = \rho_0 w_{,tt} \tag{6-17}$$

in which ρ_0 is the mass density and t is the time. These equations are equivalent to equations (1-44) to (1-46) from which the body force and the inplane and rotatory inertial effects are neglected.

In the case of plane stress the constitutive equations (1-31) for a cylindrically orthotropic material can be written as

$$\sigma_r = \frac{E_r}{1 - \nu_{r\theta}\nu_{\theta r}}(\varepsilon_r + \nu_{\theta r}\varepsilon_\theta)$$

$$\sigma_\theta = \frac{E_\theta}{1 - \nu_{r\theta}\nu_{\theta r}}(\varepsilon_\theta + \nu_{r\theta}\varepsilon_r) \tag{6-18}$$

$$\sigma_{r\theta} = G_{r\theta}\varepsilon_{r\theta}$$

in which E_i are the Young's moduli along the i principal direction of elasticity, ν_{ij} are the Poisson's ratios characterizing the contraction in the j direction during tension applied in the i direction, and $G_{r\theta}$ is shear modulus. Due to symmetry these elastic constants are related by

$$\nu_{r\theta}E_\theta = \nu_{\theta r}E_r \tag{6-19}$$

As in the classical plate theory, the membrane forces, bending moments, and transverse shear forces are defined by equations (3-2). Substituting equations

(6-18) into the first and third of expressions (3-2), taking into account equations (3-10), (6-13), and (6-14), and performing the integration, the following formulas are obtained

$$N_r = \frac{E_r h}{1 - v_{r\theta} v_{\theta r}}$$

$$\cdot \left\{ u_{r,r} + \tfrac{1}{2} w_{,r}^2 + v_{\theta r} \left[\frac{1}{r} (u_r + u_{\theta,\theta}) + \frac{1}{2r^2} w_{,\theta}^2 \right] \right\}$$

$$N_\theta = \frac{E_\theta h}{1 - v_{r\theta} v_{\theta r}} \tag{6-20}$$

$$\cdot \left\{ \frac{1}{r} (u_r + u_{\theta,\theta}) + \frac{1}{2r^2} w_{,\theta}^2 + v_{r\theta} [u_{r,r} + \tfrac{1}{2} w_{,r}^2] \right\}$$

$$N_{rs} = G_{r\theta} h \left[\frac{1}{r} (u_{r,\theta} - u_\theta) + u_{\theta,r} + \frac{1}{r} w_{,r} w_{,\theta} \right]$$

and

$$M_r = -D_r \left[w_{,rr} + v_{\theta r} \left(\frac{1}{r} w_{,r} + \frac{1}{r^2} w_{,\theta\theta} \right) \right]$$

$$M_\theta = -D_\theta \left[\frac{1}{r} w_{,r} + \frac{1}{r^2} w_{,\theta\theta} + v_{r\theta} w_{,rr} \right] \tag{6-21}$$

$$M_{r\theta} = -2D_{r\theta} \left(\frac{1}{r} w_{,r\theta} - \frac{1}{r^2} w_{,\theta} \right)$$

in which D_r and D_θ are bending rigidities given by equations (5-121) and $D_{r\theta}$ is the twisting rigidity defined by

$$D_{r\theta} = \frac{G_{r\theta} h^3}{12} \tag{6-22}$$

Now the equations of motion of the plate are derived by virtue of the classical method of integration. That is, integrating each of equations (6-15) to (6-17) with respect to z from $-h/2$ to $h/2$ and using the definitions (3-2), three equations will be obtained. Then multiplying each of equations (6-15) and (6-16) by z and integrating in a similar manner leads to the other two equations. The system of the resulting equations for the transverse motion of the plate is

$$N_{r,r} + \frac{1}{r} N_{r\theta,\theta} + \frac{1}{r} (N_r - N_\theta) = 0 \tag{6-23}$$

$$N_{r\theta,r} + \frac{1}{r} N_{\theta,\theta} + \frac{2}{r} N_{r\theta} = 0 \tag{6-24}$$

$$N_r\left(\frac{1}{r}w_{,r} + w_{,rr}\right) + N_\theta\left(\frac{1}{r^2}w_{,\theta\theta}\right) + N_{r\theta}\left(\frac{2}{r}w_{,r\theta}\right)$$

$$+ Q_{r,r} + \frac{1}{r}Q_r + \frac{1}{r}Q_{\theta,\theta} + w_{,r}\left(N_{r,r} + \frac{1}{r}N_{r\theta,\theta}\right)$$

$$+ \frac{1}{r}w_{,\theta}\left(N_{r\theta,r} + \frac{1}{r}N_{\theta,\theta}\right) + q = \rho w_{,tt} \qquad (6\text{-}25)$$

$$M_{r,r} + \frac{1}{r}M_{r\theta,\theta} + \frac{1}{r}(M_r - M_\theta) - Q_r = 0 \qquad (6\text{-}26)$$

$$M_{r\theta,r} + \frac{1}{r}M_{\theta,\theta} + \frac{2}{r}M_{r\theta} - Q_\theta = 0 \qquad (6\text{-}27)$$

in which $\rho = \rho_0 h$ is the mass per unit area of the plate and q is the transverse load intensity, and in which the boundary planes of the plate have been assumed to be free from the shear stresses. Except for body force and rotatory and inplane inertial terms, equations (6-23) to (6-27) are equivalent to equations (1-54) to (1-58).

Eliminating Q_r and Q_θ from equations (6-25) to (6-27) and using equations (6-23) and (6-24), we obtain the equation of the transverse motion of the plate

$$M_{r,rr} + \frac{2}{r}M_{r,r} + 2\left(\frac{1}{r}M_{r\theta,r\theta} + \frac{1}{r^2}M_{r\theta,\theta}\right)$$

$$- \left(\frac{1}{r}M_{\theta,r} - \frac{1}{r^2}M_{\theta,\theta\theta}\right) + N_r w_{,rr} + 2N_{r\theta}\left(\frac{1}{r}w_{,r\theta} - \frac{1}{r^2}w_{,\theta}\right)$$

$$+ N_\theta\left(\frac{1}{r}w_{,r} + \frac{1}{r^2}w_{,\theta\theta}\right) + q = \rho w_{,tt} \qquad (6\text{-}28)$$

Equations (6-23), (6-24), and (6-28) constitute a system of equations of the transverse motion of the plate. Substitution of equations (6-20) and (6-21) in these equations will yield a system of equations in three displacements u_r, u_θ, and w on the middle surface of the plate. Alternately, equations (6-23), (6-24), and (6-28) can be expressed in terms of transverse deflection w and stress function F by introducing the stress function defined by (3-6) and the equation of compatibility as follows

$$\frac{1}{r}\left(\frac{1}{r}\varepsilon_{r,\theta\theta}^\circ - \varepsilon_{r,r}^\circ\right) + \frac{1}{r}(r\varepsilon_\theta^\circ)_{,rr} - \frac{1}{r^2}(r\varepsilon_{r\theta}^\circ)_{,r\theta}$$

$$= -\frac{1}{r}w_{,r}w_{,rr} - \frac{1}{r^2}[w_{,rr}w_{,\theta\theta} - w_{,r\theta}^2] - \frac{2}{r^3}w_{,\theta}w_{,r\theta} + \frac{1}{r^4}w_{,\theta}^2 \qquad (6\text{-}29)$$

It is observed that equations (6-23) and (6-24) are exactly satisfied by the stress function defined by equation (3-6). Introduction of expressions (3-6), (3-10), and

(6-21) into equations (6-28) and (6-29) yields

$$D_r L_1 w + D_\theta L_2 w + 2D_c L_3 w + \rho w_{,tt} = q + hL(w, F) \tag{6-30}$$

$$d_\theta L_1 F + d_r L_2 F + 2d_c L_3 F = -\tfrac{1}{2}L(w, w) \tag{6-31}$$

in which L_i are the differential operators defined by

$$L_1(\ ) = (\ )_{,rrrr} + \frac{2}{r}(\ )_{,rrr}$$

$$L_2(\ ) = \frac{1}{r^4}(\ )_{,\theta\theta\theta\theta} - \frac{1}{r^2}(\ )_{,rr} + \frac{2}{r^4}(\ )_{,\theta\theta} + \frac{1}{r^3}(\ )_{,r}$$

$$L_3(\ ) = \frac{1}{r^2}(\ )_{,rr\theta\theta} - \frac{1}{r^3}(\ )_{,r\theta\theta} + \frac{1}{r^4}(\ )_{,\theta\theta}$$

$$L(w, F) = w_{,rr}\left(\frac{1}{r}F_{,r} + \frac{1}{r^2}F_{,\theta\theta}\right) \tag{6-32}$$

$$+ \left(\frac{1}{r}w_{,r} + \frac{1}{r^2}w_{,\theta\theta}\right)F_{,rr} - 2\left(\frac{1}{r}w_{,\theta}\right)_{,r}\left(\frac{1}{r}F_{,\theta}\right)_{,r}$$

$$D_c = v_{\theta r}D_r + D_{r\theta}$$

$$d_\theta = \frac{1}{E_\theta} \qquad d_r = \frac{1}{E_r} \qquad d_c = \frac{1}{2G_{r\theta}} - \frac{v_{r\theta}}{E_r}$$

Equations (6-30) and (6-31) constitute a system of two fourth-order equations in terms of transverse deflection w and stress function F. These equations in the static case reduce to those given in Ref. 6.5 where it is pointed out that they cannot be obtained by applying the transformation equation (3-1). In the case of isotropic plates equations (6-30) and (6-31) are simplified to equations (3-7) and (3-8).

The six initial conditions prescribed throughout the plate are similar to expressions (1-167) and the four boundary conditions associated with equations (6-30) and (6-31) are to be prescribed. Some boundary conditions usually encountered in engineering are given by expressions (3-11) to (3-15). Once a solution for F and w is found, the membrane forces can be calculated from equations (3-6), the bending moments from equations (6-21), and the transverse shear forces from the following

$$Q_r = -\left[D_r\left(w_{,rrr} + \frac{1}{r}w_{,rr}\right) - D_\theta\frac{1}{r}\left(\frac{1}{r}w_{,r} + \frac{1}{r^2}w_{,\theta\theta}\right)\right.$$

$$\left. + (v_{\theta r}D_r + 2D_{r\theta})\frac{1}{r}\left(\frac{1}{r}w_{,r\theta\theta} - \frac{1}{r^2}w_{,\theta\theta}\right)\right] \tag{6-33}$$

$$Q_\theta = -\left[D_\theta\frac{1}{r^2}\left(w_{,r\theta} + \frac{1}{r}w_{,\theta\theta\theta}\right) + (v_{\theta r}D_r + 2D_{r\theta})\frac{1}{r}w_{,rr\theta}\right]$$

which have been obtained from equations (6-21), (6-26), and (6-27). The stresses at an arbitrary point within the plate can be computed from formulas (3-9).

6.5 POSTBUCKLING OF CYLINDRICALLY ORTHOTROPIC ANNULAR PLATE UNDER OUTER EDGE COMPRESSION

Equations of motion for moderately large nonaxisymmetric deflections of a cylindrically orthotropic plate have been derived in the previous section. In the case of axisymmetric postbuckling, equations (6-30) and (6-31) are greatly simplified to yield (Ref. 6.3)

$$\Delta w = \frac{h}{D_r} \frac{1}{r} (w_{,r} F_{,r})_{,r} \qquad (6\text{-}34)$$

$$\Delta F = -\frac{E_\theta}{2r} (w_{,r}^2)_{,r} \qquad (6\text{-}35)$$

where

$$\Delta(\ ) = (\ )_{,rrrr} + \frac{2}{r} (\ )_{,rrr} - \frac{k^2}{r^2} (\ )_{,rr} + \frac{k^2}{r^3} (\ )_{,r}$$

$$k^2 = \frac{E_\theta}{E_r} \qquad (6\text{-}36)$$

Equations (6-34) and (6-35) can be integrated once to give

$$L_4 w = \frac{h}{D_r} w_{,r} F_{,r} + C_1 \qquad (6\text{-}37)$$

$$L_4 F = -\frac{E_\theta}{2} w_{,r}^2 + C_2 \qquad (6\text{-}38)$$

where

$$L_4(\ ) = r \left[(\ )_{,rrr} + \frac{1}{r} (\ )_{,rr} - \frac{k^2}{r^2} (\ )_{,r} \right] \qquad (6\text{-}39)$$

For a circular plate the constants of integration in equations (6-37) and (6-38) are zero because the left-hand sides vanish at $r = 0$ as does $w_{,r}$. In the case of an annular plate, the constant C_1 depends upon the boundary conditions. It can be shown that C_2 is zero by deleting the θ-dependence from the strain-displacement relations and rederiving equation (6-38) as before.

Let us apply equations (6-37) and (6-38) to a cylindrically orthotropic annular plate of outer radius a and inner radius b under uniform radial compressive load. Introducing the following parameters

$$x = \frac{r}{a} \qquad \left(\frac{b}{a} \leq x \leq 1 \qquad 0 \leq b < a \right)$$

$$\beta = -\frac{\alpha}{x} w_{,x} \qquad \eta = \frac{h}{D_r} \frac{1}{x} F_{,x} \qquad \alpha^2 = \frac{6k^2}{h^2} (1 - v_{r\theta} v_{\theta r}) \qquad (6\text{-}40)$$

equations (6-37) and (6-38) transform to

$$L^*\beta = \beta\eta - C_1\alpha\left(\frac{a}{x}\right)^2 \tag{6-41}$$

$$L^*\eta = -\beta^2 \tag{6-42}$$

where

$$L^*(\ ) = (\ )_{,xx} + \frac{3}{x}(\ )_{,x} + \frac{1-k^2}{x^2}(\ ) \tag{6-43}$$

Equations (6-41) and (6-42) constitute a system of two second-order equations to be solved in conjunction with the prescribed boundary conditions. If the plate is free along the inner edge and loosely clamped and uniformly compressed along the outer edge, these boundary conditions can be expressed as

$$x\beta_{,x} + (1 + v_{\theta r})\beta = 0 \qquad \eta = 0 \qquad \text{at} \quad x = \frac{b}{a}$$

$$\beta = 0 \qquad \eta = -N \qquad \text{at} \quad x = 1 \tag{6-44}$$

where N is the edge load parameter.

An approximate solution of equations (6-41) and (6-42) satisfying boundary conditions (6-44) is formulated by the finite-difference method associated with an iterative procedure as in Secs. 2.8 and 4.6. The operator $L^*(\ )$ in the finite-difference form is given by

$$\frac{1}{t^2}[(\ )_{i+1} - 2(\ )_i + (\ )_{i-1}] + \frac{3}{2tx_i}[(\ )_{i+1} - (\ )_{i-1}]$$

$$+ \frac{1-k^2}{x_i^2}(\ )_i \qquad i = 1, m \tag{6-45}$$

In this expression i denotes any mesh point, $t\ (= \Delta x)$ the mesh size, and m the number of mesh points. Applying this operator to equations (6-41) and (6-42) and collecting terms of like subscripts lead to

$$A_i\beta_i + B_i\beta_{i+1} + C_i\beta_{i-1} = \beta_i\eta_i \qquad i = 1, m$$

$$A_i\eta_i + B_i\eta_{i+1} + C_i\eta_{i-1} = -\beta_i^2 \qquad i = 1, m-1 \tag{6-46}$$

$$A_m\eta_m + C_m\eta_{m-1} = -\beta_m^2 - B_m N \qquad i = m$$

where

$$A_i = -\frac{2}{t^2} + \frac{1-k^2}{x_i^2}$$

$$B_i = \frac{1}{t^2} + \frac{3}{2tx_i} \tag{6-47}$$

$$C_i = \frac{1}{t^2} - \frac{3}{2tx_i}$$

Equations (6-46) may be written in the matrix form

$$[H(i, j)][\beta_j] = [\beta_i \eta_i]$$

$$[P(i, j)][\eta_j] = - \begin{bmatrix} \beta_i^2 \\ \vdots \\ \beta_m^2 + B_m N \end{bmatrix} \quad i = 1, m; j = 1, m \qquad (6\text{-}48)$$

where

$$H(i, i) = P(i, i) = A_i$$
$$H(i, i + 1) = P(i, i + 1) = B_i \qquad 1 < i < m \qquad (6\text{-}49)$$
$$H(i, i - 1) = P(i, i - 1) = C_i$$

The values of the elements in the first and last rows of these matrices are obtained from the boundary conditions. The present conditions require that

$$\begin{aligned} H(1, 1) &= A_1 + \delta C_1 & P(1, 1) &= A_1 \\ H(1, 2) &= B_1 & P(1, 2) &= B_1 \\ H(m, m - 1) &= C_m & P(m, m - 1) &= C_m \\ H(m, m) &= A_m & P(m, m) &= A_m \end{aligned} \qquad (6\text{-}50)$$

where

$$\delta = \frac{b}{a} \frac{1}{b/a - t(1 + v_{\theta r})} \qquad (6\text{-}51)$$

Equations (6-48) are the finite-difference equations equivalent to equations (6-41) and (6-42). These nonlinear algebraic equations are solved by the iterative scheme described in Sec. 4.6 for the unknowns β_i and η_i. It was found that 20 mesh points generally were sufficient to give acceptable results using double precision. When the iterations converge for a given load, the membrane forces, bending moments, and slopes can be found. In the nondimensional form the circumferential membrane force and radial and circumferential bending moments may be shown to be

$$\begin{aligned} \eta_\theta &= x\eta_{,x} + \eta \\ \zeta_r &= x\beta_{,x} + (1 + v_{\theta r})\beta \\ \zeta_\theta &= v_{r\theta} x\beta_{,x} + (1 + v_{\theta r})\beta \end{aligned} \qquad (6\text{-}52)$$

in which η is the nondimensional radial membrane force defined in equations (6-40). The nondimensional slope is given by $x\beta$ from which the deflection at a meshing point can be determined.

In the case when the buckling load of the cylindrically orthotropic annular plate (Ref. 6.6)[†] is determined, by virtue of the first of equations (3-6), equation

---

† Reprinted with permission from the American Institute of Aeronautics and Astronautics, *AIAA J.*, vol. 8, 1970.

(6-34) becomes

$$\Delta w = \frac{1}{D_r}\left(N_r w_{,rr} + \frac{1}{r}N_\theta w_{,r}\right) \tag{6-53}$$

The membrane forces in this equation can be derived independently of the transverse deflection from linearization of the compatibility equation (6-38).

$$N_{r,rr} + \frac{3}{r}N_{r,r} + (1 - k^2)\frac{1}{r^2}N_r = 0 \tag{6-54}$$

whose solution is

$$N_r = k_1 r^{(k-1)} + k_2 r^{-(k+1)} \tag{6-55}$$

in which k_1 and k_2 are constants of integration to be determined from the loading conditions at the edges. Substituting expression (6-55) into equation (6-53) and using relation (3-20), the resulting equation can be written in the form

$$\Delta_x w + \Lambda\left[(k_3 x^{k-1} + k_4 x^{-k-1})w_{,xx} + \frac{k}{x}(k_3 x^{k-1} - k_4 x^{-k-1})w_{,x}\right] = 0 \tag{6-56}$$

in which Δ_x is the operator obtained by replacing r in Δ by x and in which

$$k_3 = \frac{k_1 a^{k-1}}{N_0} \qquad k_4 = \frac{k_2 a^{-k-1}}{N_0} \qquad \Lambda = -\frac{N_0 a^2}{D_r} \tag{6-57}$$

Nontrivial solutions of equation (6-56) exist for particular values of the eigenvalue Λ. The first eigenvalue determines the lowest critical buckling load N_{cr}.

Equation (6-56) can be reduced to a second-order equation in terms of slope plus an arbitrary constant. For ease in handling the boundary conditions it is preferred here, however, to proceed with the solution of this equation. Writing equation (6-56) in the finite-difference form and collecting coefficients of terms with like subscripts yields

$$A_i^* w_i + C_i^* w_{i+1} + E_i^* w_{i+1} + F_i^* w_{i-1} + H_i^* w_{i-2}$$
$$- \Lambda(B_i^* w_i + D_i^* w_{i+1} + G_i^* w_{i-1}) = 0 \qquad i = 1, m \tag{6-58}$$

where for the plate loaded along inner and outer edges

$$A_i^* = \frac{6}{t^4} + \frac{2k^2}{t^2 x_i^2}$$

$$B_i^* = 2\left(\frac{R}{t^2}x_i^{k-1} + \frac{S}{t^2}x_i^{-k-1}\right)$$

$$C_i^* = -\frac{4}{t^4} - \frac{2}{t^3 x_i} - \frac{k^2}{t^2 x_i^2} + \frac{k^2}{2t x_i^3}$$

$$D_i^* = -R\left(\frac{1}{t^2} + \frac{k}{2t x_i}\right)x_i^{k-1} - S\left(\frac{1}{t^2} + \frac{k}{2t x_i}\right)x_i^{-k-1}$$

$$E_i^* = \frac{1}{t^4} + \frac{1}{t^3 x_i}$$

$$F_i^* = -\frac{4}{t^4} + \frac{2}{t^3 x_i} - \frac{k^2}{t^2 x_i^2} - \frac{k^2}{2tx_i^3}$$

$$G_i^* = R\left(\frac{k}{2tx_i} - \frac{1}{t^2}\right)x_i^{k-1} + S\left(\frac{k}{2tx_i} - \frac{1}{t^2}\right)x_i^{-k-1} \qquad (6\text{-}59)$$

$$H_i^* = \frac{1}{t^4} - \frac{1}{t^3 x_i}$$

$$R = \frac{1 - (b/a)^{-k-1}}{(b/a)^{-k-1} - (b/a)^{k-1}} \qquad S = \frac{(b/a)^{k-1} - 1}{(b/a)^{-k-1} - (b/a)^{k-1}}$$

Equation (6-58) can be written in the matrix form

$$([M] - \lambda[K])[w] = 0 \qquad (6\text{-}60)$$

where $[M]$ is the matrix whose elements are A_i^*, C_i^*, E_i^*, F_i^*, and H_i^*, $[K]$ is the matrix whose elements are B_i^*, D_i^*, and G_i^*, and $[w]$ is the column vector of the displacement.

The boundary conditions determine the first two and the last two rows of matrix $[M]$ and the first and last rows of matrix $[K]$. Equation (6-60) is expressed

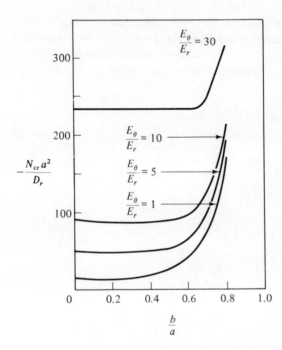

Figure 6.7 Critical buckling loads of cylindrically orthotropic annular plate with free inner edge and loosely clamped and loaded outer edge ($v_{r\theta} = v_{\theta r} = 0.3$).

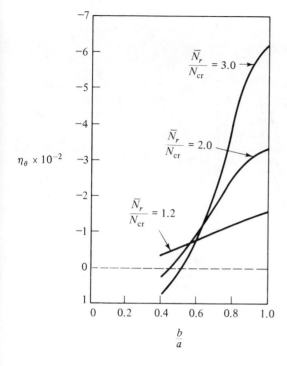

Figure 6.8 Circumferential membrane force versus radius for cylindrically orthotropic annular plate under outer-edge compression $(E_\theta/E_r = 5.0,\ \nu_{r\theta} = \nu_{\theta r} = 0.3,\ b/a = 0.4)$.

in the form amenable with the Vianello-Stodala method (Ref. 6.7).

$$[Q][w] = \frac{1}{\lambda}[I][w] \qquad [Q] = [M]^{-1}[K] \tag{6-61}$$

in which $[I]$ is the identity matrix. To determine the first eigenvalue Λ the aforementioned method was employed. It was found that reasonable convergence occurred in the neighborhood of 15–20 mesh points using double precision.

The critical buckling loads are plotted in Fig. 6.7 against the ratio of radii b/a for different values of the modulus ratio. The curve for $E_\theta/E_r = 1$ corresponds to the isotropic case. The results for the buckling loads of isotropic annular plates are in good agreement with those obtained in Ref. 6.8 for different values of the ratio b/a. The buckling loads at $b/a = 0.8$ approach those of a ring. The edge compressions corresponding to $b/a = 0$ are the buckling loads of circular plates. These values agree with those presented in Ref. 6.9 for different material properties. The postbuckling behavior of the cylindrically orthotropic annular plate is shown in Fig. 6.8 for the distribution of the circumferential membrane force and in Fig. 6.9 for the maximum circumferential membrane force. The applied uniform radial compression per unit length is represented by $\bar{N}_r$. It is observed from Fig. 6.8 that the force parameter η_θ for large loads becomes tensile in the interior of the plate, change abruptly to compression, and reach a compressive maximum at the plate periphery as in the isotropic case. This boundary-layer effect has been noted in Sec. 4.6. Figure 6.9 indicates that for given values of $\bar{N}_r/N_{cr}$ and E_θ/E_r, the

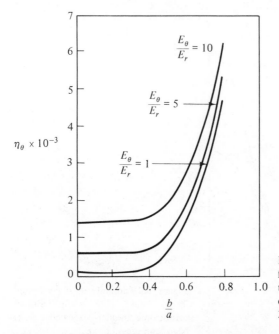

Figure 6.9 Circumferential membrane force at outer edge of cylindrically orthotropic annular plate under outer edge compression $(v_{r\theta} = v_{\theta r} = 0.3, \quad \bar{N}_r/N_{cr} = 3.0)$.

maximum η_θ is relatively constant for $b/a \leq 0.4$. As the inner radius b increases, η_θ increases markedly, especially for large values of $\bar{N}_r/N_{cr}$. This force also increases with increasing the ratio E_θ/E_r.

6.6 POSTBUCKLING OF SYMMETRICALLY LAMINATED AND HOMOGENEOUS ANISOTROPIC RECTANGULAR PLATES WITH ALL-CLAMPED AND ALL-SIMPLY SUPPORTED EDGES

The postbuckling behavior of orthotropic plates has been discussed in the previous sections for rectilinearly and cylindrically orthotropic materials. This study is concerned with the elastic behavior of a symmetrically laminated aniso-tropic rectangular plate after buckling. If the plate is defined as in Sec. 5.10, the governing equations in the nondimensional form can be obtained by deleting the transverse loading term $\lambda^4 Q$ from equations (5-201) and (5-202). The non-dimensional membrane forces and bending moments are given by expressions (5-204) and (5-206) respectively. The plate is assumed to be subjected to the inplane compressive forces per unit length, n_x in the x direction and n_y in the y direction. If the edges of the plate are all clamped and all simply supported and free from the inplane tangential boundary force, the boundary conditions for the clamped movable plate are given by equations (6-2) with notations defined in Sec. 5.10. The boundary conditions for the simply supported plate are

$$W = M_\zeta = F_{,\zeta\eta} = 0 \qquad F_{,\eta\eta} = -R \qquad \text{along} \quad \zeta = 0, 1$$

$$W = M_\eta = F_{,\zeta\eta} = 0 \qquad F_{,\zeta\zeta} = -\lambda^2 kR \qquad \text{along} \quad \eta = 0, 1 \tag{6-62}$$

where k is defined in equations (6-4) and where

$$R = \frac{n_x b^2}{A_{22} h^2} \tag{6-63}$$

Equations (5-201) and (5-202) in which $Q = 0$ are to be solved in conjunction with boundary conditions (6-2) and (6-62), respectively. The functions F and W are expressed in the form of generalized double Fourier series (Ref. 6.10) given by equations (6-5) to (6-9). In the case of clamped movable edges, the boundary conditions are all satisfied. In the case of simply supported movable edges, except for the vanishing of normal bending moment, the boundary conditions are also satisfied. The edge condition for the bending moment can be fulfilled by following a similar calculation as in Sec. 5.11.

In the case of clamped movable edges expression (6-5) can be substituted into equations (5-201) and (5-202) after deletion of the term $\lambda^4 Q$. In the case of simply supported edges, the fourth derivatives $W_{,\zeta\zeta\zeta\zeta}$, $W_{,\zeta\zeta\zeta\eta}$, $W_{,\zeta\eta\eta\eta}$, and $W_{,\eta\eta\eta\eta}$ are obtained from the cosine-sine series for $W_{,\zeta\zeta\zeta}$ and $W_{,\eta\eta\eta}$ as in Sec. 5.11, and the other derivatives of W are obtained from equation (6-5). These derivatives and expression for F are substituted into the above governing equations. In both cases, multiplying the first resulting equation by $X_i(\zeta)Y_i(\eta)$, and the second by $\phi_i(\zeta)\psi_j(\eta)$, integrating with respect to ζ and η from 0 to 1, and using the orthogonal relations (5-38) and (5-43) lead to the following equations

$$F_{ij}(\alpha_i^4 \bar{A}_{22} + \lambda^4 \alpha_j^4 \bar{A}_{11}) - \sum_{m=1}^{\infty} \sum_{n=1}^{\infty} F_{mn}$$

$$\cdot [2\lambda \alpha_m^3 \alpha_n K_9^{im} L_8^{jn} \bar{A}_{26} - \lambda^2 \alpha_m^2 \alpha_n^2 K_5^{im} L_5^{jn}(2\bar{A}_{12} + \bar{A}_{66}) - 2\lambda^3 \alpha_m \alpha_n^3 K_8^{im} L_9^{jn} \bar{A}_{16}]$$

$$= \lambda^2 \sum_{p=1}^{\infty} \sum_{q=1}^{\infty} \sum_{r=1}^{\infty} \sum_{s=1}^{\infty} W_{pq} W_{rs}(\beta_p \beta_q \beta_r \beta_s K_6^{ipr} L_6^{jqs} - \beta_p^2 \beta_s^2 K_7^{ipr} L_7^{jsq}) \tag{6-64}$$

$$W_{ij}(\beta_i^4 \bar{D}_{11} + \lambda^4 \beta_j^4 \bar{D}_{22}) + \sum_{p=1}^{\infty} \sum_{q=1}^{\infty} W_{pq}$$

$$\cdot [4\lambda \beta_p^3 \beta_q K_{11}^{ip} L_{10}^{jq} \bar{D}_{16} + 2\lambda^2 \beta_p^2 \beta_q^2 K_1^{ip} L_1^{jq}$$

$$\cdot (\bar{D}_{12} + 2\bar{D}_{66}) + 4\lambda^3 \beta_p \beta_q^3 K_{10}^{ip} L_{11}^{jq} \bar{D}_{26}]$$

$$+ \varepsilon \left\{ \sum_{r=1}^{\infty} \sum_{s=1}^{\infty} W_{rs} \beta_r \beta_s \left[\frac{32\lambda^2 \bar{D}_{16}^2}{D_{11}} \right. \right.$$

$$\cdot \left. \left(\sum_{q=1}^{\infty} \frac{\beta_q}{2} K_{12}^i C_r L_{10}^{jq} L_{10}^{qs} + \sum_{p=1}^{\infty} \sum_{q=1}^{\infty} \beta_q K_{10}^{ip} L_{10}^{jq} L_{10}^{qs} C_{pr} \right) \right.$$

▼

$$+ \frac{32\lambda^2 \bar{D}_{26}^2}{D_{22}} \left(\sum_{p=1}^{\infty} \frac{\beta_q}{2} K_{10}^{jq} K_{10}^{pr} L_{12}^j C_s + \sum_{p=1}^{\infty} \sum_{q=1}^{\infty} \beta_p K_{10}^{ip} K_{10}^{pr} L_{10}^{jq} C_{qs} \right) \right]$$

$$- \sum_{p=1}^{\infty} \sum_{q=1}^{\infty} W_{pq} \beta_p \beta_q (8\lambda \beta_i L_{10}^{jq} C_{ip} \bar{D}_{16} + 8\lambda^3 \beta_j K_{10}^{ip} C_{jq} \bar{D}_{26}) \Big\}$$

$$- \lambda^2 \sum_{m=1}^{\infty} \sum_{n=1}^{\infty} \sum_{r=1}^{\infty} \sum_{s=1}^{\infty} F_{mn} W_{rs}$$

$$\cdot (\alpha_n^2 \beta_r^2 K_2^{imr} L_3^{jns} + \alpha_m^2 \beta_s^2 K_3^{imr} L_2^{jns} - 2\alpha_m \alpha_n \beta_r \beta_s K_4^{imr} L_4^{jns})$$

$$+ \lambda^2 R \left(\sum_{p=1}^{\infty} W_{pj} \beta_p^2 K_1^{ip} + k\lambda^2 \sum_{q=1}^{\infty} W_{iq} \beta_q^2 K_1^{jq} \right) = 0 \qquad (6\text{-}65)$$

In equations (6-64) and (6-65) K_i and L_i $(i = 1, 2, \ldots, 7)$ are defined by equations (5-48) and $\varepsilon = 0$ for a clamped plate, $\varepsilon = 1$ for a simply supported plate, and

$$K_8^{im} = \frac{1}{\alpha_m} \int_0^1 X_i X_m' \, d\zeta \qquad K_9^{im} = \frac{1}{\alpha_m^3} \int_0^1 X_i X_m'' \, d\zeta$$

$$K_{10}^{ip} = \frac{1}{\beta_p H_i} \int_0^1 \phi_i \phi_p' \, d\zeta \qquad K_{11}^{ip} = \frac{1}{\beta_p^3 H_i} \int_0^1 \phi_i \phi_p''' \, d\zeta \qquad (6\text{-}66)$$

$$K_{12}^i = \frac{1}{H_i} \int_0^1 \phi_i \, d\zeta$$

$$C_i = \begin{cases} 0, & i = \text{even} \\ 1, & i = \text{odd} \end{cases} \qquad C_{ij} = \begin{cases} 0, & i + j = \text{even} \\ 1, & i + j = \text{odd} \end{cases}$$

where primes denote differentiation with respect to the corresponding coordinate. The constants, L_8 to L_{12}, in equations (6-64) and (6-65) are obtained by replacing K, i, m, p, x, ϕ, and ζ in equations (6-70) by L, j, n, q, y, ψ, and η, respectively.

Equations (6-64) and (6-65) constitute a set of simultaneous nonlinear algebraic equations which are to be solved for the coefficients W_{pq} and F_{mn}. As soon as these coefficients are determined, the deflections, membrane forces, and bending moments can be found from equations (6-5), (5-204), and (5-206), respectively.

Numerical results are presented for homogeneous and symmetric angle-ply graphite-epoxy square plates. The elastic moduli typical of this material are given by equations (5-213). In the case of a symmetric angle-ply plate, the layers are considered to be of the same thickness and the orthotropic axes in each layer are oriented alternately at $+45°$ and $-45°$ with respect to the plate axes. The elastic stiffnesses for each layer in the directions of the plate axes can be obtained by the classical equations of transformation (1-36) and (1-38). In the case of homogeneous anisotropic plate the filaments are oriented at an angle θ with respect to the plate x axis, and the values of orientation angle θ used in calculation are 0 (orthotropic), 15, 30, and 45°. In these cases A_{22} can be replaced by $E_T h$, and this change will not alter the form of other equations.

Taking a finite number of terms in each of the truncated series (6-5), the corresponding system of coupled nonlinear algebraic equations (6-64) and (6-65) is solved by an iterative procedure. The values of the applied load ratio k $(= n_y/n_x)$ and deflection coefficient W_{11} are prescribed, and an initial guess for the other W_{ij} is made. Equations (6-64) then become linear in F_{ij} and are of the form

$$\mathbf{HF} = \mathbf{B} \tag{6-67}$$

where $\mathbf{H}$ and $\mathbf{B}$ are constant matrices and where

$$\mathbf{F} = [F_{11} \ F_{12} \ ...]^T \tag{6-68}$$

The solution for F_{ij} substituted into equations (6-65) results in a set of simultaneous nonlinear algebraic equations in R and W_{ij} (not both $i, j = 1$). The resulting equations can be written as

$$\mathbf{PW} + R\mathbf{SW} = 0 \tag{6-69}$$

where $\mathbf{P}$ and $\mathbf{S}$ are constant matrices and where

$$\mathbf{W} = [W_{11}, W_{12}, ...]^T \tag{6-70}$$

This system of equations is solved by the Newton-Raphson method for R and W_{ij} (not both $i, j = 1$). These values of R and W_{ij} are substituted into equations (6-67) to obtain a set of new values for F_{ij}. This process is repeated until the desired accuracy is obtained. The convergence criterion in the iterative procedure is that the difference between the final value for the nondimensional central deflection of the plate and the average of the results of three previous iterations is less than one percent.

In order to study the convergence of the series solution, calculations were made for the central deflection w_c of a square clamped angle-ply laminate subjected to uniform biaxial edge compression and of a square simply supported homogeneous anisotropic plate under uniform uniaxial compression by use of 25 $(i, j = 1, 2, ..., 5)$ and 49 $(i, j = 1, 2, ..., 7)$ terms in each of the truncated series for F and W. The results are presented in Table 6.4 in which R_{cr} is the nondimensional buckling load defined later. It is seen that the convergence of the series solution is reasonably rapid. Based on this result, the first 49 terms in each of the truncated series for F and W are taken into calculation in this work.

The nondimensional buckling load R_{cr} is defined by $n_{cr} b^2/E_T h^3$ in which n_{cr} is the applied uniform edge compression at buckling and can be calculated by dropping all the nonlinear terms in equation (6-65). The result for the buckling load of a square anisotropic plate under uniform biaxial compression for various values of θ agrees very well with that obtained in Refs. 5.14 and 5.19. In the case of postbuckling of isotropic and orthotropic plates, the present results are in good agreement with those given in Secs. 4.3 and 6.2. The details are not presented herein.

The numerical results are graphically presented in Figs. 6.10 and 6.11 for symmetric angle-ply laminates and in Fig. 6.12 for a homogeneous anisotropic

Table 6.4 Comparison of solutions for central deflections of angle-ply and homogeneous anisotropic graphite-epoxy square plates under edge compression

	Simply supported anisotropic plate ($\theta = 15°$, $n_y = 0$)			Clamped five-layer $\pm 45°$ angle-ply laminate ($n_y = n_x$)	
	25 terms	49 terms		25 terms	49 terms
R_{cr}	31.3878	31.7128	R_{cr}	57.1917	57.5386
w_c/h	R		w_c/h	R	
0.50	32.1084	32.3856	0.65	58.4008	57.9836
1.10	33.0546	33.4062	1.30	62.5518	61.8417
1.60	34.8563	35.1515	1.95	69.0773	69.0466
2.10	37.0639	37.5632	2.25	72.8012	72.7400
2.55	39.9221	40.7612	2.50	76.5211	76.4675

plate. A simply supported plate is denoted by SS and a clamped plate by CC. Figure 6.10 shows the relation between uniform biaxial compression and central deflection w_c for homogeneous anisotropic ($n = 1$, $\theta = 45°$) and symmetrically laminated $\pm 45°$ angle-ply plates with all-simply supported and all-clamped edges. The edge compression corresponding to $w_c = 0$ is the biaxial critical buckling load. It is observed that for a given central deflection the applied edge compression increases with increasing the number of layers. The curve for a 7-layer plate (not shown here) is close to that for a plate consisting of an infinite number

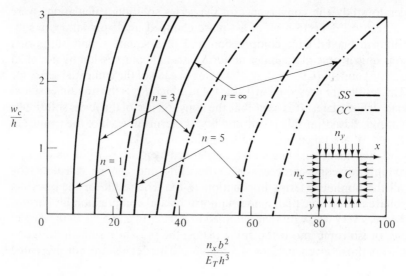

Figure 6.10 Load-deflection curves for symmetrically laminated $\pm 45°$ angle-ply graphite-epoxy square plate under biaxial compression ($n_x = n_y$).

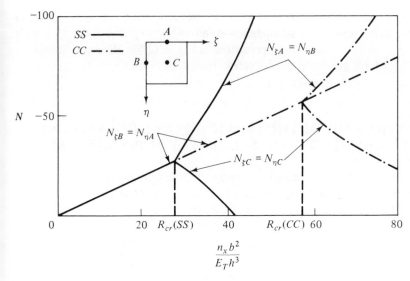

Figure 6.11 Membrane forces at various points in symmetrically laminated 5-layer $\pm 45°$ angle-ply graphite-epoxy square plate under biaxial compression.

of layers. The applied edge compression required to produce a given central deflection is larger in the case of a clamped plate than that required for a simply supported plate. The central membrane forces shown in Fig. 6.11 increase with the edge compression until the buckling load is reached and then decrease as the edge compression is further increased. The largest membrane force occurs at the middle

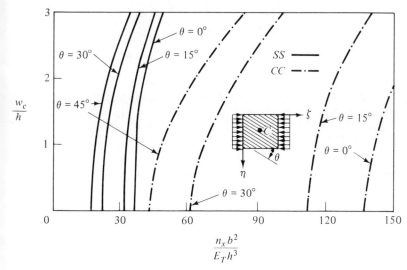

Figure 6.12 Relation between uniaxial compression and center deflection of anisotropic graphite-epoxy square plate.

points of the sides. The relation between uniaxial compression in the x direction and central deflection of a homogeneous anisotropic plate with all-simply supported and all-clamped edges is presented in Fig. 6.12 for different values of θ. It is found that for a given central deflection the edge compression decreases with increasing the orientation angle θ.

6.7 VIBRATION OF ORTHOTROPIC RECTANGULAR PLATE WITH ALL-CLAMPED AND ALL-SIMPLY SUPPORTED EDGES

Consider a thin orthotropic rectangular plate with length $2a_0$ in the x direction and width $2b_0$ in the y direction (Fig. 2.1) with its material axes of symmetry parallel to these coordinates. The plate is assumed to be excited by a transverse load of intensity q and to undergo the moderately large amplitude flexural vibration. If the edges of the plate are all simply supported and all clamped, these transverse supporting conditions are, for simply supported edges,

$$w = w_{,xx} + v_{21} w_{,yy} = 0 \quad \text{at} \quad x = \pm a_0$$

$$w = w_{,yy} + v_{12} w_{,xx} = 0 \quad \text{at} \quad y = \pm b_0$$

$$(6\text{-}71)$$

and for clamped edges,

$$w = w_{,x} = 0 \quad \text{at} \quad x = \pm a_0$$

$$w = w_{,y} = 0 \quad \text{at} \quad y = \pm b_0$$

$$(6\text{-}72)$$

The inplane boundary conditions under consideration are that the plate edges are uniformly displaced by a distribution of normal stresses with zero resultant. These conditions are

$$P_x = \psi_{,xy} = 0 \quad u^\circ = \text{constant} \quad \text{at} \quad x = \pm a_0$$

$$P_y = \psi_{,xy} = 0 \quad v^\circ = \text{constant} \quad \text{at} \quad y = \pm b_0$$

$$(6\text{-}73)$$

in which ψ is the force function and δ_x and δ_y are elongations of the plate in the x and y directions, respectively, and in which P_x and P_y are the resultants of normal boundary forces given by

$$P_x = \int_{-b_0}^{b_0} \psi_{,yy} \, dy \qquad P_y = \int_{-a_0}^{a_0} \psi_{,xx} \, dx \qquad (6\text{-}74)$$

In equations (6-73) the inplane displacements u° and v° are related to the force function by

$$u^\circ = \int_0^x \left[\frac{\psi_{,yy}}{E_1 h} - v_{21} \frac{\psi_{,xx}}{E_2 h} - \tfrac{1}{2} w_{,x}^2 \right] dx$$

$$v^\circ = \int_0^y \left[\frac{\psi_{,xx}}{E_2 h} - v_{12} \frac{\psi_{,yy}}{E_1 h} - \tfrac{1}{2} w_{,y}^2 \right] dy$$

$$(6\text{-}75)$$

It is observed that these boundary conditions in the isotropic case will reduce to Cases I(c) and II(c) given in Sec. 4.8.

As in the aforementioned section, a one-term approximate solution of the governing equations (1-158) and (1-159) satisfying the boundary conditions is formulated in each case by the Galerkin procedure (Ref. 6.11). The deflection function w is assumed to be, for simply supported movable edges,

$$w = hf(t) \cos \frac{\pi x}{2a_0} \cos \frac{\pi y}{2b_0} \tag{6-76}$$

and for clamped movable edges,

$$w = \tfrac{1}{4}hf(t)\left(1 + \cos \frac{\pi x}{a_0}\right)\left(1 + \cos \frac{\pi y}{b_0}\right) \tag{6-77}$$

which satisfy conditions (6-71) and (6-72), respectively. The force function ψ in each case is then determined from the compatibility equation (1-159) and conditions (6-73) as in Sec. 4.8. The details are not presented herein. Now equation (1-158) is satisfied approximately by the Galerkin procedure to furnish an ordinary differential equation for the time function.

In the case of free vibration this equation is given by

$$f_{,\tau\tau} + \omega_0^2 f + \varepsilon^2 f^3 = 0 \qquad \tau = \frac{t}{a_0^2}\left(\frac{D_1}{\rho}\right)^{1/2} \tag{6-78}$$

in which the coefficients ω_0^2 and ε^2 are, for simply supported movable edges,

$$\omega_0^2 = \frac{\pi^4}{16}(1 + 2\beta\lambda^2 + \gamma\lambda^4)$$

$$\varepsilon^2 = \frac{3\pi^4}{64}(1 + \lambda^4)(\gamma - v_{21}^2) \tag{6-79}$$

and for clamped movable edges,

$$\omega_0^2 = \frac{\pi^4}{9}(3 + 2\beta\lambda^2 + 3\gamma\lambda^4)$$

$$\varepsilon^2 = \frac{\pi^4}{24}\lambda^2 H(\gamma - v_{21}^2) \tag{6-80}$$

In equations (6-79) and (6-80) β, γ, λ, and H are given by

$$\beta = \frac{D_3}{D_1} = v_{21} + \frac{2G_{12}}{E_1}(1 - v_{12}v_{21}) \qquad \gamma = \frac{E_2}{E_1} \qquad \lambda = \frac{a_0}{b_0}$$

$$H = \frac{17}{8}\lambda^2 + \frac{17}{8\gamma\lambda^2} + \frac{4\lambda^2}{1 + \alpha\lambda^2 + \gamma\lambda^4} + \frac{\lambda^2}{1 + 4\alpha\lambda^2 + 16\gamma\lambda^4}$$

$$+ \frac{\lambda^2}{16 + 4\alpha\lambda^2 + \gamma\lambda^4} \tag{6-81}$$

$$\alpha = \frac{E_2}{G_{12}} - 2v_{21}$$

For the isotropic case the coefficients given by equations (6-79) and (6-80) agree exactly with those for Cases I(c) and II(c) given in Sec. 4.8. Noting that equation (6-78) is identical in form with equation (4-161), the relationship between the period T and the nondimensional amplitude A is obtained by setting $\varepsilon = \alpha$ in equation (4-166) with ω_0 given in equation (6-79) or (6-80).

In the case of static large deflections of an orthotropic rectangular plate the Galerkin procedure gives the following approximate load-deflection relation for simply supported movable edges

$$\frac{q_0 a_0^4}{D_1 h} = \frac{\pi^6}{256}\left[(1 + 2\beta\lambda^2 + \gamma\lambda^4)\frac{w_m}{h} + \tfrac{3}{4}(\gamma - v_{21}^2)(1 + \lambda^4)\left(\frac{w_m}{h}\right)^3\right] \quad (6\text{-}82)$$

and, for clamped movable edges,

$$\frac{q_0 a_0^4}{D_1 h} = \frac{\pi}{16}\left[(3 + 2\beta\lambda^2 + 3\gamma\lambda^4)\frac{w_m}{h} + \tfrac{3}{8}\lambda^2 H(\gamma - v_{21}^2)\left(\frac{w_m}{h}\right)^3\right] \quad (6\text{-}83)$$

in which q_0 is the intensity of a uniform transverse load and w_m is the maximum deflection.

6.8 MULTIMODE APPROACH TO FREE VIBRATION OF ORTHOTROPIC RECTANGULAR PLATE WITH ALL-CLAMPED AND ALL-SIMPLY SUPPORTED EDGES

In the previous section only a single-mode analysis has been made for the moderately large amplitude vibration of orthotropic plates. Hence the effect of coupling of vibrating modes on the nonlinear period or frequency of a particular vibrating mode is neglected. In this study the coupling effect is examined by use of a series solution (Ref. 6.12). Let us consider a thin orthotropic rectangular plate of length a in the x direction and width b in the y direction (Fig. 2.11). The material axes of symmetry are assumed to be parallel to the edges of the plate. The differential equations governing the nonlinear free flexural vibration of the plate obtained by deleting the transverse loading term in equations (1-158) and (1-159) can be expressed in the nondimensional form as

$$c_1 F_{,\zeta\zeta\zeta\zeta} + 2\lambda^2 c_2 F_{,\zeta\zeta\eta\eta} + \lambda^4 F_{,\eta\eta\eta\eta}$$
$$= c_1\lambda^2[W_{,\zeta\eta}^2 - W_{,\zeta\zeta} W_{,\eta\eta}] \quad (6\text{-}84)$$

$$c_1 W_{,\zeta\zeta\zeta\zeta} + 2\lambda^2 c_3 W_{,\zeta\zeta\eta\eta} + \lambda^4 W_{,\eta\eta\eta\eta} + \mu\lambda^4 W_{,\tau\tau}$$
$$= \mu\lambda^2(W_{,\zeta\zeta} F_{,\eta\eta} + W_{,\eta\eta} F_{,\zeta\zeta} - 2W_{,\zeta\eta} F_{,\zeta\eta}) \quad (6\text{-}85)$$

where

$$\zeta = \frac{x}{a} \qquad \eta = \frac{y}{b} \qquad \tau = t\left(\frac{E_2 h^3}{\rho b^4}\right)^{1/2} \qquad \lambda = \frac{a}{b}$$

▼

$$W = \frac{w}{h} \qquad F = \frac{\psi}{E_2 h^3} \qquad \mu = 12(1 - v_{12} v_{21})$$

$$c_1 = \frac{E_1}{E_2} \qquad c_2 = \frac{1}{2}\left(\frac{E_1}{G_{12}} - 2v_{12}\right) \qquad c_3 = v_{12} + \frac{\mu G_{12}}{6E_2}$$

(6-86)

The membrane forces are related to the nondimensional force function F by

$$(N_x, N_y, N_{xy}) = \frac{E_2 h^3}{b^2}\left(F_{,\eta\eta}, \frac{1}{\lambda^2} F_{,\zeta\zeta}, -\frac{1}{\lambda} F_{,\zeta\eta}\right)$$

(6-87)

If the edges of the plate are free from applied inplane forces, the boundary conditions in the nondimensional form are, for a clamped plate,

$$W = W_{,\zeta} = F_{,\eta\eta} = F_{,\zeta\eta} = 0 \qquad \text{at} \quad \zeta = 0, 1$$

$$W = W_{,\eta} = F_{,\zeta\zeta} = F_{,\zeta\eta} = 0 \qquad \text{at} \quad \eta = 0, 1$$

(6-88)

and for a simply supported plate,

$$W = W_{,\zeta\zeta} = F_{,\eta\eta} = F_{,\zeta\eta} = 0 \qquad \text{at} \quad \zeta = 0, 1$$

$$W = W_{,\eta\eta} = F_{,\zeta\zeta} = F_{,\zeta\eta} = 0 \qquad \text{at} \quad \eta = 0, 1$$

(6-89)

Equations (6-84) and (6-85) are to be solved in conjunction with boundary conditions (6-88) and (6-89) respectively.

A solution of equations (6-84) and (6-85) is sought in the form of double series

$$F = \sum_{m=1}^{\infty} \sum_{n=1}^{\infty} F_{mn}(\tau) X_m(\zeta) Y_n(\eta)$$

$$W = \sum_{p=1}^{\infty} \sum_{q=1}^{\infty} W_{pq}(\tau) \phi_p(\zeta) \psi_q(\eta)$$

(6-90)

in which X_m, Y_n, ϕ_p, and ψ_q are beam eigenfunctions given by equations (5-36) and (5-37) and F_{mn} and W_{pq} are variable coefficients, both functions of τ only. In equations (5-36) and (5-37) the coefficients α_i, β_i, γ_i, A_i, and B_i depend on the boundary conditions. The values of α_i and γ_i are given in Table 5.1. The values of β_i, A_i, and B_i are determined from equations (5-41) for a clamped plate and from equations (5-42) for a simply supported plate. Using the appropriate values of these coefficients the boundary conditions (6-88) and (6-89) are all satisfied.

Now we insert expressions (6-90) into equations (6-84) and (6-85). As in Sec. 6.6 the first of the resulting equations is multiplied by $X_i(\zeta)Y_j(\eta)$ and the second by $\phi_i(\zeta)\psi_j(\eta)$ and integrated over the domain $\zeta = 0$ to 1 and $\eta = 0$ to 1. In view of relations (5-38) and (5-43), a system of equations for the time functions F_{ij} and W_{mn} is obtained as follows

$$A_{ij}^{mn} F_{mn}(\tau) = B_{ij}^{pqrs} W_{pq}(\tau) W_{rs}(\tau)$$

(6-91)

$$\mu\lambda^4 W_{ij,\tau\tau} + C_{ij}^{pq} W_{pq}(\tau) + G_{ij}^{mnrs} F_{mn}(\tau) W_{rs}(\tau) = 0$$

(6-92)

in which repeated indices in a term except for τ indicate summation with respect to these indices. The coefficient matrices A, B, C, and G in these equations are given by

$$A_{ij}^{mn} = \delta_i^m \delta_j^n (c_1 \alpha_m^4 + \lambda^4 \alpha_n^4) + 2\lambda^2 c_2 \alpha_m^2 \alpha_n^2 K_5^{im} L_5^{jn}$$

$$B_{ij}^{pqrs} = \lambda^2 c_1 (\beta_p \beta_q \beta_r \beta_s K_6^{ipr} L_6^{jqs} - \beta_p^2 \beta_s^2 K_7^{ipr} L_7^{jsq})$$

$$C_{ij}^{pq} = \delta_i^p \delta_j^q (c_1 \beta_p^4 + \lambda^4 \beta_q^4) + 2\lambda^2 c_3 \beta_p^2 \beta_q^2 K_1^{ip} L_1^{jq} \qquad (6\text{-}93)$$

$$G_{ij}^{pqrs} = -\mu \lambda^2 (\alpha_n^2 \beta_r^2 K_2^{imr} L_3^{jns}$$

$$+ \alpha_m^2 \beta_s^2 K_3^{imt} L_2^{jns} - 2\alpha_m \alpha_n \beta_r \beta_s K_4^{imr} L_4^{jns})$$

In these expressions K_i and L_i ($i = 1$ to 7) are constants given by equations (5-48) and δ_i^j is the Kronecker delta defined by

$$\delta_i^j = \begin{cases} 1 & \text{if } i = j \\ 0 & \text{if } i \neq j \end{cases} \qquad (6\text{-}94)$$

Equations (6-91) can be solved for the coefficients F_{ij} and written as

$$F_{ij}(\tau) = N_{ij}^{pqrs} W_{pq}(\tau) W_{rs}(\tau) \qquad (6\text{-}95)$$

in which

$$[N_{ij}^{pqrs}] = [A_{mn}^{ij}]^{-1} [B_{mn}^{pqrs}] \qquad (6\text{-}96)$$

Substituting equations (6-95) into equations (6-92) leads to a system of ordinary differential equations for time functions $W_{mn}(\tau)$.

$$\mu \lambda^4 W_{ij,\tau\tau} + C_{ij}^{pq} W_{pq} + M_{ij}^{pqrskl} W_{pq} W_{rs} W_{kl} = 0 \qquad (6\text{-}97)$$

in which

$$[M_{ij}^{pqrskl}] = [G_{ij}^{mnpq}][N_{mn}^{rskl}] \qquad (6\text{-}98)$$

Since an exact solution to equations (6-97) is very difficult, an approximate solution is formulated by using the method of harmonic balance (Ref. 6.13). The time-dependent deflection coefficients $W_{ij}(\tau)$ are expanded into a Fourier cosine series in τ as

$$W_{ij}(\tau) = a_{ij}^{(1)} \cos \omega\tau + a_{ij}^{(3)} \cos 3\omega\tau + \cdots \qquad (6\text{-}99)$$

in which $a_{ij}^{(n)}$ are constant coefficients and ω is the nonlinear circular frequency. Equation (6-99) is substituted into equations (6-97), each term is converted into the first power of cosine functions, and the coefficients of like terms of cosine are set to zero. This results in a system of simultaneous nonlinear algebraic equations in $a_{ij}^{(n)}$. These equations are solved for the coefficients $a_{ij}^{(n)}$ by the Newton-Raphson method for a given set of plate parameters and the nonlinear frequency ω_{mn} of the (m, n) mode of vibration with m and n being the numbers of half-waves in the x and y directions, respectively.

Numerical computations were performed for glass-epoxy, boron-epoxy and graphite-epoxy rectangular plates. The elastic constants typical of these materials are given in Table 5.2. The first sixteen terms considered in the truncated series for

Table 6.5 Linear frequency parameter,
$\omega_{11}^{(0)} b^2 (\rho / E_T h^3)^{1/2}$, **of fundamental mode**

Material	λ	Clamped plate	Simply supported plate
Glass-epoxy	1.0	14.2041	7.3171
Boron-epoxy	1.0	22.0095	10.2048
Graphite-epoxy	1.0	41.8537	18.8052
	1.5	19.6560	9.0217
	2.0	12.4145	5.7905

deflection W are grouped into symmetric-symmetric, symmetric-antisymmetric, antisymmetric-symmetric, and antisymmetric-antisymmetric vibrating modes about two center lines of the plate parallel to x and y axes, respectively. The total deflection in each group is a combination of four similar deflections or modes which change with the time according to the law of simple harmonic motion.

The linear frequencies of a clamped orthotropic rectangular plate obtained from the present solution using the first four symmetric modes (m, $n = 1, 3$) and the first term in the time series agree well with those for the fundamental and second symmetrical modes given in Ref. 6.14, but these results are not presented here. In the presentation of numerical results, the ratio of the nonlinear frequency ω_{mn} to the corresponding linear frequency $\omega_{mn}^{(0)}$ is used and hence the linear frequency of the fundamental mode obtained by taking m, $n = 1, 3$ and the first two terms in the time series is shown in Table 6.5 for various plate materials. The nonlinear frequency of the fundamental mode for a square graphite-epoxy plate obtained by taking the same terms as above are presented in Table 6.6.

It is observed that for a given frequency the amplitude w_m predicted by the single-mode solution is appreciably less than that given by the four-mode solution. At the amplitude-to-thickness ratio 2.8, the single-mode solution yields an

Table 6.6 Frequency ratio of fundamental vibration of square graphite-epoxy plate

Simply supported plate			Clamped plate		
	w_m/h			w_m/h	
$\dfrac{\omega_{11}}{\omega_{11}^{(0)}}$	Single-mode	Four-mode	$\dfrac{\omega_{11}}{\omega_{11}^{(0)}}$	Single-mode	Four-mode
1.010	0.9808	0.9907	1.011	1.4446	1.4832
1.022	1.4334	1.4728	1.020	1.8535	1.9418
1.037	1.8773	1.9462	1.030	2.2637	2.3891
1.055	2.3012	2.4136	1.035	2.4271	2.6103
1.076	2.7037	2.8776	1.041	2.6039	2.8305

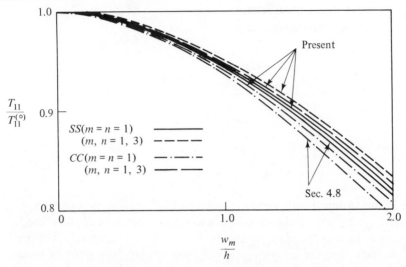

Figure 6.13 Comparison of solutions for nonlinear period of fundamental vibration of isotropic square plate.

error more than 6 percent for all-simply supported edges and 8 percent for all-clamped edges. The nonlinear period of the fundamental mode T_{11} for a square isotropic plate obtained by the present solution is compared with that obtained in Sec. 4.8 in Fig. 6.13 where SS and CC stand for all-simply supported and all-clamped edges, respectively. The present result is based on the first term in the time series and the single-mode and the multimode solutions. In the figure $T_{11}^{(0)}$ is

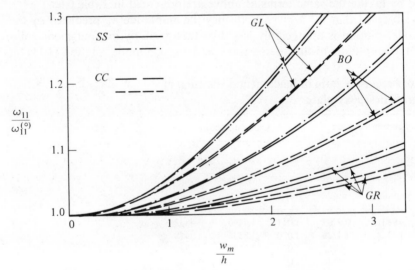

Figure 6.14 Effect of elastic properties on nonlinear frequency of orthotropic square plate (In Eq. 6-99, one term —·— and – – – – and two terms ——— and — —).

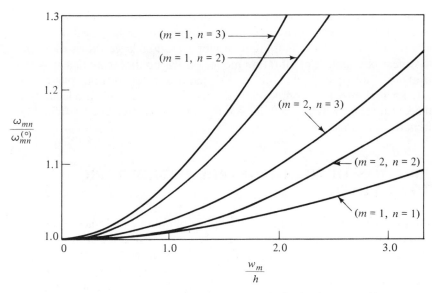

$\dfrac{\omega_{mn}}{\omega_{mn}^{(o)}}$

$(m = 1,\ n = 3)$

$(m = 1,\ n = 2)$

$(m = 2,\ n = 3)$

$(m = 2,\ n = 2)$

$(m = 1,\ n = 1)$

$\dfrac{w_m}{h}$

Figure 6.15 Nonlinear frequencies of various vibrating modes for simply supported boron-epoxy square plates.

the corresponding linear period of the fundamental mode. A good agreement between the two sets of results is noted for all-clamped and all-simply supported edges. At the amplitude twice the plate thickness, the maximum difference between the present frequencies obtained from single-mode and four-mode solutions is approximately 2.5 percent for both sets of edge conditions. Figure 6.14 shows the relation between the frequency ratio of the fundamental vibration and the relative amplitude of a square orthotropic plate for all-simply supported and all-clamped edges. In the figure *GL*, *BO*, and *GR* represent glass-epoxy, boron-epoxy, and graphite-epoxy composites, respectively. In calculation, the first term and the first two terms in the truncated time series and the first four symmetric deflections $(m, n = 1, 3)$ were used. It is seen that the time series converges very rapidly and that, for a fixed value of the amplitude and the same edge conditions, the frequency ratio is smaller for a high-modulus plate than for a low-modulus plate. However, because of different linear frequencies for different materials given in Table 6.5, the nonlinear frequency at a given amplitude is larger for a high-modulus plate than for a low-modulus plate. Similarly, the nonlinear frequency of a clamped plate is higher than that of the corresponding simply supported plate. In Fig. 6.15 the amplitude-frequency response curves are presented for various vibrating modes of a simply supported orthotropic square plate. These results are obtained by taking $m, n = 1, 3$ for a symmetric-symmetric mode; $m = 1, 3$, $n = 2, 4$ for a symmetric-antisymmetric mode; and $m = n = 2, 4$ for an antisymmetric-antisymmetric mode.

From this study it is seen that the nonlinear frequency of a glass-epoxy, boron-epoxy, or graphite-epoxy plate with all-clamped and all-simply supported edges increases with its amplitude, and hence only a hardening type of nonlinearity is observed. The accuracy of a single-mode solution for the nonlinear frequency decreases with increasing the amplitude of vibration. For large values of amplitude, the effect of coupling of vibrating modes on the nonlinear frequency is less significant for isotropic plates but more significant for orthotropic plates, especially for high-modulus composite plates. However, the single-mode analysis of nonlinear vibration will be made for the rest of this chapter due to difficulties of multimode solutions.

6.9 VIBRATION OF RECTILINEARLY ORTHOTROPIC CIRCULAR PLATE

Consider a rectilinearly orthotropic circular plate of radius a and thickness h. The origin of a rectangular cartesian coordinate system x, y, z is located at the center of the plate and the x and y axes are taken to be parallel to the material axes of symmetry (Fig. 6.16). The plate is assumed to be subjected to the transverse axisymmetric load $q(r)$ with r being the polar radius. In the case of moderately large amplitude flexural vibration of the plate, the governing equations may be given by equations (1-158) and (1-159). If the edge of the plate is clamped but free to move in the radial direction, these boundary conditions are

$$w = w_{,r} = 0$$

$$x\psi_{,yy} - y\psi_{,xy} = 0 \qquad \text{along} \quad (x^2 + y^2)^{1/2} = a \qquad (6\text{-}100)$$

$$x\psi_{,xy} - y\psi_{,xx} = 0$$

The fundamental-mode analysis is made by virtue of the Galerkin procedure (Ref. 6.15) furnishing an ordinary differential equation for the time function. The

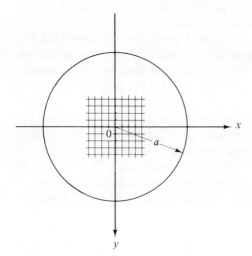

Figure 6.16 Geometry and elastic directions of rectilinearly orthotropic circular plate.

geometrical boundary conditions prescribed in equations (6-100) are satisfied by choosing the deflection function in the separate form

$$w = w_0(t)\left(1 - \frac{r^2}{a^2}\right)^2 \tag{6-101}$$

in which $w_0(t)$ is an unknown function of time. Substitution of expression (6-101) in the compatibility equation (1-159) yields

$$\psi_{,xxxx} + \alpha\psi_{,xxyy} + \gamma\psi_{,yyyy} = (4a^2r^2 - 3r^4 - a^4)f(t) \tag{6-102}$$

where α and γ are defined in equation (6-81) and where

$$f(t) = \frac{16}{a^8} E_2 h w_0^2(t) \tag{6-103}$$

A particular solution of this equation suitable for this study possesses the following form

$$\psi = \frac{1}{30 \cdot 56}(A_1 x^8 + A_2 y^8) + \frac{1}{12 \cdot 30}(A_3 x^6 + A_4 y^6)$$

$$+ \frac{1}{24}(A_5 x^4 + A_6 y^4) + \frac{1}{2}(A_7 x^2 + A_8 y^2)$$

$$+ \frac{1}{12 \cdot 30}(B_1 x^6 y^2 + B_2 x^2 y^6) + \frac{1}{24}(B_3 x^4 y^2 + B_4 x^2 y^4)$$

$$+ \frac{1}{24} B_5 x^4 y^4 + \frac{1}{4} B_6 x^2 y^2 \tag{6-104}$$

in which A's and B's are fourteen coefficients, all functions of time, and are to be determined from equation (6-102), and the statical boundary conditions given in equations (6-100). Inserting expression (6-104) in equation (6-102) six relations for these coefficients are obtained. The satisfaction of the last two boundary conditions in equations (6-100) yields eight additional relations among these coefficients. Thus there are fourteen equations for fourteen unknown coefficients A and B. This system of equations can be split into partial systems from which all the coefficients can be determined by a step-by-step procedure. The result is

$$B_1 = -\frac{6f}{\Delta_1}(7 + 14\alpha + 382\gamma + 3\alpha^2 + 87\gamma^2 + 62\alpha\gamma)$$

$$B_2 = -\frac{6f}{\Delta_1}(87 + 62\alpha + 382\gamma + 3\alpha^2 + 7\gamma^2 + 14\alpha\gamma)$$

$$B_5 = -\frac{1}{6\alpha}(B_1 + \gamma B_2 + 6f)$$

$$A_1 = \frac{1}{6\alpha}[B_1(\gamma - \alpha^2) + B_2\gamma^2 + 6f(\gamma - 3\alpha)]$$

▼

$$A_2 = \frac{1}{6\alpha\gamma}[B_1 + B_2(\gamma - \alpha^2) + 6f(1 - 3\alpha)]$$

$$B_3 = \frac{2a^2}{\Delta_2}[3A_1(\alpha + 10\gamma) + 3A_2(5\gamma - \gamma^2) + B_1(8\alpha - 85\gamma - \gamma^2)$$
$$- B_2(\alpha + 50\gamma - 8\gamma^2) + 55B_5(\alpha + 15\gamma - \gamma^2)$$
$$+ 10f(5 + \alpha + 9\gamma)]$$

$$B_4 = \frac{2a^2}{\Delta_2}[3A_1(5\gamma - 1) + 3A_2(10\gamma + \alpha\gamma) + B_1(8 - 50\gamma - \alpha\gamma)$$
$$+ B_2(1 - 85\gamma - 8\alpha\gamma) + 55B_5(15\gamma + \alpha\gamma - 1)$$
$$+ 10f(9 + \alpha + 5\gamma)]$$

$$A_3 = 4a^2f - \alpha B_3 - \gamma B_4$$

$$A_4 = \frac{1}{\gamma}(4a^2f - B_3 - \alpha B_4)$$

$$A_5 = -\frac{1}{\Delta_3}\Big\{3\alpha a^4[A_1(\alpha + 3\gamma) - 3\gamma A_2] + 5\alpha a^2[A_3(\alpha + 3\gamma)$$
$$- 3\gamma A_4] - \frac{11\alpha a^4}{2}[B_1(\alpha + 3\gamma) - 3\gamma B_2]$$
$$- 5\alpha a^2[B_3(7\alpha + 27\gamma) - B_4(2\alpha + 27\gamma)] + 20a^4\alpha^2 B_5 + 45\alpha a^4f\Big\}$$

$$A_6 = \frac{1}{\Delta_3}\Big\{3\alpha a^4[3A_1 - A_2(3 + \alpha)] + 5\alpha a^2[3A_3 - A_4(3 + \alpha)]$$
$$- \frac{11\alpha a^4}{2}[3B_1 - B_2(3 + \alpha)] - 5\alpha a^2[B_3(27 + 2\alpha) - B_4(27 + 7\alpha)]$$
$$- 20\alpha^2 a^4 B_5 + 45\alpha a^4f\Big\}$$

$$B_6 = -\frac{1}{\alpha}(a^4f + A_5 + \gamma A_6)$$

$$A_7 = -\frac{a^2}{60}[2a^4(A_1 - B_1) + 5a^2(A_3 - B_3) + 30(A_5 - 2B_6)]$$

$$A_8 = -\frac{a^2}{60}[2a^4(A_2 - B_2) + 5a^2(A_4 - 4B_4) + 30(A_6 - 2B_6)]$$

(6-105)

where

$$\Delta_1 = 35\alpha(1 + \gamma^2) + 390\alpha\gamma + 21\alpha^2(1 + \gamma) + \alpha^3$$
$$+ 469\gamma(1 + \gamma) + 7(1 + \gamma^3)$$
$$\Delta_2 = 5(5 + 10\alpha + 10\alpha\gamma + \alpha^2 + 74\gamma + 5\gamma^2)$$
$$\Delta_3 = 15\alpha(3 + \alpha + 3\gamma)$$

(6-106)

The Galerkin procedure is now applied to the equation of motion (1-158). To this end we substitute equations (6-101) and (6-104) into (1-158), multiply the resulting equation by the spatial part of expression (6-101), $(1 - r^2/a^2)^2$, and integrate the result over the domain of the plate. After a lengthy calculation the following nonlinear differential equation for the time function $w_0(t)$ is obtained

$$w_{0,tt} + \mu^2 w_0 + \varepsilon^2 w_0^3 - \frac{5q_0}{3\rho} = 0 \qquad (6\text{-}107)$$

in which a uniform transverse load of intensity $q_0(t)$ has been used and in which

$$\mu^2 = \frac{40D_1}{3\rho a^4}(3 + 2\beta + 3\gamma) \qquad \varepsilon^2 = \frac{E_2 hS}{63\rho a^{10}} \qquad a_i = \frac{A_i}{f} \qquad b_i = \frac{B_i}{f}$$

$$S = a^6(a_1 + a_2) + 7a^4(a_3 + a_4) + 168a^2(a_5 + a_6) + \tfrac{2}{3}a^6(b_1 + b_2) \mid (6\text{-}108)$$
$$+ 21a^4(b_3 + b_4) + 6a^6 b_5 + 336a^2 b_6 + 3360(a_7 + a_8)$$

with β given in equations (6-81). Now equation (6-107) is specified for the following cases.

In the case of linear free vibration, μ is the circular frequency of the orthotropic plate which is also given on page 432 of Ref. 4.20, using an energy method and expression (6-101) for the deflection. In the isotropic case ($\beta = \gamma = 1$), the value of μ reduces to that given in Ref. 6.16 as a first approximation. It is observed that the value of μ increases monotonously with an increasing β and an increasing γ. By a suitable reinforcement the linear frequency of an orthotropic plate in the range of values of $E_2/E_1 \leq 4$ can be varied by -39 percent to $+46$ percent as compared with an isotropic plate (Ref. 6.15).

In the static case w_0 is the constant deflection at the center of the plate and hence, by virtue of equations (6-108), equation (6-107) simplifies to yield

$$\frac{2(3 + 2\beta + 3\gamma)}{3\gamma(1 - \gamma v_{12}^2)}\left(\frac{w_0}{h}\right) + \frac{S}{105a^6}\left(\frac{w_0}{h}\right)^3 = \frac{q_0 a^4}{E_2 h^4} \qquad (6\text{-}109)$$

When this load-deflection relation is specified for the isotropic case, by taking $v = 0.3$ we find

$$\frac{1600}{273}\frac{w_0}{h} + \frac{6}{7}\left(\frac{w_0}{h}\right)^3 = \frac{q_0 a^4}{E h^4} \qquad (6\text{-}110)$$

which agrees with the result obtained on page 188 of Ref. 3.10 by use of the same deflection function.

In the case of nonlinear free vibration we adopt a more convenient representation

$$w_0(t) = w_m \, \phi(t) \tag{6-111}$$

which permits us to utilize the normalized initial conditions

$$\phi(0) = 1 \qquad \phi_{,t}(0) = 0 \tag{6-112}$$

By rejecting the loading term, equation (6-107) can be written as

$$\phi_{,tt} + \mu^2\phi + \varepsilon^2 w_m^2 \, \phi^3 = 0 \tag{6-113}$$

This equation is identical in form with equation (4-161). In view of equations (6-108) the modulus k can be expressed as

$$k^2 = \frac{1}{2}\left[1 + \frac{70a^6(3 + 2\beta + 3\gamma)}{S\gamma(1 - \gamma v_{12}^2)}\left(\frac{h}{w_m}\right)^2\right]^{-1} \tag{6-114}$$

and the ratio of nonlinear period T to linear period T_0 as

$$\frac{T}{T_0} = \frac{2K(k)}{\pi}\left[1 + \frac{S\gamma(1 - \gamma v_{12}^2)}{70a^6(3 + 2\beta + 3\gamma)}\left(\frac{w_m}{h}\right)^2\right]^{-1/2} \tag{6-115}$$

in which K is the complete elliptic integral of the first kind and the ratio w_m/h represents the maximum relative amplitude of the free vibration at the center of the plate. In the isotropic case expression (6-115) reduces to

$$\frac{T}{T_0} = \frac{2K}{\pi}\left[1 + \tfrac{9}{56}(1 - v^2)\left(\frac{w_m}{h}\right)^2\right]^{-1/2} \tag{6-116}$$

which is in agreement with the result given in Ref. 6.17 using a similar method.

Numerical calculations were performed for two real wooden materials with their properties given in Table 6.7 where the elastic constants of an isotropic material are also included. The dependence of the period ratio T/T_0 on the relative amplitude w_m/h is depicted in Fig. 6.17 for three different combinations of the elastic moduli given in the table. It is seen that the decrease of the period ratio with increasing the relative amplitude is less pronounced for the two orthotropic cases considered. By virtue of equations (6-104) and (6-105) the membrane stresses σ_x^m and σ_y^m can be calculated. Figure 6.18 shows the maximum values of nondimensional membrane stresses at the center of the plate, denoted by σ_ζ^m and σ_η^m, for

Table 6.7 Values of elastic constants

Case	Material	v_{12}	v_{21}	α	β	γ
I	Plywood	0.05	0.025	5	0.223	0.5
II	Delta product	0.2	0.01	1	0.108	0.05
III	Isotropic	0.3	0.3	2	1	1

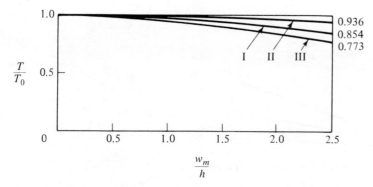

Figure 6.17 Period ratio versus relative amplitude for loosely clamped circular plate having different types of rectilinear orthotropy.

$\phi(t) = 1$ and for the isotropic and two orthotropic cases. These nondimensional stresses are defined by

$$[\sigma_\zeta^m, \sigma_\eta^m] \equiv \frac{a^2}{E_2 h^2} [\sigma_x^m, \sigma_y^m] = \frac{16}{fa^6} \left(\frac{w_m}{h}\right)^2 [A_8, A_7] \qquad (6\text{-}117)$$

This figure indicates that the membrane stresses increase rapidly with amplitude. Apparently, these stresses can be reduced or raised by an appropriate type of reinforcement. In the case considered the variation of stress, for $w_m/h = 2$, amounts

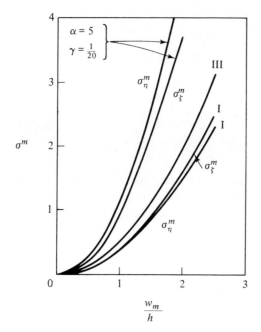

Figure 6.18 Membrane stresses at plate center versus relative amplitude for loosely clamped circular plate having different degrees of rectilinear orthotropy.

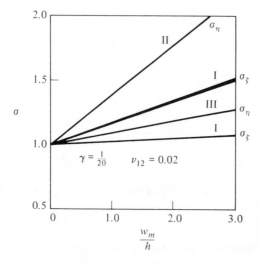

Figure 6.19 Total stresses at plate center versus amplitude for loosely clamped circular plate with different types of rectilinear orthotropy.

to -26 percent and $+130$ percent as the lower and upper bounds, if compared with the isotropic case. The bending moments can be expressed in the form

$$M_x = \frac{4(1 + v_{21})D_1 w_m}{a^2}\phi(t) \qquad M_y = \frac{4(1 + v_{12})D_2 w_m}{a^2}\phi(t) \qquad (6\text{-}118)$$

and hence the maximum nondimensional bending stresses are

$$[\sigma_\zeta^b, \sigma_\eta^b] \equiv \frac{a^2}{E_2 h^2}[\sigma_x^b, \sigma_y^b] = \frac{2}{\gamma(1 - \gamma v_{12}^2)}\frac{w_m}{h}[1 + \gamma v_{12}, 1 + v_{12}] \qquad (6\text{-}119)$$

The maximum total stresses at the plate center are then written in the nondimensional form as

$$\sigma_\zeta \equiv \frac{\sigma_\zeta^m + \sigma_\zeta^b}{\sigma_\zeta^b} = 1 + \frac{8\gamma(1 - \gamma v_{12}^2)}{1 + \gamma v_{12}}\frac{A_8}{fa^6}\frac{w_m}{h}$$

$$\sigma_\eta \equiv \frac{\sigma_\eta^m + \sigma_\eta^b}{\sigma_\eta^b} = 1 + \frac{8(1 - \gamma v_{12}^2)}{1 + v_{12}}\frac{A_7}{fa^6}\frac{w_m}{h} \qquad (6\text{-}120)$$

which are plotted in Fig. 6.19 against the relative amplitude w_m/h for different elastic properties. Obviously, as a consequence of the nonlinear character of vibration the maximum stresses at the center of the plate increase considerably with an increasing amplitude. The effect of anisotropy on the total stresses is similar to that on membrane stresses.

Finally we turn to the large-amplitude forced vibration of the plate. After the steady state of vibration has been established, the vibrating frequency of the plate is equal to that of pulsation of a uniform transverse load. Let then

$$q_0 = q_0^* \cos \omega t \qquad \phi(t) = \cos \omega t \qquad (6\text{-}121)$$

in which q_0^* is the amplitude of pulsation of the external load. We substitute equations (6-121) into (6-107) and apply the Galerkin procedure by multiplying the resulting equation by $\cos \omega t$ and integrating over the cycle 2π. Thus the following relation is obtained

$$\omega^2 = \frac{40D_1(3 + 2\beta + 3\gamma)}{3\rho a^4} + \frac{E_2 hS}{84\rho a^{10}} w_m^2 - \frac{5q_0^*}{3\rho w_m} \tag{6-122}$$

The period of large-amplitude free harmonic vibrations, associated with the value $q_0^* = 0$, becomes

$$T_h = \frac{2\pi}{\omega} \tag{6-123}$$

where

$$\omega = \omega_0 \left[1 + \frac{E_2 S w_m^2}{1120 D_1 a^6 (3 + 2\beta + 3\gamma)} \right]^{1/2} \tag{6-124}$$

with ω_0 being the frequency of small harmonic vibrations. The desired ratio of nonlinear period to linear period $T_h^{(o)}$ thus yields

$$\frac{T_h}{T_h^{(o)}} = \left[1 + \frac{3\gamma S(1 - \gamma v_{12}^2)}{280 a^6 (3 + 2\beta + 3\gamma)} \left(\frac{w_m}{h} \right)^2 \right]^{-1/2} \tag{6-125}$$

6.10 OSCILLATION OF LOOSELY CLAMPED ORTHOTROPIC SKEW PLATE

The present investigation is concerned with the moderately large amplitude vibration of an orthotropic skew plate. The geometry and coordinate system of the plate are shown in Fig. 4.24. The material axes of symmetry are with reference to the orthogonal system of axes. These rectangular coordinates x and y are related to the oblique coordinates ζ and η by equations (4-232). By the coordinate transformation the nonlinear equations of motion of the plate given by (1-158) and (1-159) can be expressed in terms of ζ and η as follows

$$w_{,\zeta\zeta\zeta\zeta} + a_1 w_{,\zeta\zeta\zeta\eta} + a_2 w_{,\zeta\zeta\eta\eta} + a_3 w_{,\zeta\eta\eta\eta} + a_4 w_{,\eta\eta\eta\eta}$$

$$= \frac{c^3}{H} (cq - c\rho w_{,tt} + w_{,\zeta\zeta} \psi_{,\eta\eta} + w_{,\eta\eta} \psi_{,\zeta\zeta} - 2w_{,\zeta\eta} \psi_{,\zeta\eta}) \tag{6-126}$$

$$\psi_{,\zeta\zeta\zeta\zeta} + a_5 \psi_{,\zeta\zeta\zeta\eta} + a_6 \psi_{,\zeta\zeta\eta\eta} + a_7 \psi_{,\zeta\eta\eta\eta} + a_8 \psi_{,\eta\eta\eta\eta}$$

$$= cE_2 h(w_{,\zeta\eta}^2 - w_{,\zeta\zeta} w_{,\eta\eta}) \tag{6-127}$$

where

$$a_1 = -4s \qquad a_2 = 2c^2 \left[3\left(\frac{s}{c} \right)^2 + v_{21} + 2k \right]$$

▼

$$a_3 = -4c^2s\left[\left(\frac{s}{c}\right)^2 + v_{21} + 2k\right]$$

$$a_4 = c^4\left[\gamma + 2(2k + v_{21})\left(\frac{s}{c}\right)^2 + \left(\frac{s}{c}\right)^4\right] \qquad a_5 = -4s$$

$$a_6 = Bc^2 + 6s^2 \qquad a_7 = -2s(Bc^2 + 2s^2)$$

$$a_8 = \gamma c^4 + Bc^2s^2 + s^4 \qquad \gamma = \frac{E_2}{E_1} \qquad\qquad\qquad \text{(6-128)}$$

$$k = \frac{G_{12}}{E_1}(1 - v_{12}v_{21}) \qquad B = \frac{1}{k}(\gamma - v_{21}^2 - 2kv_{21})$$

$$H = \frac{G_{12}h^3}{12k} \qquad c = \cos\theta \qquad s = \sin\theta$$

with θ being the skew angle.

For the isotropic case, $\gamma = 1$, $v_{12} = v_{21} = v$, $k = \frac{1}{2}(1 - v)$, and $B = 2$, and hence equations (6-126) and (6-127) will reduce to equations (4-234) and (4-235) without initial deflection.

If the edges of the orthotropic plate are clamped but free to move in the plane of the plate, the boundary conditions are given by equations (4-238) and (4-247). Now a single-mode solution of the problem is formulated by virtue of Galerkin's method (Ref. 6.18). The deflection satisfying conditions (4-238) is taken to be

$$w = \frac{hf(\tau)}{4}\left(1 + \cos\frac{2\pi\zeta}{a}\right)\left(1 + \cos\frac{2\pi\eta}{b}\right) \qquad \text{(6-129)}$$

in which τ is the nondimensional time defined by

$$\tau = \frac{4t}{a^2}\sqrt{\frac{H}{\rho}} \qquad \text{(6-130)}$$

When expression (6-129) is substituted into equation (6-127), a particular integral is obtained as

$$\begin{aligned}
\psi(\zeta, \eta, \tau) = \frac{a^4 g(\tau)}{16\pi^4}\Bigg[& b_1 \cos\frac{2\pi\zeta}{a}\cos\frac{2\pi\eta}{b} + b_2 \sin\frac{2\pi\zeta}{a}\sin\frac{2\pi\eta}{b} \\
& + b_3 \cos\frac{2\pi\zeta}{a} + b_4 \cos\frac{2\pi\eta}{b} + b_5 \cos\frac{4\pi\zeta}{a} + b_6 \cos\frac{4\pi\eta}{b} \\
& + b_7 \cos\frac{4\pi\zeta}{a}\cos\frac{2\pi\eta}{b} + b_8 \sin\frac{4\pi\zeta}{a}\sin\frac{2\pi\eta}{b} \\
& + b_9 \cos\frac{2\pi\zeta}{a}\cos\frac{4\pi\eta}{b} + b_{10} \sin\frac{2\pi\zeta}{a}\sin\frac{4\pi\eta}{b}\Bigg]
\end{aligned} \qquad \text{(6-131)}$$

where

$$b_1 = \frac{2c_1}{c_1^2 - c_2^2} \qquad b_2 = \frac{2c_2}{c_1^2 - c_2^2} \qquad b_3 = 1 \qquad b_4 = \frac{1}{a_8 \lambda}$$

$$b_5 = \frac{1}{16} \qquad b_6 = \frac{1}{16 a_8 \lambda^4} \qquad b_7 = \frac{c_3}{c_3^2 - c_4^2}$$

$$b_8 = \frac{c_4}{c_3^2 - c_4^2} \qquad b_9 = \frac{c_5}{c_5^2 - c_6^2} \qquad b_{10} = \frac{c_6}{c_5^2 - c_6^2}$$

$$g(\tau) = \frac{c\pi^4 E_2 h^2}{2a^2 b^2} f^2(\tau) \qquad \lambda = \frac{a}{b}$$

$$c_1 = 1 + a_6 \lambda^2 + a_8 \lambda^4 \qquad c_2 = \lambda(a_5 + a_7 \lambda^2)$$

$$c_3 = 16 + 4a_6 \lambda^2 + a_8 \lambda^4 \qquad c_4 = 2\lambda(4a_5 + a_7 \lambda^2)$$

$$c_5 = 1 + 4a_6 \lambda^2 + 16 a_8 \lambda^4 \qquad c_6 = 2\lambda(a_5 + 4a_7 \lambda^2)$$

$$(6\text{-}132)$$

As in Sec. 4.12 the contribution to the average stresses of the bracketed terms of expression (6-131) is zero at the corresponding edges. Thus conditions (4-247) are fulfilled.

With the trial function w given by expression (6-129) and the force function given by expression (6-131), instead of satisfaction of equation (6-126) use is made of Galerkin's method to furnish the following nonlinear ordinary differential equation for the time functions $f(\tau)$

$$f_{,\tau\tau} + \omega_0^2 f + \varepsilon^2 f^3 = \frac{q_0 a^4}{9Hh} \qquad (6\text{-}133)$$

in which a uniform transverse load of intensity q_0 has been considered and in which

$$\omega_0^2 = \frac{\pi^4}{9c^4}(3 + a_2 \lambda^2 + 3a_4 \lambda^4)$$

$$\varepsilon^2 = \frac{\pi^4 \lambda^4 d}{24}(\gamma - v_{21}^2)$$

$$(6\text{-}134)$$

where

$$d = \frac{17}{8} + \frac{17}{8 a_8 \lambda^4} + \frac{4c_1}{c_1^2 - c_2^2} + \frac{c_3}{c_3^2 - c_4^2} + \frac{c_5}{c_5^2 - c_6^2} \qquad (6\text{-}135)$$

It is observed that equation (6-133) is a Duffing's equation which can reduce to equation (4-249) in the case of an isotropic skew plate with no initial curvature, and to equation (6-78) in the case of an orthotropic rectangular plate ($\theta = 0$) with clamped edges.

In the static case f is independent of τ and hence equation (6-133) is simplified to yield

$$\frac{\pi^4}{c^4 \lambda^4}\left(3 + a_2 \lambda^2 + 3a_4 \lambda^4\right)\frac{w_m}{h} + \frac{3\pi^4 d}{8}(\gamma - v_{21}^2)\left(\frac{w_m}{h}\right)^3 = \frac{q_0 b^4}{Hh} \quad (6\text{-}136)$$

in which w_m is the maximum deflection of the orthotropic skew plate.

When equation (6-133) is specified for the case of nonlinear free vibrations, the resulting time equation is solved by means of the standard procedure as applied to equation (4-161). The relative period is then given by

$$\frac{T}{T_0} = \frac{2\omega_0 K(\kappa)}{\pi\sqrt{\omega_0^2 + \varepsilon^2 A^2}} \quad (6\text{-}137)$$

in which T and $T_0 = (2\pi/\omega_0)$ are nonlinear and linear periods respectively, A $(= w_m/h)$ is the nondimensional amplitude, and K is the complete elliptic integral of the first kind with κ given by

$$\kappa = \left[\frac{\varepsilon^2 A^2}{2(\omega_0^2 + \varepsilon^2 A^2)}\right]^{1/2} \quad (6\text{-}138)$$

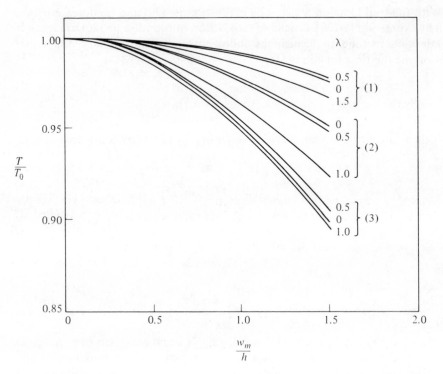

Figure 6.20 Period ratio versus nondimensional amplitude for loosely clamped orthotropic skew plate with skew angle $\theta = 30°$.

Table 6.8 Numerical values of elastic constants

Case	Material	E_2/E_1	ν_{21}	$(G_{12}/E_1)(1 - \nu_{12}\nu_{21})$
(1)	Orthotropic I	0.05	0.010	0.05
(2)	Orthotropic II	0.50	0.025	0.10
(3)	Isotropic	1.00	0.300	0.35

The amplitude-period response curves for skew plates of different aspect ratios are shown in Fig. 6.20 for an isotropic material and two types of orthotropic materials. The elastic constants of these materials are given in Table 6.8. It is seen that the relative period decreases with increasing the amplitude. Hence only a hardening type of nonlinearity is observed. This phenomenon is more pronounced for the aspect ratio $\lambda = 1$.

6.11 VIBRATIONS OF ORTHOTROPIC RIGHT AND ISOSCELES TRIANGULAR PLATES WITH ALL-LOOSELY AND ALL-RIGIDLY CLAMPED EDGES

In this section the moderately large amplitude flexural vibrations of orthotropic right and isosceles triangular plates are investigated. The boundary conditions under consideration are all-loosely and all-rigidly clamped along the edges. The differential equations governing the dynamic behavior of these plates are given by equations (1-109) to (1-111) for rigidly clamped plates and by equations (1-158) and (1-159) for loosely clamped plates. An approximate solution for the fundamental-mode vibration will be formulated in each case.

a Loosely Clamped Orthotropic Right Triangular Plate

The geometry, coordinate system, and elastic directions of the plate are shown in Fig. 5.17. The boundary conditions for loosely clamped edges are given by equations (5-105). An approximate solution (Ref. 5.11) to equations (1-158) and (1-159) is obtained by slight modification of the static solution presented in Sec. 5.7. In the present case w_c and ψ_c in equations (5-108) and (5-112) are replaced by $\phi(t)$ and $\xi(t)$, respectively. In addition, $L_2(w, \psi)$ in (5-110) represents the compatibility equation (1-159), and $L_1(w, \psi)$ the dynamic equation (1-158). Corresponding to equation (5-113) we find

$$\phi_{,tt} + \frac{\alpha_1 D_1}{\rho}\phi + \frac{\alpha_2 E_2 h}{\rho}\phi^3 - \frac{\alpha_3 q_0}{\rho} = 0 \qquad (6\text{-}139)$$

in which α_1, α_2, and α_3 are given by expressions (5-114), D_1 is defined in equations (1-112), and ρ is the mass per unit area of the plate.

In the static case equation (6-139) reduces to equation (5-113). In the case of free linear vibrations the nonlinear and the loading terms in equation (6-139) are to be rejected. The circular frequency thus appears to be

$$\omega_0 = \frac{63.28}{a^2}\left[\frac{D_1}{\rho}\left(1 + \frac{D_3}{D_1}c^2 + \frac{D_2}{D_1}c^4\right)\right]^{1/2} \tag{6-140}$$

which is the same value as given by equation (94.15) of Ref. 4.19, using Lagrange's equation of motion and the spatial function identical with equation (5-109). When equation (6-139) is specified for nonlinear free vibrations, the resulting time equation can be solved by the standard method discussed in Sec. 4.8 with the relative period given by

$$\frac{T}{T_0} = \frac{2K(\kappa)}{\pi[1 + (\alpha_2 E_2 h^3/\alpha_1 D_1)(w_c/h)^2]^{1/2}} \tag{6-141}$$

in which T is the period of nonlinear vibrations, $T_0[= 2\pi(\alpha_1 D_1/\rho)^{-1/2}]$ is the period of linear vibrations, w_c is the amplitude or the maximum deflection at the centroid of the plate, and K is the complete elliptic integral of the first kind with the modulus given by

$$\kappa = \left[2 + \frac{2\alpha_1 D_1}{\alpha_2 E_2 h^3}\left(\frac{w_c}{h}\right)^{-2}\right]^{-1/2} \tag{6-142}$$

For the other cases approximate solutions will be formulated by a modified form of the Galerkin procedure, known as Kantorovich's method (Ref. 6.19)†.

b Rigidly Clamped Orthotropic Right Triangular Plate

In this case the boundary conditions are

$$u^\circ = v^\circ = w = w_{,x} = 0 \qquad \text{at} \quad x = 0$$
$$u^\circ = v^\circ = w = w_{,y} = 0 \qquad \text{at} \quad y = 0 \tag{6-143}$$
$$u^\circ = v^\circ = w = w_{,n} = 0 \qquad \text{at} \quad 1 - \frac{x}{a} - \frac{y}{b} = 0$$

Since these boundary conditions are explicitly expressed in terms of three displacement components in the middle surface, equations (1-109) to (1-111) are appropriate for the problem considered. Because of the plate geometry, essentially the solution will be inseparable with respect to the space coordinates.

An approximate solution to equations (1-109) to (1-111) is sought in the separable form of space and time functions

$$w = f_1(x, y)\phi(t) \qquad u^\circ = f_2(x, y)\zeta(t) \qquad v^\circ = f_3(x, y)\eta(t) \tag{6-144}$$

---

† Reprinted with permission from the American Institute of Aeronautics and Astronautics, *AIAA J.*, vol. 11, 1973.

Of the many possible spatial functions the following nondimensional forms are adopted

$$f_1 = \frac{x^2 y^2}{a^2 b^2}\left(1 - \frac{x}{a} - \frac{y}{b}\right)^2$$

$$f_2 = \frac{xy}{ab}\left(1 - \frac{x}{a} - \frac{y}{b}\right)\left(1 + \frac{x}{a} - \frac{y}{b}\right) \qquad (6\text{-}145)$$

$$f_3 = \frac{xy}{ab}\left(1 - \frac{x}{a} - \frac{y}{b}\right)\left(1 - \frac{x}{a} + \frac{y}{b}\right)$$

which satisfy boundary conditions (6-143). These spatial functions in equations (1-109) and (1-110) are eliminated by using the Galerkin procedure which yields

$$0.07937\left(\frac{3K_1}{a^2} + \frac{5K_2}{b^2}\right)\zeta(t) + 0.12897\frac{K_2 + K_3}{ab}\eta(t)$$

$$= 0.26429 \times 10^{-5}\frac{5K_2 + K_3}{ab^2}\phi^2(t)$$

$$\qquad\qquad\qquad\qquad\qquad\qquad\qquad (6\text{-}146)$$

$$0.12897\frac{K_2 + K_3}{ab}\zeta(t) + 0.07937\left(\frac{5K_2}{a^2} + \frac{3K_4}{b^2}\right)\eta(t)$$

$$= 0.26429 \times 10^{-5}\frac{5K_2 + K_3}{a^2 b}\phi^2(t)$$

where

$$K_1 = \frac{E_1 h}{1 - v_{12} v_{21}} \qquad K_2 = G_{12} h$$

$$\qquad\qquad\qquad\qquad\qquad\qquad\qquad (6\text{-}147)$$

$$K_3 = v_{21} K_1 = v_{12} K_4 \qquad K_4 = \frac{E_2 h}{1 - v_{12} v_{21}}$$

Solving these algebraic equations for $\zeta(t)$ and $\eta(t)$ we find

$$\zeta(t) = \frac{ad_1}{b^2 d_3}\phi^2(t) \qquad \eta(t) = \frac{d_2}{bd_3}\phi^2(t) \qquad (6\text{-}148)$$

where

$$d_1 = 0.20975(5K_2 + K_3)(5K_2 + 3c^2 K_4)$$

$$\quad - 0.34085(K_2 + K_3)(5K_2 + K_3)$$

$$d_2 = 0.20975(3K_1 + 5c^2 K_2)(5K_2 + K_3)$$

$$\quad - 0.34085c^2(K_2 + K_3)(5K_2 + K_3) \qquad (6\text{-}149)$$

$$d_3 = 0.62988 \times 10^4(3K_1 + 5c^2 K_2)(5K_2 + 3c^2 K_4)$$

$$\quad - 0.16633 \times 10^5 c^2(K_2 + K_3)^2$$

$$c = \frac{a}{b}$$

It is observed that terms with d_1 and d_2 represent the contribution due to the inplane displacement only, which is small compared to the transverse deflection.

Applying the Galerkin procedure to equation (1-111) and using equations (6-144) and (6-148) leads to the following differential equation for $\phi(t)$

$$\phi_{,tt} + \frac{\alpha_1 D_1}{\rho} \phi + \frac{\delta}{\rho} \phi^3 - 0.12515 \times 10^4 \frac{q_0}{\rho} = 0 \qquad (6\text{-}150)$$

in which α_1 is given in equations (5-114), q_0 is the intensity of uniform lateral load, and the coefficient of ϕ^3 represents the contribution due to stretching of the plate, and in which

$$
\delta = \frac{1}{a^4} \left[0.12509 \times 10^{-3}(K_1 + c^4 K_4) + 0.35963 \times 10^{-3} c^2 K_3 \right.
$$

$$
+ 0.15637 \times 10^{-4} c^2 K_2 + \frac{d_1}{3d_3}(3c^2 K_1 - 4c^4 K_2 + c^4 K_3)
$$

$$
\left. + \frac{d_2}{3d_3}(3c^4 K_4 - 4c^2 K_2 + c^2 K_3) \right] \qquad (6\text{-}151)
$$

In the static case ϕ is independent of time t and may be taken to be the deflection at the centroid of the plate, denoted by w_c, and hence equation (6-150) reduces to

$$
\frac{a^4 \alpha_1 D_1}{0.12515 \times 10^4 E_1 h^3} \frac{w_c}{h} + \frac{a^4 \delta}{0.12515 \times 10^4 E_1 h} \left(\frac{w_c}{h}\right)^3 = \frac{q_0 a^4}{E_1 h^4} \qquad (6\text{-}152)
$$

which is plotted in Fig. 5.18 for comparison.

In the case of nonlinear free vibration ($q_0 = 0$), equation (6-150) becomes

$$
\phi_{,tt} + \frac{\alpha_1 D_1}{\rho} \phi + \frac{\delta}{\rho} \phi^3 = 0 \qquad (6\text{-}153)
$$

which can be solved by the method discussed in Sec. 4.8. The ratio of the periods T/T_0 is related to the relative amplitude w_c/h by

$$
\frac{T}{T_0} = \frac{2K(\kappa)}{[1 + (\delta/\alpha_1 D_1)(729h)^2 (w_c/h)^2]^{1/2}} \qquad (6\text{-}154)
$$

where

$$
\kappa = \left[2 + \frac{2\alpha_1 D_1}{\delta(729h)^2 (w_c/h)^2} \right]^{-1/2} \qquad (6\text{-}155)
$$

c Loosely Clamped Orthotropic Isosceles Triangular Plate

The geometry, coordinate system, and elastic directions of the plate are shown in Fig. 6.21. The boundary conditions for the clamped plate with edges free of in-plane stresses are

$$
w = w_{,y} = N_y = N_{xy} = 0 \qquad \text{at} \quad y = b
$$

$$
w = w_{,n} = N_n = N_{ns} = 0 \qquad \text{at} \quad \frac{y}{b} = \pm \frac{x}{a_0} \qquad (6\text{-}156)
$$

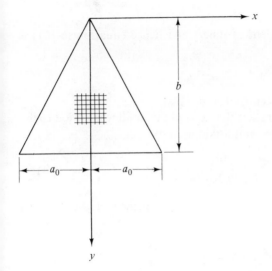

Figure 6.21 Geometry and elastic directions of isosceles triangular plate.

in which n and s are normal and tangent to the inclined face, respectively. Evidently, equations (1-158) and (1-159) are suitable for these boundary conditions. To obtain an approximate solution to these equations, transverse deflection w and force function ψ are expressed as

$$w = f(x, y)\phi(t) \qquad \psi = g(x, y)\xi(t) \tag{6-157}$$

The boundary conditions (6-156) are satisfied by taking

$$f = g = \left(\frac{y}{b} - 1\right)^2 \left(\frac{y}{b} - \frac{x}{a_0}\right)^2 \left(\frac{y}{b} + \frac{x}{a_0}\right)^2 \tag{6-158}$$

Applying the Galerkin procedure to equation (1-159) leads to

$$\xi(t) = -0.79920 \times 10^{-2} \frac{E_2 h r^2}{1 + \alpha r^2 + 9\gamma r^4} \phi^2(t) \tag{6-159}$$

where α and γ are given in equations (6-81) and where

$$r = \frac{a_0}{b} \tag{6-160}$$

Similarly, applying Galerkin's technique to equation (1-158) and using expressions (6-157) to (6-159), the following equation for the time function $\phi(t)$ is obtained

$$\phi_{,tt} + \frac{\mu}{\rho}\phi + \frac{\delta}{\rho}\phi^3 - 0.78203 \times 10^2 \frac{q_0}{\rho} = 0 \tag{6-161}$$

where

$$\mu = 0.25025 \times 10^3 (1 + 2\beta r^2 + 9\gamma r^4) \frac{D_1}{a_0^4}$$

$$\delta = 0.19688 \times 10^3 \frac{E_2 r^4}{1 + \alpha r^2 + 9\gamma r^4} \tag{6-162}$$

with β given in equations (6-81).

In the static case ϕ is independent of time t and hence equation (6-161) is simplified to yield

$$\mu w_c + \delta w_c^3 = 78.203 q_0 \qquad (6\text{-}163)$$

in which w_c is the deflection at the centroid of the plate.

In the case of nonlinear free vibration the ratio of the nonlinear period to the linear period is related to the relative amplitude w_c/h by

$$\frac{T}{T_0} = \frac{2K(\kappa)}{[1 + (\delta/\mu)(729h/16)^2(w_c/h)^2]^{1/2}} \qquad (6\text{-}164)$$

where κ is given by equation (6-155). The circular frequency of the clamped isosceles triangular plate is given by

$$\omega_0 = \left[0.25025 \times 10^3 (1 + 2\beta r^2 + 9\gamma r^4) \frac{D_1}{a_0^4 \rho} \right]^{1/2} \qquad (6\text{-}165)$$

d Rigidly Clamped Orthotropic Isosceles Triangular Plate

In the present case the appropriate boundary conditions are

$$u^\circ = v^\circ = w = w_{,y} = 0 \qquad \text{at} \quad y = b$$

$$u^\circ = v^\circ = w = w_{,n} = 0 \qquad \text{at} \quad \frac{y}{b} = \pm \frac{x}{a_0} \qquad (6\text{-}166)$$

A single-mode solution to equations (1-109) to (1-111) is assumed in the form

$$w = f_1(x, y)\phi(t) \qquad u^\circ = f_2(x, y)\zeta(t) \qquad v^\circ = f_3(x, y)\eta(t) \qquad (6\text{-}167)$$

where the nondimensional coordinate functions satisfying the above boundary conditions may be expressed as

$$f_1 = \left(\frac{y}{b} - 1 \right)^2 \left(\frac{y}{b} - \frac{x}{a_0} \right)^2 \left(\frac{y}{b} + \frac{x}{a_0} \right)^2$$

$$f_2 = \frac{x}{a_0} \left(\frac{y}{b} - 1 \right) \left(\frac{y}{b} - \frac{x}{a_0} \right) \left(\frac{y}{b} + \frac{x}{a_0} \right) \qquad (6\text{-}168)$$

$$f_3 = \left(\frac{y}{b} - 1 \right) \left(\frac{y}{b} - \frac{x}{a_0} \right) \left(\frac{y}{b} + \frac{x}{a_0} \right)$$

Applying Galerkin's method to equations (1-109) and (1-110) and solving the resulting algebraic equations, we find

$$\zeta(t) = -\frac{m_1 r}{bm_3} \phi^2(t) \qquad \eta(t) = -\frac{m_2}{bm_3} \phi^2(t) \qquad (6\text{-}169)$$

where

$$m_1 = 0.60140(K_2 - K_3)(5K_2 + 3K_4 r^2)$$
$$- 0.17183(K_2 + K_3)(2K_2 + K_3 - 3K_4 r^2)$$

$$m_2 = 0.17183r^2(K_2 - K_3)(K_2 + K_3)$$
$$- 0.04296(3K_1 + 5K_2 r^2)(2K_2 + K_3 - 3K_4 r^2)$$

$$m_3 = 0.35273 \times 10^2(3K_1 + 5K_2 r^2)(K_2 + 3K_4 r^2)$$
$$- 0.40312 \times 10^2 r^2(K_2 + K_3)^2$$

(6-170)

Employing Galerkin's techniques to equation (1-111) and substituting expressions (6-167) to (6-170) into the resulting equation, we will arrive at equation (6-160) for the time function $\phi(t)$. In this equation μ is given in equations (6-162) and

$$\delta = 0.20014 \times 10^{-2}(K_1 + 9K_4 r^4) + 0.19014 \times 10^{-1}K_3 r^2$$

$$- 0.70050 \times 10^{-2}K_2 r^2 + \frac{m_1 r^2}{3m_3}(3K_1 + 2K_2 r^2 + 7K_3 r^2)$$

$$+ \frac{m_2 r^2}{3m_3}(2K_2 + K_3 - 3K_4 r^2)$$

(6-171)

The corresponding static deflection is given by equation (6-163), and the relation between the period ratio and the relative amplitude by equation (6-164) for non-linear free vibration. In the present case, however, expression (6-171) for δ is to be used.

The amplitude-period response is depicted in Figs. 6.22 and 6.23 for clamped right and isosceles triangular plates. The elastic properties of two orthotropic

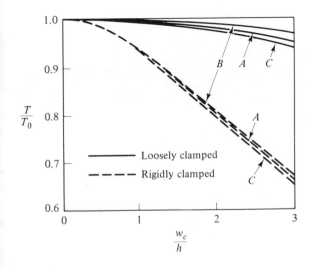

Figure 6.22 Period ratio versus relative amplitude for clamped right triangular plates with $c = 1$ and for different material properties.

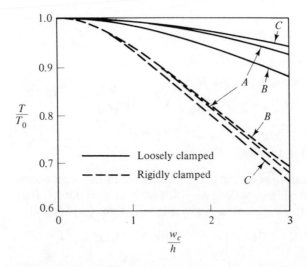

Figure 6.23 Period ratio versus relative amplitude for clamped isosceles triangular plate with $r = 1$ and different material properties.

materials, Cases A and B, and an isotropic material, Case C, given in Table 5.6 are used herein. These figures show that the effect of inplane boundary conditions for immovable edges on the nonlinear period is very pronounced. The effect of orthotropicity on the nonlinear behavior is more pronounced in the case of loosely clamped edges. For the latter case nonlinear periods do not differ greatly from linear. This indicates a possible method of achieving nonlinear-frequency stabilization by proper choice of geometry, material, and boundary conditions.

PROBLEMS

6.1 Suppose that an orthotropic rectangular plate under uniform uniaxial edge compression is rigidly supported against the transverse deflection along all edges. Opposite edges are taken to be elastically restrained against rotation to the same degree.

Find an approximate solution to this postbuckling problem.

6.2 A simply supported orthotropic skew plate shown in Fig. 4.24 is under the action of uniform inplane compressive force resultants P_ζ and P_η $(= C_1^2 P_\zeta)$ and constant shear force resultant $P_{\zeta\eta}$ $(= C_2^2 P_\zeta)$. As an approximate solution the transverse deflection satisfying the boundary conditions for loosely clamped edges is taken to be

$$w = \frac{w_0}{4}\left(1 + \cos\frac{2\pi\zeta}{a}\right)\left(1 + \cos\frac{2\pi\eta}{b}\right)$$

Determine the force function ψ from the compatibility equation (6-127) with the following inplane boundary conditions

$$\psi_{,\eta\eta} = -\frac{P_\zeta}{b} \qquad -\psi_{,\zeta\eta} = \frac{P_{\zeta\eta}}{b}$$

$$\psi_{,\zeta\zeta} = -\frac{P_\eta}{a} \qquad -\psi_{,\zeta\eta} = \frac{P_{\zeta\eta}}{a}$$

Also find the postbuckling load-deflection relation for $a = b$, $C_1 = C_2 = 1$.

6.3 Taking the first terms in expressions (6-90), derive an approximate relation between moderately large amplitude and nonlinear frequency (or period) for a free vibrating orthotropic rectangular plate with boundary conditions given by equations (6-89).

6.4 Use the Galerkin procedure to obtain an approximate solution for a clamped, cylindrically orthotropic, circular plate undergoing moderately large amplitude free flexural vibrations.

REFERENCES

6.1. | C. Y. Chia and M. Sathyamoorthy: Nonlinear Vibration of Anisotropic Skew Plates, *Fiber Sci. Technol.* 1979 (in press).

6.2. S. Yusuff: Large Deflection Theory for Orthotropic Rectangular Plates Subjected to Edge Compression, *ASME J. Appl. Mech.*, vol. 19, pp. 446–450, 1952.

6.3. E. B. Uthgenannt and R. S. Brand: Postbuckling of Orthotropic Annular Plates, *ASME J. Appl. Mech.*, vol. 40, pp. 559–564, 1973.

6.4. S. A. Ambartsumyan: "Theory of Anisotropic Plates," ed. by J. E. Ashton and translated from Russian (1st ed.) by T. Cheron, Technomic Publishing Co., Inc., 1970.

6.5. M. K. Shen: On the Non-linear Differential Equations of Cylindrically Anisotropic Plates, *Acta Mech.*, vol. 2, pp. 210–216, 1966.

6.6. E. B. Uthgenannt and R. S. Brand: Buckling of Orthotropic Annular Plates, *AIAA J.*, vol. 8, pp. 2102–2104, 1970.

6.7. F. B. Hildebrand: "Methods of Applied Mathematics," 2d ed., Prentice-Hall, pp. 62–65, 1965.

6.8. M. Rozsa: Stability Analysis of Thin Annular Plates Compressed Along the Outer or Inner Edge of Uniformly Distributed Radial Forces, *Acta Tech. Acad. Sci. Hunqaricae*, vol. 53, pp. 359–377, 1966.

6.9. S. Woinowsky-Krieger: Buckling Stability of Circular Plates with Circular Cylindrical Aeolotropy, *Ing. Arch.*, vol. 26, pp. 129–131, 1958.

6.10. M. K. Prabhakara and C. Y. Chia: Postbuckling of Angle-ply and Anisotropic Plates, *Ing. Arch.*, vol. 45, Springer-Verlag KG (Berlin), pp. 131–140, 1976.

6.11. M. Sathyamoorthy and K. A. V. Pandalai: Nonlinear Flexural Vibrations of Orthotropic Rectangular Plates, *J. Aeronaut. Soc. India*, vol. 22, pp. 264–266, 1970.

6.12. M. K. Prabhakara and C. Y. Chia: Non-linear Flexural Vibrations of Orthotropic Rectangular Plates, *J. Sound Vib.*, vol. 52, Academic Press, pp. 511–518, 1977.

6.13. C. Hayashi: "Non-linear Oscillations in Physical Systems," McGraw-Hill Book Company, 1964.

6.14. M. Dickinson: The Flexural Vibration of Rectangular Orthotropic Plates, *ASME J. Appl. Mech.*, vol. 36, pp. 101–106, 1969.

6.15. J. L. Nowinski: Nonlinear Vibrations of Elastic Circular Plates Exhibiting Rectilinear Orthotropy, *Z. Angew. Math. Phys.*, vol. 14, Redaction ZAMP (Germany), pp. 112–124, 1963.

6.16. S. P. Timoshenko: "Vibration Problems in Engineering," Van Nostrand Co., p. 449, 1937.

6.17. E. I. Grigoliuk: Nonlinear Vibrations and Stability of Shallow Shells and Rods (in Russian), *Izv. Akad. Nauk SSR, Otd. Tech. Note* no. 3, pp. 33–68, 1955.

6.18. M. Sathyamoorthy and K. A. V. Pandalai: Non-linear Flexural Vibration of Orthotropic Skew Plates, *J. Sound Vib.*, vol. 24, Academic Press, pp. 115–120, 1972.

6.19. C. P. Vendhan and B. L. Dhoopar: Nonlinear Vibration of Orthotropic Triangular Plates, *AIAA J.*, vol. 11, pp. 704–709, 1973.

ADDITIONAL REFERENCES

Benveniste, Y. and J. Aboudi: The Nonlinear Response of a Fibre-reinforced Thin Plate Under Dynamic Loading, *Fibre Sci. Technol.*, vol. 7, pp. 223–236, 1974.

Chou, P. C., and J. Carleone: Transverse Shear in Laminated Plate Theories, *AIAA J.*, vol. 11, pp. 1333–1336, 1973.

Kanaka Raju, K., and G. Venkateswara Rao: Non-linear Vibrations of Orthotropic Plates by a Finite Element Method (Letter to the editor), *J. Sound Vib.*, vol. 48, pp. 301–303, 1976.

Nowinski, J. L., and S. R. Woodall: Finite Vibrations of a Free Rotating Anisotropic Membrane, *J. Acoust. Soc. Am.*, vol. 36, pp. 2113–2118, 1964.

Pandalai, K. A. V., and M. Sathyamoorthy: Postbuckling Behavior of Orthotropic Skew Plates, *AIAA J.*, vol. 11, pp. 731–733, 1973.

Schultz, H. G., Post-buckled Strength of Orthotropic Plate, *Jahrb., Schiffbautach, Ges.*, vol. 56, p. 184, 1964.

Wu, C., and J. R. Vinson: On the Nonlinear Oscillations of Plates Composed of Composite Materials, *J. Comp. Mater.*, vol. 3, pp. 548–561, 1969.

MODERATELY LARGE DEFLECTIONS OF UNSYMMETRICALLY LAMINATED ANISOTROPIC PLATES

Based on the moderately large deflection theory the homogeneous and symmetrically laminated anisotropic plates in both static and dynamic cases have been discussed in the previous chapters. The moderately large deflection behavior of unsymmetric laminates is considered in this chapter. Solutions for angle-ply plates under combined lateral and inplane loads, for cross-ply plates under transverse load, and for angle-ply laminates under uniform edge moment, all with simply supported edges, are presented by use of double Fourier series for the transverse deflection and generalized double Fourier series for the force function. Approximate solutions are formulated by the perturbation technique for loosely clamped angle-ply and cross-ply plates and for rigidly clamped general laminates, all uniformly loaded. Accurate solutions are obtained by the generalized double Fourier series for all-loosely and all-rigidly clamped general laminates under the combined action of nonuniformly distributed transverse load and inplane forces.

7.1 SIMPLY SUPPORTED UNSYMMETRIC ANGLE-PLY RECTANGULAR PLATE UNDER TRANSVERSE AND INPLANE LOADS

In the previous two chapters the elastic behavior of homogeneous anisotropic and symmetrically laminated anisotropic plates has been studied for various elastic properties, plate shapes, loading conditions, and boundary conditions. It should be noted that the bending and stretching of these plates are not coupled. In the case of unsymmetric laminates, however, a coupling phenomenon between transverse bending and inplane stretching occurs even in the range of small deflections. Thus the elastic problem of unsymmetric laminates is generally more complicated than the corresponding homogeneous plates and symmetric laminates.

Suppose an unsymmetrically laminated anisotropic rectangular plate of length a in the x direction, width b in the y direction, and thickness h in the z direction. The middle plane of the undeformed plate contains the x, y axes. The plate under consideration consists of an even number of perfectly bonded layers, n, of thin orthotropic sheets all of the same thickness and elastic properties. The orthotropic axes in each ply are alternately oriented at angles $+\theta$ and $-\theta$ to the plate axes. The differential equations governing the moderately large deflection behavior of the unsymmetric angle-ply plate under transverse load q may be specified from equations (1-135) and (1-136) and written in the dimensionless form

$$W_{,\zeta\zeta\zeta\zeta} + 2a_2\lambda^2 W_{,\zeta\zeta\eta\eta} + a_4\lambda^4 W_{,\eta\eta\eta\eta} + a_6\lambda F_{,\zeta\zeta\zeta\eta} + a_8\lambda^3 F_{,\zeta\eta\eta\eta}$$

$$= \frac{\lambda^4 Q}{\bar{D}_{11}^*} + \frac{\lambda^2}{\bar{D}_{11}^*}(W_{,\zeta\zeta}F_{,\eta\eta} + W_{,\eta\eta}F_{,\zeta\zeta} - 2W_{,\zeta\eta}F_{,\zeta\eta}) \qquad (7\text{-}1)$$

$$F_{,\zeta\zeta\zeta\zeta} + 2b_2\lambda^2 F_{,\zeta\zeta\eta\eta} + b_4\lambda^4 F_{,\eta\eta\eta\eta} - b_6\lambda W_{,\zeta\zeta\zeta\eta} - b_8\lambda^3 W_{,\zeta\eta\eta\eta}$$

$$= \frac{\lambda^2}{\bar{A}_{22}^*}[W_{,\zeta\eta}^2 - W_{,\zeta\zeta}W_{,\eta\eta}] \qquad (7\text{-}2)$$

where

$$\zeta = \frac{x}{a} \qquad \eta = \frac{y}{b} \qquad \lambda = \frac{a}{b}$$

$$W = \frac{w}{h} \qquad F = \frac{\psi}{A_{22}h^2} \qquad Q = \frac{qb^4}{A_{22}h^3}$$

$$a_2 = \frac{1}{\bar{D}_{11}^*}(\bar{D}_{12}^* + 2\bar{D}_{66}^*) \qquad a_4 = \frac{\bar{D}_{22}^*}{\bar{D}_{11}^*}$$

$$a_6 = \frac{1}{\bar{D}_{11}^*}(2\bar{B}_{26}^* - \bar{B}_{61}^*) \qquad a_8 = \frac{1}{\bar{D}_{11}^*}(2\bar{B}_{16}^* - \bar{B}_{62}^*) \qquad (7\text{-}3)$$

$$b_2 = \frac{1}{2\bar{A}_{22}^*}(2\bar{A}_{12}^* + \bar{A}_{66}^*) \qquad b_4 = \frac{\bar{A}_{11}^*}{\bar{A}_{22}^*}$$

$$b_6 = \frac{1}{\bar{A}_{22}^*}(2\bar{B}_{26}^* - \bar{B}_{61}^*) \qquad b_8 = \frac{1}{\bar{A}_{22}^*}(2\bar{B}_{16}^* - \bar{B}_{62}^*)$$

$$\bar{A}_{ij}^* = A_{22}A_{ij}^* \qquad \bar{B}_{ij}^* = \frac{B_{ij}^*}{h} \qquad \bar{D}_{ij}^* = \frac{D_{ij}^*}{A_{22}h^2} \qquad (i, j = 1, 2, 6)\dagger$$

The plate is assumed to be simply supported along its edges and subjected to inplane compressive forces, per unit length, n_x in the x direction and n_y in the y

† See equations (8-16) for A_{ij}^*, B_{ij}^* and D_{ij}^*.

direction, but not the tangential boundary forces. The dimensionless form of these boundary conditions is given by

$$W = W_{,\zeta\zeta} = F_{,\zeta\eta} = 0 \qquad F_{,\eta\eta} = -R \qquad \text{at} \quad \zeta = 0, 1$$

$$W = W_{,\eta\eta} = F_{,\zeta\eta} = 0 \qquad F_{,\zeta\zeta} = -\lambda^2 kR \qquad \text{at} \quad \eta = 0, 1 \tag{7-4}$$

in which k and R are the load ratio and the dimensionless load parameter defined by

$$k = \frac{n_y}{n_x} \qquad R = \frac{n_x b^2}{A_{22} h^2} \tag{7-5}$$

Equations (7-1) and (7-2) are to be solved in conjunction with boundary conditions (7-4). The dependent functions F and W are assumed to be of the form (Refs. 7.1, 7.2)

$$F = -\frac{R}{2}(\eta^2 + k\lambda^2\zeta^2) + \sum_{m=1}^{\infty}\sum_{n=1}^{\infty} F_{mn} X_m(\zeta) Y_n(\eta)$$

$$W = \sum_{p=1}^{\infty}\sum_{q=1}^{\infty} W_{pq} \sin p\pi\zeta \sin q\pi\eta \tag{7-6}$$

in which X_m and Y_n are the beam eigenfunctions defined by equations (5-36). The series for W satisfies all out-of-plane conditions in equations (7-4). Introducing the series for F into the inplane boundary conditions we obtain

$$\gamma_i = \frac{\cosh \alpha_i - \cos \alpha_i}{\sinh \alpha_i - \sin \alpha_i} \tag{7-7}$$

$$1 - \cos \alpha_m \cosh \alpha_m = 0$$

The roots of the last equation are given in Table 5.1.

Inserting expressions (7-6) into equations (7-1) and (7-2), multiplying the first of the resulting equations by $\sin i\pi\zeta \sin j\pi\eta$ and the second by $X_i(\zeta)Y_j(\eta)$, integrating from 0 to 1 with respect to ζ and η, and using the orthogonality properties (5-38), the following system of algebraic equations is obtained

$$W_{ij}\left[i^4 + 2a_2\lambda^2 i^2 j^2 + a_4\lambda^4 j^4 - \frac{\lambda^2 R}{\pi^2 \bar{D}_{11}^*}(i^2 + k\lambda^2 j^2) \right]$$

$$+ \frac{4}{\pi^4}\sum_{m=1}^{\infty}\sum_{n=1}^{\infty} F_{mn}\left(a_6 \lambda\alpha_m^3\alpha_n K_1^{mi} S_2^{nj} + a_8\lambda^3\alpha_m\alpha_n^3 K_2^{mi} S_1^{nj}\right)$$

$$+ \frac{4\lambda^3}{\pi^2 \bar{D}_{11}^*}\sum_{k=1}^{\infty}\sum_{l=1}^{\infty}\sum_{r=1}^{\infty}\sum_{s=1}^{\infty} F_{kl} W_{rs}$$

$$\cdot \left(\alpha_k^2 s^2 K_3^{kir} S_4^{ljs} + \alpha_l^2 r^2 K_4^{kir} S_3^{ljs} + 2\alpha_k\alpha_l rs K_5^{kir} S_5^{ljs}\right)$$

$$= \frac{\lambda^4 Q_{ij}}{\pi^4 \bar{D}_{11}^*} \qquad i, j = 1, 2, 3, \ldots \tag{7-8}$$

$$F_{ij}(\alpha_i^4 + b_4 \lambda^4 \alpha_j^4) + \sum_{m=1}^{\infty} \sum_{n=1}^{\infty} 2F_{mn} b_2 \lambda^2 \alpha_m^2 \alpha_n^2 K_6^{im} S_6^{jn}$$

$$= - \sum_{p=1}^{\infty} \sum_{q=1}^{\infty} \pi^4 W_{pq} (b_6 \lambda p^3 q + b_8 \lambda^3 pq^3) K_7^{ip} S_7^{jq}$$

$$+ \frac{\pi^4 \lambda^2}{A_{22}^*} \sum_{r=1}^{\infty} \sum_{s=1}^{\infty} \sum_{k=1}^{\infty} \sum_{l=1}^{\infty} W_{rs} W_{kl} (rskl K_8^{ikr} S_8^{jls} - k^2 s^2 K_4^{ikr} S_4^{jls})$$

$$i, j = 1, 2, 3, \ldots \quad (7\text{-}9)$$

in which Q_{ij} and K_1 to K_8 are constants given by

$$Q = \sum_{i=1}^{\infty} \sum_{j=1}^{\infty} Q_{ij} \sin i\pi\zeta \sin j\pi\eta$$

$$K_1^{im} = \frac{1}{\alpha_i^3} \int_0^1 X_i''' \sin m\pi\zeta \, d\zeta$$

$$K_2^{im} = \frac{1}{\alpha_i} \int_0^1 X_i' \sin m\pi\zeta \, d\zeta$$

$$K_3^{ikr} = \frac{1}{\alpha_i^2} \int_0^1 X_i'' \sin k\pi\zeta \sin r\pi\zeta \, d\zeta$$

$$K_4^{ikr} = \int_0^1 X_i \sin k\pi\zeta \sin r\pi\zeta \, d\zeta \quad (7\text{-}10)$$

$$K_5^{ikr} = \frac{1}{\alpha_i} \int_0^1 X_i' \sin k\pi\zeta \cos r\pi\zeta \, d\zeta$$

$$K_6^{im} = \frac{1}{\alpha_i^2} \int_0^1 X_i'' X_m \, d\zeta$$

$$K_7^{im} = \int_0^1 X_i \cos m\pi\zeta \, d\zeta$$

$$K_8^{ikr} = \int_0^1 X_i \cos k\pi\zeta \cos r\pi\zeta \, d\zeta$$

with the primes denoting differentiation with respect to the corresponding coordinate, and the constants S_1 to S_8 being obtained by replacing $X, \zeta, i, k, m,$ and r in expressions (7-10) by $Y, \eta, j, l, n,$ and s, respectively.

Taking a finite number of terms in each of the series for F and W, equations (7-8) and (7-9) can be solved for F_{mn} and W_{mn} for a given set of values of aspect ratio, load parameter, orthotropic properties, number of layers, and the orientation of the orthotropic axes of the constituent layer with respect to the plate axes. By virtue of equations (1-125) and (1-138) the dimensionless membrane forces and bending moments can be found from the following

$$N_\zeta = F_{,\eta\eta} \qquad N_\eta = \frac{1}{\lambda^2} F_{,\zeta\zeta} \qquad N_{\zeta\eta} = -\frac{1}{\lambda} F_{,\zeta\eta} \qquad (7\text{-}11)$$

and

$$M_\zeta = \frac{1}{\lambda} \bar{B}_{61}^* F_{,\zeta\eta} - \frac{1}{\lambda^2} \bar{D}_{11}^* W_{,\zeta\zeta} - \bar{D}_{12}^* W_{,\eta\eta}$$

$$M_\eta = \frac{1}{\lambda} \bar{B}_{62}^* F_{,\zeta\eta} - \frac{1}{\lambda^2} \bar{D}_{12}^* W_{,\zeta\zeta} - \bar{D}_{22}^* W_{,\eta\eta} \tag{7-12}$$

$$M_{\zeta\eta} = -\bar{B}_{16}^* F_{,\eta\eta} - \frac{1}{\lambda^2} \bar{B}_{26}^* F_{,\zeta\zeta} - \frac{2}{\lambda} \bar{D}_{66}^* W_{,\zeta\eta}$$

where

$$(N_\zeta, N_\eta, N_{\zeta\eta}) = \frac{b^2}{A_{22} h^2} (N_x, N_y, N_{xy})$$

$$(M_\zeta, M_\eta, M_{\zeta\eta}) = \frac{b^2}{A_{22} h^3} (M_x, M_y, M_{xy}) \tag{7-13}$$

Numerical results are presented for unsymmetric graphite-epoxy laminates with elastic constants given by equations (5-213). The constant A_{22} in equations (7-3), (7-5), and (7-13) can be replaced by $E_T h$ without affecting the form of the other equations. The nondimensional edge compression is also simplified to $R = n_x b^2 / E_T h^3$. To check the convergence of the present series solution, calculations are performed by taking the first four and nine terms in each series. The result for the central deflection w_c of a simply supported two-layer angle-ply plate under uniform transverse pressure q_0 and uniaxial compression $(n_y = 0)$ is shown in Table 7.1. The dimensionless uniaxial compression is defined by $\beta = n_x/n_{cr}$ in which n_{cr} is the critical buckling load per unit length for the plate under uniaxial compression in the x direction and will be determined in Sec. 8.1. The table indicates that the present series solution converges quite rapidly. In the case of small deflections of a simply supported unsymmetric $\pm 45°$ angle-ply square plate for the number of layers† $n = 2, 4, \infty$, the present results for central deflections agree very well with those obtained in Ref. 7.3, but are not presented herein.

The numerical results are graphically presented in Figs. 7.1 to 7.3 by the use of the first nine terms in each of the truncated series for F and W. The relation

Table 7.1 Comparison of solutions for the dimensionless central deflection, w_c/h, of a simply supported two-layer $\pm 45°$ angle-ply square plate under the combined loading

$\dfrac{q_0 b^4}{E_T h^4}$	100		200		300	
β	0.0	1.0	0.0	1.0	0.0	1.0
4 terms	0.7032	2.0894	1.2846	2.6761	1.7352	3.1317
9 terms	0.6973	2.0590	1.2619	2.6457	1.7095	3.0717

† For the uncoupled solution $(n = \infty)$ coupling rigidities B_{ij} vanish.

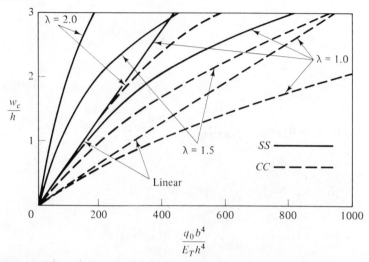

Figure 7.1 Relation between uniform transverse load and central deflection for two-layer $\pm 45°$ angle-ply graphite-epoxy plate with various aspect ratios.

between uniform transverse pressure q_0 and central deflection w_c is shown in Fig. 7.1 for a simply supported unsymmetric angle-ply plate denoted by *SS*. For a given pressure the central deflection increases with the aspect ratio λ. The curves for a clamped unsymmetric angle-ply plate (*CC*) obtained from a solution in Section 7.3 will be discussed later. Figure 7.2 indicates that for large values of q_0 and n_x the location of the maximum bending moment for a simply supported

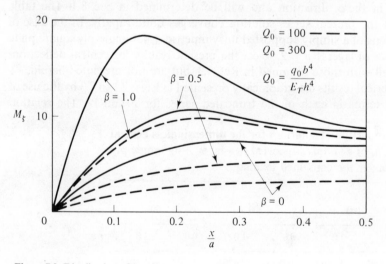

Figure 7.2 Distribution of bending moment M_ζ along the longitudinal center line of square simply supported two-layer $\pm 45°$ angle-ply graphite-epoxy plate under uniform transverse load and uniaxial edge compression in ζ-direction.

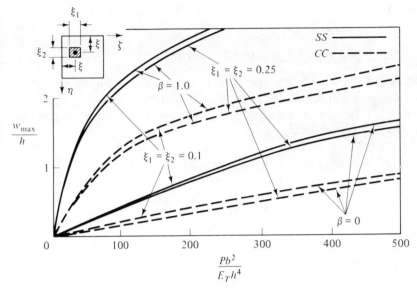

Figure 7.3 Relation between combined loading and maximum deflection for square four-layer $\pm 45°$ angle-ply graphite-epoxy plate under eccentric partial loading and uniaxial edge compression in ζ-direction ($\xi = 0.25$).

angle-ply plate is no longer at the center but shifts toward the edges of the plate. In Fig. 7.3 the load-deflection curves for a four-layer angle-ply plate are presented for combined loading and eccentric partial load alone. The total transverse load denoted by P is uniformly distributed over the loaded area $\xi_1 \times \xi_2$. For the two loading areas shown, the location of the maximum deflection varies slightly with the loading and is very close to the point $\zeta = \eta = 0.4$. Thus the deflection at the point is plotted herein. It may be observed that the difference between maximum deflections for these two loading areas is small even for large values of the eccentric partial load.

7.2 SIMPLY SUPPORTED UNSYMMETRIC CROSS-PLY RECTANGULAR PLATE SUBJECTED TO TRANSVERSE LOAD

By virtue of equations (1-141) and (1-142), the differential equations governing the moderately large deflection of unsymmetrically laminated cross-ply rectangular plates can be written in the nondimensional form

$$\bar{A}_{22}^* F_{,\zeta\zeta\zeta\zeta} + 2\lambda^2 (\bar{A}_{12}^* + \tfrac{1}{2}\bar{A}_{66}^*) F_{,\zeta\zeta\eta\eta} + \lambda^4 \bar{A}_{11}^* F_{,\eta\eta\eta\eta} - \bar{B}_{21}^* W_{,\zeta\zeta\zeta\zeta}$$

$$- \lambda^2 (\bar{B}_{11}^* + \bar{B}_{22}^*) W_{,\zeta\zeta\eta\eta} - \lambda^4 \bar{B}_{12}^* W_{,\eta\eta\eta\eta}$$

$$= \lambda^2 [W_{,\zeta\eta}^2 - W_{,\zeta\zeta} W_{,\eta\eta}] \tag{7-14}$$

$$\bar{D}_{11}^* W_{,\zeta\zeta\zeta\zeta} + 2\lambda^2(\bar{D}_{12}^* + 2\bar{D}_{66}^*)W_{,\zeta\zeta\eta\eta} + \lambda^4\bar{D}_{22}^* W_{,\eta\eta\eta\eta} + \bar{B}_{21}^* F_{,\zeta\zeta\zeta\zeta}$$

$$+ \lambda^2(\bar{B}_{11}^* + \bar{B}_{22}^*)F_{,\zeta\zeta\eta\eta} + \lambda^4\bar{B}_{12}^* F_{,\eta\eta\eta\eta}$$

$$= \lambda^4 Q + \lambda^2(W_{,\zeta\zeta} F_{,\eta\eta} + W_{,\eta\eta} F_{,\zeta\zeta} - 2W_{,\zeta\eta} F_{,\zeta\eta}) \tag{7-15}$$

in which ζ, η, λ, F, Q, W, $\bar{A}_{ij}^*$, $\bar{B}_{ij}^*$, and $\bar{D}_{ij}^*$ are as defined in equations (7-3).

The nondimensional membrane forces N_ζ, N_η, and $N_{\zeta\eta}$ are given by equations (7-11) and (7-13). In view of expressions (1-144), the nondimensional bending moments may be expressed as

$$M_\zeta = -\bar{B}_{11}^* F_{,\eta\eta} + \frac{1}{\lambda^2}\bar{B}_{21}^* F_{,\zeta\zeta} - \frac{1}{\lambda^2}\bar{D}_{11}^* W_{,\zeta\zeta} - \bar{D}_{12}^* W_{,\eta\eta}$$

$$M_\eta = -\bar{B}_{12}^* F_{,\eta\eta} - \frac{1}{\lambda^2}\bar{B}_{22}^* F_{,\zeta\zeta} - \frac{1}{\lambda^2}\bar{D}_{12}^* W_{,\zeta\zeta} - \bar{D}_{22}^* W_{,\eta\eta} \tag{7-16}$$

$$M_{\zeta\eta} = -\frac{2}{\lambda}\bar{D}_{66}^* W_{,\zeta\eta}$$

where M_ζ, M_η and $M_{\zeta\eta}$ are defined in equations (7-13).

In a case when the plate consists of an even number of plies, all of the same thickness, the following relations† hold

$$\bar{A}_{22}^* = \bar{A}_{11}^* \qquad \bar{B}_{22}^* = -\bar{B}_{11}^* \qquad \bar{B}_{21}^* = -\bar{B}_{12}^* \qquad \bar{D}_{22}^* = \bar{D}_{11}^* \tag{7-17}$$

The edges of the plate are assumed to be simply supported and free from boundary forces. The corresponding nondimensional boundary conditions are

$$W = F_{,\eta\eta} = F_{,\zeta\eta} = 0 \qquad W_{,\zeta\zeta} = \frac{\bar{B}_{21}^*}{\bar{D}_{11}^*} F_{,\zeta\zeta} \qquad \text{at} \quad \zeta = 0, 1$$

$$\tag{7-18}$$

$$W = F_{,\zeta\zeta} = F_{,\zeta\eta} = 0 \qquad W_{,\eta\eta} = -\frac{\bar{B}_{12}^*}{\bar{D}_{22}^*} F_{,\eta\eta} \qquad \text{at} \quad \eta = 0, 1$$

A solution of eqs. (7-14, 7-15) is sought in the form of double series (Ref. 7.4)

$$F = \sum_{m=1}^{\infty} \sum_{n=1}^{\infty} F_{mn} X_m(\zeta) Y_n(\eta)$$

$$W = \sum_{p=1}^{\infty} \sum_{q=1}^{\infty} W_{pq} \sin p\pi\zeta \cos q\pi\eta \tag{7-19}$$

$$Q = \sum_{r=1}^{\infty} \sum_{s=1}^{\infty} Q_{rs} \sin r\pi\zeta \sin s\pi\eta$$

in which X_i and Y_j are given by equations (5-36). These double series for W and F with the use of Table 5.1 satisfy the boundary conditions (7-18) except for the vanishing of normal bending moment. If $F_{,\zeta\zeta}$ at $\zeta = 0, 1$ and $F_{,\eta\eta}$ at $\eta = 0, 1$ are allowed to have whatever values given by the first series of equations (7-19), then

---

† The third relation also holds for the thickness of even layers different from that of odd layers.

the series for W cannot be differentiated term by term beyond the second order (Ref. 7.5). Thus the derivative $W_{,\zeta\zeta\zeta}$ is expanded into a Fourier cosine-sine series as

$$W_{,\zeta\zeta\zeta} = \sum_{q=1}^{\infty} R_{0q} \sin q\pi\eta + \sum_{p=1}^{\infty} \sum_{q=1}^{\infty} R_{pq} \cos p\pi\zeta \sin q\pi\eta \qquad (7\text{-}20)$$

in which the Fourier coefficients can be related to those in the second series of equations (7-19) by a partial integration of expression (7-20) with respect to ζ. The result is

$$R_{0q} = \tfrac{1}{2} b_q \qquad R_{pq} = b_q - p^3\pi^3 W_{pq} \qquad \text{for } p = \text{even}$$
$$R_{pq} = a_q - p^3\pi^3 W_{pq} \qquad \text{for } p = \text{odd} \qquad (7\text{-}21)$$

where

$$a_q = -4 \int_0^1 \{W_{,\zeta\zeta}(1, \eta) + W_{,\zeta\zeta}(0, \eta)\} \sin q\pi\eta \, d\eta$$

$$b_q = 4 \int_0^1 \{W_{,\zeta\zeta}(1, \eta) - W_{,\zeta\zeta}(0, \eta)\} \sin q\pi\eta \, d\eta \qquad (7\text{-}22)$$

The second derivative $X_i''(\zeta)$ is, at the plate edges,

$$X_i''(0) = 2\alpha_i^2 \qquad X_i''(1) = \begin{cases} 2\alpha_m^2, & m = \text{odd} \\ -2\alpha_m^2, & m = \text{even} \end{cases} \qquad (7\text{-}23)$$

In view of equations (7-22) and (7-23) and the boundary condition for zero bending moment given in equations (7-18), a_q and b_q become

$$a_q = -\frac{16\bar{B}_{12}^*}{\bar{D}_{11}^*} \sum_{m=1}^{\infty} \sum_{n=1}^{\infty} F_{mn} c_m \alpha_m^2 L_1^{nq}$$

$$b_q = -\frac{16\bar{B}_{12}^*}{\bar{D}_{11}^*} \sum_{m=1}^{\infty} \sum_{n=1}^{\infty} F_{mn} d_m \alpha_m^2 L_1^{nq} \qquad (7\text{-}24)$$

in which

$$c_m = \begin{cases} 1, & m = \text{odd} \\ 0, & m = \text{even} \end{cases} \qquad d_m = \begin{cases} 0, & m = \text{odd} \\ 1, & m = \text{even} \end{cases}$$

$$L_1^{nq} = \int_0^1 Y_n \sin q\pi\eta \, d\eta \qquad (7\text{-}25)$$

Introduction of equations (7-21) and (7-24) in (7-20) yield

$$W_{,\zeta\zeta\zeta} = -\frac{8\bar{B}_{12}^*}{\bar{D}_{11}^*} \sum_{q=1}^{\infty} \left(\sum_{m=1}^{\infty} \sum_{n=1}^{\infty} F_{mn} d_m \alpha_m^2 L_1^{nq} \right) \sin q\pi\eta$$

$$- \frac{16\bar{B}_{12}^*}{\bar{D}_{11}^*} \sum_{p=1}^{\infty} \sum_{q=1}^{\infty} \sum_{m=1}^{\infty} \sum_{n=1}^{\infty} F_{mn} \alpha_m^2 L_1^{nq} (c_p c_m + d_p d_m)$$

$$\cdot \cos p\pi\zeta \sin q\pi\eta - \sum_{p=1}^{\infty} \sum_{q=1}^{\infty} W_{pq} (p\pi)^3 \cos p\pi\zeta \sin q\pi\eta \qquad (7\text{-}26)$$

Similarly, the Fourier sine-cosine series representation of $W_{,\eta\eta\eta}$ can be written as

$$W_{,\eta\eta\eta} = \frac{8\bar{B}_{12}^*}{\bar{D}_{11}^*} \sum_{p=1}^{\infty} \left(\sum_{m=1}^{\infty} \sum_{n=1}^{\infty} F_{mn} d_n \alpha_n^2 K_1^{mp} \right) \sin p\pi\zeta$$

$$+ \frac{16\bar{B}_{12}^*}{\bar{D}_{11}^*} \sum_{p=1}^{\infty} \sum_{q=1}^{\infty} \sum_{m=1}^{\infty} \sum_{n=1}^{\infty} F_{mn} \alpha_n^2 K_1^{mp} (c_q c_n + d_q d_n)$$

$$\cdot \sin p\pi\zeta \cos q\pi\eta - \sum_{p=1}^{\infty} \sum_{q=1}^{\infty} W_{pq}(q\pi)^3 \sin p\pi\zeta \cos q\pi\eta \qquad (7\text{-}27)$$

where

$$K_1^{mp} = \int_0^1 X_m \sin p\pi\zeta \, d\zeta \qquad (7\text{-}28)$$

Thus higher-order derivatives can now be obtained from a term-by-term differentiation.

Substituting F from equation (7-19) and the appropriate derivatives of W from equations (7-19), (7-26), and (7-27) into (7-14) and (7-15), multiplying the first of the resulting equations by $X_i(\zeta)Y_j(\eta)$, and the second by $\sin i\pi\zeta \sin j\pi\eta$, integrating from 0 to 1 with respect to ζ and η, and using the orthogonality relations (5-38), the following system of equations is obtained

$$F_{ij} \bar{A}_{11}^* (\alpha_i^4 + \lambda^4 \alpha_j^4) + \sum_{m=1}^{\infty} \sum_{n=1}^{\infty} F_{mn}$$

$$\cdot \left\{ \lambda^2 K_2^{im} L_2^{jn} (2\bar{A}_{12}^* + \bar{A}_{66}^*) \right.$$

$$+ \frac{16\bar{B}_{12}^{*2}}{\bar{D}_{11}^*} \sum_{p=1}^{\infty} \sum_{q=1}^{\infty} [p\pi \alpha_m^2 L_1^{nq} (c_p c_m + d_p d_m)$$

$$\left. + \lambda^4 q\pi \alpha_n^2 K_1^{mp} (c_q c_n + d_q d_n)] \right\}$$

$$= -\pi^4 \bar{B}_{12}^* \sum_{p=1}^{\infty} \sum_{q=1}^{\infty} W_{pq} K_2^{ip} L_2^{jq} (p^4 - \lambda^4 q^4)$$

$$+ \pi^4 \lambda^2 \sum_{p=1}^{\infty} \sum_{q=1}^{\infty} \sum_{r=1}^{\infty} \sum_{s=1}^{\infty} W_{pq} W_{rs} (pqrs K_3^{ipr} L_3^{jqs} - p^2 s^2 k_4^{ipr} L_4^{jqs})$$

$$i, j = 1, 2, 3, \ldots \qquad (7\text{-}29)$$

$$\pi^4 W_{ij} \{ \bar{D}_{11}^* i^4 + 2\lambda^2 i^2 j^2 (\bar{D}_{12}^* + 2\bar{D}_{66}^*) + \bar{D}_{11}^* \lambda^4 j^4 \}$$

$$- 4\bar{B}_{12}^* \sum_{m=1}^{\infty} \sum_{n=1}^{\infty} F_{mn} \{ K_1^{mi} L_1^{nj} (\alpha_m^4 - \lambda^4 \alpha_n^4) - 4\pi$$

$$\cdot [i\alpha_m^2 L_1^{nj} \cdot (c_i c_m + d_i d_m) - \lambda^4 j\alpha_n^2 K_1^{mi} (c_j c_n + d_j d_n)] \} \qquad \blacktriangledown$$

$$+ 4\pi^2\lambda^2 \sum_{p=1}^{\infty} \sum_{q=1}^{\infty} \sum_{r=1}^{\infty} \sum_{s=1}^{\infty} W_{pq}F_{rs}$$

$$\cdot (q^2 K_5^{rip}L_4^{sjq} + p^2 K_4^{rip}L_5^{sjq} + 2pqK_6^{rip}L_6^{sjq}) = \lambda^4 Q_{ij}$$

$$i, j = 1, 2, 3, \ldots \quad (7\text{-}30)$$

The constants K_2 to K_6 in equations (7-29) and (7-30) are defined by

$$K_2^{im} = \int_0^1 X_i X_m'' \, d\zeta$$

$$K_3^{ipr} = \int_0^1 X_i \cos p\pi\zeta \cos r\pi\zeta \, d\zeta$$

$$K_4^{ipr} = \int_0^1 X_i \sin p\pi\zeta \sin r\pi\zeta \, d\zeta \quad (7\text{-}31)$$

$$K_5^{ipr} = \int_0^1 X_i'' \sin p\pi\zeta \sin r\pi\zeta \, d\zeta$$

$$K_6^{ipr} = \int_0^1 X_i' \sin p\pi\zeta \cos r\pi\zeta \, d\zeta$$

and constants L_2 to L_6 are obtained by replacing $X, \zeta, i, m, p,$ and r in expressions (7-31) by $Y, \eta, j, n, q,$ and s, respectively.

Equations (7-29) and (7-30) which constitute a system of simultaneous nonlinear algebraic equations are to be solved for coefficients F_{mn} and W_{pq} for a given set of values of aspect ratio, transverse load, orthotropic properties, and number of layers. As soon as these coefficients are determined, the deflections can be found from the second of equations (7-19) and the membrane forces and bending moments from equations (7-11) and (7-16).

Numerical examples are presented for unsymmetric cross-ply graphite-epoxy plates consisting of an even number of plies all of the same thickness and elastic properties. The elastic constant ratios typical of graphite-epoxy composites are given by equation (5-213). As in the previous section, A_{22} is replaced by $E_T h$. The first nine terms in each of the truncated series for F and W are considered in the numerical computation. After eliminating coefficients F_{mn} from equations (7-29) and (7-30), the resulting nine nonlinear simultaneous algebraic equations are solved for W_{pq} by an iterative procedure. In order to check the convergence of the present series solution, calculations were performed by taking the first four and nine terms, respectively, in each of these series. The results presented in Table 7.2 indicate that the series solution converges rapidly. In the case of small deflections of simply supported unsymmetric cross-ply plates, a close agreement is found between the present solution and that given in Ref. 7.6 for $n = 2, 4, \infty$.

The numerical results are presented graphically in Figs. 7.4 to 7.7. The curves for clamped laminates under lateral and inplane loads are obtained from the solution which will be discussed in Sec. 7.3. The effect of the number of layers, n,

Table 7.2 Comparison of solutions for nondimensional central deflection w_c/h of a simply supported two-layer cross-ply square plate under uniform pressure q_0

$\dfrac{q_0 b^4}{E_T h^4}$	200	400	600
4 terms	1.7080	2.5317	3.0685
9 terms	1.6679	2.4459	2.9913

on the load-deflection relation is shown in Fig. 7.4 for square laminates under uniform transverse load. The curves for $n = \infty$ correspond to the uncoupled solution. It is observed that the central deflection w_c decreases with increasing the number of layers, and that the result tends very rapidly to the solution for an uncoupled plate. Figure 7.5 shows the relation between central deflection and central partial load for square two-layer laminates. For any given total transverse load P in the range of values of w_c shown here the maximum difference between central deflections is less that 6 percent for the two loading areas shown in the figure. In Fig. 7.6 the bending-moment distribution is presented for a square simply supported two-layer plate under central partial loading. The maximum bending moments for both M_ζ and M_η occur at the center of the plate. The bending moment M_η along the center line, $\zeta = 0.5$, is positive for the values of Q

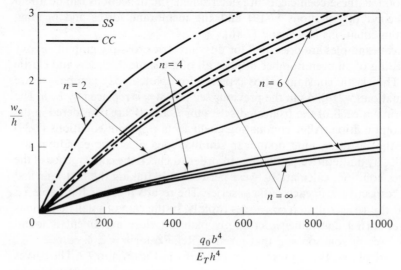

Figure 7.4 Effect of number of layers on load-deflection curve for square cross-ply graphite-epoxy plate under uniform transverse pressure.

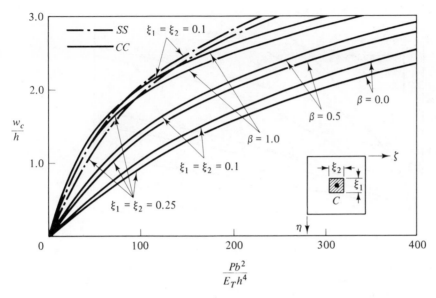

Figure 7.5 Load-deflection curves for square two-layer cross-ply graphite-epoxy plate under central partial load and uniaxial compression in ζ-direction.

under consideration whereas the bending moment M_ζ along the center line, $\eta = 0.5$, becomes negative in some regions between the center and the edges of the plate for large values of Q. This arises from the fact that coupling coefficient $\bar{B}^*_{11}$ is greater than the coupling coefficient $\bar{B}^*_{12}$. For tensile membrane forces the sum of the first two terms in expressions (7-16) is negative for M_ζ but positive for M_η. In addition the membrane forces normal to the plate edges vanish and the change in

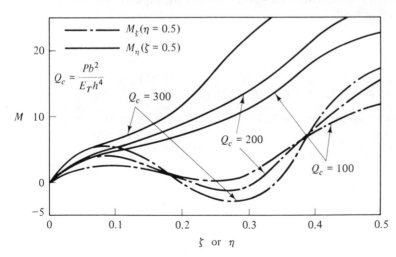

Figure 7.6 Distribution of bending moments along center lines in square simply supported two-layer cross-ply graphite-epoxy plate under central partial loading ($\xi_1 = \xi_2 = 0.1$).

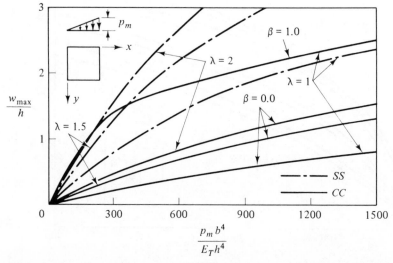

Figure 7.7 Relation between load and maximum deflection for four-layer cross-ply graphite-epoxy plates under combined hydrostatic loading and uniaxial compression in x-direction.

bending curvature is predominant in the neighborhood of the partial loading. The relation between hydrostatic loading and maximum deflection is shown in Fig. 7.7 for four-layer laminates with various aspect ratios. The hydrostatic pressure is uniform in the y direction and varies linearly from zero at $x = 0$ to the maximum intensity p_m at $x = a$. The maximum deflection is found to occur near the point $\zeta = 0.55$ and $\eta = 0.5$, and to increase with the aspect ratio.

It may be observed that all the numerical results presented in these two sections have been subjected to the condition that the inplane load is not greater than the buckling load.

7.3 LOOSELY CLAMPED GENERALLY LAMINATED ANISOTROPIC RECTANGULAR PLATE UNDER TRANSVERSE AND INPLANE LOADS

In the previous two sections the large deflections of unsymmetric angle-ply and cross-ply laminates have been discussed for simply supported edges. Now let us consider a generally laminated anisotropic rectangular plate with clamped edges. The differential equations (1-129) and (1-131) for the plate in the static case may be expressed in the nondimensional form

$$
\begin{aligned}
W_{,\zeta\zeta\zeta\zeta} &+ a_1 \lambda W_{,\zeta\zeta\zeta\eta} + 2a_2 \lambda^2 W_{,\zeta\zeta\eta\eta} + a_3 \lambda^3 W_{,\zeta\eta\eta\eta} \\
&+ a_4 \lambda^4 W_{,\eta\eta\eta\eta} + a_5 F_{,\zeta\zeta\zeta\zeta} + a_6 \lambda F_{,\zeta\zeta\zeta\eta} + a_7 \lambda^2 F_{,\zeta\zeta\eta\eta} \\
&+ a_8 \lambda^3 F_{,\zeta\eta\eta\eta} + a_9 \lambda^4 F_{,\eta\eta\eta\eta} \\
&= \frac{\lambda^4 Q}{\bar{D}_{11}^*} + \frac{\lambda^2}{\bar{D}_{11}^*} (W_{,\zeta\zeta} F_{,\eta\eta} + W_{,\eta\eta} F_{,\zeta\zeta} - 2 W_{,\zeta\eta} F_{,\zeta\eta})
\end{aligned}
\tag{7-32}
$$

$$F_{,\zeta\zeta\zeta\zeta} - b_1 \lambda F_{,\zeta\zeta\zeta\eta} + 2b_2 \lambda^2 F_{,\zeta\zeta\eta\eta} - b_3 \lambda^3 F_{,\zeta\eta\eta\eta}$$

$$+ b_4 \lambda^4 F_{,\eta\eta\eta\eta} - b_5 W_{,\zeta\zeta\zeta\zeta} - b_6 \lambda W_{,\zeta\zeta\zeta\eta}$$

$$- b_7 \lambda^2 W_{,\zeta\zeta\eta\eta} - b_8 \lambda^3 W_{,\zeta\eta\eta\eta} - b_9 \lambda^4 W_{,\eta\eta\eta\eta}$$

$$= \frac{\lambda^2}{\bar{A}_{22}^*} [W_{,\zeta\eta}^2 - W_{,\zeta\zeta} W_{,\eta\eta}] \qquad (7\text{-}33)$$

in which $\zeta, \eta, \lambda, F, Q, W, a_i$, and b_i $(i = 2, 4, 6, 8)$ are given by equations (7-3) and in which

$$a_1 = \frac{4\bar{D}_{16}^*}{\bar{D}_{11}^*} \qquad a_3 = \frac{4\bar{D}_{26}^*}{\bar{D}_{11}^*} \qquad a_5 = \frac{\bar{B}_{21}^*}{\bar{D}_{11}^*}$$

$$a_7 = \frac{1}{\bar{D}_{11}^*} (\bar{B}_{11}^* + \bar{B}_{22}^* - 2\bar{B}_{66}^*) \qquad a_9 = \frac{\bar{B}_{12}^*}{\bar{D}_{11}^*}$$

$$b_1 = \frac{2\bar{A}_{26}^*}{\bar{A}_{22}^*} \qquad b_3 = \frac{2\bar{A}_{16}^*}{\bar{A}_{22}^*} \qquad b_5 = \frac{\bar{B}_{21}^*}{\bar{A}_{22}^*}$$

$$b_7 = \frac{1}{\bar{A}_{22}^*} (\bar{B}_{11}^* + \bar{B}_{22}^* - 2\bar{B}_{66}^*) \qquad b_9 = \frac{\bar{B}_{12}^*}{\bar{A}_{22}^*}$$

$$(7\text{-}34)$$

The nondimensional membrane forces are given by expressions (7-11) and the bending moments (1-128) can be written in the nondimensional form

$$M_\zeta = -\bar{B}_{11}^* F_{,\eta\eta} - \frac{1}{\lambda^2} \bar{B}_{21}^* F_{,\zeta\zeta} + \frac{1}{\lambda} \bar{B}_{61}^* F_{,\zeta\eta}$$

$$- \frac{1}{\lambda^2} \bar{D}_{11}^* W_{,\zeta\zeta} - \bar{D}_{12}^* W_{,\eta\eta} - \frac{2}{\lambda} \bar{D}_{16}^* W_{,\zeta\eta}$$

$$M_\eta = -\bar{B}_{12}^* F_{,\eta\eta} - \frac{1}{\lambda^2} \bar{B}_{22}^* F_{,\zeta\zeta} + \frac{1}{\lambda} \bar{B}_{62}^* F_{,\zeta\eta}$$

$$- \frac{1}{\lambda^2} \bar{D}_{12}^* W_{,\zeta\zeta} - \bar{D}_{22}^* W_{,\eta\eta} - \frac{2}{\lambda} \bar{D}_{26}^* W_{,\zeta\eta}$$

$$(7\text{-}35)$$

$$M_{,\zeta\eta} = -\bar{B}_{16}^* F_{,\eta\eta} - \frac{1}{\lambda^2} \bar{B}_{26}^* F_{,\zeta\zeta} + \frac{1}{\lambda} \bar{B}_{66}^* F_{,\zeta\eta}$$

$$- \frac{1}{\lambda^2} \bar{D}_{16}^* W_{,\zeta\zeta} - \bar{D}_{26}^* W_{,\eta\eta} - \frac{2}{\lambda} \bar{D}_{66}^* W_{,\zeta\eta}$$

where M_ζ, M_η, and $M_{\zeta\eta}$ are defined in equations (7-13).

The plate under consideration is subjected to uniform inplane compressive forces, per unit length, n_x in the x direction and n_y in the y direction. The boundary conditions for loosely clamped edges are

$$W = W_{,\zeta} = F_{,\zeta\eta} = 0 \qquad F_{,\eta\eta} = -R \qquad \text{at} \quad \zeta = 0, 1$$

$$W = W_{,\eta} = F_{,\zeta\eta} = 0 \qquad F_{,\zeta\zeta} = -\lambda^2 kR \qquad \text{at} \quad \eta = 0, 1$$

$$(7\text{-}36)$$

in which k and R are given by equations (7-5).

A solution of equations (7-32) and (7-33) is assumed in the form of generalized double Fourier series (Refs. 7.1, 7.2)

$$F = -\frac{R}{2}(\eta^2 + k\lambda^2\zeta^2) + \sum_{m=1}^{\infty}\sum_{n=1}^{\infty} F_{mn} X_m(\zeta) Y_n(\eta) \tag{7-37}$$

$$W = \sum_{p=1}^{\infty}\sum_{q=1}^{\infty} W_{pq} X_p(\zeta) Y_q(\eta) \tag{7-38}$$

All the boundary conditions (7-36) are satisfied by use of expressions (5-36) for X_m and Y_m with the values of α_m and γ_m given in Table 5.1. Following a similar calculation as in equations (7-8) and (7-9) we obtain

$$
\begin{aligned}
W_{ij}(\alpha_i^4 + a_4 \lambda^4 \alpha_j^4) &+ \sum_{p=1}^{\infty}\sum_{q=1}^{\infty} W_{pq}(a_1 \lambda \alpha_p^3 \alpha_q K_1^{ip} L_3^{jq} \\
&+ 2a_2 \lambda^2 \alpha_p^2 \alpha_q^2 K_2^{ip} L_2^{jq} + a_3 \lambda^3 \alpha_p \alpha_q^3 K_3^{ip} L_1^{jq}) + F_{ij}(a_5 \alpha_i^4 + a_9 \lambda^4 \alpha_j^4) \\
&+ \sum_{m=1}^{\infty}\sum_{n=1}^{\infty} F_{mn}(a_6 \lambda \alpha_m^3 \alpha_n K_1^{im} L_3^{jn} + a_7 \lambda^2 \alpha_m^2 \alpha_n^2 K_2^{im} L_2^{jn} \\
&+ a_8 \lambda^3 \alpha_m \alpha_n^3 K_3^{im} L_1^{jn}) - \frac{\lambda^2}{\bar{D}_{11}^*} \sum_{k=1}^{\infty}\sum_{l=1}^{\infty}\sum_{r=1}^{\infty}\sum_{s=1}^{\infty} F_{kl} W_{rs} \\
&\cdot (\alpha_r^2 \alpha_l^2 K_5^{irk} L_5^{jls} + \alpha_k^2 \alpha_s^2 K_5^{ikr} L_5^{jsl} - 2\alpha_k \alpha_l \alpha_r \alpha_s K_4^{irk} L_4^{jsl}) \\
&+ \frac{\lambda^2 R}{\bar{D}_{11}^*}\left(\sum_{p=1}^{\infty} W_{pj} \alpha_p^2 K_2^{ip} + \rho\lambda^2 \sum_{q=1}^{\infty} W_{iq} \alpha_q^2 L_2^{jq}\right) \\
&= \frac{\lambda^4 Q_{ij}}{\bar{D}_{11}^*} \qquad i, j = 1, 2, 3, \ldots
\end{aligned}
\tag{7-39}
$$

$$
\begin{aligned}
F_{ij}(\alpha_i^4 + b_4 \lambda^4 \alpha_j^4) &- \sum_{m=1}^{\infty}\sum_{n=1}^{\infty} F_{mn}(b_1 \lambda \alpha_m^3 \alpha_n K_1^{im} L_3^{jn} \\
&- 2b_2 \lambda^2 \alpha_m^2 \alpha_n^2 K_2^{im} L_2^{jn} + b_3 \lambda^3 \alpha_m \alpha_n^3 K_3^{im} L_1^{jn}) \\
&= W_{ij}(b_5 \alpha_i^4 + b_9 \lambda^4 \alpha_j^4) + \sum_{p=1}^{\infty}\sum_{q=1}^{\infty} W_{pq}(b_6 \lambda \alpha_p^3 \alpha_q K_1^{ip} L_3^{jq} \\
&+ b_7 \lambda^2 \alpha_p^2 \alpha_q^2 K_2^{ip} L_2^{jq} + b_8 \lambda^3 \alpha_p \alpha_q^3 K_3^{ip} L_1^{jq}) \\
&+ \frac{\lambda^2}{\bar{A}_{22}^*} \sum_{r=1}^{\infty}\sum_{s=1}^{\infty}\sum_{k=1}^{\infty}\sum_{l=1}^{\infty} W_{rs} W_{kl}(\alpha_r \alpha_s \alpha_k \alpha_l K_4^{irk} L_4^{jsl} - \alpha_r^2 \alpha_l^2 K_5^{irk} L_5^{jls})
\end{aligned}
$$

$$i, j = 1, 2, 3, \ldots \tag{7-40}$$

in which Q_{ij}, K's and L's are defined by equations (5-212). Equations (7-39) and (7-40) can be solved by taking a finite number of terms in each of the truncated series for F and W.

Table 7.3 Comparison of solutions for nondimensional maximum deflection, $W(0.4, 0.4)$, of clamped graphite-epoxy four-layer cross-ply square plate under eccentric partial load $(\xi_1 = \xi_2 = 0.1, \xi = 0.25)$ and uniaxial compression

$\dfrac{Pb^2}{E_T h^4}$	100		200		300	
β	0.0	1.0	0.0	1.0	0.0	1.0
4 terms	0.1693	1.3102	0.3670	1.7086	0.5401	1.9834
9 terms	0.1785	1.2435	0.3550	1.5929	0.5276	1.8627

Numerical results are presented for two special cases, unsymmetric angle-ply and cross-ply plates. Each plate consists of an even number of plies, all of the same thickness. The vanishing elastic constants for the former are given by equation (1-134) and those for the latter by equation (1-140). Calculations were performed for graphite-epoxy laminates with elastic constants given by equation (5-213). To examine the convergence of the generalized Fourier series (7-37) and (7-38), the results obtained by taking the first four and nine terms in each of these series are presented in Table 7.3 for the maximum deflection of a cross-ply laminate under lateral load and inplane compression. In the table $\xi_1 \xi_2$, ξ, P, and β are defined in Section 7.1. It is seen that the series solution converges reasonably rapidly. The first nine terms in the truncated series for F and W which should give a good approximation are used in calculation. The numerical results are presented graphically in Fig. 7.1 for a two-layer $\pm 45°$ angle-ply plate of different aspect ratios subjected to uniform transverse load, in Fig. 7.3 for a square four-layer $\pm 45°$ angle-ply plate under eccentric partial loading and uniaxial compression, in Fig. 7.4 for a laterally loaded square cross-ply plate with various values of the total number of layers, in Fig. 7.5 for a square two-layer cross-ply plate under central partial load and uniaxial compression, and in Fig. 7.7 for a four-layer cross-ply plate of different aspect ratios under combined hydrostatic pressure and uniaxial compression. Based on the numerical results shown in Figs. 7.1 to 7.7, Tables 7.1 to 7.3, and some other numerical results (not presented herein) the following remarks may be drawn:

(i) The edge compression increases the maximum deflection, bending moments, and membrane forces for a given lateral load. The maximum deflection of an unsymmetric laminate increases with the aspect ratio but decreases with the number of layers. For given values of transverse load and inplane force (not greater than the critical load) the maximum deflection of a two-layer plate is largest among the corresponding laminated plates. As the number of layers increases, the result rapidly approaches that given by the uncoupled (specially orthotropic) solution.

(ii) In the case of maximum deflection at the center of a composite plate, the central deflection of a simply supported angle-ply plate is smaller than that of a corresponding cross-ply plate, whereas the central deflection of a clamped angle-ply plate is slightly larger than that of the corresponding cross-ply plate. In the cases of eccentric partial loading and hydrostatic pressure, the maximum deflection and maximum positive bending moment occur somewhere in the region between the center of the plate and the point of application of the resultant of the transverse load. The maximum deflection of the plate under partial loading is not affected to a great extent by small loading areas.

(iii) For large values of transverse load, the formation of boundary layers in the bending-moment distribution is observed for simply supported plates under uniform load, eccentric partial load, and hydrostatic load. The boundary layers are developed for smaller values of transverse load in the case of combined loads than in the case of transverse load alone. The largest value of membrane forces occurs at the edge midpoint in the cases of uniform transverse load, central partial load, and triangular load, and near some point along the edges close to the point of application of the resultant of the transverse load in the cases of eccentric and hydrostatic loads.

7.4 PERTURBATION SOLUTION FOR LOOSELY CLAMPED UNSYMMETRIC CROSS-PLY AND ANGLE-PLY RECTANGULAR PLATE UNDER UNIFORM LATERAL PRESSURE

Consider a thin general-ply anisotropic rectangular plate of length $2a_0$ in the x direction, width $2b_0$ in the y direction, and thickness h in the z direction subjected to uniform transverse load of intensity q_0. The origin of coordinates is taken at the center of the middle plane of the undeformed plate which contains the x and y axes. The nondimensional equations (7-1) and (7-2) for unsymmetric angle-ply plates and (7-14) and (7-15) for unsymmetric cross-ply plates can be expressed as

$$L_1 W + L_3 F = \tfrac{1}{16}\lambda^4 Q + \lambda^2(W_{,\zeta\zeta} F_{,\eta\eta} + W_{,\eta\eta} F_{,\zeta\zeta} - 2W_{,\zeta\eta} F_{,\zeta\eta}) \qquad (7\text{-}41)$$

$$L_2 F - L_3 W = \lambda^2[W_{,\zeta\eta}^2 - W_{,\zeta\zeta} W_{,\eta\eta}] \qquad (7\text{-}42)$$

where

$$\zeta = \frac{x}{a_0} \qquad \eta = \frac{y}{b_0} \qquad F = \frac{\psi}{E_T h^3}$$

$$Q = \frac{q_0(2b_0)^4}{E_T h^4} \qquad \bar{A}_{ij}^* = E_T h \bar{A}_{ij}^* \qquad \bar{D}_{ij}^* = \frac{D_{ij}^*}{E_T h^3} \qquad (7\text{-}43)$$

$$L_1( ) = \bar{D}_{11}^*( )_{,\zeta\zeta\zeta\zeta} + 2\lambda^2(\bar{D}_{12}^* + 2\bar{D}_{66}^*)( )_{,\zeta\zeta\eta\eta} + \lambda^4 \bar{D}_{22}^*( )_{,\eta\eta\eta\eta}$$

$$L_2( ) = \bar{A}_{22}^*( )_{,\zeta\zeta\zeta\zeta} + 2\lambda^2(\bar{A}_{12}^* + \tfrac{1}{2}\bar{A}_{66}^*)( )_{,\zeta\zeta\eta\eta} + \lambda^4 \bar{A}_{11}^*( )_{,\eta\eta\eta\eta}$$

and where, for unsymmetric angle-ply plates,

$$L_3( ) = \lambda(2\bar{B}_{26}^* - \bar{B}_{61}^*)( )_{,\zeta\zeta\zeta\eta} + \lambda^3(2\bar{B}_{16}^* - \bar{B}_{62}^*)( )_{,\zeta\eta\eta\eta} \qquad (7\text{-}44)$$

and, for unsymmetric cross-ply plates consisting of layers of equal thickness,

$$L_3(\ ) = -\bar{B}_{12}^*[(\ )_{,\zeta\zeta\zeta\zeta} - \lambda^4(\ )_{,\eta\eta\eta\eta}] \tag{7-45}$$

In these equations W, λ, and $\bar{B}_{ij}^*$ are defined in equation (7-3).

Due to the present nondimensional coordinates ζ and η, the nondimensional membrane forces become

$$N_\zeta = 4F_{,\eta\eta} \qquad N_\eta = \frac{4}{\lambda^2} F_{,\zeta\zeta} \qquad N_{\zeta\eta} = -\frac{4}{\lambda} F_{,\zeta\eta} \tag{7-46}$$

in which

$$(N_\zeta, N_\eta, N_{\zeta\eta}) = \frac{(2b_0)^2}{E_T h^3} (N_x, N_y, N_{xy}) \tag{7-47}$$

The nondimensional bending moments can be obtained by replacing ζ and η by $\zeta/2$ and $\eta/2$, respectively, in expressions (7-12) and (7-16) for unsymmetric angle-ply and cross-ply laminates, respectively.

If the four edges of the plate are clamped but free from applied inplane forces, the boundary conditions can be written in the nondimensional form

$$\begin{aligned} W = W_{,\zeta} = F_{,\eta\eta} = F_{,\zeta\eta} = 0 \qquad \text{at} \quad \zeta = \pm 1 \\ W = W_{,\eta} = F_{,\zeta\zeta} = F_{,\zeta\eta} = 0 \qquad \text{at} \quad \eta = \pm 1 \end{aligned} \tag{7-48}$$

An approximate solution of equations (7-41) and (7-42) satisfying boundary conditions (7-48) is formulated by making use of the perturbation method (Ref. 7.7). The load parameter Q and the variables F and W are expressed in the perturbation series with respect to the nondimensional central deflection $W(0, 0)$ denoted by W_0.

$$Q = \sum_{n=1}^{\infty} q_n W_0^n \qquad F = \sum_{n=1}^{\infty} f_n(\zeta, \eta) W_0^n \qquad W = \sum_{n=1}^{\infty} w_n(\zeta, \eta) W_0^n \tag{7-49}$$

By definition it requires that

$$w_1(0, 0) = 1 \qquad \text{and} \qquad w_i(0, 0) = 0 \qquad i = 2, 3, 4, \dots \tag{7-50}$$

Substituting equations (7-49) into (7-41) and (7-42) and equating like powers of W_0 lead to an infinite set of linear differential equations. Equating the coefficients of W_0 results in the following differential equations

$$\begin{aligned} L_1 w_1 + L_3 f_1 = \tfrac{1}{16}\lambda^4 q_1 \\ L_2 f_1 - L_3 w_1 = 0 \end{aligned} \tag{7-51}$$

which govern the small deflections of unsymmetric angle-ply and cross-ply laminates. The second approximation is given by the solution of the equations

$$\begin{aligned} L_1 w_2 + L_3 f_2 &= \tfrac{1}{16}\lambda^4 q_2 + \lambda^2(w_{1,\zeta\zeta} f_{1,\eta\eta} \\ &\quad + w_{1,\eta\eta} f_{1,\zeta\zeta} - 2w_{1,\zeta\eta} f_{1,\zeta\eta}) \\ L_2 f_2 - L_3 w_2 &= \lambda^2[(w_{1,\zeta\eta})^2 - w_{1,\zeta\zeta} w_{1,\eta\eta}] \end{aligned} \tag{7-52}$$

and the third approximation by the solution of the following

$$L_1 w_3 + L_3 f_3 = \tfrac{1}{16}\lambda^4 q_3 + \lambda^2(w_{1,\zeta\zeta}\, f_{2\,,\eta\eta} + w_{2\,,\zeta\zeta}\, f_{1,\eta\eta}$$

$$+ w_{1,\eta\eta}\, f_{2\,,\zeta\zeta} + w_{2\,,\eta\eta}\, f_{1,\zeta\zeta} - 2w_{1,\zeta\zeta}\, f_{2\,,\zeta\eta} - 2w_{2\,,\zeta\eta}\, f_{1,\zeta\eta}) \qquad (7\text{-}53)$$

$$L_2 f_3 - L_3 w_3 = \lambda^2(2w_{1,\zeta\eta} w_{2\,,\zeta\eta} - w_{1,\zeta\zeta} w_{2\,,\eta\eta} - w_{1,\eta\eta} w_{2\,,\zeta\zeta})$$

Differential equations in higher-order approximations can be similarly obtained. The associated boundary conditions in the ith approximation are, from equations (7-48) and (7-49),

$$w_i = w_{i,\zeta} = f_{i\,,\eta\eta} = f_{i\,,\zeta\eta} = 0 \qquad \text{at} \quad \zeta = \pm 1$$

$$w_i = w_{i,\eta} = f_{i\,,\zeta\zeta} = f_{i\,,\zeta\eta} = 0 \qquad \text{at} \quad \eta = \pm 1 \qquad (7\text{-}54)$$

in which i takes the values 1, 2, 3, and so forth.

The solution of any set of equations in the foregoing approximations may be assumed in the form of polynomials as follows

$$f_i = (1 - \zeta^2)^2(1 - \eta^2)^2(A_{i00} + A_{i10}\zeta + A_{i01}\eta + A_{i20}\zeta^2$$

$$+ A_{i11}\zeta\eta + A_{i02}\eta^2 + \cdots + A_{i60}\zeta^6 + \cdots + A_{i06}\eta^6)$$

$$w_i = (1 - \zeta^2)^2(1 - \eta^2)^2(B_{i00} + B_{i10}\zeta + B_{i01}\eta + B_{i20}\zeta^2 \qquad (7\text{-}55)$$

$$+ B_{i11}\zeta\eta + B_{i20}\eta^2 + \cdots + B_{i60}\zeta^6 + \cdots + B_{i06}\eta^6)$$

in which the expression in each pair of parentheses is a complete polynomial of degree six. In view of conditions (7-50)

$$B_{100} = 1 \qquad \text{and} \qquad B_{i00} = 0 \qquad i = 2, 3, 4, \dots \qquad (7\text{-}56)$$

It is observed that expressions (7-55) satisfy the boundary conditions (7-54) for any value of i. In the case of unsymmetric angle-ply plates the nondimensional stress function and the transverse deflection possess the following properties

$$F_{,\alpha\beta}(-\zeta, -\eta) = F_{,\alpha\beta}(\zeta, \eta) \qquad (\alpha, \beta = \zeta \ \text{or} \ \eta)$$

$$F_{,\alpha\beta}(-\zeta, \eta) = F_{,\alpha\beta}(\zeta, -\eta) \qquad (7\text{-}57)$$

$$W(-\zeta, -\eta) = W(\zeta, \eta) \qquad W(-\zeta, \eta) = W(\zeta, -\eta)$$

These conditions are satisfied by taking in equations (7-55)

$$A_{imn} = B_{imn} = 0 \qquad \text{for} \quad m + n = \text{odd} \qquad (7\text{-}58)$$

In the case of unsymmetric cross-ply plates, these membrane forces and transverse deflection respectively possess the properties of twofold symmetry. These physical requirements are satisfied by taking in equations (7-55)

$$A_{imn} = B_{imn} = 0 \qquad \text{for} \quad m, n = 1, 3, 5 \qquad (7\text{-}59)$$

in addition to equations (7-58).

Substituting equations (7-55) for $i = 1$ into equations (7-51) and equating the coefficients of like powers of ζ and η, a set of algebraic equations can be generated

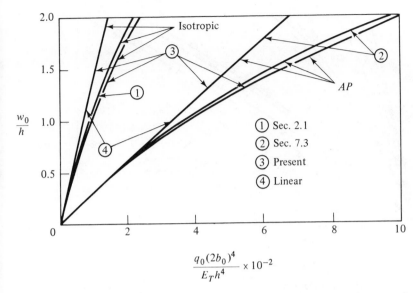

Figure 7.8 Relations between uniform transverse load and central deflection for square isotropic and two-layer $\pm 45°$ angle-ply plates.

as the number of nonzero coefficients q_1, A_{imn}, and B_{imn} in each case, and then solved simultaneously for these coefficients. The procedure for determining q_i, f_i, and w_i in other approximations is similar to that used in the first approximation. In the analysis, numerical results are presented by taking the first three terms in the perturbation series. It will be shown later that the three-term approximation agrees closely with the previous solutions. Therefore equations (7-49) may be approximated by

$$Q = q_1 W_0 + q_2 W_0^2 + q_3 W_0^3$$
$$F = f_1 W_0 + f_2 W_0^2 + f_3 W_0^3 \qquad (7\text{-}60)$$
$$W = w_1 W_0 + w_2 W_0^2 + w_3 W_0^3$$

As soon as the unknowns q_n, f_n, and w_n in equation (7-60) are determined, the nondimensional membrane forces and bending moments can be calculated.

Numerical examples are presented for unsymmetric angle-ply (AP) and cross-ply (CP) graphite-epoxy plates. The elastic constants given by equations (5-213) are used. In order to study the validity of the three-term approximation given by equations (7-60), the present results for the central deflection w_0 of isotropic and two-layer angle-ply plates are shown in Fig. 7.8 with the two previous solutions. A comparison of the load-deflection curves shows that the first three terms in the present truncated series give good approximations for the ratio of central deflection to thickness up to the value of 2. Figure 7.9 shows the relation between uniform transverse load and central deflection for unsymmetric laminates with various values of the aspect ratio λ and total number of layers n. It is seen that for

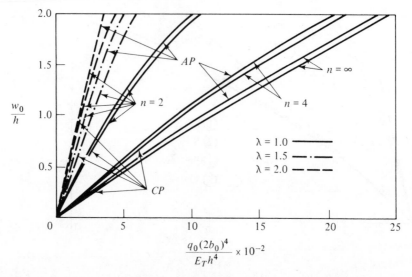

Figure 7.9 Load-deflection curves for cross-ply and $\pm 45°$ angle-ply plates for various values of aspect ratio and total number of layers.

both cross-ply and angle-ply plates the central deflection for a given load increases with increasing the aspect ratio but decreases with increasing the total number of layers, and that the curve for $n = 6$ (not presented here) is close to that for the uncoupled solution ($n = \infty$). At any fixed value of the load, the central deflection of an angle-ply plate is slightly larger than that of a corresponding cross-ply plate. These results are consistent with observations in the foregoing section. The membrane forces at the plate center and the middle point of a side are shown in Fig. 7.10 for unsymmetric angle-ply and cross-ply plates. In the case of a cross-ply

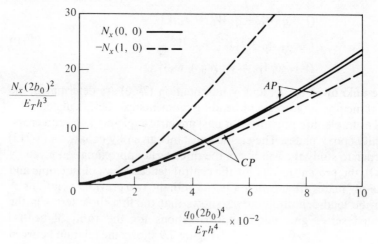

Figure 7.10 Membrane force N_x in square graphite-epoxy two-layer cross-ply and $\pm 45°$ angle-ply plates subjected to uniform pressure.

plate the largest value of N_x occurs at the midpoints of the sides $\eta = \pm 1$ and is in compression. In the case of an angle-ply plate, it occurs at the centre of the plate and is in tension. The membrane force N_x at the centre of an angle-ply plate is slightly larger than that in a corresponding cross-ply plate.

7.5 APPROXIMATE SOLUTION FOR RIGIDLY CLAMPED GENERALLY LAMINATED ANISOTROPIC RECTANGULAR PLATE UNDER UNIFORM TRANSVERSE LOAD

In the previous problems of unsymmetric laminates the inplane boundary conditions are associated with membrane forces and transverse deflection or membrane forces alone, and hence the differential equations expressed in terms of transverse deflection and force function have been used. In the case of a rigidly clamped plate, the boundary conditions are described by three displacement components. It is, therefore, better to adopt the system of equations for three displacement components in the analysis. These differential equations for a generally laminated anisotropic rectangular plate of length $2a_0$ in the x direction, width $2b_0$ in the y direction, and thickness h in the z direction under uniform transverse load q_0 obtained from the static version of equation (1-66) to (1-68) can be written in the nondimensional form

$$\lambda L_1 U + \lambda L_2 V - L_3 W = -W_{,\zeta} L_1 W - \lambda W_{,\eta} L_2 W \qquad (7\text{-}61)$$

$$\lambda L_2 U + \lambda L_4 V - L_5 W = -W_{,\zeta} L_2 W - \lambda W_{,\eta} L_4 W \qquad (7\text{-}62)$$

$$\lambda L_3 U + \lambda L_5 V - L_6 W = -\lambda^4 Q - [\lambda U_{,\zeta} + \tfrac{1}{2} W_{,\zeta}^2] L_7 W$$
$$\quad - \lambda^2 [V_{,\eta} + \tfrac{1}{2} W_{,\eta}^2] L_8 W - \lambda (\lambda U_{,\eta} + V_{,\zeta} + W_{,\zeta} W_{,\eta}) L_9 W$$
$$\quad - W_{,\zeta} L_3 W - \lambda W_{,\eta} L_5 W - 2\lambda^2 (b_{12} - b_{66})[W_{,\eta}^2 - W_{,\zeta\zeta} W_{,\eta\eta}] \qquad (7\text{-}63)$$

in which the nondimensional parameters and constants are defined by

$$\zeta = \frac{x}{a_0} \qquad \eta = \frac{y}{b_0} \qquad \lambda = \frac{a_0}{b_0} \qquad Q = \frac{q_0 b_0^4}{A_{22} h^3}$$

$$U = \frac{u^\circ b_0}{h^2} \qquad V = \frac{v^\circ b_0}{h^2} \qquad W = \frac{w}{h} \qquad (7\text{-}64)$$

$$a_{ij} = \frac{A_{ij}}{A_{22}} \qquad b_{ij} = \frac{B_{ij}}{A_{22} h} \qquad d_{ij} = \frac{D_{ij}}{A_{22} h^2} \qquad (i, j = 1, 2, 6)$$

and the nondimensional linear differential operators L_i by

$$L_1(\ ) = a_{11}(\ )_{,\zeta\zeta} + 2\lambda a_{16}(\ )_{,\zeta\eta} + \lambda^2 a_{66}(\ )_{,\eta\eta}$$

$$L_2(\ ) = a_{16}(\ )_{,\zeta\zeta} + \lambda(a_{12} + a_{66})(\ )_{,\zeta\eta} + \lambda^2 a_{26}(\ )_{,\eta\eta}$$

$$L_3(\ ) = b_{11}(\ )_{,\zeta\zeta\zeta} + 3\lambda b_{16}(\ )_{,\zeta\zeta\eta} + \lambda^2 (b_{12} + 2b_{66})(\ )_{,\zeta\eta\eta}$$
$$\quad + \lambda^3 b_{26}(\ )_{,\eta\eta\eta}$$

▼

$$L_4(\ ) = a_{66}(\ )_{,\zeta\zeta} + 2\lambda a_{26}(\ )_{,\zeta\eta} + \lambda^2(\ )_{,\eta\eta}$$

$$L_5(\ ) = b_{16}(\ )_{,\zeta\zeta\zeta} + \lambda(b_{12} + 2b_{66})(\ )_{,\zeta\zeta\eta} + 3\lambda^2 b_{26}(\ )_{,\zeta\eta\eta}$$
$$\qquad + \lambda^3 b_{22}(\ )_{,\eta\eta\eta}$$

$$L_6(\ ) = d_{11}(\ )_{,\zeta\zeta\zeta\zeta} + 4\lambda d_{16}(\ )_{,\zeta\zeta\zeta\eta} + 2\lambda^2(d_{12} + 2d_{66})(\ )_{,\zeta\zeta\eta\eta}$$
$$\qquad + 4\lambda^3 d_{26}(\ )_{,\zeta\eta\eta\eta} + \lambda^4 d_{22}(\ )_{,\eta\eta\eta\eta} \qquad (7\text{-}65)$$

$$L_7(\ ) = a_{11}(\ )_{,\zeta\zeta} + 2\lambda a_{16}(\ )_{,\zeta\eta} + \lambda^2 a_{12}(\ )_{,\eta\eta}$$

$$L_8(\ ) = a_{12}(\ )_{,\zeta\zeta} + 2\lambda a_{26}(\ )_{,\zeta\eta} + \lambda^2(\ )_{,\eta\eta}$$

$$L_9(\ ) = a_{16}(\ )_{,\zeta\zeta} + 2\lambda a_{66}(\ )_{,\zeta\eta} + \lambda^2 a_{26}(\ )_{,\eta\eta}$$

If the plate is rigidly clamped along its edges, the appropriate nondimensional boundary conditions are

$$U = V = W = W_{,\zeta} = 0 \qquad \text{at} \quad \zeta = \pm 1$$
$$U = V = W = W_{,\eta} = 0 \qquad \text{at} \quad \eta = \pm 1 \qquad (7\text{-}66)$$

An approximate solution of the boundary-value problem is formulated by use of the perturbation method (Ref. 7.8). The parameters in load, deflection, and two inplane displacements are developed into the perturbation series with respect to the nondimensional central deflection, $W(0, 0)$, of the plate, denoted by W_0.

$$Q = \sum_{n=1}^{\infty} q_n W_0^n \qquad W = \sum_{n=1}^{\infty} w_n(\zeta, \eta) W_0^n$$
$$U = \sum_{n=1}^{\infty} u_n(\zeta, \eta) W_0^n \qquad V = \sum_{n=1}^{\infty} v_n(\zeta, \eta) W_0^n \qquad (7\text{-}67)$$

By definition, it requires that

$$w_1(0, 0) = 1 \qquad w_i(0, 0) = 0 \qquad i = 2, 3, 4, \ldots \qquad (7\text{-}68)$$

Substituting equation (7-67) into equations (7-61) to (7-63) and (7-66), and equating like powers of W_0, a series of differential equations and boundary conditions is obtained. In the first approximation, the terms in the first power of W_0 are equated. The corresponding set of differential equations is given by

$$\lambda L_1 u_1 + \lambda L_2 v_1 - L_3 w_1 = 0$$
$$\lambda L_2 u_1 + \lambda L_4 v_1 - L_5 w_1 = 0 \qquad (7\text{-}69)$$
$$\lambda L_3 u_1 + \lambda L_5 v_1 - L_6 w_1 = -\lambda^4 q_1$$

which governs the small deflection of unsymmetrically laminated anisotropic plates. The second approximation requires that

$$\lambda L_1 u_2 + \lambda L_2 v_2 - L_3 w_2 = -w_{1,\zeta} L_1 w_1 - \lambda w_{1,\eta} L_2 w_1$$
$$\lambda L_2 u_2 + \lambda L_4 v_2 - L_5 w_2 = -w_{1,\zeta} L_2 w_1 - \lambda w_{1,\eta} L_4 w_1$$

$$\lambda L_3 u_2 + \lambda L_5 v_2 - L_6 w_2 = -\lambda^4 q_2 - \lambda u_{1,\zeta} L_7 w_1 - \lambda^2 v_{1,\eta} L_8 w_1$$
$$- \lambda(\lambda u_{1,\eta} + v_{1,\zeta}) L_9 w_1 - w_{1,\zeta} L_3 w_1 - \lambda w_{1,\eta} L_5 w_1 \qquad (7\text{-}70)$$
$$- 2\lambda^2(b_{12} - b_{16})(w_{1,\zeta\eta}2 - w_{1,\zeta\zeta} w_{1,\eta\eta})$$

The third approximation is given by the solution of the equations

$$\lambda L_1 u_3 + \lambda L_2 v_3 - L_3 w_3 = -w_{1,\zeta} L_1 w_2 - w_{2,\zeta} L_1 w_1$$
$$- \lambda(w_{1,\eta} L_2 w_2 + w_{2,\eta} L_2 w_1)$$

$$\lambda L_2 u_3 + \lambda L_4 v_3 - L_5 w_3 = -w_{1,\zeta} L_2 w_2 - w_{2,\zeta} L_2 w_1$$
$$- \lambda(w_{1,\eta} L_4 w_2 + w_{2,\eta} L_4 w_1)$$

$$\lambda L_3 u_3 + \lambda L_5 v_3 - L_6 w_3 = -\lambda^4 q_3 - \lambda u_{1,\zeta} L_7 w_2$$
$$- (\lambda u_{2,\zeta} + \tfrac{1}{2} w_{1,\zeta}^2) L_7 w_1 \qquad (7\text{-}71)$$
$$- \lambda^2 v_{1,\eta} L_8 w_2 - \lambda^2 (v_{2,\eta} + \tfrac{1}{2} w_{1,\eta}^2) L_8 w_1$$
$$- \lambda(\lambda u_{1,\eta} + v_{1,\zeta}) L_9 w_2 - \lambda(\lambda u_{2,\eta} + v_{2,\zeta} + w_{1,\zeta} w_{1,\eta}) L_9 w_1$$
$$- w_{1,\zeta} L_3 w_2 - w_{2,\zeta} L_3 w_1 - \lambda(w_{1,\eta} L_5 w_2 + w_{2,\eta} L_5 w_1)$$
$$- 2\lambda^2 (b_{12} - b_{66})(2w_{1,\zeta\eta} w_{2,\zeta\eta} - w_{1,\zeta\zeta} w_{2,\eta\eta} - w_{2,\zeta\zeta} w_{1,\eta\eta})$$

The other sets of differential equations in higher-order approximations can be similarly obtained. The boundary conditions in any approximations are obtained from equations (7-66) and (7-67).

$$\text{Along } \zeta = \pm 1 \qquad u_n = v_n = w_n = w_{n,\zeta} = 0$$
$$\qquad\qquad\qquad\qquad\qquad\qquad\qquad\qquad n = 1, 2, 3, \ldots \quad (7\text{-}72)$$
$$\text{Along } \eta = \pm 1 \qquad u_n = v_n = w_n = w_{n,\eta} = 0$$

In equations (7-67), q_1, w_1, u_1, and v_1 are then determined from equations (7-69) and (7-72) for $n = 1$; q_2, w_2, u_2, and v_2 are determined from equations (7-70) and (7-72) for $n = 2$; and so forth. The solution of any set of the foregoing differential equations is assumed to be in the form of polynomial

$$w_n = (1 - \zeta^2)^2 (1 - \eta^2)^2 F(\zeta, \eta)$$
$$u_n = (1 - \zeta^2)(1 - \eta^2) G(\zeta, \eta) \qquad n = 1, 2, 3, \ldots \quad (7\text{-}73)$$
$$v_n = (1 - \zeta^2)(1 - \eta^2) H(\zeta, \eta)$$

In these expressions, F, G, and H are the complete polynomials given by

$$F = R_{n00} + R_{n10}\zeta + R_{n01}\eta + \cdots + R_{n60}\zeta^6 + R_{n51}\zeta^5\eta$$
$$+ R_{n42}\zeta^4\eta^2 + R_{n33}\zeta^3\eta^3 + R_{n24}\zeta^2\eta^4 + R_{n15}\zeta\eta^5 + R_{n06}\eta^6$$

$$G = S_{n00} + S_{n10}\zeta + S_{n01}\eta + \cdots + S_{n50}\zeta^5 + S_{n41}\zeta^4\eta \qquad (7\text{-}74)$$
$$+ S_{n32}\zeta^3\eta^2 + S_{n23}\zeta^2\eta^3 + S_{n14}\zeta\eta^4 + S_{n05}\eta^5$$

$$H = T_{n00} + T_{n10}\zeta + T_{n01}\eta + \cdots + T_{n50}\zeta^5 + T_{n41}\zeta^4\eta$$
$$T_{n32}\zeta^3\eta^2 + T_{n23}\zeta^2\eta^3 + T_{n14}\zeta\eta^4 + T_{n05}\eta^5$$

where R's, S's, and T's are constant coefficients. In view of equations (7-68) it follows that

$$R_{100} = 1 \qquad R_{n00} = 0 \qquad n = 2, 3, 4, \ldots \qquad (7\text{-}75)$$

It is observed that equations (7-73) satisfy all the boundary conditions (7-72) for any value of n. The evaluation of the constants in equation (7-74) follows the standard line.

As an approximate solution the series (7-67) may be truncated as

$$Q = \sum_{n=1}^{3} q_n W_0^n \qquad W = \sum_{n=1}^{3} w_n(\zeta, \eta) W_0^n$$

$$U = \sum_{n=1}^{3} u_n(\zeta, \eta) W_0^n \qquad V = \sum_{n=1}^{3} v_n(\zeta, \eta) W_0^n \qquad (7\text{-}76)$$

Once the unknowns, q_n, w_n, u_n, and v_n in equations (7-76) are determined, in view of equations (1-70) and (1-71), the nondimensional membrane stress resultants and stress couples can be calculated from the following

$$
\begin{Bmatrix} N_\zeta \\ N_\eta \\ N_{\zeta\eta} \\ M_\zeta \\ M_\eta \\ M_{\zeta\eta} \end{Bmatrix}
=
\begin{bmatrix}
a_{11} & a_{12} & a_{16} & b_{11} & b_{12} & b_{16} \\
a_{12} & a_{22} & a_{26} & b_{12} & b_{22} & b_{26} \\
a_{16} & a_{26} & a_{66} & b_{16} & b_{26} & b_{66} \\
b_{11} & b_{12} & b_{16} & d_{11} & d_{12} & d_{16} \\
b_{12} & b_{22} & b_{26} & d_{12} & d_{22} & d_{26} \\
b_{16} & b_{26} & b_{66} & d_{16} & d_{26} & d_{66}
\end{bmatrix}
\begin{Bmatrix} \xi_1 \\ \xi_2 \\ \xi_3 \\ -\dfrac{W_{,\zeta\zeta}}{\lambda^2} \\ -W_{,\eta\eta} \\ -\dfrac{2W_{,\zeta\eta}}{\lambda} \end{Bmatrix}
\qquad (7\text{-}77)
$$

in which the nondimensional membrane forces N and bending moments M are defined in equations (7-13), and in which

$$\xi_1 = \frac{1}{\lambda^2}[\lambda U_{,\zeta} + \tfrac{1}{2}W_{,\zeta}^2] \qquad \xi_2 = V_{,\eta} + \tfrac{1}{2}W_{,\eta}^2$$

$$\xi_3 = \frac{1}{\lambda}(\lambda U_{,\eta} + V_{,\zeta} + W_{,\zeta}W_{,\eta}) \qquad (7\text{-}78)$$

The solution presented above is simplified for special cases as follows:

(a) In the case of unsymmetric angle-ply plates it can be shown that

$$a_{16} = a_{26} = b_{11} = b_{12} = b_{22} = b_{66} = d_{16} = d_{26} = 0 \qquad (7\text{-}79)$$

In this case the deflection and two inplane displacements possess the following properties

$$w_n(-\zeta, -\eta) = w_n(\zeta, \eta) \qquad w_n(\zeta, -\eta) = w_n(-\zeta, \eta)$$
$$u_n(-\zeta, -\eta) = -u_n(\zeta, \eta) \qquad u_n(\zeta, -\eta) = -u_n(-\zeta, \eta)$$
$$v_n(-\zeta, -\eta) = -v_n(\zeta, \eta) \qquad v_n(\zeta, -\eta) = -v_n(-\zeta, \eta)$$
$$u_n(0, 0) = v_n(0, 0) = 0 \qquad n = 1, 2, 3 \tag{7-80}$$

To satisfy equations (7-78), we take, in equations (7-74),

$$R_{n10} = R_{n01} = R_{n30} = R_{n21} = R_{n12} = R_{n03} = 0$$

$$R_{n50} = R_{n41} = R_{n32} = R_{n23} = R_{n14} = R_{n05} = 0$$

$$Z_{n00} = Z_{n20} = Z_{n11} = Z_{n02} = Z_{n40} = Z_{n31} = 0 \tag{7-81}$$

$$Z_{n22} = Z_{n13} = Z_{n04} = 0 \qquad n = 1, 2, 3$$

where

$$Z_{nij} = S_{nij} \quad \text{or} \quad T_{nij} \tag{7-82}$$

(b) For unsymmetric cross-ply plates composed of layers of equal thickness, it is found that

$$a_{16} = a_{26} = b_{12} = b_{16} = b_{26} = b_{66} = d_{16} = d_{26} = 0$$
$$a_{11} = 1 \qquad b_{22} = -b_{11} \qquad d_{22} = d_{11} \tag{7-83}$$

To satisfy the twofold symmetry with respect to the xz and yz planes, in addition to equations (7-81) we take

$$R_{n11} = R_{n31} = R_{n13} = R_{n51} = R_{n33} = R_{n15} = 0$$

$$S_{n01} = S_{n21} = S_{n03} = S_{n41} = S_{n23} = R_{n05} = 0 \tag{7-84}$$

$$T_{n10} = T_{n30} = T_{n12} = T_{n50} = T_{n32} = T_{n14} = 0$$

(c) In the case of symmetrically laminated anisotropic plates, the material coupling phenomenon does not occur between transverse bending and inplane stretching. Consequently

$$b_{ij} = 0 \qquad i, j = 1, 2, 6 \tag{7-85}$$

In view of equations (7-65) and of geometric symmetry with respect to the middle plane, the following is obtained

$$L_3 = L_5 = u_1 = v_1 = w_2 = u_3 = v_3 = 0 \tag{7-86}$$

(d) For material homogeneity we have

$$A_{ij} = hC_{ij} \quad \text{and} \quad D_{ij} = \frac{C_{ij}h^3}{12} \qquad i, j = 1, 2, 6 \tag{7-87}$$

in addition to equations (7-85) and (7-86). The general solution presented in this study, therefore, can reduce to those for anisotropic, orthotropic, and isotropic plates.

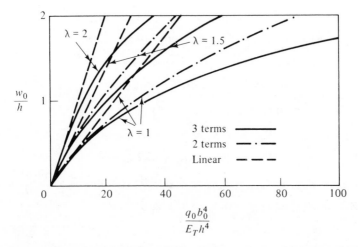

Figure 7.11 Relation between uniform pressure and central deflection of two layer $\pm 45°$ angle-ply graphite-epoxy plate for various aspect ratios.

The validity of the three-term approximation given by equation (7-76) is examined by comparison with the two-term approximation. In the case of $\pm 45°$ angle-ply two-layer graphite-epoxy plates with elastic constants given by equation (5-213), the load-deflection relations given by the one-term, two-term, and three-term solutions are shown in Fig. 7.11 for $\lambda = 1.0$, 1.5, and 2.0. It is seen from the figure that the values of the central deflection w_0 given by the two-term and three-term solutions are subjected to a maximum difference of approximately 5 percent for the central deflection equal to the plate thickness. Thus the first three terms in series (7-67) do not yield good approximations for the maximum deflection greater than the plate thickness. In view of the numerical results given in Sec. 7.4 the first three terms in series (7-49) give good approximations for the ratio of maximum deflection to thickness up to the value of 2. This may arise from the fact that the nonlinear load-deflection curve for a loosely clamped composite plate given in Sec. 7.4 deviates less from the corresponding linear load-deflection curve than from that for a rigidly clamped laminate. This is also true in the case of isotropic plates.

7.6 MORE ACCURATE SOLUTION FOR RIGIDLY CLAMPED LAMINATED ANISOTROPIC RECTANGULAR PLATE UNDER TRANSVERSE LOAD

In the previous section an approximate solution for the moderately large deflection of generally laminated anisotropic rectangular plates with rigidly clamped edges subjected to uniform lateral pressure has been presented on the basis of the perturbation method. In this section a more accurate solution of the plate problem for arbitrary lateral loading $q(x, y)$ is formulated by use of the generalized double Fourier series (Ref. 7.9). If the length and width of the plate are denoted by a in the x direction and by b in the y direction, then the governing differential equations are given by equations (7-61) to (7-63) with a_0, b_0, and q_0 in expressions (7-64) replaced by a, b, and q, respectively. The boundary conditions for a rigidly clamped plate are of the form

$$U = V = W = W_{,\zeta} = 0 \qquad \text{at} \quad \zeta = \pm\tfrac{1}{2}$$
$$U = V = W = W_{,\eta} = 0 \qquad \text{at} \quad \eta = \pm\tfrac{1}{2} \tag{7-88}$$

in which the origin of the plate coordinate system has been chosen to coincide with the center of the midplane of the undeformed plate.

A solution of equations (7-61) to (7-63) satisfying boundary conditions (7-88) is sought in the form of double series

$$U = \sum_{m=1}^{\infty} \sum_{n=1}^{\infty} u_{mn} R_m(\zeta) Y_n(\eta)$$

$$V = \sum_{m=1}^{\infty} \sum_{n=1}^{\infty} v_{mn} X_m(\zeta) S_n(\eta) \tag{7-89}$$

$$W = \sum_{m=1}^{\infty} \sum_{n=1}^{\infty} w_{mn} X_m(\zeta) Y_n(\eta)$$

where

$$R_m = \sin 2m\pi\zeta \qquad S_n = \sin 2n\pi\eta$$

$$X_m = \frac{\cosh \alpha_m \zeta}{\cosh (\alpha_m/2)} - \frac{\cos \alpha_m \zeta}{\cos (\alpha_m/2)} \tag{7-90}$$

$$Y_n = \frac{\cosh \alpha_n \eta}{\cosh (\alpha_n/2)} - \frac{\cos \alpha_n \eta}{\cos (\alpha_n/2)}$$

All the boundary conditions are satisfied if the values $\alpha_k/2$ are the roots of the transcendental equation

$$\tanh (\alpha_k/2) + \tan (\alpha_k/2) = 0 \tag{7-91}$$

whose roots are given in Table 2.1 in which $\lambda_k = \alpha_k/2$.

The functions X_m, Y_n satisfy the following orthogonality relations

$$\int_{-1/2}^{1/2} X_i X_j \, d\zeta = \begin{cases} 0 & i \neq j \\ 1 & i = j \end{cases}$$

$$\int_{-1/2}^{1/2} Y_i Y_j \, d\eta = \begin{cases} 0 & i \neq j \\ 1 & i = j \end{cases} \tag{7-92}$$

Substituting expressions (7-89) into equations (7-61) to (7-63), multiplying the first of the resulting equations by $\sin (2i\pi\zeta) Y_j(\eta)$, the second by $X_i(\zeta) \sin (2j\pi\eta)$, and the third by $X_i(\zeta)Y_i(\eta)$, integrating from $-1/2$ to $1/2$ with respect to ζ and η, and using equations (7-92), we obtain*

$$2\pi^2\lambda a_{11}i^2 u_{ij} - \tfrac{1}{2}\lambda^3 a_{66}\sum_{n=1}^{\infty}u_{in}\alpha_n^2 L_1^{jn}$$

$$- 2\pi\lambda^2(a_{12}+a_{66})\sum_{m=1}^{\infty}\sum_{n=1}^{\infty}v_{mn}\alpha_m n K_2^{im}L_3^{jn}$$

$$= -b_{11}\sum_{m=1}^{\infty}w_{mj}\alpha_m^3 K_4^{im} - \lambda^2(b_{12}+2b_{66})\sum_{m=1}^{\infty}\sum_{n=1}^{\infty}w_{mn}\alpha_m\alpha_n^2 K_2^{im}L_1^{jn}$$

$$+ \sum_{p=1}^{\infty}\sum_{q=1}^{\infty}\sum_{r=1}^{\infty}\sum_{s=1}^{\infty}w_{pq}w_{rs}[a_{11}\alpha_p\alpha_r^2 K_5^{ipr}L_7^{jqs} + \lambda^2 a_{66}\alpha_p\alpha_s^2 K_6^{ipr}L_8^{jqs}$$

$$+ \lambda^2(a_{12}+a_{66})\alpha_q\alpha_r\alpha_s K_6^{irp}L_9^{jqs}] \qquad\qquad i,j=1,2,3,\dots \quad (7\text{-}93)$$

$$2\pi^2\lambda^3 j^2 v_{ij} - 2\pi\lambda^2(a_{12}+a_{66})\sum_{m=1}^{\infty}\sum_{n=1}^{\infty}u_{mn}m\alpha_n K_3^{im}L_2^{jn}$$

$$- \tfrac{1}{2}\lambda a_{66}\sum_{m=1}^{\infty}v_{mj}\alpha_m^2 K_1^{im} = -\lambda^3 b_{22}\sum_{n=1}^{\infty}w_{in}\alpha_n^3 L_4^{jn}$$

$$- \lambda(b_{12}+2b_{66})\sum_{m=1}^{\infty}\sum_{n=1}^{\infty}w_{mn}\alpha_m^2\alpha_n K_1^{im}L_2^{jn}$$

$$+ \lambda\sum_{p=1}^{\infty}\sum_{q=1}^{\infty}\sum_{r=1}^{\infty}\sum_{s=1}^{\infty}w_{pq}w_{rs}[(a_{12}+a_{66})\alpha_p\alpha_r\alpha_s K_9^{ipr}L_6^{jsq}$$

$$+ a_{66}\alpha_q\alpha_r^2 K_8^{ipr}L_6^{jqs} + \lambda^2\alpha_q\alpha_s^2 K_7^{ipr}L_5^{jqs}] \qquad\qquad i,j=1,2,3,\dots \quad (7\text{-}94)$$

$$(d_{11}\alpha_i^4 + \lambda^4 d_{22}\alpha_j^4)w_{ij} + 2\lambda^2(d_{12}+2d_{66})\sum_{m=1}^{\infty}\sum_{n=1}^{\infty}w_{mn}\alpha_m^2\alpha_n^2 K_1^{im}L_1^{jn}$$

$$= \lambda^4 q_{ij} - 8\pi^3\lambda\left(b_{11}\sum_{m=1}^{\infty}u_{mj}m^3 K_3^{im} + \lambda^3 b_{22}\sum_{n=1}^{\infty}v_{in}n^3 L_3^{jn}\right)$$

$$+ 2\pi\lambda^2(b_{12}+2b_{66})\sum_{m=1}^{\infty}\sum_{n=1}^{\infty}(u_{mn}m\lambda\alpha_n^2 K_3^{im}L_1^{jn} + v_{mn}\alpha_m^2 n K_1^{im}L_3^{jn})$$

$$+ 2\lambda\sum_{p=1}^{\infty}\sum_{q=1}^{\infty}\sum_{r=1}^{\infty}\sum_{s=1}^{\infty}u_{pq}w_{rs}(\pi a_{11}p\alpha_r^2 K_{12}^{ipr}L_7^{jqs} + \pi\lambda^2 a_{12}p\alpha_s^2 K_{11}^{ipr}L_8^{jqs}$$

$$+ \lambda^2 a_{66}\alpha_q\alpha_r\alpha_s K_6^{pri}L_9^{jqs}) + 2\lambda^2\sum_{p=1}^{\infty}\sum_{q=1}^{\infty}\sum_{r=1}^{\infty}\sum_{s=1}^{\infty}v_{pq}w_{rs}$$

$$\cdot(\pi a_{12}q\alpha_r^2 K_8^{ipr}L_{11}^{jqs} + \pi\lambda^2 q\alpha_s^2 K_7^{ipr}L_{12}^{jqs} + a_{66}\alpha_p\alpha_r\alpha_s K_9^{ipr}L_6^{qsj})$$

$$+ \sum_{p=1}^{\infty}\sum_{q=1}^{\infty}\sum_{r=1}^{\infty}\sum_{s=1}^{\infty}w_{pq}w_{rs}[b_{11}\alpha_p\alpha_r^3 K_{10}^{ipr}L_7^{jqs} + \lambda^2(b_{12}+2b_{66})$$

$$\cdot(\alpha_p\alpha_r\alpha_s^2 K_9^{ipr}L_8^{jqs} + \alpha_q\alpha_r^2\alpha_s K_8^{ipr}L_9^{jqs})$$

▼

---

* Integrations of all odd functions such as $X_m'' \sin(2i\pi\zeta)$, $X_i X_m'$, etc. over $[-1/2, 1/2]$ are zero.

$$+ \lambda^4 b_{22} \alpha_q \alpha_s^3 K_7^{ipr} L_{10}^{jqs}$$ ▲

$$+ 2\lambda^2 (b_{12} - b_{66})(\alpha_q \alpha_s K_7^{ipr} L_9^{jqs} - \alpha_p^2 \alpha_s^2 K_8^{irp} L_8^{jqs})]$$

$$+ \tfrac{1}{2} \sum_{p=1}^{\infty} \sum_{q=1}^{\infty} \sum_{r=1}^{\infty} \sum_{s=1}^{\infty} \sum_{k=1}^{\infty} \sum_{l=1}^{\infty} w_{pq} w_{rs} w_{kl} [a_{11} \alpha_p \alpha_r \alpha_k^2 K_{16}^{iprk} L_{13}^{jqsl}$$

$$+ \lambda^2 a_{12}(\alpha_p \alpha_r \alpha_l^2 K_{15}^{iprk} L_{14}^{jqsl} + \alpha_q \alpha_s \alpha_k^2 K_{14}^{iprk} L_{15}^{jsql})$$ ▲

$$+ \lambda^4 \alpha_q \alpha_s \alpha_l^2 K_{13}^{iprk} L_{16}^{jqsl} + 4\lambda^2 a_{66} \alpha_p \alpha_s \alpha_k \alpha_l K_{15}^{ipkr} L_{15}^{jslq}] \quad i,j = 1, 2, 3, \dots \quad (7\text{-}95)$$

In equations (7-93) to (7-95) q_{ij} and K_1 to K_{16} are constants defined by

$$Q = \sum_{i=1}^{\infty} \sum_{j=1}^{\infty} q_{ij} X_i(\zeta) Y_j(\eta)$$

$$K_1^{im} = \frac{1}{\alpha_m^2} \int_{-1/2}^{1/2} X_i X_m'' \, d\zeta$$

$$K_2^{im} = \frac{1}{\alpha_m} \int_{-1/2}^{1/2} \sin(2i\pi\zeta) X_m' \, d\zeta$$

$$K_3^{im} = \int_{-1/2}^{1/2} X_i \cos(2m\pi\zeta) \, d\zeta$$

$$K_4^{im} = \frac{1}{\alpha_m^3} \int_{-1/2}^{1/2} \sin(2i\pi\zeta) X_m''' \, d\zeta$$

$$K_5^{ipr} = \frac{1}{\alpha_p \alpha_r^2} \int_{-1/2}^{1/2} \sin(2i\pi\zeta) X_p' X_r'' \, d\zeta$$

$$K_6^{ipr} = \frac{1}{\alpha_p} \int_{-1/2}^{1/2} \sin(2i\pi\zeta) X_p' X_r \, d\zeta \qquad (7\text{-}96)$$ ▼

$$K_7^{ipr} = \int_{-1/2}^{1/2} X_i X_p X_r \, d\zeta$$

$$K_8^{ipr} = \frac{1}{\alpha_r^2} \int_{-1/2}^{1/2} X_i X_p X_r'' \, d\zeta$$

$$K_9^{ipr} = \frac{1}{\alpha_p \alpha_r} \int_{-1/2}^{1/2} X_i X_p' X_r' \, d\zeta$$

$$K_{10}^{ipr} = \frac{1}{\alpha_p \alpha_r^3} \int_{-1/2}^{1/2} X_i X_p' X_r''' \, d\zeta$$

$$K_{11}^{ipr} = \int_{-1/2}^{1/2} X_i \cos(2p\pi\zeta) X_r \, d\zeta$$

$$K_{12}^{ipr} = \frac{1}{\alpha_r^2} \int_{-1/2}^{1/2} X_i \cos(2p\pi\zeta) X_r'' \, d\zeta$$ ▼

$$K_{13}^{iprk} = \int_{-1/2}^{1/2} X_i X_p X_r X_k \, d\zeta \qquad \blacktriangle$$

$$K_{14}^{iprk} = \frac{1}{\alpha_k^2} \int_{-1/2}^{1/2} X_i X_p X_r X_k'' \, d\zeta$$

$$K_{15}^{iprk} = \frac{1}{\alpha_p \alpha_r} \int_{-1/2}^{1/2} X_i X_p' X_r' X_k \, d\zeta$$

$$K_{16}^{iprk} = \frac{1}{\alpha_p \alpha_r \alpha_k^2} \int_{-1/2}^{1/2} X_i X_p' X_r' X_k'' \, d\zeta$$

where the primes denote differentiation with respect to the corresponding coordinate, and the constants L_1 to L_{16} are obtained by replacing X, ζ, i, k, m, p, and r in equations (7-96) by Y, η, j, l, n, q, and s, respectively. It is observed that the integrands in expressions (7-96) are even functions and that these definite integrals can be evaluated. For example,

$$K_1^{im} = \frac{2}{\alpha_m^2} \int_0^{1/2} X_i X_m'' \, d\zeta \qquad (i \neq m)$$

$$= 4 \left[\frac{\alpha_i \sinh(\alpha_i/2) \cos(\alpha_m/2) + \alpha_m \cosh(\alpha_i/2) \sin(\alpha_m/2)}{(\alpha_i^2 + \alpha_m^2) \cosh(\alpha_i/2) \cos(\alpha_m/2)} \right.$$

$$\left. - \frac{2}{\cos(\alpha_i/2) \cos(\alpha_m/2)} \left[\frac{\sin(\alpha_i/2 + \alpha_m/2)}{\alpha_i + \alpha_m} + \frac{\sin(\alpha_i/2 - \alpha_m/2)}{\alpha_i - \alpha_m} \right] \right] \qquad (7\text{-}97)$$

Some of these integrals, however, will lead to tedious expressions and hence are not evaluated herein.

It is to be noted that plate constants $a_{16}, a_{26}, b_{16}, b_{26}, d_{16}$, and d_{26} or $A_{16}, A_{26}, B_{16}, B_{26}, D_{16}$, and D_{26} disappear in equations (7-93) to (7-95). This arises from the fact that in the present coordinate system with its origin at the center of the plate, all the integrations of odd functions of ζ or η such as $X_i(\zeta) X_m'(\zeta)$ and $\sin(2i\pi\zeta) X_m''(\zeta)$ in the form of expressions (7-96) are zero. These six plate constants are associated with the vanishing integrations. Therefore, the present solution is not valid for generally laminated plates but applicable for a class of unsymmetrically laminated plates such as unsymmetric cross-ply laminates.

7.7 UNSYMMETRIC ANGLE-PLY RECTANGULAR PLATE BENT BY UNIFORM EDGE MOMENT

Based on the solution presented in Sec. 7.1, the titled problem can be discussed for the plate simply supported along its edges and subjected to uniformly distributed moment M_0 along the edges $x = 0, a$ (Fig. 7.12). If the edges of the plate are free from inplane boundary forces, the dimensionless boundary conditions are of the form

$$F_{,\eta\eta} = F_{,\zeta\eta} = W = 0 \qquad \bar{D}_{11}^* W_{,\zeta\zeta} = -\lambda^2 \tau \qquad \text{at} \quad \zeta = 0, 1$$

$$F_{,\zeta\zeta} = F_{,\zeta\eta} = W = W_{,\eta\eta} = 0 \qquad \text{at} \quad \eta = 0, 1 \qquad (7\text{-}98)$$

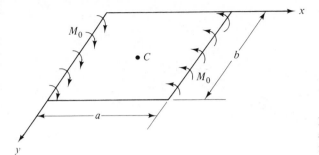

Figure 7.12 Geometry of rectangular plate subjected to uniform edge moment.

in which the notations defined in Sec. 7.1 are used and in which τ is the dimensionless uniform edge moment given by

$$\tau = \frac{M_0 b^2}{E_T h^4} \tag{7-99}$$

The dimensionless differential equations governing large deflections of the plate is obtained by setting the transverse load parameter $Q = 0$ in equations (7-1) and (7-2). A solution to this boundary-value problem is sought in the form of double series (Ref. 7.10)

$$F = \sum_{m=1,\,3,\,\ldots}^{\infty} \sum_{n=1,\,3,\,\ldots}^{\infty} F_{mn} X_m(\zeta) Y_n(\eta) \tag{7-100}$$

$$W = \sum_{r=1,\,3,\,\ldots}^{\infty} \sum_{s=1,\,3,\,\ldots}^{\infty} W_{rs} \sin r\pi\zeta \sin s\pi\eta$$

which are a special case of solution (7-6). Expressions (7-100) for F and W satisfy the boundary conditions (7-98) except for that involving $W_{,\zeta\zeta}$ along the loading edges $\zeta = 0$ and 1. Thus the series for W cannot be differentiated term-by-term with respect to ζ beyond the second order. Following a similar calculation as in Secs. 5.11 and 7.2, the derivative $W_{,\zeta\zeta\zeta}$ is represented by a cosine-sine series. Integrating the series by parts and using the second of expressions (7-100) and the conditions for $W_{,\zeta\zeta}$ at $\zeta = 0$ and 1 in equations (7-98), we obtain

$$W_{,\zeta\zeta\zeta} = \sum_{r=1,\,3,\,\ldots}^{\infty} \sum_{s=1,\,3,\,\ldots}^{\infty} \left(\frac{16\lambda^2 \tau}{s\pi \bar{D}_{11}^*} - r^3\pi^3 W_{rs} \right) \cos r\pi\zeta \sin s\pi\eta \tag{7-101}$$

Higher-order derivatives of W with respect to ζ are to be obtained from this expression. The other derivatives of W and those of F can be obtained from expressions (7-100).

Inserting the series for F and the appropriate derivatives of W in equations (7-1) and (7-2), multiplying the first of the resulting equations by $\sin i\pi\zeta \sin j\pi\eta$ and the second by $X_i(\zeta) Y_j(\eta)$, integrating from 0 to 1 with respect to ζ and η and

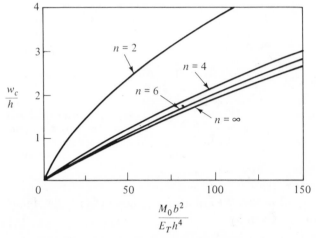

Figure 7.13 Relation between edge moment and central deflection of square $\pm 45°$ angle-ply graphite-epoxy plate for various values of the number of layers.

using the orthogonality relations (5-38) lead to an infinite set of algebraic equations. This set of equations can be obtained by setting $R = 0$ and $Q_{ij} = 0$ in equation (7-8) and adding the terms

$$\frac{16i\lambda^2 \tau}{j\pi^4 \bar{D}^*_{11}} \quad \text{and} \quad \frac{16b_6 \lambda^3 \tau}{\bar{D}^*_{11}} \sum_{r=1,3,\dots}^{\infty} \sum_{s=1,3,\dots}^{\infty} R_7^{ir} S_7^{js}$$

to the right-hand sides of equations (7-8) and (7-9), respectively. The resulting nonlinear algebraic equations can be solved for coefficients F_{mn} and W_{rs} by taking a finite number of terms in each of the series (7-100).

As in Sec. 7.1 the first nine terms in each of the truncated series (7-100) and (7-101) are taken into account. The relation between edge moment M_0 and central deflection w_c of an unsymmetric graphite-epoxy laminate is shown in Fig. 7.13 for various values of the number of layers denoted by n. The material properties are given by equations (5-213). This figure indicates that the central deflection at a fixed value of M_0 decreases with increasing the number of layers, and the results tend rapidly to decrease for an uncoupled plate.

The present solution can reduce to those for anisotropic and isotropic plates by specifying the elastic properties and orientation of the layers accordingly.

PROBLEMS

7.1 Formulate an approximate solution for moderately large deflections of an unsymmetric angle-ply plate under uniform lateral load if the edges of the plate are simply supported and free from inplane stresses.

7.2 A generally laminated anisotropic rectangular plate under the action of a concentrated load at its center is loosely clamped along its edges. Find an approximate load-deflection relation in the range of moderately large deflections.

REFERENCES

7.1. C. Y. Chia and M. K. Prabhakara: Postbuckling Behavior of Unsymmetrically Layered Anisotropic Rectangular Plates, *ASME J. Appl. Mech.*, vol. 41, pp. 155–162, 1974.

7.2. M. K. Prabhakara and C. Y. Chia: Finite Deflections of Unsymmetrically Layered Anisotropic Rectangular Plates Subjected to the Combined Action of Transverse and In-plane Loads, *ASME J. Appl. Mech.*, vol. 42, pp. 517–518, 1975.

7.3. Y. R. Kan and Y. M. Ito: Analysis of Unbalanced Angle-ply Rectangular Plates, *Int. J. Solids Struct.*, vol. 8, pp. 1283–1297, 1972.

7.4. M. K. Prabhakara and C. Y. Chia: Nonlinear Analysis of Laminated Cross-ply Plates, *J. Eng. Mech. Div., Proc. ASCE*, vol. 103, no. EM4, pp. 749–753, 1977.

7.5. A. E. Green and R. F. S. Hearmon: The Buckling of Flat Rectangular Plywood Plates, *Philos. Mag.*, series 7, vol. 36, pp. 659–688, 1945.

7.6. Y. R. Kan and Y. M. Ito: On the Analysis of Unsymmetrical Cross-ply Rectangular Plates, *ASME J. Appl. Mech.*, vol. 39, pp. 615–617, 1972.

7.7. C. Y. Chia and M. K. Prabhakara: Large Deflection of Unsymmetric Cross-ply and Angle-ply Plates, *J. Mech. Eng. Sci.*, vol. 18, Institution of Mechanical Engineers (London), pp. 179–183, 1976.

7.8. C. Y. Chia: Large Deflections of Heterogeneous Anisotropic Rectangular Plates, *Int. J. Solids Struct.*, vol. 10, Pergamon Press, pp. 965–976, 1974.

7.9. C. Y. Chia and C. L. Wang: Nonlinear Bending of Generally Laminated Anisotropic Rectangular Plates, Res. Rep. no. CE78-16, Dept. of Civ. Eng., Univ. of Calgary, 1978.

7.10. M. K. Prabhakara: Finite Deflections of Unsymmetric Angle-ply Anisotropic Rectangular Plate Under Edge Moments, *ASME J. Appl. Mech.*, vol. 44, pp. 171–172, 1977.

ADDITIONAL REFERENCES

Habip, L. M.: Moderately Large Deflection of Asymmetrically Layered Elastic Plate, *Int. J. Solids Struct.*, vol. 3, pp. 207–215, 1967.

Pao, Y. C.: Simple Bending Analysis of Laminated Plates by Large Deflection, *J. Comp. Mater.*, vol. 4, pp. 380–389, 1970.

Turvey, G. J., and W. H. Wittrick: The Large Deflection and Postbuckling Behaviour of Some Laminated Plates, *Aeronaut. Q.*, vol. 24, pp. 77–86, 1973.

Zaghloul, S. A., and J. B. Kennedy: Nonlinear Analysis of Unsymmetrically Laminated Plates, *J. Eng. Mech. Div., Proc. ASCE*. vol. 101, no. EM3, pp. 169–186, 1975.

EIGHT

POSTBUCKLING BEHAVIOR AND NONLINEAR FLEXURAL VIBRATION OF UNSYMMETRICALLY LAMINATED ANISOTROPIC PLATES

In this chapter nonlinear buckling and vibration of unsymmetric rectangular laminates are considered. The first three sections deal with postbuckling behavior and the last three sections with moderately large-amplitude free flexural vibrations. In a postbuckling problem the plate is subjected to uniaxial or biaxial inplane compressive forces. Only perfect flat plates are treated. The edges of the plate are all-clamped and all-simply supported with zero tangential boundary forces. The methods used in these studies are the generalized double Fourier series for general laminates, and a combination of double Fourier series and generalized double Fourier series for unsymmetric angle-ply and cross-ply laminates. For the simply supported plate Green's procedure is used in the fulfillment of the zero-moment condition at the boundary.

In the vibration problems the single-mode analysis is presented in Secs. 8.4 and 8.5 for unsymmetric angle-ply and cross-ply laminates, respectively. The angle-ply plate is assumed to be all-clamped and all-simply supported with all-movable and all-immovable edges. The cross-ply laminate is taken to be simply supported along two opposite edges and clamped along the other two edges. For the inplane boundary conditions, the plate edges are free from normal and tangential membrane forces. In each case the Galerkin procedure is employed for the equations of motion, and the perturbation technique for the time equation. In the last section multimode solutions are discussed for these laminates. The plate considered is all-clamped and all-simply supported along its four edges which are free from membrane boundary forces. Generalized double Fourier series are used for clamped plates and a combination of double Fourier series and generalized double Fourier series for simply supported plates. In these series the coefficients are treated as functions of time. Green's procedure is applied to a simply supported cross-ply plate for the fulfillment of the zero-moment condition. In each case the resulting set of nonlinear ordinary differential equations for the time-dependent deflection coefficients is solved by use of the method of harmonic balance.

8.1 POSTBUCKLING OF SIMPLY SUPPORTED UNSYMMETRIC ANGLE-PLY RECTANGULAR PLATE

Consider an unsymmetric angle-ply rectangular plate under uniform inplane compressive forces, per unit length, n_x in the x direction and n_y in the y direction. The buckling stress of the plate is assumed to be in the elastic range and hence the elastic behavior of the plate after buckling can be investigated. The differential equations governing the postbuckling behavior of the plate may be obtained in the dimensional form by deleting the loading and inertia terms in equations (1-135) and (1-136), or in the nondimensional form by deleting the transverse loading term in equations (7-1) and (7-2). If the plate is simply supported along its edges and compressed frictionlessly, then the appropriate nondimensional boundary conditions can be expressed in the form (7-4). Therefore, the postbuckling problem is nearly a special case of the boundary-value problem discussed in Sec. 7.1 where the inplane load has been assumed to be not greater than the corresponding buckling load. A solution of equations (7-1) and (7-2) satisfying boundary conditions (7-4) for the postbuckling problem (Ref. 7.1) reduces to that of simultaneous nonlinear algebraic equations (7-8) and (7-9), in which the transverse loading term is to be deleted. For a given set of values of the aspect ratio, inplane load parameter, orthotropic properties, number of layers, and the degree of anisotropy of the constituent layer, these equations can be solved as in Sec. 7.1. As soon as the coefficients F_{mn} and W_{pq} in the series for the nondimensional force function F and the nondimensional deflection W are determined, the deflection can be found from the second of equations (7-6). The nondimensional membrane forces and bending moments can be computed from equations (7-11) and (7-12), respectively.

Calculations are performed for glass-epoxy (GL), boron-epoxy (BO), and graphite-epoxy (GR) composites. The elastic constants typical of these materials with respect to their orthotropic axes L, T are listed in Table 8.1. As in Sec. 7.1 the constant A_{22} is replaced by $E_T h$. The orthotropic axes of the layers in the unsymmetric angle-ply plate are assumed to be oriented alternately at angles of $+45°$ and $-45°$ to the plate axes. In calculation the first nine terms in the truncated series for F and W are taken into account. The computation procedure is briefly described in the following.

From equation (7-9) each of the coefficients F_{mn} is expressed as a quadratic in coefficients W_{pq}. Substituting in equation (7-8), a set of nine simultaneous cubic

Table 8.1 Elastic constants

Material	E_L/E_T	G_{LT}/E_T	ν_{LT}
Glass-epoxy	3.0	0.5	0.25
Boron-epoxy	10.0	1/3	0.22
Graphite-epoxy	40.0	0.5	0.25

equations for W_{pq} is obtained. Each of these equations consists of 229 terms. The method of solution consists in prescribing one of W_{pq} and solving these equations for R and the other W_{pq} by the Newton-Raphson method. The particular W_{pq} whose value is prescribed is chosen in accordance with the buckling mode of the plate. In the case of a square plate which buckles into one half-wave in both ζ and η directions, the coefficient W_{11} is dominant and is prescribed. For a small value of W_{11}, the value of R may be taken to be the nondimensional critical load and the other W_{pq} may be assumed to be zero for the initial guess. For the next prescribed value of W_{11}, the true values of R and other W_{pq} in the previous result are used as initial values for the iterative process. The value of W_{11} is increased with small increment $\Delta W_{11} = 0.1$ in the calculation. The convergence criterion in the iterative procedure for the solution of the nonlinear algebraic equations is that the difference between the final value for each W_{pq} and R and the average of the results of three previous iterations is less than 0.1 percent. Generally, the solution converged within eight iterations for the present numerical results.

The nondimensional critical buckling load defined by $R_{cr} = n_{cr} b^2/E_T h^3$, in which n_{cr} is the applied edge compression n_x at which the plate buckles, can be calculated by dropping all the nonlinear terms in equations (7-8) and (7-9). The resulting equation for R is of the matrix form

$$\mathbf{SZ} = R\mathbf{TZ} \qquad (8\text{-}1)$$

in which $\mathbf{S}$ and $\mathbf{T}$ are the coefficient matrices and $\mathbf{Z} = [W_{11}, W_{12}, \ldots]^T$. The lowest eigenvalue of the system of homogeneous equations (8-1) corresponds to the critical load. In calculation the characteristic polynomial is obtained by use of Leverrier's method (Ref. 8.1) and then solved by use of the modified Bairstow method (Ref. 8.2).

In order to gain some idea of the convergence of the series solution, the numerical values of the nondimensional central deflection $W(\frac{1}{2}, \frac{1}{2})$ for a square 4-layer graphite-epoxy plate under uniaxial compression by using the first four terms in the series for F and W, are compared with those obtained by using the first nine terms for various loads. An excellent agreement is found between these two approximations. The buckling loads of a simply supported $\pm 45°$ angle-ply graphite-epoxy square plate obtained from the nine-term solution agree closely with the graphical results given in Ref. 8.3 for $n = 2, 4, \infty$. In the case of postbuckling of isotropic and graphite-epoxy orthotropic square plates the present results for the central deflection are in good agreement with those obtained in Secs. 4.3,

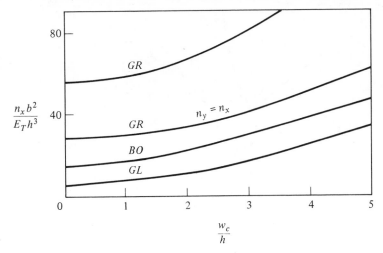

Figure 8.1 Load-deflection curves for simply supported 4-layer $\pm 45°$ angle-ply square plates under uniaxial and biaxial compression ($n_y = 0$ unless specified).

6.1, and 6.2 for various postbuckling loads. None of these results is presented herein.

The load-deflection curves for square $\pm 45°$ angle-ply plates are shown in Fig. 8.1 for different material properties. The edge compression corresponding to the central deflection $w_c = 0$ is the critical load. For a given deflection a large compression is required for a high-modulus material. For lower values of the deflection the load required for a plate under uniaxial compression is nearly twice as large as that for the corresponding plate under biaxial compression. Figure 8.2

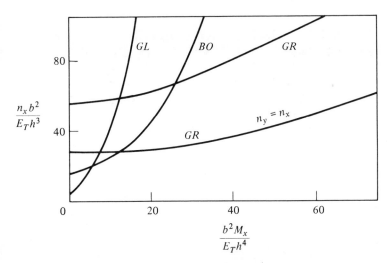

Figure 8.2 Bending moments at center of simply supported 4-layer $\pm 45°$ angle-ply square plates of different materials under uniaxial and biaxial compression ($n_y = 0$ unless specified).

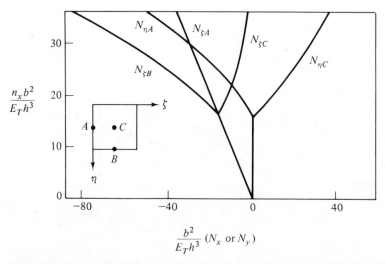

Figure 8.3 Membrane forces at various points in simply supported 4-layer $\pm45°$ angle-ply boron-epoxy square plate under uniaxial compression.

shows the relation between load and bending moment M_x at the center of the plate for different materials. For a fixed value of the load the bending moment is small for a low-modulus material. In view of Fig. 8.1 this small value of the bending moment is accompanied by a large deflection. Membrane forces at different points in a boron-epoxy plate are shown in Fig. 8.3 for different edge loads. The largest magnitude of membrane forces occurs at the midpoints of unloaded edges in the loading direction. The postbuckling behavior of a rectangular plate ($\lambda > 1$) will be illustrated graphically in Sec. 8.3.

8.2 POSTBUCKLING OF SIMPLY SUPPORTED UNSYMMETRIC CROSS-PLY RECTANGULAR PLATE

The method used in the study of the moderately large deflection of an unsymmetrically laminated cross-ply plate can be applied also to the postbuckling behavior of the plate. The nondimensional governing equations in the case of postbuckling may be obtained by deleting the transverse loading term in equations (7-14) and (7-15). The corresponding nondimensional membrane forces, N_ζ, N_η, and $N_{\zeta\eta}$, are given by equations (7-11) and the nondimensional bending moments, M_ζ, M_η, and $M_{\zeta\eta}$ by equations (7-16). If the plate is simply supported along its edges and frictionlessly compressed by uniform inplane forces, per unit length, n_x in the x direction and n_y in the y direction, the boundary conditions can be written in the nondimensional form

$$W = F_{,\zeta\eta} = 0 \qquad F_{,\eta\eta} = -R \qquad W_{,\zeta\zeta} = \frac{1}{\bar{D}_{11}^*}\left(\lambda^2 \bar{B}_{11}^* R - \bar{B}_{21}^* F_{,\zeta\zeta}\right)$$

$$W = F_{,\zeta\eta} = 0 \qquad F_{,\zeta\zeta} = -\lambda^2 kR \qquad W_{,\eta\eta} = \frac{1}{\bar{D}_{22}^*}\left(k\bar{B}_{22}^* R - \bar{B}_{12}^* F_{,\eta\eta}\right)$$

$$(8\text{-}2)$$

in which k and R are the load ratio and the nondimensional load parameter, respectively, defined in equations (7-5).

A solution of equations (7-14) and (7-15) in which $Q = 0$ is formulated by use of the double series (Ref. 8.4). Thus the variables F and W are expressed in the form

$$F = -\frac{R}{2}(\eta^2 + k\lambda^2\zeta^2) + \sum_{m=1}^{\infty}\sum_{n=1}^{\infty} F_{mn} X_m(\zeta) Y_n(\eta)$$

$$W = \sum_{p=1}^{\infty}\sum_{q=1}^{\infty} W_{pq} \sin p\pi\zeta \sin q\pi\eta \tag{8-3}$$

which are expressions (7-6) and in which X_m and Y_n are defined by equations (5-36). As in Sec. 7.2 the expressions (8-3) satisfy boundary conditions (8-2) except for the vanishing of the normal bending moment. Following a similar calculation as in the above-mentioned section, the Fourier series expansions of the derivatives $W_{,\zeta\zeta\zeta}$ and $W_{,\eta\eta\eta}$ can be expressed in terms of coefficients F_{mn} and W_{pq} as

$$W_{,\zeta\zeta\zeta} = \frac{8\bar{B}_{21}^*}{\bar{D}_{11}^*} \sum_{q=1}^{\infty}\left(\sum_{m=1}^{\infty}\sum_{n=1}^{\infty} F_{mn} d_m \alpha_m^2 L_1^{nq}\right) \sin q\pi\eta$$

$$- \sum_{p=1}^{\infty}\sum_{q=1}^{\infty}\left[W_{pq}(p\pi)^3 + \frac{16}{q\pi\bar{D}_{11}^*}\lambda^2 R c_p c_q(\bar{B}_{11}^* + k\bar{B}_{21}^*)\right.$$

$$\left. - \frac{16\bar{B}_{21}^*}{\bar{D}_{11}^*}\sum_{m=1}^{\infty}\sum_{n=1}^{\infty} F_{mn}\alpha_m^2 L_1^{nq}(c_p c_m + d_p d_m)\right]$$

$$\cdot \cos p\pi\zeta \sin q\pi\eta \tag{8-4}$$

$$W_{,\eta\eta\eta} = \frac{8\bar{B}_{12}^*}{\bar{D}_{22}^*} \sum_{p=1}^{\infty}\left(\sum_{m=1}^{\infty}\sum_{n=1}^{\infty} F_{mn} d_n \alpha_n^2 K_1^{mp}\right) \sin p\pi\zeta$$

$$- \sum_{p=1}^{\infty}\sum_{q=1}^{\infty}\left[W_{pq}(q\pi)^3 + \frac{16}{p\pi\bar{D}_{22}^*} R c_p c_q(\bar{B}_{12}^* + k\bar{B}_{22}^*)\right.$$

$$\left. - \frac{16\bar{B}_{12}^*}{\bar{D}_{22}^*}\sum_{m=1}^{\infty}\sum_{n=1}^{\infty} F_{mn}\alpha_n^2 K_1^{mp}(c_n c_q + d_n d_q)\right]$$

$$\cdot \sin p\pi\zeta \cos q\pi\eta$$

in which c_i, d_i, K_1^{mp}, and L_1^{mq} are given by equations (7-25) and (7-28), respectively. From expressions (8-4) higher derivatives can be obtained through term-by-term differentiation.

Upon substitution, multiplication, and integration as in Sec. 7.2, equations (7-14) and (7-15) in which $Q = 0$ transform to the following system of nonlinear algebraic equations

$$F_{ij}(\bar{A}_{22}^*\alpha_i^4 + \bar{A}_{11}^*\lambda^4\alpha_j^4) + \sum_{m=1}^{\infty}\sum_{n=1}^{\infty} F_{mn}\left\{\lambda^2 K_2^{im} L_2^{jn}(2\bar{A}_{12}^* + \bar{A}_{66}^*)\right.$$

$$+ 16\sum_{p=1}^{\infty}\sum_{q=1}^{\infty} K_1^{ip} L_1^{jq}\left[\frac{1}{\bar{D}_{11}^*} p\pi\alpha_m^2 L_1^{nq}\bar{B}_{21}^{*2}(c_p c_m + d_p d_m)\right.$$

▼

$$+ \frac{1}{\bar{D}_{22}^*} \lambda^4 q \pi \alpha_n^2 K_1^{mp} \bar{B}_{12}^{*2}(c_n c_q + d_n d_q) \Bigg] \Bigg\}$$

$$= \sum_{p=1}^{\infty} \sum_{q=1}^{\infty} K_1^{ip} L_1^{jq} \Bigg\{ 16\lambda^2 R c_p c_q \Bigg[\frac{1}{\bar{D}_{11}^*} \frac{p}{q} \bar{B}_{21}^*(\bar{B}_{11}^* + k\bar{B}_{21}^*)$$

$$+ \frac{1}{\bar{D}_{22}^*} \frac{q}{p} \lambda^2 \bar{B}_{12}^*(\bar{B}_{12}^* + k\bar{B}_{22}^*) \Bigg] + \pi^4 W_{pq}[\bar{B}_{21}^* p^4$$

$$+ \lambda^2 p^2 q^2 (\bar{B}_{11}^* + \bar{B}_{22}^*) + \bar{B}_{12}^* \lambda^4 q^4] \Bigg\}$$

$$+ \lambda^2 \pi^2 \sum_{p=1}^{\infty} \sum_{q=1}^{\infty} \sum_{r=1}^{\infty} \sum_{s=1}^{\infty} W_{pq} W_{rs}(pqrs K_3^{ipr} L_3^{jqs} - p^2 s^2 K_3^{ipr} L_3^{jqs}) \quad (8\text{-}5)$$

$$W_{ij}\{\pi^4[\bar{D}_{11}^* i^4 + 2\lambda^2 i^2 j^2 (\bar{D}_{12}^* + 2\bar{D}_{66}^*) + \bar{D}_{22}^* \lambda^4 j^4] - \lambda^2 \pi^2 R(i^2 + k\lambda^2 j^2)\}$$

$$+ 16\lambda^2 R c_i c_j \Bigg[\frac{i}{j} (\bar{B}_{11}^* + k\bar{B}_{21}^*) + \frac{j}{i} \lambda^2 (\bar{B}_{12}^* + k\bar{B}_{22}^*) \Bigg]$$

$$+ 4 \sum_{m=1}^{\infty} \sum_{n=1}^{\infty} F_{mn}\{K_1^{mi} L_1^{nj}(\bar{B}_{21}^* \alpha_m^4 + \bar{B}_{12}^* \lambda^4 \alpha_n^4)$$

$$+ \lambda^2 K_7^{mi} L_7^{nj}(\bar{B}_{11}^* + \bar{B}_{22}^*) - 4[i\pi\alpha_m^2 L_1^{nj} \bar{B}_{21}^*(c_m c_i + d_m d_i)$$

$$+ \lambda^4 j \pi \alpha_n^2 K_1^{mi} \bar{B}_{12}^*(c_n c_j + d_n d_j)]\}$$

$$+ 4\lambda^2 \pi^2 \sum_{p=1}^{\infty} \sum_{q=1}^{\infty} \sum_{r=1}^{\infty} \sum_{s=1}^{\infty} W_{pq} F_{rs}(p^2 K_4^{rip} L_5^{sjq} + q^2 K_5^{rip} L_4^{sjq}$$

$$- 2pq K_6^{rip} L_6^{sjq}) = 0 \quad (8\text{-}6)$$

in which c_m, d_m, K_i and L_i ($i = 1, 2, \ldots, 6$) are given by equations (7-25), (7-28), and (7-31) and in which

$$K_7^{im} = \int_0^1 X_i'' \sin m\pi\zeta \, d\zeta \qquad L_7^{jn} = \int_0^1 Y_j'' \sin n\pi\eta \, d\eta \quad (8\text{-}7)$$

Equations (8-5) and (8-6) can be solved for W_{mn} and F_{ij} as in Sec. 8.1.

In calculation the unsymmetric cross-ply plate is assumed to consist of an even number of layers n, all of the same thickness, and hence relations (7-17) hold. The plate is taken to be composed of the high-modulus graphite-epoxy composites with elastic properties given by equation (5-213). The procedure for determining the nondimensional buckling load, $R_{cr} = n_{cr} b^2/E_T h^3$, and solving the system of equations (8-5) and (8-6), is the same as that described in Sec. 8.1 except for replacing equation (8-1) by

$$SZ - RTZ = RM \quad (8\text{-}8)$$

in which **M** is a column vector corresponding to the uniform bending moment M_x caused by the load n_x. The buckling load corresponds to the lowest eigenvalue of

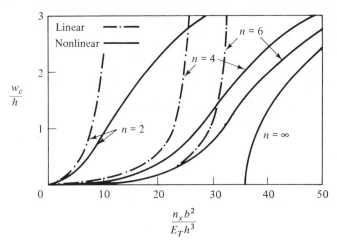

Figure 8.4 Effect of number of layers on central deflection of simply supported cross-ply graphite-epoxy square plate under uniaxial compression n_x.

the system of homogeneous equations obtained by setting $\mathbf{M} = 0$ in equation (8-8).

Calculations were performed by taking the first four and nine terms in the truncated series for F and W. The four-term solution for the central deflection w_c of a 2-layer square plate under uniaxial compression agrees closely with the nine-term solution even for w_c being three times the plate thickness. The values of the buckling load, $n_{cr} b^2/\pi^2 D_{22}$, obtained by the use of the nine-term approximation are in excellent agreement with those given in Ref. 8.5 for a simply supported cross-ply graphite-epoxy square plate under uniaxial compression having different values of the number of layers. The buckling values thus obtained for the plate are

$$\frac{n_{cr} b^2}{E_T h^3} = 12.6282,\ 30.0301,\ 33.2527,\ 35.8307$$

for $n = 2, 4, 6, \infty$, respectively.

The relationship between uniaxial compression and central deflection w_c for a square plate is shown in Fig. 8.4 for different values of the number of layers. For a given load the deflection obtained from the linear theory is much higher than that given by the nonlinear solution. As the number of layers increases, the deflection decreases and tends rapidly to that of an uncoupled plate. It is to be noted that the lateral deflection in the unsymmetric cross-ply plate occurs even for the edge compression less than the buckling load. This unusual behavior arises from the fact that the normal bending moments given by equations (7-16), which depend not only upon the curvatures of the plate but also upon the normal membrane forces, do not vanish for any values of the inplane compressive load. Figure 8.5 indicates that at the center of the plate under uniaxial compression n_x, the bending moment M_y is larger than M_x, and this difference decreases with increasing n.

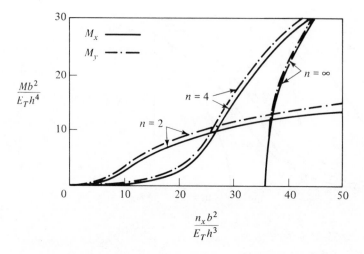

Figure 8.5 Bending moments at center of simply supported cross-ply graphite-epoxy square plate under uniaxial compression n_x for different values of number of layers.

This is because the tensile membrane forces in equations (7-16) have a tendency to decrease the bending moment M_x and increase the value of M_y on account of the coupling rigidities B_{ij}.

8.3 POSTBUCKLING OF GENERALLY LAMINATED ANISOTROPIC RECTANGULAR PLATE WITH CLAMPED EDGES

In Sec. 7.3 a loosely clamped general laminate has been assumed to be under the combined action of lateral load and inplane edge compression. A solution for the geometrically nonlinear behavior of the plate has been formulated by use of the generalized double Fourier series. Thus the governing equations have reduced to an infinite set of algebraic equations which can be solved numerically. The solution is exact in the sense that the set of equations can be truncated to obtain any desired degree of accuracy. However, in the numerical examples considered, the inplane load has been restricted to those values which are not beyond the buckling load. Therefore the plate has not buckled although it has been allowed to undergo the moderately large deflections. Evidently this solution can be utilized in the study of the postbuckling behavior of the plate by deletion of the transverse loading term from equations (7-32) and (7-39).

In calculation we consider the unsymmetrically laminated cross-ply and angle-ply plates as defined in Sec. 7.3 with material properties given in Table 8.1. Following a similar calculation as in Sec. 8.1, the nondimensional buckling load, $R_{cr} = n_{cr} b^2 / E_T h^3$, and the coefficients in the series (7-37) and (7-38) for F and W can be determined for a given set of values of orthotropic properties, lamination

Table 8.2 Comparison of solutions for central deflection w_c/h, of clamped 4-layer $\pm 45°$ angle-ply graphite-epoxy square plate under uniaxial compression

$\dfrac{R}{R_{cr}}$	4 Terms $R_{cr} = 114.71$	9 Terms $R_{cr} = 113.67$
1.02	0.6942	0.6592
1.09	1.4100	1.3081
1.60	3.6293	3.5458
2.22	4.7436	4.9730

parameters, aspect ratio, and load parameter. The results for buckling load and central deflection w_c obtained by use of the first four and nine terms in the truncated series for F and W are presented in Table 8.2 for a square angle-ply plate. These two sets of values agree fairly with one another and hence the nine-term approximation is used in the following results.

The relation between uniaxial compression n_x and central deflection w_c of a cross-ply graphite-epoxy laminate is shown in Fig. 8.6 for various values of the number of layers n. The edge compression corresponding to $w_c = 0$ is the critical buckling load. For a given deflection the edge compression increases as the number of layers increases. The curve for a 6-layer plate is close to that given by the uncoupled solution ($n = \infty$) for which the coupling coefficients $B_{ij} = 0$. The

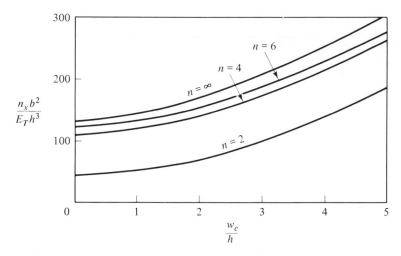

Figure 8.6 Effect of number of layers on load-deflection relation for clamped cross-ply graphite-epoxy square plate under uniaxial compression.

Table 8.3 Buckling load for 4-layer graphite-epoxy rectangular plate under uniaxial compression

	λ	R_{cr}	m	λ	R_{cr}	m
Clamped cross-ply plate	1.5	87.74	2	2.0	76.83	3
Clamped $\pm 45°$ angle-ply plate	1.5	95.73	2	2.0	89.86	3
Simply supported $\pm 45°$ angle-ply plate	1.5	58.64	2	2.0	56.09	2

effect of coupling between bending and stretching, therefore, reduces the stiffness of the plate and decreases with increasing the number of layers. Before presentation of some graphical results for a rectangular laminate, the critical buckling load of a 4-layer laminate under uniaxial compression is shown in Table 8.3 where m represents the number of half-waves in the ζ direction. In these cases the plate buckles into one half-wave in the η direction. For a clamped plate the buckling load decreases as the aspect ratio λ increases. The buckling loads for simply supported plates obtained found from Sec. 8.1 are one half-wave for $\lambda = 1$ and two half-waves for $\lambda = 2$ as in the case of isotropic plates. The plates with $\lambda = 2$, 3, ... are expected to buckle into square panels. The load-deflection curves are shown in Fig. 8.7 for all-clamped and all-simply supported plates with $\lambda = 1.5$. The buckling result for the simply supported plate is also obtained from Sec. 8.1. The deflection under consideration is that evaluated at $\zeta = \frac{1}{4}$, $\eta = \frac{1}{2}$ since the plate buckles into two half-waves in the ζ direction and one half-wave in the η direction. For a given deflection the load carried by a simply supported plate is smaller than that carried by a clamped plate.

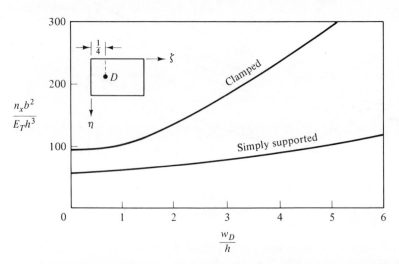

Figure 8.7 Load-deflection curves for 4-layer $\pm 45°$ angle-ply graphite-epoxy rectangular plate ($\lambda = 1.5$) under uniaxial compression.

Based on the previous results some concluding remarks may be drawn.

1. The critical buckling load of a square $\pm 45°$ angle-ply plate is nearly the same as that of the corresponding cross-ply plate in the case of clamped edges, whereas the former is about twice as large as the latter in the case of simply supported edges. In general this critical value decreases with increasing the plate aspect ratio. Furthermore, the critical load of a composite square plate under uniform biaxial compression is just half of that under uniform uniaxial compression.

2. The deflection at the center of a cross-ply or angle-ply plate under inplane edge compression decreases as the plate elastic moduli or the number of layers increases. Thus the coupling between bending and stretching reduces the plate stiffness.

3. The central deflection of a square plate under uniform biaxial compression is nearly twice as large as that under uniaxial compression. The post-buckling behavior of a rectangular plate for one half wavelength is similar to that of the corresponding square plate.

8.4 VIBRATION OF UNSYMMETRIC ANGLE-PLY PLATE WITH VARIOUS EDGE CONDITIONS

The postbuckling behavior of unsymmetric rectangular laminates has been discussed in the previous three sections. For the rest of this chapter the moderately large amplitude flexural vibrations of these laminates are investigated for various boundary conditions. Let us consider an unsymmetric angle-ply rectangular plate of length a in the x direction and width b in the y direction as shown in Fig. 2.11. The equations of motion governing the nonlinear free flexural vibration of the plate can be obtained by deleting the transverse loading term in equations (1-77) to (1-79) for three displacement components or in equations (1-135) and (1-136) for transverse deflection and force function. The boundary conditions under consideration are as follows:

(a) Simply supported laminate with zero average normal and zero tangential boundary forces

$$w = w_{,xx} = \psi_{,xy} = 0 \qquad \text{at} \quad x = 0, a$$
$$w = w_{,yy} = \psi_{,xy} = 0 \qquad \text{at} \quad y = 0, b$$
$$\int_0^b (\psi_{,yy})_{x=0, a} \, dy = 0 \tag{8-9}$$
$$\int_0^a (\psi_{,xx})_{y=0, b} \, dx = 0$$

(b) Simply supported laminate with zero tangential force and zero normal displacement at the edges

$$w = w_{,xx} = \psi_{,xy} = u° = 0 \qquad \text{at} \quad x = 0, a$$
$$w = w_{,yy} = \psi_{,xy} = v° = 0 \qquad \text{at} \quad y = 0, b \tag{8-10}$$

(c) Clamped laminate with zero average normal and tangential boundary forces

$$w = w_{,x} = 0 \quad \text{at} \quad x = 0, a$$

$$\int_0^b (\psi_{,yy})_{x=0,a}\, dy = 0 \qquad \int_0^b (\psi_{,xy})_{x=0,a}\, dy = 0$$

$$w = w_{,y} = 0 \quad \text{at} \quad y = 0, b \tag{8-11}$$

$$\int_0^a (\psi_{,xx})_{y=0,b}\, dx = 0 \qquad \int_0^b (\psi_{,xy})_{y=0,b}\, dx = 0$$

(d) Clamped laminate with zero average shear force and zero tangential displacement at the edges

$$w = w_{,x} = v^\circ = 0 \quad \text{at} \quad x = 0, a$$

$$\int_0^b (\psi_{,xy})_{y=0,a}\, dy = 0$$

$$w = w_{,y} = u^\circ = 0 \quad \text{at} \quad y = 0, b \tag{8-12}$$

$$\int_0^b (\psi_{,xy})_{y=0,b}\, dx = 0$$

where

$$u^\circ = \int_0^a \left(\varepsilon_x^\circ - \tfrac{1}{2} w_{,x}^2\right) dx \qquad v^\circ = \int_0^b \left(\varepsilon_y^\circ - \tfrac{1}{2} w_{,y}^2\right) dy \tag{8-13}$$

The single-mode analysis is carried out in this study by use of Galerkin's method for the equations of motion and the perturbation technique for the time equation (Ref. 8.6). Before formulation of approximate solutions of the foregoing problems, the nonvanishing components of A_{ij}^*, B_{ij}^*, and D_{ij}^* for the plate are nondimensionalized.

In view of equations (1-36) to (1-38) and (1-76) we have

$$(A_{11}, A_{12}, A_{22}, A_{66}) = h(C_{11}, C_{12}, C_{22}, C_{66}) = \frac{E_L h}{\mu}(a_{11}, a_{12}, a_{22}, a_{66})$$

$$(B_{16}, B_{26}) = -\frac{h^2}{2n_1}(C_{16}, C_{26}) = \frac{E_L h^2}{\mu}(b_{16}, b_{26}) \tag{8-14}$$

$$(D_{11}, D_{12}, D_{22}, D_{66}) = \frac{E_L h^3}{\mu}(d_{11}, d_{12}, d_{22}, d_{66})$$

in which n_1 represents the number of layers of the laminate and in which

$$a_{11} = c^4 + 2c^2 s^2\left(v_{TL} + \frac{2\mu G_{LT}}{E_L}\right) + s^4 \frac{E_T}{E_L}$$

$$a_{12} = c^2 s^2\left(1 + \frac{E_T}{E_L} - \frac{4\mu G_{LT}}{E_L}\right) + (c^4 + s^4)v_{TL}$$

▼

$$a_{22} = s^4 + 2c^2s^2\left(v_{TL} + \frac{2\mu G_{LT}}{E_L}\right) + c^4\frac{E_T}{E_L}$$

$$a_{66} = c^2s^2\left(1 + \frac{E_T}{E_L} - 2v_{TL}\right) + (c^2 - s^2)^2\frac{\mu G_{LT}}{E_L}$$

$$b_{16} = -\frac{cs}{2n_1}\left[c^2 - s^2\frac{E_T}{E_L} - (c^2 - s^2)\left(v_{TL} + \frac{2\mu G_{LT}}{E_L}\right)\right] \tag{8-15}$$

$$b_{26} = -\frac{cs}{2n_1}\left[s^2 - c^2\frac{E_T}{E_L} + (c^2 - s^2)\left(v_{TL} + \frac{2\mu G_{LT}}{E_L}\right)\right]$$

$$(d_{11}, d_{12}, d_{22}, d_{66}) = \tfrac{1}{12}(a_{11}, a_{12}, a_{22}, a_{66})$$

$$c = \cos\theta \qquad s = \sin\theta$$

The nonvanishing A_{ij}^*, B_{ij}^* and D_{ij}^* are from equations (1-127)

$$(A_{11}^*, A_{12}^*, A_{22}^*, A_{66}^*) = \frac{\mu}{E_L h}\left(\frac{1}{a_{11}^*}, \frac{1}{a_{12}^*}, \frac{1}{a_{22}^*}, \frac{1}{a_{66}^*}\right)$$

$$(B_{16}^*, B_{26}^*, B_{61}^*, B_{62}^*) = h(b_{16}^*, b_{26}^*, b_{61}^*, b_{62}^*) \tag{8-16}$$

$$(D_{11}^*, D_{12}^*, D_{22}^*, D_{66}^*) = \frac{E_L h^3}{\mu}(d_{11}^*, d_{12}^*, d_{22}^*, d_{66}^*)$$

where

$$a_{11}^* = a_{11} - \frac{a_{12}^2}{a_{22}} \qquad a_{12}^* = -a_{11}^*\frac{a_{22}}{a_{12}}$$

$$a_{22}^* = a_{11}^*\frac{a_{22}}{a_{11}} \qquad a_{66}^* = a_{66}$$

$$b_{16}^* = -\left(\frac{b_{16}}{a_{11}^*} + \frac{b_{26}}{a_{12}^*}\right) \qquad b_{26}^* = -\left(\frac{b_{26}}{a_{22}^*} + \frac{b_{16}}{a_{12}^*}\right) \tag{8-17}$$

$$b_{61}^* = -\frac{b_{16}}{a_{66}^*} \qquad b_{62}^* = -\frac{b_{26}}{a_{66}^*}$$

$$d_{11}^* = d_{11} + b_{16}b_{61}^* \qquad d_{12}^* = d_{12} + b_{16}b_{62}^*$$

$$d_{22}^* = d_{22} + b_{62}b_{26}^* \qquad d_{66}^* = d_{66} + b_{16}b_{16}^* + b_{26}b_{26}^*$$

The transverse supporting conditions given in equations (8-9) to (8-12) are satisfied by assuming the deflection function of the laminate corresponding to the (m, n) mode in the separable form

$$w = h\xi(t)\sin\frac{m\pi x}{a}\sin\frac{n\pi y}{b} \tag{8-18}$$

for simply supported edges and, corresponding to the fundamental mode,

$$w = h\xi(t)\left(1 - \cos\frac{2\pi x}{a}\right)\left(1 - \cos\frac{2\pi y}{b}\right) \tag{8-19}$$

for clamped edges.

Substituting the expression for w into the compatibility equation (1-136) and solving the resulting equation, the force function ψ is obtained as

$$\psi = \psi_h + \psi_p \tag{8-20}$$

in which ψ_h and ψ_p are homogeneous and particular solutions, respectively. In each case these solutions satisfying the corresponding inplane boundary conditions are

(a) $\psi_h = 0$

$$\psi_p = \frac{H_1}{H_2} h\xi(t) \cos\frac{m\pi x}{a} \cos\frac{n\pi y}{b} \tag{8-21}$$

$$+ \frac{h^2\xi^2(t)}{32}\left[\frac{(n\pi/b)^2}{A_{22}^*(m\pi/a)^2}\cos\frac{2m\pi x}{a} + \frac{(m\pi/a)^2}{A_{11}^*(n\pi/b)^2}\cos\frac{2n\pi y}{b}\right]$$

in which

$$H_1 = \left(\frac{m\pi}{a}\right)^3\left(\frac{n\pi}{b}\right)(B_{61}^* - 2B_{26}^*) + \left(\frac{m\pi}{a}\right)\left(\frac{n\pi}{b}\right)^3(B_{62}^* - 2B_{16}^*)$$

$$H_2 = \left(\frac{m\pi}{a}\right)^4 A_{22}^* + \left(\frac{m\pi}{a}\right)^2\left(\frac{n\pi}{b}\right)^2(2A_{12}^* + A_{66}^*) + \left(\frac{n\pi}{b}\right)^4 A_{11}^* \tag{8-22}$$

(b) $\psi_h = K_1 x^2 + K_2 y^2$ $\tag{8-23}$

where

$$K_1 = -\frac{h^2\xi^2(t)}{16}\left[\left(\frac{m\pi}{a}\right)^2 A_{12}^* - \left(\frac{n\pi}{b}\right)^2 A_{11}^*\right](A_{11}^* A_{22}^* - A_{12}^{*2})^{-1}$$

$$K_2 = \frac{h^2\xi^2(t)}{16}\left[\left(\frac{m\pi}{a}\right)^2 A_{22}^* - \left(\frac{n\pi}{b}\right)^2 A_{12}^*\right](A_{11}^* A_{22}^* - A_{12}^{*2})^{-1} \tag{8-24}$$

In this case the particular solution ψ_p is the same as in Case (a) and the homogeneous solution ψ_h is identical with that for the inplane conditions being zero tangential boundary force and displacement.

(c) $\psi_h = 0$

$$\psi_p = -\frac{E_L h^3}{\mu}\left[\frac{\lambda^2\xi^2(t)}{2}\left(-a_{22}^*\cos\frac{2\pi x}{a} - \frac{a_{11}^*}{\lambda^4}\cos\frac{2\pi y}{b}\right.\right.$$

$$\left.+ \frac{a_{22}^*}{16}\cos\frac{4\pi x}{a} + \frac{a_{11}^*}{16\lambda^4}\cos\frac{4\pi y}{b} + \frac{2}{H_3}\cos\frac{2\pi x}{a}\cos\frac{2\pi y}{b}\right)$$

▼

$$\left. -\frac{1}{H_4}\cos\frac{2\pi x}{a}\cos\frac{4\pi y}{b} - \frac{1}{H_5}\cos\frac{4\pi x}{a}\cos\frac{2\pi y}{b} \right.$$

▲

▲

$$\left. + \frac{H_6\xi(t)}{H_3}\sin\frac{2\pi x}{a}\sin\frac{2\pi y}{b} \right] \tag{8-25}$$

in which

$$H_3 = \frac{1}{a_{22}^*} + \lambda^2\left(\frac{2}{a_{12}^*} + \frac{1}{a_{66}^*}\right) + \frac{\lambda^4}{a_{11}^*} \qquad \lambda = \frac{a}{b}$$

$$H_4 = \frac{1}{a_{22}^*} + 4\lambda^2\left(\frac{2}{a_{12}^*} + \frac{1}{a_{66}^*}\right) + \frac{16\lambda^4}{a_{11}^*}$$

$$H_5 = \frac{16}{a_{22}^*} + 4\lambda^2\left(\frac{2}{a_{12}^*} + \frac{1}{a_{66}^*}\right) + \frac{\lambda^4}{a_{11}^*} \tag{8-26}$$

$$H_6 = \lambda(2b_{26}^* - b_{61}^*) + \lambda^3(2b_{16}^* - b_{62}^*)$$

(d) $\psi_h = K_3 x^2 + K_4 y^2$ $\tag{8-27}$

where

$$K_3 = \frac{3\pi^2 E_L h^3 \xi^2(t)}{4a^2\mu} \cdot \frac{a_{12}^* a_{22}^* (a_{11}^* - \lambda^2 a_{12}^*)}{a_{11}^* a_{22}^* - a_{12}^{*2}}$$

$$K_4 = \frac{3\pi^2 E_L h^3 \xi^2(t)}{4a^2\mu\lambda^2} \cdot \frac{a_{11}^* a_{12}^* (\lambda^2 a_{22}^* - a_{12}^*)}{a_{11}^* a_{22}^* - a_{12}^{*2}}$$

In the case the particular solution ψ_p is the same as in Case (c).

Applying the Galerkin procedure to the equation of motion (1-138), taking $q = 0$ and using expressions for w and ψ lead to an ordinary differential equation for the time function $\xi(t)$ in each case

$$\xi_{,\tau\tau} + \omega_0^2 \xi + \alpha^2 \xi^3 = 0 \tag{8-28}$$

where

$$\tau = \frac{t}{a^2}\left(\frac{D_{11}^*}{\rho}\right)^{1/2} \qquad \text{for Cases } (a) \text{ and } (b)$$

$$\tau = \frac{t}{a^2}\left(\frac{E_L h^3}{\mu\rho}\right)^{1/2} \qquad \text{for Cases } (c) \text{ and } (d) \tag{8-29}$$

The coefficients ω_0^2 and α^2 in equation (8-28) are given below for each case

(a) $\omega_0^2 = \pi^4 \left\{ m^4 + 2m^2n^2\lambda^2\frac{d_{12}^* + 2d_{66}^*}{d_{11}^*} + n^4\lambda^4\frac{d_{22}^*}{d_{11}^*} \right.$

$$\left. + \frac{\lambda^2}{d_{11}^*}\frac{[m^3n(b_{61}^* - 2b_{26}^*) + mn^3(b_{62}^* - 2b_{16}^*)]^2}{m^4/a_{22}^* + m^2n^2\lambda^2(2/a_{22}^* + 1/a_{66}^*) + n^4\lambda^4/a_{11}^*} \right\} \tag{8-30}$$

$$\alpha^2 = \frac{\pi^4}{16d_{11}^*}(m^4 a_{11}^* + n^4\lambda^4 a_{22}^*)$$

(b) The linear frequency in this case is the same as in Case (a) and the coefficient α^2 is

$$\alpha^2 = \frac{\pi^4}{16d_{11}^*}(m^4 a_{11}^* + n^4 \lambda^4 a_{22}^*) + \frac{\pi^4}{8d_{11}^*}\frac{a_{12}^*}{a_{12}^{*2} - a_{11}^* a_{22}^*}$$

$$\cdot (n^4 \lambda^4 a_{12}^* a_{22}^* - 2m^2 n^2 \lambda^2 a_{11}^* a_{22}^* + m^4 a_{11}^* a_{12}^*) \tag{8-31}$$

(c) $$\omega_0^2 = \frac{16\pi^4}{9}\left[3d_{11}^* + 2\lambda^2(d_{12}^* + 2d_{66}^*) + 3\lambda^4 d_{22}^* + \frac{H_6^2}{H_3}\right]$$

$$\alpha^2 = \frac{8\pi^4}{9}\left[\frac{17}{8}(a_{11}^* + \lambda^4 a_{22}^*) + \lambda^4\left(\frac{4}{H_3} + \frac{1}{H_4} + \frac{1}{H_5}\right)\right] \tag{8-32}$$

(d) The linear frequency ω_0 in the case is the same as in Case (c) and the coefficient α^2 is given by

$$\alpha^2 = \frac{8\pi^4}{9}\left[\frac{17}{8}(a_{11}^* + \lambda^4 a_{22}^*) + \lambda^4\left(\frac{4}{H_3} + \frac{1}{H_4} + \frac{1}{H_5}\right)\right]$$

$$+ \frac{2\pi^4 a_{12}^*(2\lambda^2 a_{11}^* a_{22}^* - \lambda^4 a_{12}^* a_{22}^* - a_{11}^* a_{12}^*)}{a_{11}^* a_{22}^* - a_{12}^{*2}} \tag{8-33}$$

It is observed that the coefficients in equation (8-28) for Case (b) agree well with the corresponding expressions of Ref. 8.7, and the coefficient α^2 of the nonlinear term is independent of the coupling rigidities B_{ij}, but the linear frequency ω_0 does depend on B_{ij}.

Equation (8-28) is now solved by the perturbation method (Ref. 4.22). Replacing the independent variable τ by $\Gamma = \omega\tau$, equation (8-28) becomes

$$\omega^2 \xi_{,\Gamma\Gamma} + \omega_0^2 \xi + \alpha^2 \xi^3 = 0 \tag{8-34}$$

in which ω is the unknown frequency of the periodic solution. Clearly, the time function ξ is of period 2π in Γ. Since small but finite amplitude vibrations are of interest, the desired solution ξ and the unknown frequency ω are developed into the perturbation series with respect to a nondimensional amplitude A

$$\xi = \xi_0(\Gamma) + A\xi_1(\Gamma) + A^2\xi_2(\Gamma) + A^3\xi_3(\Gamma) + \cdots$$
$$\omega = \omega_0 + A\omega_1 + A^2\omega_2 + A^3\omega_3 + \cdots \tag{8-35}$$

The initial conditions are taken to be

$$\xi(0) = A \qquad \xi_{,\Gamma}(0) = 0 \tag{8-36}$$

for which it follows that

$$\xi_1(0) = 1 \qquad \xi_0(0) = \xi_2(0) = \xi_3(0) = \cdots = 0 \tag{8-37}$$

Note that $A = w_{max}$ in Cases (a) and (b) and $A = w_{max}/4h$ in Cases (c) and (d). Substituting expressions (8-35) into equation (8-34) and equating like powers of A, a series of equations is obtained. The first is

$$A^0: \quad \omega_0^2 \xi_{0,\,\Gamma\Gamma} + \omega_0^2 \xi_0 + \alpha^2 \xi_0^3 = 0 \tag{8-38}$$

which, by virtue of equation (8-37), has as its solution

$$\xi_0(\Gamma) = 0 \tag{8-39}$$

and next

$$A^1: \quad \xi_{1,\,\Gamma\Gamma} + \xi_1 = 0 \tag{8-40}$$

whose solution is

$$\xi_1(\Gamma) = \cos \Gamma \tag{8-41}$$

Continuing, we obtain

$$A^2: \quad \xi_{2,\,\Gamma\Gamma} + \xi_2 = 2\frac{\omega_1}{\omega_0} \cos \Gamma \tag{8-42}$$

If the coefficient of $\cos \Gamma$ were not zero, the solution of this equation would contain a secular term $\Gamma \cos \Gamma$ which grows up indefinitely when $t \to \infty$. To ensure a periodic solution it is necessary that

$$\omega_1 = 0 \tag{8-43}$$

The solution to equation (8-42) becomes

$$\xi_2(\Gamma) = \cos \Gamma \tag{8-44}$$

Finally

$$A^3: \quad \xi_{3,\,\Gamma\Gamma} + \xi_3 = \frac{1}{\omega_0^2}\left(2\omega_0\omega_2 - \frac{3\alpha^2}{4}\right) \cos \Gamma - \frac{\alpha^2}{4\omega_0^2} \cos 3\Gamma \tag{8-45}$$

Once again, to ensure a periodic solution it requires that

$$2\omega_0\omega_2 - \tfrac{3}{4}\alpha^2 = 0 \tag{8-46}$$

Thus the second of the perturbation series (8-35) may be approximated by

$$\omega^2 = \omega_0^2 + \tfrac{3}{4}\alpha^2 A^2 \tag{8-47}$$

Noting that expressions (8-18) and (8-19) both represent the deflection function of the unsymmetric angle-ply plate corresponding to the (m, n) mode, equation (8-47) can be written as

$$\frac{\omega_{mn}}{\omega_{mn}^{(0)}} = \left[1 + \frac{3}{4}\left(\frac{\alpha}{\omega_{mn}^{(0)}}\right)^2 A_{mn}^2\right]^{1/2} \tag{8-48}$$

in which the linear frequency $\omega_{mn}^{(0)}$ $(= \omega_0)$ and the coefficient α^2 of the nonlinear term are given by equations (8-30) to (8-33) for different cases.

Numerical results are presented in Fig. 8.8 for the fundamental mode $(m = n = 1)$ of vibrations of clamped square plates and in Fig. 8.9 for simply supported square plates corresponding to the mode $m = 1$ and $n = 2$. In these figures θ represents the angle of orientation of fibers in each ply with respect to the plate axes and the specially orthotropic curves are obtained by neglecting B_{ij} in

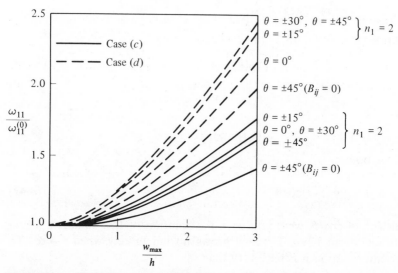

Figure 8.8 Amplitude-frequency response curves for fundamental vibration of clamped square plates ($E_T/E_L = 0.1315$, $G_{LT}/E_L = 0.0538$, $\nu_{LT} = 0.3$).

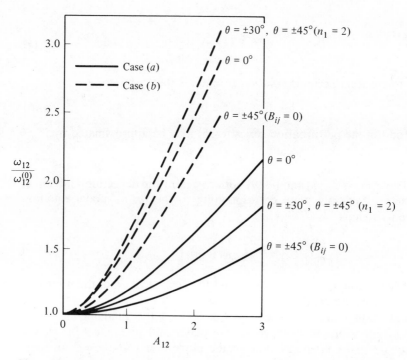

Figure 8.9 Amplitude-frequency response curves for simply supported square plate ($m = 1$, $n = 2$; $E_T/E_L = 0.1315$, $G_{LT}/E_T = 0.0538$, $\nu_{LT} = 0.3$).

the solution. These figures indicate that the effects of lamination and inplane boundary conditions are quite significant. In the case of clamped plates the frequency ratio for $\theta = 15°$, $30°$ and $45°$ is generally higher than that for $\theta = 0°$ at any amplitude. For simply supported plates no general trend regarding the variation of the backbone curves with respect to θ seems to exist.

8.5 VIBRATION OF UNSYMMETRIC CROSS-PLY RECTANGULAR PLATE WITH TWO OPPOSITE EDGES SIMPLY SUPPORTED AND OTHER EDGES CLAMPED

Suppose that an unsymmetric cross-ply rectangular plate of length a and width b executes moderately large amplitude free flexural vibrations. The governing equations obtained by deleting the loading term in equations (1-141) and (1-142) can be written in the nondimensional form as

$$
\begin{aligned}
L_{11}W + L_{13}F - \lambda^2 L_n(W, F) + W_{,\tau\tau} &= 0 \\
L_{12}F - L_{13}W - \tfrac{1}{2}\lambda^2 L_n(W, W) &= 0
\end{aligned}
\tag{8-49}
$$

where

$$
W = \frac{w}{h} \qquad F = \frac{\psi}{C_{11}h^3} \qquad \tau = \frac{t}{a^2}\left(\frac{C_{11}h^3}{\rho}\right)^{1/2} \qquad \lambda = \frac{a}{b}
$$

$$
L_{11}(\;) = d_{11}^*(\;)_{,\zeta\zeta\zeta\zeta} + 2\lambda^2(d_{12}^* + 2d_{66}^*)(\;)_{,\zeta\zeta\eta\eta} + \lambda^4(\;)_{,\eta\eta\eta\eta}
$$

$$
L_{12}(\;) = \frac{1}{a_{22}^*}(\;)_{,\zeta\zeta\zeta\zeta} + \lambda^2\left(\frac{2}{a_{12}^*} + \frac{1}{a_{66}^*}\right)(\;)_{,\zeta\zeta\eta\eta} + \lambda^4\frac{1}{a_{11}^*}(\;)_{,\eta\eta\eta\eta}
\tag{8-50}
$$

$$
L_{13}(\;) = b_{21}^*(\;)_{,\zeta\zeta\zeta\zeta} + \lambda^2(b_{22}^* - b_{11}^*)(\;)_{,\zeta\zeta\eta\eta} + \lambda^4 b_{12}^*(\;)_{,\eta\eta\eta\eta}
$$

$$
L_n(W, F) = W_{,\zeta\zeta}F_{,\eta\eta} + W_{,\eta\eta}F_{,\zeta\zeta} - 2W_{,\zeta\eta}F_{,\zeta\eta}
$$

In these expressions ζ, η, a_{ij}^*, b_{ij}^*, and d_{ij}^* are given by

$$
\zeta = \frac{x}{a} \qquad \eta = \frac{y}{b} \qquad a_{11}^* = a_{11} - \frac{v_{TL}^2}{a_{22}}
$$

$$
a_{12}^* = v_{TL} - \frac{a_{11}a_{22}}{v_{TL}} \qquad a_{22}^* = a_{22} - \frac{v_{TL}^2}{a_{11}} \qquad a_{66}^* = a_{66}
$$

$$
b_{11}^* = \frac{b_{11}}{a_{11}^*} \qquad b_{12}^* = \frac{b_{11}}{a_{12}^*} \qquad b_{21}^* = -b_{12}^*
\tag{8-51}
$$

$$
b_{22}^* = \frac{b_{11}}{a_{22}^*} \qquad d_{11}^* = d_{11} - b_{11}b_{11}^* \qquad d_{12}^* = d_{12} + b_{11}b_{12}^*
$$

$$
d_{22}^* = d_{22} - b_{11}b_{22}^* \qquad d_{66}^* = d_{66}
$$

where

$$a_{11} = \frac{\gamma + R}{1 + \gamma} \qquad a_{12} = \nu_{TL} \qquad a_{22} = \frac{1 + \gamma R}{1 + \gamma}$$

$$a_{66} = \frac{G_{LT}}{E_T}(1 - \nu_{LT}\nu_{TL}) \qquad b_{11} = \frac{\gamma(R-1)}{n(1+\gamma)^2} \qquad b_{22} = -b_{11}$$

$$d_{11} = \tfrac{1}{12}[1 + k(R-1)] \qquad d_{12} = \frac{\nu_{TL}}{12} \qquad d_{22} = \tfrac{1}{12}[R + k(1-R)]$$

$$d_{66} = \frac{1}{12}\frac{G_{LT}}{E_L}(1 - \nu_{LT}\nu_{TL})$$

(8-52)

with n, R, γ, and k being given in equations (1-83).

The plate is assumed to be simply supported along the edges $x = 0$, a and clamped along the edges $y = 0$, b. For the inplane boundary conditions the edges are assumed to be free from the normal and tangential membrane forces. These conditions are expressed in the nondimensional form as

$$W = M_\zeta = F_{,\eta\eta} = F_{,\zeta\eta} = 0 \qquad \text{at} \quad \zeta = 0, 1$$

$$W = W_{,\eta} = F_{,\zeta\zeta} = F_{,\zeta\eta} = 0 \qquad \text{at} \quad \eta = 0, 1$$

(8-53)

in which M_ζ is a nondimensional bending moment. By virtue of the first of equations (1-144), the zero moment condition becomes

$$d_{11}^* W_{,\zeta\zeta} + d_{12}^* W_{,\eta\eta} - b_{11}^* F_{,\eta\eta} + b_{21}^* F_{,\zeta\zeta} = 0 \qquad \text{at} \quad \zeta = 0, 1 \qquad (8\text{-}54)$$

A single-mode is carried for the fundamental vibration of the plate by use of the Galerkin procedure and the perturbation technique (Ref. 8.8). The nondimensional deflection function satisfying the geometric boundary conditions in equations (8-53) is assumed in the separable form

$$W = \tfrac{1}{2}A(\tau)\sin\pi\zeta\,(1 - \cos 2\pi\eta) \qquad (8\text{-}55)$$

The nondimensional force function is taken to be

$$F = B(\tau)\sin\pi\zeta\,\sin\pi\eta \qquad (8\text{-}56)$$

which satisfies the inplane boundary conditions in equations (8-53). Substituting expressions (8-55) and (8-56) into the second of equations (8-49) and orthogonalizing the trial function with respect to F we find

$$B(\tau) = \frac{4}{\pi k_1}\left(b_{21}^* + \frac{k_2}{3}\right)\frac{A(\tau)}{2} - \frac{1024\lambda^2}{25\pi^2 k_1}\frac{A^2(\tau)}{4} \qquad (8\text{-}57)$$

where

$$k_1 = \frac{1}{a_{22}^*} + \lambda^2\left(\frac{2}{a_{12}^*} + a_{66}^*\right) + \frac{\lambda^4}{a_{11}^*}$$

$$k_2 = b_{21}^* + 4\lambda^2(b_{22}^* - b_{11}^*) + 16\lambda^4 b_{12}^*$$

(8-58)

Inserting expressions (8-55) to (8-57) into the first of equations (8-49) and applying the Galerkin procedure to the resulting equation lead to the ordinary differential equation for the time function

$$A_{,\tau\tau} + \omega_0^2 A + \alpha A^2 + \beta A^3 = 0 \tag{8-59}$$

where

$$\omega_0^2 = \frac{\pi^4}{3}(2d_{11}^* + k_3) + \frac{128\pi^2 k_4}{9k_1}\left(b_{21}^* + \frac{k_2}{3}\right)$$

$$\alpha = -\frac{4096\pi\lambda^2}{135k_1}\left(b_{21}^* + \frac{k_2}{3} + \frac{4k_4}{3}\right)$$

$$\beta = \frac{2}{3}\left(\frac{512}{45}\right)^2 \frac{\lambda^4}{k_1} \tag{8-60}$$

$$k_3 = d_{11}^* + 8\lambda^2(d_{12}^* + 2d_{66}^*) + 16\lambda^4 d_{22}^*$$

$$k_4 = b_{21}^* + \lambda^2(b_{22}^* - b_{11}^*) + \lambda^4 b_{12}^*$$

An approximate solution of equation (8-59) obtained by the perturbation method as in the previous section yields the nonlinear frequency ω

$$\frac{\omega}{\omega_0} = \left[1 + \left(\frac{3\beta}{4\omega_0^2} - \frac{5\alpha^2}{6\omega_0^4}\right)A^2\right] \tag{8-61}$$

It may be observed that the foregoing approximate solution could be improved by introducing expression (8-55) into the compatibility equations (8-49) and solving the resulting equation for F in conjunction with the membrane conditions in equations (8-53), rather than assuming a particular spatial function for F.

8.6 MULTIMODE APPROACH TO VIBRATION OF UNSYMMETRIC CROSS-PLY AND ANGLE-PLY RECTANGULAR LAMINATES WITH ALL-CLAMPED AND ALL-SIMPLY SUPPORTED EDGES

Nonlinear flexural free vibrations of unsymmetric angle-ply and cross-ply plates have been discussed in the previous two sections. However, the effect of coupling of the vibrating modes on the nonlinear frequency of a particular mode has been neglected in these studies. The present investigation is concerned with this coupling effect. Let us consider unsymmetrically laminated cross-ply and angle-ply rectangular plates of length a in the x direction and width b in the y direction (Fig. 2.11) which consist of an even number of plies, all of the same thickness. The undeformed middle surface of the plate contains the x, y axes. The differential equations governing the moderately large amplitude free flexural vibrations of the plate may be expressed in the nondimensional form as

$$\bar{A}_{22}^* F_{,\zeta\zeta\zeta\zeta} + \lambda^2 (2\bar{A}_{12}^* + \bar{A}_{66}^*) F_{,\zeta\zeta\eta\eta} + \lambda^4 \bar{A}_{11}^* F_{,\eta\eta\eta\eta}$$
$$+ L(W) = \lambda^2 [W_{,\zeta\eta}^2 - W_{,\zeta\zeta} W_{,\eta\eta}] \tag{8-62}$$

$$\bar{D}_{11}^* W_{,\zeta\zeta\zeta\zeta} + 2\lambda^2 (\bar{D}_{12}^* + 2\bar{D}_{66}^*) W_{,\zeta\zeta\eta\eta} + \lambda^4 \bar{D}_{22}^* W_{,\eta\eta\eta\eta}$$
$$- L(F) + \lambda^4 W_{,\tau\tau} = \lambda^2 (W_{,\zeta\zeta} F_{,\eta\eta} + W_{,\eta\eta} F_{,\zeta\zeta} - 2W_{,\zeta\eta} F_{,\zeta\eta}) \tag{8-63}$$

in which ζ, η, λ, W, F, $\bar{A}_{ij}^*$, $\bar{B}_{ij}^*$, and $\bar{D}_{ij}^*$ are defined in equations (7-3) and in which

$$\tau = \frac{t}{b^2} \left(\frac{A_{22} h^2}{\rho} \right)^{1/2} \tag{8-64}$$

The differential operator in equations (8-62) and (8-63) is, for a cross-ply plate,

$$L(\ ) = \bar{B}_{12}^* (\ )_{,\zeta\zeta\zeta\zeta} - \lambda^4 \bar{B}_{12}^* (\ )_{,\eta\eta\eta\eta} \tag{8-65}$$

and, for an angle-ply plate,

$$L(\ ) = \lambda (\bar{B}_{61}^* - 2\bar{B}_{26}^*) (\ )_{,\zeta\zeta\zeta\eta} + \lambda^3 (\bar{B}_{62}^* - 2\bar{B}_{16}^*) (\ )_{,\zeta\eta\eta\eta} \tag{8-66}$$

The nondimensional force function F is related to the membrane forces by equations (7-11) and (7-13). If the edges of the plate are free from the inplane boundary forces, the boundary conditions are

(a) For clamped cross-ply and angle-ply plates

$$W = W_{,\zeta} = F_{,\eta\eta} = F_{,\zeta\eta} = 0 \quad \text{at} \quad \zeta = 0, 1$$
$$W = W_{,\eta} = F_{,\zeta\zeta} = F_{,\zeta\eta} = 0 \quad \text{at} \quad \eta = 0, 1 \tag{8-67}$$

(b) For a simply supported angle-ply plate

$$W = W_{,\zeta\zeta} = F_{,\eta\eta} = F_{,\zeta\eta} = 0 \quad \text{at} \quad \zeta = 0, 1$$
$$W = W_{,\eta\eta} = F_{,\zeta\zeta} = F_{,\zeta\eta} = 0 \quad \text{at} \quad \eta = 0, 1 \tag{8-68}$$

(c) For a simply supported cross-ply plate

$$W = F_{,\eta\eta} = F_{,\zeta\eta} = 0 \qquad W_{,\zeta\zeta} = \frac{\bar{B}_{21}^*}{\bar{D}_{11}^*} F_{,\zeta\zeta} \qquad \zeta = 0, 1$$

$$W = F_{,\zeta\zeta} = F_{,\zeta\eta} = 0 \qquad W_{,\eta\eta} = -\frac{\bar{B}_{12}^*}{\bar{D}_{11}^*} F_{,\eta\eta} \qquad \eta = 0, 1 \tag{8-69}$$

which are equations (7-18).

Equations (8-62) and (8-63) are solved in conjunction with the boundary conditions in each case by using the series method for equations of motion and the method of harmonic balance for the time equations (Refs. 8.9) as in Sec. 6.8. The nondimensional force function is expressed as

$$F = \sum_{p=1}^{\infty} \sum_{q=1}^{\infty} F_{pq}(\tau) X_p(\zeta) Y_q(\eta) \tag{8-70}$$

and the nondimensional transverse deflection as

$$W = \sum_{m=1}^{\infty} \sum_{n=1}^{\infty} W_{mn}(\tau) X_m(\zeta) Y_q(\eta) \tag{8-71}$$

for clamped plates and

$$W = \sum_{m=1}^{\infty} \sum_{n=1}^{\infty} W_{mn}(\tau) \sin \eta\pi\zeta \sin \eta\pi\eta \tag{8-72}$$

for simply supported plates.

In expressions (8-70) to (8-72), F_{pq} and W_{mn} are the undetermined functions of the nondimensional time τ, and X_i and Y_i are beam eigenfunctions given by equations (5-36). Using the values of the coefficients α_i and γ_i given in Table 5.1, the expression (8-70) for F satisfies all the inplane boundary conditions in equations (8-67) to (8-69). Expression (8-71) for W meets all the other requirements in boundary conditions (8-67) for a clamped plate. Expression (8-72) for W satisfies the transverse boundary conditions in equations (8-68) for a simply supported angle-ply plate, and those in equations (8-69) except for the zero bending moment for a simply supported cross-ply plate. The zero moment condition is fulfilled by use of the procedure as in Secs. 5.11 and 7.2. If $F_{,\zeta\zeta}$ at $\zeta = 0$, 1 and $F_{,\eta\eta}$ at $\eta = 0$, 1 in equations (8-69) are allowed to have whatever values given by series (8-70), then the series for W cannot be differentiated term by term beyond the second order. The derivatives $W_{,\zeta\zeta\zeta}$ and $W_{,\eta\eta\eta}$ are thus represented by cosine-sine and sine-cosine series, respectively. The coefficients in these series can be related to those in series (8-72) by partial integration of these new series and by use of the boundary condition for zero bending moment in equations (8-69). Higher-order derivatives can now be obtained from term-by-term differentiation for a simply supported cross-ply plate. The details are not presented herein.

Equations (8-70) and (8-71) for a clamped plate, equations (8-70) and (8-72) for a simply supported angle-ply plate, and equations (8-70) and (8-72) with appropriate derivatives of W for a simply supported cross-ply plate, are substituted into equations (8-62) and (8-63). The first resulting equation is multiplied by $X_i(\zeta)Y_j(\eta)$, and the second by $X_i(\zeta)Y_j(\eta)$ in the case of a clamped plate and by $\sin i\pi\zeta \sin j\pi\eta$ in the case of a simply supported plate. Integrating each of these equations with respect to ζ and η from 0 to 1 and using the orthogonality relations (5-38) for X_i and Y_j yield the following system of equations

$$G_{ij}^{mn} F_{mn}(\tau) = H_{ij}^{pq} W_{pq}(\tau) + K_{ij}^{pqrs} W_{pq}(\tau) W_{rs}(\tau) \tag{8-73}$$

and

$$W_{ij,\tau\tau} + L_{ij}^{pq} W_{pq}(\tau) + P_{ij}^{mn} F_{mn}(\tau) + Q_{ij}^{pqrs} W_{pq}(\tau) F_{rs}(\tau) = 0 \tag{8-74}$$

in which repeated Latin indices in a term indicate summation with respect to these indices. In the case of a clamped plate the coefficients G, H, K, L, P, and Q in equations (8-73) and (8-74) are given by

$$G_{ij}^{mn} = \delta_i^m \delta_j^n (\bar{A}_{22}^* \alpha_m^4 + \lambda^4 \bar{A}_{11}^* \alpha_n^4) + \lambda^2 I_1^{im} J_1^{jn} (2\bar{A}_{12}^* + \bar{A}_{66}^*)$$

$$K_{ij}^{pqrs} = \lambda^2 (I_2^{ipr} J_2^{jqs} - I_3^{ipr} J_3^{jqs})$$

$$L_{ij}^{pq} = \delta_i^p \delta_j^q (\bar{D}_{11}^* \alpha_p^4 + \lambda^4 \bar{D}_{22}^* \alpha_q^4) + 2\lambda^2 I_1^{ip} J_1^{jq} (\bar{D}_{12}^* + 2\bar{D}_{66}^*)$$

$$Q_{ij}^{pqrs} = -\lambda^2 (I_3^{ipr} J_3^{jsq} + I_3^{irp} J_3^{jqs} - 2I_2^{ipr} J_2^{jqs})$$

(8-75)

for unsymmetric cross-ply and angle-ply plates,

$$H_{ij}^{pq} = -\bar{B}_{12}^* \delta_i^p \delta_j^q (\alpha_p^4 - \lambda^4 \alpha_q^4)$$

$$P_{ij}^{mn} = -\bar{B}_{12}^* \delta_i^m \delta_j^n (\alpha_m^4 - \lambda^4 \alpha_n^4)$$

(8-76)

for unsymmetric cross-ply plates, and

$$H_{ij}^{pq} = \lambda I_4^{ip} J_5^{jq} (2\bar{B}_{26}^* - \bar{B}_{61}^*) + \lambda^3 I_5^{ip} J_4^{jq} (2\bar{B}_{16}^* - \bar{B}_{62}^*)$$

$$P_{ij}^{mn} = \lambda I_4^{im} J_5^{jn} (2\bar{B}_{26}^* - \bar{B}_{61}^*) + \lambda^3 I_5^{in} J_4^{jn} (2\bar{B}_{16}^* - \bar{B}_{62}^*)$$

(8-77)

for unsymmetric angle-ply plates.

In the case of simply supported plates, the coefficients G, H, K, L, P and Q are given by

$$G_{ij}^{mn} = \delta_i^m \delta_j^n (\bar{A}_{22}^* \alpha_m^4 + \lambda^4 \bar{A}_{11}^* \alpha_n^4) + \lambda^2 I_1^{im} J_1^{jn} (2\bar{A}_{12}^* + \bar{A}_{66}^*)$$

$$+ \frac{16\bar{B}_{12}^{*2}}{\bar{D}_{11}^*} \sum_{p=1}^{\infty} \sum_{q=1}^{\infty} \{p\pi\alpha_m^2 J_6^{nq} (c_p c_m + d_p d_m)$$

$$+ \lambda^4 q\pi\alpha_n^2 I_6^{mp} (c_q c_n + d_q d_n)\}$$

$$H_{ij}^{pq} = -\pi^4 \bar{B}_{12}^* (I_6^{ip} J_6^{jq} (p^4 - \lambda^4 q^4)$$

$$P_{ij}^{mn} = -4\bar{B}_{12}^* \{I_6^{mi} J_6^{nj} (\alpha_m^4 - \lambda^4 \alpha_n^4)$$

$$- 4\pi [i\alpha_m^2 J_6^{nj} (c_i c_m + d_j d_m) - \lambda^4 j\alpha_n^2 I_6^{mi} (c_j c_n + d_j d_n)]\}$$

(8-78)

for unsymmetric cross-ply plates,

$$G_{ij}^{mn} = \delta_i^m \delta_j^n (\bar{A}_{22}^* \alpha_m^4 + \lambda^4 \bar{A}_{11}^* \alpha_n^4) + \lambda^2 I_1^{im} J_1^{jn} (2\bar{A}_{12}^* + \bar{A}_{66}^*)$$

$$H_{ij}^{pq} = -\pi^4 I_7^{ip} J_7^{jq} \{\lambda p^3 q (2\bar{B}_{26}^* - \bar{B}_{61}^*) + \lambda^3 pq^3 (2\bar{B}_{16}^* - \bar{B}_{62}^*)\}$$

$$P_{ij}^{mn} = \lambda I_8^{mi} J_9^{nj} (2\bar{B}_{26}^* - \bar{B}_{61}^*) + \lambda^3 I_9^{mi} J_8^{nj} (2\bar{B}_{16}^* - \bar{B}_{62}^*)$$

(8-79)

for unsymmetric angle-ply plates, and

$$K_{ij}^{pqrs} = \lambda^2 \pi^4 (^{pqrs} I_{10}^{ipr} J_{10}^{jqs} - p^2 s^2 I_{11}^{ipr} J_{11}^{jqs})$$

$$L_{ij}^{pq} = \delta_i^p \delta_j^q \pi^4 \{\bar{D}_{11}^* p^4 + 2\lambda^2 p^2 q^2 (\bar{D}_{12}^* + 2\bar{D}_{66}^*) + \lambda^4 q^4 \bar{D}_{22}^*\}$$

$$Q_{ij}^{pqrs} = 4\lambda^2 \pi^2 (p^2 I_{11}^{rip} J_{12}^{sjq} + q^2 I_{12}^{rip} J_{11}^{sjq} + 2pq I_{13}^{jip} J_{13}^{sjq})$$

(8-80)

for unsymmetric cross-ply and angle-ply plates. In equations (8-75) to (8-80) δ_i^j, c_m, and d_n are given by

$$\delta_i^j = \begin{cases} 1, & i = j \\ 0, & i \neq j \end{cases} \qquad c_m = \begin{cases} 1, & m = \text{odd} \\ 0, & m = \text{even} \end{cases} \qquad d_n = \begin{cases} 0, & n = \text{odd} \\ 1, & n = \text{even} \end{cases} \qquad (8\text{-}81)$$

and I_1 to I_{13} are constants defined by

$$I_1^{im} = \int_0^1 X_i X_m'' \, d\zeta \qquad I_2^{imn} = \int_0^1 X_i X_m' X_n' \, d\zeta$$

$$I_3^{imn} = \int_0^1 X_i X_m'' X_n \, d\zeta \qquad I_4^{im} = \int_0^1 X_i X_m''' \, d\zeta$$

$$I_5^{im} = \int_0^1 X_i X_m' \, d\zeta \qquad I_6^{im} = \int_0^1 X_i \sin m\pi\zeta \, d\zeta$$

$$I_7^{im} = \int_0^1 X_i \cos m\pi\zeta \, d\zeta \qquad I_8^{im} = \int_0^1 X_i''' \sin m\pi\zeta \, d\zeta \qquad (8\text{-}82)$$

$$I_9^{im} = \int_0^1 X_i' \sin m\pi\zeta \, d\zeta \qquad I_{10}^{imn} = \int_0^1 X_i \cos m\pi\zeta \cos n\pi\zeta \, d\zeta$$

$$I_{11}^{imn} = \int_0^1 X_i \sin m\pi\zeta \sin n\pi\zeta \, d\zeta \qquad I_{12}^{imn} = \int_0^1 X_i'' \sin m\pi\zeta \sin n\pi\zeta \, d\zeta$$

$$I_{13}^{imn} = \int_0^1 X_i' \sin m\pi\zeta \cos n\pi\zeta \, d\zeta$$

where primes denote the differentiation with respect to the corresponding coordinate. Expressions for J_1 to J_{13} are obtained from equations (8-82) by replacing I, X and ζ by L, Y and η, respectively.

Equations (8-73) can be solved for F_{ij} coefficients and written as

$$F_{ij}(\tau) = M_{ij}^{pq} W_{pq}(\tau) + N_{ij}^{pqrs} W_{pq}(\tau) W_{rs}(\tau) \qquad (8\text{-}83)$$

where

$$[M_{ij}^{pq}] = [G_{mn}^{ij}]^{-1} [H_{mn}^{pq}]$$
$$[N_{ij}^{pqrs}] = [G_{mn}^{ij}]^{-1} [K_{mn}^{pqrs}] \qquad (8\text{-}84)$$

Substituting equations (8-83) into equations (8-74) leads to a system of equations for time functions $W_{ij}(\tau)$

$$W_{ij,\tau\tau} + \beta_{ij}^{pq} W_{pq} + \kappa_{ij}^{pqrs} W_{pq} W_{rs} + \mu_{ij}^{pqrskl} W_{pq} W_{rs} W_{kl} = 0 \qquad (8\text{-}85)$$

in which the quadratic terms for unsymmetric angle-ply plates vanish automatically and in which

$$[\beta_{ij}^{pq}] = [L_{ij}^{pq}] + [P_{ij}^{mn}][M_{mn}^{pq}]$$
$$[\kappa_{ij}^{pqrs}] = [P_{ij}^{mn}][N_{mn}^{pqrs}] + [Q_{ij}^{pqmn}][M_{mn}^{rs}] \qquad (8\text{-}86)$$
$$[\mu_{ij}^{pqrskl}] = [Q_{ij}^{pqmn}][N_{mn}^{rskl}]$$

In the application of the method of harmonic balance (Ref. 6.13), the time-dependent deflection coefficients $W_{ij}(\tau)$ are expanded into Fourier cosine series as

$$W_{ij}(\tau) = \sum_{k=0}^{\infty} W_{ij}^{(k)} \cos k\omega\tau \qquad (8\text{-}87)$$

where $W_{ij}^{(k)}$ are constant Fourier coefficients and vanish for $k = 0, 2, 4, \ldots$ in the case of unsymmetric angle-ply plates. This assumed solution is inserted in equation (8-85) and each term is converted into the first power of cosine function. Equating the coefficients of like terms of cosine to zero, a system of simultaneous nonlinear algebraic equations is obtained. These equations can be solved for $W_{ij}^{(k)}$ by the Newton-Raphson method for a given set of plate parameters and nonlinear frequency ω_{mn} of the (m, n) mode of vibration with m and n being the numbers of half-waves in the x and y directions, respectively.

Once Fourier coefficients $W_{ij}^{(k)}$ and hence $W_{ij}(\tau)$ are found, $F_{ij}(\tau)$ can be computed from equation (8-83). Force function F and transverse deflection W represented by series (8-70) and (8-71) for clamped edges and by series (8-70) and (8-72) for simply supported edges are uniquely determined. Any physical quantities of the plate, therefore, can be calculated without difficulty.

Numerical results are presented for unsymmetric cross-ply and angle-ply plates with all-clamped and all-simply supported edges. The materials of these plates under consideration are glass-epoxy, boron-epoxy and graphite-epoxy composites. The values of elastic constants typical of these materials are given in Table 8.1. The first sixteen terms in the truncated series for W are grouped into symmetric-symmetric, symmetric-antisymmetric, antisymmetric-symmetric and antisymmetric-antisymmetric vibrating modes about two center lines of the plate. In each case the total deflection for a particular mode of vibration is a combination of four similar deflections or modes which change with the time according to the law of simple harmonic motion.

The fundamental linear frequencies $\omega_{11}^{(0)}$ of simply-supported angle-ply and cross-ply laminates obtained by using the first four symmetric-symmetric modes $(m, n = 1, 3)$ and the term $W_{ij}^{(1)} \cos \omega\tau$ in the time series are compared in Table 8.4 with the graphic results given in Refs. 8.3 and 8.5. In the table E_T is the tensile

Table 8.4 Fundamental linear frequency, $\omega_{11}^{(0)} b^2 (\rho/E_T h^3)^{1/2}$, of simply-supported graphite-epoxy square plates

Number of Layers	±45° Angle-ply		Cross-ply	
	Present	Ref. 8.3	Present	Ref. 8.5
2	14.6357	~ 14.2	11.6141	11.6150
4	23.5238	~ 23.4	17.2270	17.2267
∞	25.8199	~ 25.8	18.8193	18.8193

Table 8.5 Fundamental linear frequency, $\omega_{11}^{(0)} b^2 (\rho/E_T h^3)^{1/2}$ of square unsymmetric laminates

Number of Layers	Material	Cross-ply		± 45° Angle-ply	
		SS	CC	SS	CC
2	GR	11.1641	24.0332	14.6353	23.5848
2	BO	7.5638	15.7735	9.4451	
2	GL	6.8143	12.9760	7.3272	
4	GR	17.2159	38.1153		
∞	GR	18.8052	41.7673		

modulus of the plate material perpendicular to the fiber direction. A good agreement is noted between these values. In the case of orthotropic plates the present results reduce to those given in Sec. 6.8. For an unsymmetric 2-layer $\pm 45°$ angle-ply square plate ($E_L/E_T = 7.6$, $G_{LT}/E_T = 0.4$, $v_{TL} = 0.3$) with edges all clamped and all simply supported the present results agree closely with those obtained in Sec. 8.4 although the inplane boundary conditions are slightly different in these two analyses. The maximum difference between the present results using the single mode and the first four symmetric modes is approximately 5 percent for both sets of edge conditions. The details are not presented herein.

In the presentation of numerical results, unless specified otherwise the first four terms in the truncated time series are used. The ratio of the nonlinear frequency ω_{mn} to the corresponding linear frequency $\omega_{mn}^{(0)}$ is also used and hence fundamental linear frequencies are presented in Table 8.5 where SS and CC represent all-simply supported edges and all-clamped edges, respectively, and GR, BO and GL denote graphite-epoxy, boron-epoxy, and glass-epoxy composites, respectively.

The nonlinear fundamental frequencies of a square angle-ply plate calculated by taking $m, n = 1$ and $m, n = 1, 3$ are shown in Table 8.6 for comparison in

Table 8.6 Comparison of nonlinear fundamental frequencies of unsymmetric 2-layer $\pm 45°$ angle-ply graphite-epoxy square plate

Simply Supported			Clamped		
	w_c/h			w_c/h	
$\omega_{11}/\omega_{11}^{(0)}$	Single mode	Four modes	$\omega_{11}/\omega_{11}^{(0)}$	Single mode	Four modes
1.034	0.9836	0.9839	1.037	0.9303	0.9610
1.071	1.4274	1.4506	1.075	1.3449	1.3971
1.139	2.0491	2.1075	1.143	1.9031	1.9803
1.163	2.2305	2.3159	1.168	2.0370	2.1574
1.213	2.5801	2.7187	1.217	2.2519	2.4903

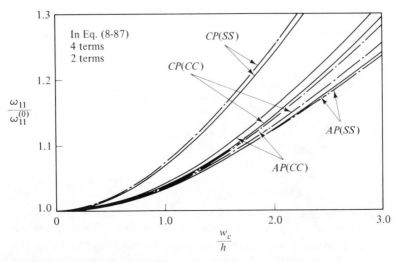

Figure 8.10 Convergence of time series for fundamental vibration of two-layer cross-ply and $\pm 45°$ angle-ply graphite-epoxy square plates.

which w_c is the maximum central deflection or amplitude. The result shows that the amplitude of the fundamental mode obtained by using the first four symmetric-symmetric modes is higher than that given by the single-mode solution with the term $W_{ij}^{(1)} \cos \omega\tau$ in the time series. At an amplitude of the order of two-and-a-half times the plate thickness, the difference is more than 6 percent for a simply supported plate and more than 10 percent for a clamped plate. The effect of numbers of terms in the time series on the amplitude-frequency response is shown in Fig. 8.10 for square cross-ply (CP) and $\pm 45°$ angle-ply (AP) laminates. The numerical results obtained from the first two and four terms in each time series (8-87) indicate that these series converge rapidly. The first four terms in each time series should give a good approximation to the series.

The results presented graphically in Figs. 8.11 to 8.13 were obtained by taking the first four modes in the double series for W, depending on the vibrating mode considered. It is seen from Fig. 8.11 and Table 8.5 that the fundamental frequency of a simply supported angle-ply plate for a given w_c decreases with the aspect ratio but increases with the ratio E_L/E_T. The nondimensional linear frequencies are defined by $\Omega_{mn}^{(0)} = \omega_{mn}^{(0)} b^2 (\rho/E_T h^3)^{1/2}$. The amplitude-frequency response curves for a graphite-epoxy composite plate having different values of the total number of layers, n_1, are shown in Fig. 8.12 for the symmetric-antisymmetric mode with one half-wave in the x direction and two half-waves in the y direction. The four terms, $m = 1, 3$ and $n = 2, 4$, were used in calculation. The amplitude occurs nearly at the point, $\zeta = 0.50$ and $\eta = 0.25$. The linear frequencies $\Omega_{12}^{(0)}$ appearing in the figure are 33.7223 for $n_1 = 2$, 53.6752 for $n_1 = 4$, and 58.8419 for $n_1 = \infty$ in the case of simply supported edges, and 47.5386 for $n_1 = 2$, 75.0409 for $n_1 = 4$, and 82.1880 for $n_1 = \infty$ in the case of a clamped plate. This figure indicates that the frequency

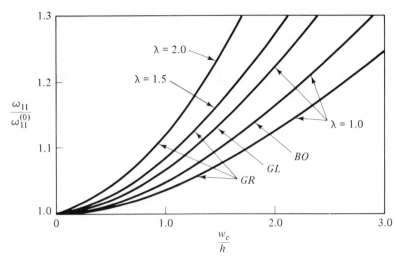

Figure 8.11 Effect of aspect ratio and elastic properties on fundamental frequency of simply supported two-layer $\pm 45°$ angle-ply plate ($\Omega_{11}^{(0)} = 10.2378$ for $\lambda = 1.5$ and $\Omega_{11}^{(0)} = 8.4306$ for $\lambda = 2$).

of a symmetric-antisymmetric mode increases with increasing the total number of layers as in the case of the fundamental mode. In Fig. 8.13 the frequencies of various vibrating modes are presented for a cross-ply plate. The four terms taken from the series for W are m, $n = 1, 3$ for symmetric-symmetric mode; $m = 1, 3$ and $n = 2, 4$ for symmetric-antisymmetric mode; $m, n = 2, 4$ for antisymmetric-antisymmetric mode. The amplitude w_{max} occurs nearly at the point $(0.50, 0.50)$ for ω_{11}, $(0.50, 0.25)$ for ω_{12}, $(0.25, 0.25)$ for ω_{22}, $(0.50, 0.33)$ for

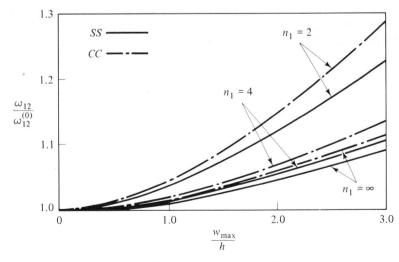

Figure 8.12 Effect of number of layers on frequency of $\pm 45°$ angle-ply graphite-epoxy square plate for symmetric-antisymmetric vibrating mode ($m = 1, n = 2$).

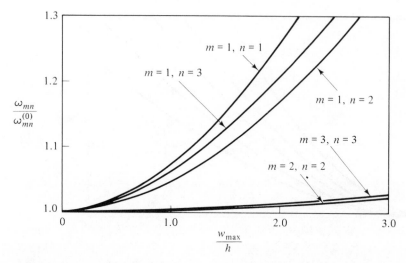

Figure 8.13 Frequencies of simply supported two-layer cross-ply boron-epoxy plate for various vibrating modes.

ω_{13}, and (0.33, 0.33) for ω_{33}. The corresponding linear frequencies are $\Omega_{12}^{(0)} = 20.7261$, $\Omega_{22}^{(0)} = 30.2554$, $\Omega_{13}^{(0)} = 44.0714$, and $\Omega_{33}^{(0)} = 68.0747$.

Based on this study some concluding remarks may be made. The nonlinear frequency of a composite plate with all-clamped and all-simply supported edges increases with the amplitude and hence only a hardening type of nonlinearity is noted. For a given amplitude the nonlinear frequency decreases with the aspect ratio but increases with the total number of layers or the tensile moduli of the plate. The accuracy of a single-mode solution for the nonlinear frequency decreases with the amplitude of vibration. For large amplitudes the effect of coupling of vibrating modes on the nonlinear frequency is significant for composite plates, especially for clamped high-modulus laminates.

PROBLEMS

8.1 Formulate an approximate load-deflection relation for the postbuckling of a loosely clamped unsymmetric cross-ply square plate under uniform uniaxial inplane compression.

8.2 Taking the first terms in equations (8-70) and (8-72) and applying Galerkin's method, derive the time equation for a simply-supported unsymmetric angle-ply rectangular plate with stress-free edges.

REFERENCES

8.1. D. K. Faddeev and V. N. Faddeeva: "Computational Method in Linear Algebra," W. H. Freeman, Publishers, San Francisco, 1963.

8.2. R. W. Hamming: "Numerical Methods for Scientists and Engineers," McGraw-Hill Book Co., 1962.

8.3.   J. M. Whitney and A. W. Leissa: Analysis of a Simply Supported Laminated Anisotropic Rectangular Plate, *AIAA J.*, vol. 8, pp. 28–33, 1970.

8.4.   M. K. Prabhakara: Post-buckling Behaviour of Simply-Supported Cross-ply Rectangular Plate, *Aeronaut. Q.*, vol. 27, Royal Aeronautical Society (London), pp. 309–316, 1977.

8.5.   R. M. Jones: Buckling and Vibration of Unsymmetrically Laminated Cross-ply Rectangular Plates, *AIAA J.*, vol. 11, pp. 1626–1632, 1973.

8.6.   R. Chandra and B. Basava Raju: Large Deflection Vibration of Angle Ply Laminated Plates, *J. Sound Vib.*, vol. 40, Academic Press, pp. 393–408, 1975.

8.7.   J. A. Bennett: Nonlinear Vibration of Simply Supported Angle-ply Laminated Plates, *AIAA J.*, vol. 9, pp. 1997–2033, 1971.

8.8.   R. Chandra: Large Deflection Vibration of Cross-ply Laminated Plates with Certain Edge Conditions, *J. Sound Vib.*, vol. 47, Academic Press, pp. 509–514, 1976.

8.9.   C. Y. Chia and M. K. Prabhakara: A General Mode Approach to Nonlinear Flexural Vibrations of Laminated Rectangular Plates, *ASME J. Appl. Mech.*, vol. 45, pp. 623–628, 1978.

ADDITIONAL REFERENCES

Bert, C. W.: Nonlinear Vibration of a Rectangular Plate Arbitrarily Laminated of Anisotropic Materials, *ASME J. Appl. Mech.*, vol. 40, pp. 452–458, 1973.

Chailleux, A., Y. Hans, and G. Verchery: Experimental Study of the Buckling of Laminated Composite Columns and Plates, *Int. J. Mech. Sci.*, vol. 17, pp. 489–498, 1975.

Chandra, R.: Postbuckling Analysis of Cross-ply Laminated Plates, *AIAA J.*, vol. 13, pp. 1388–1389, 1975.

———— and B. Basava Raju: Large Amplitude Flexural Vibration of Cross-ply Laminated Composite Plates, *Fibre Sci. Technol.*, vol. 8, pp. 243–263, 1975.

Harris, G. Z.: The Buckling and Post-buckling Behaviour of Composite Plates under Biaxial Loading, *Int. J. Mech. Sci.*, vol. 17, pp. 187–202, 1975.

VALUES OF COEFFICIENTS IN EQUATIONS (2-80) TO (2-82)

Numerical values of the coefficients in equations (2-80) to (2-82) are tabulated below for $v = \frac{1}{3}$. The corresponding coefficients q_1 and q_3 in the load-deflection relation given by the first of equations (2-83) are also given in the last columns of Tables A.1 and A.4.

Table A.1 Coefficients in equation (2-80)

λ	A_1	A_2	A_3	A_4	A_5	q_1
0.00	+0.0000	+2.0000	+0.0000	+3.0000	+0.0000	+24.0000
0.10	+0.0000	+1.9950	−0.0000	+2.6355	+0.0021	+23.9998
0.20	+0.0003	+1.9315	−0.0000	+1.8480	+0.0245	+23.9963
0.30	+0.0029	+1.7305	−0.0003	+1.0950	+0.0759	+24.0273
0.40	+0.0116	+1.4061	−0.0009	+0.5772	+0.1306	+24.3208
0.50	+0.0293	+1.0622	−0.0016	+0.2872	+0.1639	+25.2606
0.60	+0.0564	+0.7779	−0.0017	+0.1421	+0.1752	+27.1842
0.70	+0.0920	+0.5693	−0.0011	+0.0719	+0.1750	+30.3550
0.80	+0.1356	+0.4225	+0.0008	+0.0373	+0.1714	+35.0452
0.90	+0.1869	+0.3193	+0.0044	+0.0196	+0.1686	+41.5860
1.00	+0.2457	+0.2457	+0.0101	+0.0101	+0.1676	+50.3815

Table A.2 Coefficients in equation (2-81)

λ	B_1	B_2	B_3	B_4	B_5	B_6
0.00	+0.6095	−2.0571	−0.5333	+1.1429	+2.6667	−3.2000
0.10	+0.6115	−2.0569	−0.5819	+1.1428	+0.7023	−3.1428
0.20	+0.6115	−2.0544	−0.5526	+1.1395	−2.8143	−2.4890
0.30	+0.6026	−2.0454	−0.4056	+1.1105	−5.1957	−0.6912
0.40	+0.5742	−2.0265	−0.2045	+1.0228	−5.5712	+1.8040
0.50	+0.5477	−2.0065	+0.0286	+0.8605	−4.4921	+4.0439
0.60	+0.5362	−1.9932	+0.2113	+0.6380	−2.9145	+5.5298
0.70	+0.5341	−1.9903	+0.2882	+0.3746	−1.4492	+6.2840
0.80	+0.5375	−1.9910	+0.2452	+0.0905	−0.2924	+6.4845
0.90	+0.5437	−1.9859	+0.1016	−0.1975	+0.5728	+6.2821
1.00	+0.5499	−1.9646	−0.1136	−0.4713	+1.2115	+5.7642

Table A.3 Coefficients in equation (2-81)

λ	C_1	C_2	C_3	C_4	C_5	C_6
0.00	+0.0000	+0.0000	+0.0000	+0.0000	+0.0000	+0.0000
0.10	−0.1527	−0.0127	+0.9216	+0.0026	+2.9317	−0.3388
0.20	−0.1749	−0.0837	+0.7125	+0.0618	+3.0236	−1.8064
0.30	−0.1049	−0.2786	+0.4431	+0.3062	+2.6342	−3.5505
0.40	+0.1334	−0.5780	+0.3099	+0.7485	+1.7125	−4.1144
0.50	+0.2949	−0.8136	−0.0962	+1.2261	+0.5469	−3.1398
0.60	+0.3612	−0.8836	−0.6114	+1.5809	−0.2954	−1.2628
0.70	+0.4054	−0.7931	−1.0666	+1.7519	−0.6884	+0.8262
0.80	+0.4518	−0.5962	−1.4293	+1.7398	−0.7624	+2.7534
0.90	+0.5010	−0.3527	−1.7200	+1.5577	−0.6595	+4.4026
1.00	+0.5499	−0.1136	−1.9646	+1.2115	−0.4713	+5.7642

Table A.4 Coefficients in equation (2-82)

λ	H_1	H_2	H_3	H_4	H_5	q_3
0.00	+0.02032	+0.11429	+0.00000	−0.27429	+0.00254	+1.46286
0.10	+0.02003	+0.10151	+0.00002	−0.00671	+0.00456	+1.44505
0.20	+0.01925	+0.11185	+0.00019	+0.33551	−0.00475	+1.39816
0.30	+0.01776	+0.13658	+0.00057	+0.35007	−0.01927	+1.31326
0.40	+0.01632	+0.12420	+0.00092	+0.21433	−0.01987	+1.23302
0.50	+0.01517	+0.09606	+0.00025	+0.10524	−0.00671	+1.19704
0.60	+0.01442	+0.07161	−0.00183	+0.04291	+0.01301	+1.20642
0.70	+0.01459	+0.05282	−0.00487	+0.01105	+0.03145	+1.27934
0.80	+0.01611	+0.03922	−0.00801	−0.00379	+0.04453	+1.43447
0.90	+0.01911	+0.02980	−0.01035	−0.00972	+0.05171	+1.68170
1.00	+0.02351	+0.02351	−0.01118	−0.01118	+0.05384	+2.03143

VALUES OF DEFLECTION COEFFICIENTS IN SECTION 4.3

The values of the deflection coefficients w_{mn} shown in Table 4.2 are presented in Tables B.1 to B.4 for various edge loads and amplitudes of initial deflection and for $v = \frac{1}{3}$.

Table B.1 Case I

Case	ξ_{11}	Ω	w_{11}	$-w_{13}$	$-w_{31}$	w_{33}
I(a)	0	0.375	0	0	0	0
		0.497	1.0	0.0103	0.00608	0.00035
		0.839	2.0	0.0829	0.0355	0.0100
		1.364	3.0	0.2940	0.0953	0.7160
	0.1	0.356	0.5	0.00199	0.00138	0.000025
		0.487	1.0	0.0129	0.00782	0.00053
		0.865	2.0	0.0933	0.0414	0.0124
		1.414	3.0	0.320	0.1020	0.0820
I(b)	0	0.375	0	0	0	0
		0.457	1.0	0.0095	0.0101	0.00088
		0.798	2.5	0.1054	0.1169	0.0264
		1.273	4.0	0.2830	0.3360	0.1250
	0.1	0.438	1.0	0.0117	0.0131	0.00115
		0.672	2.0	0.0673	0.0755	0.0135
		0.963	3.0	0.1690	0.1940	0.0559
		1.300	4.0	0.2930	0.5350	0.1330

Table B.2 Case II

Case	ξ_{11}	Ω	w_{11}	w_{12}	$-w_{21}$	$-w_{22}$
II(a)	0	0.956	0	0	0	0
		1.162	0.25	0.0165	0.0241	0.0052
		1.783	0.50	0.0506	0.0805	0.0198
		2.036	0.5625	0.0827	0.1050	0.0307
	0.025	0.879	0.125	0.00667	0.00994	0.00192
		1.122	0.25	0.0147	0.0257	0.00513
		1.822	0.50	0.0497	0.0857	0.0206
		2.096	0.5625	0.0848	0.1116	0.3240
II(b)	0	0.956	0	0	0	0
		1.150	0.25	0.0153	0.0239	0.00458
		1.702	0.50	0.0300	0.768	0.0105
		2.098	0.625	0.0366	0.1135	0.0100
	0.025	0.874	0.125	0.0065	0.0090	0.00182
		1.105	0.25	0.0133	0.0254	0.00433
		1.726	0.50	0.0255	0.0808	0.00912
		2.134	0.625	0.0263	0.1167	0.00544

Table B.3 Case III

Case	ξ_{11}	Ω	w_{11}	w_{12}	$-w_{31}$	$-w_{32}$
III(a)	0	0.632	0	0	0	0
		0.765	0.5	0.00536	0.00659	0.000743
		1.143	1.0	0.0147	0.0365	0.00442
		1.755	1.5	0.0545	0.0841	0.0144
	0.05	0.574	0.25	0.00242	0.00148	0.000136
		0.734	0.5	0.00504	0.00832	0.000894
		1.163	1.0	0.0151	0.0403	0.00481
		1.806	1.5	0.0564	0.0889	0.0153
III(b)	0	0.632	0	0	0	0
		0.740	0.5	0.00301	0.00861	-0.000158
		1.192	1.25	-0.0201	0.0822	0.00803
		1.843	2.0	-0.1420	0.1850	0.0774
	0.05	0.566	0.25	0.00198	0.00192	-0.000045
		0.703	0.5	0.00213	0.0110	-0.00012
		1.205	1.25	-0.0241	0.0887	0.00989
		1.876	2.0	-0.1530	0.1910	0.0850

Table B.4 Case IV

Case	ξ_{12}	Ω	w_{12}	$-w_{22}$	w_{32}	w_{16}
IV(a)	0	0.724	0	0	0	0
		0.951	0.4	0.0566	0.0115	0.00033
		1.235	0.6	0.1213	0.0235	0.00091
		1.646	0.8	0.2210	0.0469	0.00185
	0.05	0.524	0.1	0.00948	0.00214	0.000018
		0.937	0.4	0.0640	0.0122	0.00044
		1.275	0.6	0.1373	0.0266	0.00110
		1.733	0.8	0.2460	0.0536	0.0022
IV(b)	0	0.724	0	0	0	0
		0.949	0.4	0.0569	0.0112	0.00038
		1.231	0.6	0.1228	0.0239	0.00110
		1.637	0.8	0.2270	0.0488	0.00242
	0.05	0.524	0.1	0.00949	0.00214	0.000020
		0.934	0.4	0.0643	0.0122	0.00051
		1.269	0.6	0.1391	0.0271	0.00134
		1.721	0.8	0.2520	0.0559	0.0029

AUTHOR INDEX

Aalami, B., 106(3)*, 280
Abdelmigid, S. B., 146
Aboudi, J., 335
Adimurthy, N. K., 51
Adotte, G. A., 280
Aggarwala, B. D., 220
Ahmad, J., 218(2)
Allen, H. G., 51
Alwan, A. M., 51(2)
Alwar, R. S., 51, 218
Almroth, B. O., 51
Alzheimer, W. E., 146
Ambartsymyan, S. A., 51, 335
Armenakas, A. E., 51
Ashton, J. E., 48, 51, 280
Ashwell, D. G., 146, 219

Balachandra, M., 106
Banerjee, B., 49(3), 50(2), 146(3), 220(2), 280, 281
Banerjee, M. M., 49(2), 146
Banks, W. M., 281
Basava Raju, B., 403(2)
Basu, A. K., 280
Basuli, S., 49(2), 146(2)
Batdorf, S. B., 218
Bauer, F., 106

Bauer, H. F., 218
Bauer, L., 106
Becker, E. B., 146
Becker, W., 106
Bennett, J. A., 403
Benveniste, Y., 335
Bera, R., 49, 218
Berger, H. M., 49, 106, 146
Bernhart, W. D., 52
Bernstein, E. L., 51, 106
Bert, C. W., 403
Biot, M. A., 48
Bleich, H., 51, 218
Bodner, S. R., 217
Boley, S. R., 218
Bolton, R., 146
Brand, R. S., 335(2)
Bromberg, E., 146
Brown, J. C., 106
Brush, D. O., 51
Bulkeley, P. Z., 220
Bulson, P. S., 51, 218

Calcote, L. R., 51
Carleone, J., 335
Carlson, R. L., 218

* The number in parentheses denotes the number of the indicated author's references on the same page.

411

SUBJECT INDEX